Contents

KU-703-250

A Stanley Gibbons checklist
of the stamps of Great Britain

ect **British** *Stamps*

72nd Edition
2021

STANLEY
GIBBONS

By Appointment to
Her Majesty The Queen
Philatelists
Stanley Gibbons Ltd
London

Published by Stanley Gibbons Ltd
Editorial, Publications Sales Offices
and Distribution Centre:
7 Parkside, Christchurch Road, Ringwood,
Hants BH24 3SH

British Library Cataloguing in
Publication Data.
A catalogue record for this book is available
from the British Library.

Errors and omissions excepted. The colour
reproduction of stamps is only as accurate as
the printing process will allow.

ISBN-13: 978–1–911304–69–2

Item No. R0289-21

Printed by Stephens & George, Wales

The 2021 Edition

COLLECT BRITISH STAMPS has been the standard guide for collectors of Great Britain ever since the first edition was published in September 1967.

It provides a straightforward, easy-to-use work of reference, with every stamp design illustrated in colour and clear, uncomplicated listings ideally suited to the newer collector, while at the same time providing a handy checklist for the more advanced philatelist – small wonder that over four million copies have been sold to collectors around the world.

Collect British Stamps appears in the autumn of each year: for a more detailed listing, the *Great Britain Concise Catalogue* is published in the spring, incorporating many additional features and is ideal for the collector who needs more information about GB stamps.

Scope. Collect British Stamps comprises:

- All stamps with different watermark (wmk) or perforation (perf).
- Visible plate numbers on Victorian issues.
- Graphite-lined and phosphor issues, including variations in the numbers of phosphor bands.
- First Day Covers for Definitives from 1936, Regionals and all Special Issues.
- Presentation, Gift and Souvenir Packs.
- Post Office Yearbooks and year packs.
- Regional issues and War Occupation stamps of Guernsey and Jersey.
- Postage Due and Official Stamps.
- Post Office Picture Cards (PHQ cards).
- Commemorative gutter pairs and 'Traffic Light' gutter pairs listed as mint sets.
- Royal Mail Postage Labels priced as sets and on P.O. First Day Cover.
- Royal Mail Post & Go Stamps
- The introduction includes a Great Britain collector's glossary and articles giving helpful advice on a range of collecting topics
- A fully revised and updated design index now appears at the end of the catalogue.

Stamps of the independent postal administrations of Guernsey, Isle of Man and Jersey are contained in *Collect Channel Islands and Isle of Man Stamps*.

New for this edition

- A thorough review of all prices has been carried out, with revisions being made to several sections.
- Issues up to *Star Trek* 2020 have been added and the listings of earlier issues carefully checked and updated.
- All decimal Machin definitives have been combined in a separate section at the end of the commemorative issues. The edge of these pages have been tinted to make them easier to locate.

Layout

Stamps are set out chronologically by date of issue. In the catalogue lists the first numeral is the Stanley Gibbons catalogue number; the black (boldface) numeral alongside is the type number referring to the respective illustration. A blank in this column implies that the number immediately

above is repeated. The denomination and colour of the stamp are then shown. Before February 1971 British currency was:

£1 = 20s. One pound = twenty shillings and

1s = 12d. One shilling = twelve pence.

Upon decimalisation this became:

£1 = 100p.

One pound = one hundred (new) pence.

The catalogue list then shows two price columns. The left-hand is for unused stamps and the right-hand for used. Corresponding small boxes are provided in which collectors may wish to check off the items in their collection. Our method of indicating prices is: Numerals for pence, e.g. 10 denotes 10p. (10 pence). Numerals for pounds and pence, e.g. 4·25 denotes £4·25 (4 pounds and 25 pence). For £100 and above, prices are in whole pounds and so include the £ sign and omit the zeros for pence.

Where a stamp is described as 'As' another stamp, it means similar in appearance to that stamp, but differing in some key respect, such as gum, paper, perforation or printing method. It does not mean that it is the *same* as that stamp.

Note that stamps which only appear within miniature sheets are not seperately listed as individual items. However stamps which come from booklets are listed individually.

It should be noted that if a stamp or set is self-adhesive this is specifically noted in the set heading. If there is no reference to a stamp being self adhesive it will have ordinary gum.

Colour illustrations

The colour illustrations of stamps are intended as a guide only; they may differ in shade from the originals.

Size of illustrations

To comply with Post Office regulations stamp illustrations are three-quarters linear size. Separate illustrations of surcharges, overprints and watermarks are actual size.

Prices

The prices quoted in this catalogue are the estimated selling prices of Stanley Gibbons Ltd at the time of publication. They are *unless it is specifically stated otherwise*, for examples in very fine condition for the issue concerned. Superb examples are worth more; those of a lower quality considerably less. For more details on catalogue prices, see page xiv

The unused prices for stamps of Queen Victoria to King George V are for lightly hinged examples. Unused prices for King Edward VIII to Queen Elizabeth II are for unmounted mint (though when not available unmounted, mounted stamps are often supplied at a lower price). Prices for used stamps refer to very fine postally used examples, for issues from about 1880 with a very fine circular or oval dated cancellation. For further guidance on condition, see 'The Stanley Gibbons Guide to Stamp Pricing on page xiv. All prices are subject to change without prior notice and we give no guarantee to supply all stamps priced, since it is not possible to keep every catalogued item in stock. Commemorative issues may only be available in complete sets.

In the price columns:

† = Does not exist.

(—) or blank = Exists, or may exist, but price cannot be quoted.

* = Not normally issued (the so-called 'Abnormals' of 1862–1880).

Minimum price

The minimum price quoted is 10 pence. For individual stamps prices between 10 pence and 95 pence are provided as a guide for catalogue users. The lowest price *charged* for individual stamps or sets purchased from Stanley Gibbons is £1.

Perforations

The 'perforation' is the number of holes in a length of 2 cm, as measured by the Gibbons Instanta gauge. The stamp is viewed against a dark background with the transparent gauge put on top of it. Perforations are quoted to the nearest half. Stamps without perforation are termed 'imperforate'. From 1992 certain stamps occur with a large elliptical (oval) hole inserted in each line of vertical perforations. The £10 definitive, No. 1658, is unique in having two such holes in the horizontal perforations.

Elliptical perforations

Se-tenant combinations

Se-tenant means 'joined together'. Some sets include stamps of different design arranged *se-tenant* as blocks or strips and these are generally collected unsevered as issued. Where such combinations exist the stamps are priced both mint and used, as singles or complete sets. The set price refers to the unsevered combination plus singles of any other values in the set.

Miniature sheets sold singly include a barcode and other information in a panel at the left-hand edge. Sheets from presentation packs have this panel trimmed off. Catalogue prices are the same, either way.

First day covers

Prices for first day covers are for complete sets used on plain covers (Nos. 430/438, 453/460, 462/478*b*, 485/490, and 503/512) or on special covers (Nos. 461, 479/484, 491/502 and 513 onwards), the stamps of which are cancelled with ordinary operational postmarks (1924–1962) or by the standard 'First Day of Issue' postmarks (1963 onwards). The British Post Office did not provide 'First Day' treatment for every definitive issued after 1963. Where the stamps in a set were issued on different days, prices are for a cover from each day.

For all decimal issues (from 1971), first day cover prices are for official Royal Mail philatelic bureau products. Others may be worth more, but will frequently be worth less. If there was no official bureau first day cover service for a particular stamp or set, no price will be quoted.

Presentation Packs

Special packs comprising slip-in cards with printed information inside a protective covering, were introduced for the 1964 Shakespeare issue. Collectors packs, containing commemoratives from the preceding 12 months, were issued from 1967. Some packs with text in German from 1968–1969, exist as does a Japanese version of the pack for Nos. 916/917. Yearbooks, hardbound and illustrated in colour within a slip cover, joined the product range in 1984.

Many modern presentation packs include the relevant miniature sheet, however not all do so. If the miniature sheet is to be found in the presentation pack this is now noted.

It should be noted that prices given for presentation packs are for items as originally sold, including any additional inserts such as questionaire forms and publicity material.

PHQ cards

Since 1973 the Post Office has produced a series of picture cards, which can be sent through the post as postcards. Each card shows an enlarged colour reproduction of a current British stamp, either of one or more values from a set or of all values. Cards are priced here in fine mint condition for sets complete as issued. The Post Office gives each card a 'PHQ' serial number, hence the term. The cards are usually on sale shortly before the date of issue of the stamps, but there is no officially designated 'first day'. Used prices are for cards franked with the stamp depicted, on the obverse or reverse; the stamp being cancelled with an official postmark for first day of issue. For 1973–1976 issues cards with stamps on the obverse are worth about 25% more than the prices quoted.

Gutter pairs

Almost all modern Great Britain commemoratives are produced in sheets containing two panes of stamps separated by a blank horizontal or vertical margin known as a gutter. This feature first made its appearance on some supplies of the 1972 Royal Silver Wedding 3p., and marked the introduction of Harrison & Sons' new 'Jumelle' stamp-printing press. There are advantages for both the printer and the Post Office in such a layout which has now been used for nearly all commemorative issues since 1974. The term 'gutter pair' is used for a pair of stamps separated by part of the blank gutter margin. We do not list gutter pairs for self-adhesive stamps since, although the production format is the same, the stamps are separated by die-cutting.

Gutter pair

Most printers include some form of colour check device on the sheet margins, in addition to the cylinder or plate numbers. Harrison & Sons used round 'dabs' or spots of colour, resembling 'traffic lights'. For the period from the 1972 Royal Silver Wedding until the end of 1979 these colour dabs appeared in the gutter margin. Gutter pairs showing these 'traffic lights' are worth considerably more than the normal version. From the 2004 Entente Cordiale set, Walsall reintroduced traffic lights in the gutters of certain sets. Where these extend over more than one section of gutter margin on any stamp they are priced as blocks rather than pairs.

Traffic light gutter pair

No Value Indicated Stamps

From 22 August 1989 various definitive and special stamps appeared inscribed '2nd', '1st' or 'E' instead of a face value. These were sold at the current minimum rates for these services which were as follows:

Inland Postage Rate	2nd Class	1st Class
5 September 1988	14p.	19p.
2 October 1989	15p.	20p.
17 September 1990	17p.	22p.
16 September 1991	18p.	24p.
1 November 1993	19p.	25p.
8 July 1996	20p.	26p.
26 April 1999	19p.	26p.
17 April 2000	19p.	27p.
8 May 2003	20p.	28p.
1 April 2004	21p.	28p.
7 April 2005	21p.	30p.
3 April 2006	23p.	32p.
2 April 2007	24p.	34p.
7 April 2008	27p.	36p.
6 April 2009	30p.	39p.
6 April 2010	32p.	41p.
4 April 2011	36p.	46p.
30 April 2012	50p.	60p.
31 March 2014	53p.	62p.
30 March 2015	54p.	63p.
29 March 2016	55p.	64p.
27 March 2017	56p.	65p.
26 March 2018	58p.	67p.
25 March 2019	61p.	70p.
23 March 2020	65p.	76p.

European Airmail Rate	
26 April 1999	30p.
25 October 1999	34p.
27 April 2000	36p.
2 July 2001	37p.
27 March 2003	38p.
1 April 2004	40p.

From June 2004, European Airmail rate stamps reverted to showing a face value.

From 21 August 2006 'Large' letters were charged at a higher rate following the introduction of 'Pricing in Proportion'. Rates as follows:

Inland Postage Rate	2nd Class Large	1st Class Large
21 August 2006	37p.	44p.
2 April 2007	40p.	48p.
7 April 2008	42p.	52p.
6 April 2009	47p.	61p.
6 April 2010	51p.	66p.
4 April 2011	58p.	75p.
30 April 2012	69p.	90p.
31 March 2014	73p.	93p.
30 March 2015	74p	95p
29 March 2016	75p.	96p.
27 March 2017	76p.	98p.
26 March 2018	79p.	£1·01
25 March 2019	83p.	£1·06
23 March 2020	80p.	£1·15

Catalogue numbers used

This checklist uses the same catalogue numbers as other current Stanley Gibbons catalogues.

Latest issue date for stamps recorded in this edition is 13 November 2020.

We regret we do not give opinions as to the genuineness of stamps, nor do we identify stamps or number them by our Catalogue

Collecting Stamps – the Basics

It seems reasonable to assume, since you are reading this, that you already collect British stamps – but of course there are many ways of building on any collection and, if you are relatively new to it, we hope that the following will be of some guidance.

Traditionally, stamp collectors were introduced to the hobby with a quantity of world stamps, some still on envelopes and cards, which were then sorted and mounted in an album. In due course, many would decide to concentrate on a single country or group of countries and 'specialisation' would begin, based on the experience built up as a 'world collector'.

More recently, an alternative route has become prevalent, in which, often as a gift, collections may be built on a 'standing order' from a philatelic bureau, with stamps or covers arriving automatically, as they are issued, to be mounted in an album or stockbook. Albums are conveniently designed to meet the needs of this type of collection, with an illustrated space in which to mount every stamp.

This type of collection has much to recommend it – but one big disadvantage – it will be exactly the same as thousands of others, built up in the same way.

For this reason, many collectors are now returning to the delights of general collecting while maintaining their existing collections, and finding that the fun they had as children is very easy to recapture!

If you came to the hobby via 'the standing order' route and would like to start a second 'general collection', here are a few tips and suggestions.

Obtaining your stamps

Children were encouraged to buy – or persuade their parents to buy – the largest packet of stamps they could, as just sorting them into countries would prove enormously useful and interesting. Unfortunately large packets of world stamps are not as easy to obtain as they used to be, but you can still buy existing collections of all sorts at stamp fairs, shops or at auction, prices to suit every pocket. Just sorting and remounting such a collection will prove tremendously exciting.

Sooner or later, of course, you will identify gaps in your collection that you want to fill. It is useful to keep a note of these in a book that you can take with you when you visit a stamp shop or stamp fair – no one can remember everything and it is always annoying to discover that you have just bought a stamp you didn't need!

It is vitally important of course that you keep your 'wants' book up-to-date and cross out items as you acquire them.

As well as visiting stamp fairs, you can check out the advertisements in the press; establish a good relationship with a dealer you like and, he will be happy to receive a 'wants list' from you. He will then supply you with any items on it he has currently in stock and keep a record of anything else so that he can send it on to you if he gets one. All such items are usually 'on approval', so that if you have found them somewhere else, you are not obliged to purchase them.

More expensive items can be purchased at auction. Many of the larger auction houses do not like to sell items of lower value and therefore, in the main, offer more expensive single stamps and covers or complete collections and accumulations.

Other auctions offer single items of lower value and these can be a great way of picking up items you need and, once again, it is good to identify an auction house which regularly offers the type of material you are looking for and provides a reliable service.

Another method of buying stamps is 'kiloware'. These are stamps sold by weight and generally assumed to be 'unsorted' i.e. no one has been through them before and picked the good ones out. Many collectors enjoy this approach to stamp collecting and they will tell you of the wonderful 'finds' they have made – but inevitably you will be left with a vast majority of stamps that you do not want because they duplicate items already in your collection. Charity shops will always be happy to receive them – and they will eventually finish up in someone else's 'genuinely unsorted kiloware' – so once again, if this is your kind of collecting, establish a good relationship with a reliable supplier.

'Kiloware' is generally supplied in the form of stamps on paper, torn or cut from envelopes – so this is probably a good point at which to discuss one of the real basics of stamp collecting – soaking stamps off paper.

It is helpful to carry out some rudimentary sorting before you start. Soaking stamps is quite a time-consuming process, so you do not want to waste time on stamps you don't need or don't want, maybe because they are damaged.

Once you have sorted out the stamps you want to soak off, pour some clean water (warm but *not* hot) into a bowl; then float each stamp (face uppermost) on the surface of the water. You can float as many stamps at one time as you have room for.

Leave the stamps for 15 minutes or so to give the water time to soak the gum that is sticking the stamp to the paper. Most stamps can then be gently peeled away. If they do not come away easily do not try to tear them off the paper. Leave them for another five minutes or so and try again.

Providing your hands are clean it's better to handle the stamps with your fingers when peeling off the envelope paper. The paper of stamps is weakened when it is damp and picking them up with tweezers may damage them.

When you have peeled the stamps off the envelope there will probably be some damp gum still on the back of them. Use a soft brush dipped in water to remove this, a paint brush is ideal. Alternatively let the stamp float on the water for a few minutes – the gum will dissolve away. However, do not immerse the stamp in water. For most stamps this would be safe enough but for some it would be dangerous as the ink may run.

Then shake off any excess water and place the stamps face upwards on a sheet of clean kitchen paper towel. This is why it is so important to clean all the gum off. If you do not, your stamps will stick to the paper and you will have to float them off all over again. When all the stamps are laid out cover them with more paper towel then make a kind of sandwich by putting a few sheets of ordinary paper on top.

Place a heavy book on this sandwich. This will flatten the stamps as they dry. After half an hour open up the sandwich and carefully remove the stamps. Spread them out on another piece of clean paper and leave to dry in the air for a little while. When completely dry they are ready for mounting in your album.

Or you can just lay the stamps face down on paper towel and allow them to dry out in the air. If you use this method do not try to speed up the drying by putting the stamps in the sun or close to a hot radiator as they will curl up and you may damage them when you flatten them out to put them in your album.

There are two things which you must be very careful about when floating stamps. Firstly, many old stamps were printed in special inks which run, change colour, or even disappear completely in water. Fewer modern stamps are affected in this way but even so it is best to be safe, so avoid letting water get on the surface of the stamp when you are floating-off. Be careful when floating stamps to keep separate stamps affixed to white and coloured envelopes. Take out any stamp which are stuck to bits of coloured paper and float these separately. Floating can easily make the ink run and so damage your stamps by staining them with unwanted colours.

These days, many countries produce 'self-adhesive' stamps and these may not come away from their backing paper at all. If you believe that a stamp may be 'self-adhesive', it would be better to leave it on the paper, carefully trimming round it with scissors, making sure you do not cut into the stamp.

Finally, always think twice before tearing a stamp off an envelope. Most old stamps and some modern ones too, if they have interesting postmarks, will be more valuable if left on the envelope. If in doubt always try to ask a more experienced collector's advice.

Choosing an Album and Mounting your stamps

These are two different topics but really need to be considered together, as the way you mount your stamps will depend on the album you choose and your choice of album may depend on the way you wish to mount your stamps. Here are some of the options:

New Age album

Printed Albums

You may be used to an album printed with a space for every stamp, and these may be obtained for larger groups of countries, such as the Stanley Gibbons New Age Album, with spaces for all Commonwealth Queen Elizabeth stamps up to 1962. If this is the sort of collection you hope to build they are fine albums – but as they have a space for every stamp, filling one would be a time-consuming business!

Blank albums

These are made up of blank pages, printed with a faint quadrille (tiny squares) which help you lay your stamps out neatly. These give you freedom to lay your collection out as you wish, leaving spaces for stamps you are hoping to obtain, or a neat display of the stamps you have. The former option may mean that you have a lot of gaps on the page, the latter may mean fairly regular rearrangement of your collection – the choice is yours.

Blank albums come in a wide range of prices and binding types, from inexpensive ring binders, through traditional springbacks to high quality peg-fitting types. Again, the choice is yours.

Stockbooks

In the past, collectors used stockbooks to hold duplicates and stamps awaiting mounting in the main album, but due to their convenience and cost, many collectors are now using stockbooks to house their main collections.

They certainly make it easy to mount your stamps – you just slip them into the strips on the pages and you can move them around easily to accommodate new acquisitions too! You can even write notes regarding different stamps or sets and slip those into the strips.

Stock albums

These are loose-leaf stockbooks, which have the added benefit of being able to insert extra pages in the book. Also, because the strips come in a number of formats, they look better than a stockbook layout which is a bit restricting and does not show larger items, such as covers, blocks and miniature sheets, very well.

Mounting your stamps

Before we come on to cover albums, let's return to the matter of mounting your stamps. If you have chosen either the stockbook or stock album option, this is not really an issue as you can just slip your stamps into the strips on the page. If you have opted for a printed or blank album, on the other hand, the question of mounting is important.

The traditional stamp hinge is generally the preferred option for used stamps. Instructions for their use are generally given on the packet, so we will not repeat them here, but we must stress that the key points are to *lightly* moisten the hinge before attaching it to the stamp or album page and *not to try to remove it* until it's dry or you may damage the page – or even more important, the stamp.

For unused stamps that have been previously mounted, stamp hinges are also perfectly acceptable, but for stamps which still have 'full original gum' and show no evidence of having been previously hinged, most collectors now favour 'hingeless mounts', which allow you to attach the stamp to the page without disturbing the gum (keeping the stamp 'unmounted'').

For most of the frequently encountered stamp sizes, cut-to-size mounts are available for immediate use. Less common sizes will have to be cut from larger strips, but even large blocks and miniature sheets can be mounted in this way.

Although hingeless mounts are gummed, ready for use, many collectors prefer to use hinges to attach them to the album page as this makes them easier to move around when new stamps are added.

Covers

Many collectors like to include covers in their collections – either 'first day' or 'souvenir' covers or simply envelopes that show examples of the stamps in use. This is especially desirable in the case of early covers, which might show unusual postmarks or other features.

Cover album

Covers can be mounted on blank pages using gummed photograph corners, but may also be accommodated in purpose-built cover albums. There are even albums, which are designed to hold stamp and cover pages together (and booklet pages too!).

What else?

So, that's covered the choice of album and the mounting of stamps: What else do you need? This comes under two headings: equipment and information.

Information

You can manage without background information, but it would be a bit like setting out on a journey to somewhere you've never been without a map.

The first thing is a catalogue to tell you what exists and will help you to identify what you have. The Stanley Gibbons catalogue range includes something for every collector from the beginner to the specialist.

Beyond that there are specialist handbooks on just about everything, but many are printed in quite small numbers and, once sold, are unlikely to be reprinted. However, specialist dealers and auction houses can be a useful source of out-of-print literature.

You should also try to keep up with what is going on in the philatelic world and, again, Stanley Gibbons is able to help, via its monthly magazine, *Gibbons Stamp Monthly*, recently described as 'the best magazine for stamp collectors published anywhere'. For a free sample copy and subscription details, please write to Stanley Gibbons Publications, *(the address is at the front of this checklist)*.

Of course, as with everything else, much information may also be found on the internet and you will almost certainly find it worth joining the local society in your area, other stamp collectors are always happy to help a newcomer.

Equipment

Again, what you need in the way of equipment will depend largely on what you are collecting, the degree of specialisation you intend to achieve and the type of album you use.

We have already discussed albums and stamp mounts, the only other item every stamp collector must have is a pair of tweezers. All stamps should be handled with tweezers; they ensure that the natural oils in our fingers do not get on to the stamps and, after a bit of practice, they are easier to use than fingers as well. They come in different lengths, with different points and made from different materials (generally stainless steel or gold-plated). Find a style that suits you and stick with it.

From then on the equipment you need is up to you. Most collectors like to have a magnifying glass so they can look at their stamps more closely. Again, they come in a wide range, from the fairly basic, offering 2 or 3× magnification to pocket microscopes giving 30× magnification, and digital microscopes that you can attach to your computer for really detailed examination of your stamps.

Another useful type of magnifier is one that incorporates a millimetre scale – ideal for measuring overprints and other features.

Even a quick look in any catalogue will show that differences in perforation, watermark and colour can make an enormous difference to the price of a stamp. So most collectors like to have the necessary equipment to measure perforations, view watermarks and identify colours and shades.

Fortunately, as far as perforations are concerned, the perforation gauge used by most of the world's top collectors and dealers is accessible to all – it's the Stanley Gibbons Instanta – which measures perforations to a decimal point and is easy to use. There is an electronic perforation measurer which is even easier to use – but it is a bit more expensive than the Instanta.

Watermark detectors also come in a variety of types and designs at different prices, so it is useful to seek the advice of an experienced collector before deciding on the one to buy.

If you are collecting older stamps, watermarks are generally clearer and can be identified simply by placing the stamps face down on a dark background or watermark tray and, if necessary, adding a few drops of lighter fluid or watermark fluid. The Morley Bright products are an excellent alternative if you do not like using fluids, which many collectors do not.

More modern stamps, especially mint ones are more difficult to sort and for these one of the electric watermark detectors will probably be the answer. The Stanley Gibbons Detectamark Spectrum and other similar products take a bit of practice to get used to, but are very effective. Their drawback is that they can only handle single stamps and cannot accommodate blocks or sheets. If you are able to, visit a shop where you can see the different products demonstrated and make your choice.

Happily, the standard colour guide for stamp collectors, the Stanley Gibbons Colour Key, is another relatively inexpensive item which will provide years of use. It features 200 different colours and will allow you to tell the difference between 'mauve', 'purple', 'lilac' and 'violet' with ease.

Finally and especially if you are collecting the modern stamps of Great Britain at a more specialised level, you will probably want an ultraviolet lamp to identify different papers and phosphor types. Again, these come in a range of designs at different prices, so it is useful to seek the advice of an experienced collector before deciding on the one to buy. If you collect Great Britain stamps, you really need a 'short wave' lamp to identify different phosphors, but some lamps incorporate both 'long' and 'short' wave bulbs, which give them wider potential use.

A lamp with a 'hood' or viewing eyepiece is generally to be recommended, firstly because direct exposure to prolonged ultraviolet light is damaging to the eyes, so you should avoid lamps which cause you to see the bulb itself while you are using it. Also, such lamps are more effective in the dark, so anything which shields the stamp being examined from other light sources, including daylight, will improve the effectiveness of the lamp.

The Stanley Gibbons Ultraviolet lamp, introduced in 2012, offers a broad spectrum light, suitable for detecting all phosphors, while the unique eyepiece makes it suitable for use wherever you are.

Philatelic accessories of all types are available from Stanley Gibbons Publications or at the SG shop in London. The current product guide is available on request. Alternatively, a host of useful information can be found here: www.stanleygibbons.com

Stanley Gibbons Numbers

When Stanley Gibbons published his first stamp catalogue in 1865 the stamps in it were simply listed by country and description. It was not long, however, before there were just too many stamps to be listed in this way and in order to simplify the way in which stamps could be ordered by customers, each was given its unique and individual number.

Nowadays, as each stamp is added to the catalogue in the supplement published in *Gibbons Stamp Monthly*, it is assigned its number; sets being listed according to the date on which they were issued and then by face value within that set. If several stamps of the same value belong to one set, usually issued in the form of a sheet or sheetlet, the numbering starts at the top left-hand stamp and runs down to the stamp at bottom right.

Long definitive series are listed together for the convenience of collectors so this often involves adding new numbers to an existing series. It can also happen that a stamp or set of stamps are discovered which were unknown at the time of issue – these also have to be inserted in their correct chronological sequence.

Easy identification

The Stanley Gibbons number appears in the left-hand column of the stamp listing and should not be confused with the bold number that often appears to its right and refers to its illustration. So, by using the country name and catalogue number, every stamp can be easily identified and, rather than having to order Great Britain 1924 10d. turquoise-blue on Block Cypher watermarked paper, all you have to do is order a Great Britain SG 428 and state whether you want it used or unused.

In order to render them immediately identifiable, certain types of stamps are given a prefix to their catalogue number thus a number prefixed with a 'D' is a postage due stamp, while an 'O' means it's an official stamp. Some countries' stamps also have a prefix to allow them to be easily identified. Thus, in this catalogue, Scotland stamp numbers are prefixed with an 'S' and those for Wales with a 'W'.

Changes

Once a number has been assigned it is not changed unless absolutely necessary. The reason, for this is that collectors often maintain their 'wants lists' using SG numbers, while auction houses around the world quote them in their descriptions, as do books and articles in the philatelic press.

Expertising bodies, including the expert committee of the Royal Philatelic Society London and the British Philatelic Association also quote SG numbers in their certificates, which generally identify scarcer or more valuable stamps, so regular changing of those numbers would render such certificates out-of-date.

Nevertheless, sometimes complete sections of the catalogue, occasionally even complete countries, have to be re-organised, and under such circumstances renumbering does take place – but this is infrequent.

Usually, new stamps added into the middle of listings have a letter suffix. This can occur in two forms. If the stamp is listable in its own right the suffix forms a part of the 'main' number in the left-hand column of the listing. Thus, when the Wilding 4½d. and 5d. values with phosphor bands appeared, in 1961 and 1967 respectively, but the 4d. and 6d., both issued in 1960, had already been given the numbers 616 and 617, the 4½d. became 616*a* and the 5d. was listed as 616*b*.

Varieties of such 'main' stamps, such as errors, booklet panes and watermark varieties are given letter suffixes in a different way, so that the phosphor version of the 1963 6d. Paris Postal Conference stamp (SG 636) has a 'p' suffix which appears in the listing itself, to differentiate it from the normal, non-phosphor stamp – so to order one, all you need to ask for is SG 636p.

Sometimes, of course, so many stamps are subsequently added to a listing that the use of suffix letters would just become too complicated and, so far as Great Britain is concerned, this has happened with the decimal Machin series, which are prefixed 'X' for the conventionally perforated series, first issued in 1971, and 'Y' for the series with elliptical perforations at each side, first issued in 1993. In 2009 a new series with additional security features began to appear and these are listed with a 'U' prefix.

Adding new numbers

Thus when new stamps are added to such series – and several are appearing each year – adding new numbers does not have to mean changing those of subsequently issued commemorative issues.

Within the 'U' series, new 'main' values are initially added with a suffix letter, so the numbers of previously issued stamps do not have to be adjusted with each new catalogue, but every four or five years the complete listing is updated to eliminate the suffix letters and maintain a 'clean' listing of numbers. When ordering stamps from these series it is as well to mention which edition of the catalogue you are using as, if your dealer is using a different one, you may not receive what you expect!

The Stanley Gibbons numbering system represents an easy-to-use and universally recognised system of stamp identification. Collectors all over the world use it to keep their collections in order and dealers sort and classify their stocks by it, so its use makes life easier for everyone.

Stanley Gibbons numbers are fully protected by copyright and, while their use is encouraged, they may not be reproduced without the prior permission of Stanley Gibbons Limited.

The Stanley Gibbons Guide to Stamp Pricing

Catalogue editor and lifelong collector, Hugh Jefferies, offers a few tips.

It is a common fallacy that the prices in this catalogue show what a stamp is 'worth', should you wish to sell it.

They are, instead, the price at which Stanley Gibbons will sell a very fine example of the stamp in question, but that price includes a lot of other factors, as well as the inherent 'value' of the stamp itself. There are costs in running any business and these are built into the price of any stamp shown in the catalogue, although the proportion of the price that relates to the stamp and that which relates to 'business overheads' will vary from stamp to stamp.

What is true is that the prices shown in this catalogue represent an accurate 'guide' to the value of the stamps listed in it. **Stanley Gibbons are now the only major philatelic publisher whose stamp catalogue is also their price list**. Naturally, if the prices are set too high, no one will buy our stamps, if they are too low, we will have difficulty replacing our stocks. It is therefore vitally important to the future of the company that the prices in this catalogue are set as accurately as possible. As a result, a great deal of care is taken over those prices – which is why they are held in such regard by collectors, dealers and stamp auction houses throughout the world.

A very accurate picture

Each year, every price in our annual catalogues is checked and amended if necessary, having regard to the prices being achieved at auction as well as the demands of our customers at 399 Strand and orders coming in via the post, email and our website. Prices are held, increased or reduced according to those factors, giving a very accurate picture of the state of the market for each and every stamp.

Can stamps be purchased for less than the prices quoted in this catalogue? Of course they can. Stanley Gibbons themselves will frequently have stamps in stock at prices lower than 'full catalogue'. Every business offers discounts and makes 'special offers' from time to time and Stanley Gibbons is no different. That apart, however, it should always be remembered that the prices quoted in this catalogue are for stamps in very fine condition. Stamps with minor defects, heavy postmarks, slight fading and other flaws will frequently be offered at lower prices, both by Stanley Gibbons and by other dealers and auction houses.

Checking condition

It is very important that, when you are thinking of buying a stamp for your collection, you carefully consider the condition of the item in question. Does it match up to the Stanley Gibbons definition of 'Very Fine'? If it doesn't, is the price at which it is being offered too high? If you believe that the price is higher that it should be, leave it alone – or if you are really desperate, haggle for a better deal.

The knowledge as to what is 'very fine' and therefore worthy of 'full catalogue' is one that you will gain with experience and will vary from stamp to stamp. Any stamp less than 100 years old should really be perfect in every way, but one can be more forgiving with older issues.

Briefly, here are a few of the things to consider.

- **Gum** – for unused stamps issued after 1936 prices are for unmounted mint – stamps never previously hinged. Modern stamps with hinge marks should be substantially discounted. For earlier stamps, heavy mounts and multiple hinges will also detract from the value, while unused stamps with the gum removed are worth considerably less.

- **Margins** – for imperforate stamps these should be clear on all sides – the design should not be cut into or even touching the edge of the stamp.

- **Perforations** – check that these are complete, that none are missing or short, especially at the stamp corners. Ideally the margin between the stamp design and the perforations should be even and well balanced – known as 'well-centred'.

- **Paper** – Check that there are no tears or thins to the paper – on the front as well as the back – and that there are no bends or creases. Again, the greater the damage the further away from 'full catalogue' the stamp is worth.

- **Postmarks** – these should be clear, clean and should not disfigure the stamp. **The prices for all British stamps issued after 1880 assume used stamps to be cancelled with a clean, clear circular datestamp. Heavy parcel, wavy line or slogan cancellations reduce stamp values significantly**. On the other hand, very lightly cancelled stamps should sometimes be viewed with suspicion. There needs to be enough of the postmark showing to prove that the stamp has really been used!

If the above notes seem complicated, don't worry. You will soon become adept at viewing every stamp in the light of its condition and deciding what proportion of catalogue you are prepared to pay. If you are not certain, ask the dealer for a guarantee that he will refund your money if you're not happy with your purchase. All good dealers will be happy to provide this.

So, buy carefully – but, above all, have fun!

It should always be remembered that the prices quoted in this catalogue are for stamps in very fine condition.

Great Britain Stamp Collector's Glossary

Adhesive A gummed stamp

Albino A design impression without colour

Aniline A fugitive (water soluble) ink or dye

Bisect Part of a stamp that has been cut in two for separate use; usually during a shortage of stamps

Blind perforation A perforation which has not been punched out

Block A group of four or more unseparated stamps

Bogus A spurious, pretend stamp

Booklet A small book containing 'panes' of stamps

Booklet pane A leaf or page of stamps from a booklet

Cachet A commemorative marking, usually applied by rubber stamp

Cancellation Any authorised defacing mark on a stamp

Centre The position of a stamp design within its perforations, e.g. 'well-centred' or 'off-centre'

Chalk-surfaced paper Stamp paper coated with a chalky solution for security purposes. Attempted removal of the postmark damages the surface of the stamp

Charity stamp One bearing a premium or surcharge for charitable purposes

Classic A country's early stamp issues, mostly up to about 1875; a choice stamp

Coil stamp One from a roll of stamps used in vending machines

Coil join A tab uniting two sections of a roll of stamps

Commemorative A stamp issued to mark a special anniversary or event

Country stamp See Regional

Cover A postally used envelope, letter-sheet or wrapper

Cylinder number Letters/numerals in sheet margins identifying printing cylinders. Normally collected in 'Cylinder block' of six stamps. Also see 'Plate number'

Die An engraved plate for impressing design etc. on softer metal

Doctor blade A steel blade which removes surplus ink from the printing cylinder in the press – faulty wiping by this blade will cause a 'Doctor blade' flaw

Embossing A form of printing in relief, now rarely used

Error A mistake in stamp design, printing or production

Essay A trial stamp design, sometimes differing from the issued stamps

Face value The denomination of a stamp, expressed on its face

Fake A genuine stamp doctored in some way to deceive collectors

First Day Cover A cover bearing stamps postmarked on their day of issue

Flaw A fortuitous blemish on a stamp; a printing fault

Forgery A fraudulent copy of a genuine postage stamp, overprint or postmark

Frama stamps See Machine label

Graphite lines Black vertical lines printed on the back of GB definitives, 1957–1959, for use with automatic letter-sorting equipment'. Also see 'Phosphor' stamps

Greetings stamp Stamp intended for use on birthday or other greetings mail

Gum Mucilage on the back of adhesive stamps. Not 'glue'

Gutter The narrow space between stamps in the sheet permitting perforation

Gutter margin The blank margins dividing a sheet of stamps into panes

Handstamp A postmark or overprint applied by hand

Imperforate Stamps printed and issued without perforations, deliberately or in error

Imprint The name of the printer or issuing authority inscribed on the stamps or in the sheet margins

Imprinted stamps Stamps other than adhesives, printed direct on postal stationery items (postcards, envelopes, etc)

Jubilee line Coloured line found in the sheet margin of British stamps

Local A stamp with geographical limits of postal use and validity. These are not normally listed in the Stanley Gibbons catalogues

Machin The name given to GB definitives, first issued in 1967, bearing the Queen's head designed by Arnold Machin

Machine label Postage stamp produced by a micro-processor machine after the insertion of coins of the required value, popularly known as Frama stamps

Maltese cross Name given to the cross-shaped cancellation used on the first British stamps

Margin The unprinted edging surrounding or dividing a sheet of stamps. See also 'Gutter margin'

Maximum card A picture postcard bearing a stamp and cancellation relevant to the picture on the card

Miniature sheet A small sheet of one or several stamps, usually with decorative margins, issued as a souvenir for collectors

Mint A stamp in its original pristine state, with full gum (if so issued), when it is said to have its 'original gum' ('O.G.'). 'Unmounted mint' stamps have not been hinged. Also see 'Unused'

Mulready Envelopes and letter sheets issued by Britain in 1840 with a pictorial motif designed by William Mulready

Non Value Indicator stamp (NVI) A stamp which bears no monetary inscription, but shows the class of postage (1st, 2nd, etc) instead

Obsolete A stamp no longer sold by a post office though it may still be valid for postage

Overprint A printed addition to a stamp. Also see 'Surcharge'

Pair Two unseparated stamps, joined as originally issued

Pane A formation or group of stamps within the sheet. Also see 'Booklet pane'

Perforations Holes punched between stamps in sheets to enable easy separation

Personalised stamp Stamp with an attached non-postal label bearing an image taken from a personal photograph

Phosphor stamps Stamps overprinted or coated with phosphorescent materials recognised by high technology letter sorting machinery

Plate number Letters/numerals in sheet margins identifying printing plates. Also see 'Cylinder number' many Victorian stamps included the plate number in the design; these are listed in this catalogue

Post & Go stamp Illustrated self-adhesive label dispensed from a machine with inkjet printed indicator of the service required. This catalogue only lists Post & Go stamps available from machines within post offices, it does not include those from stamp exhibitions or non-post office establishments.

Postmark Any mark, such as a cancellation, connected with the postal service and found on items transmitted by post

Presentation pack A philatelic souvenir containing a set of stamps and descriptive text

Prestige booklet Stamp booklet devoted to a particular subject or event and containing special panes of stamps with descriptive text printed alongside

Proof A trial impression taken from an original die or printing plate

Regional Name given by collectors to stamps issued by Royal Mail (who term them Country stamps) for use in England, Scotland, Wales or Northern Ireland. Issues were also made for Guernsey and Jersey (until 1969) and the Isle of Man (until 1973)

Seahorse Name given to the high value definitive stamps of King George V

Self-adhesive Gummed stamps (with protective backing) which do not require moistening

Se-tenant Stamps of different design or face value that are joined together

Specimen Sample stamp usually with 'specimen' overprinted or perforated on it

Strip Three or more stamps joined in a row

Tête-bêche A stamp inverted in relation to the adjoining stamp in a pair

Traffic lights Collectors' term for the colour check dots found in sheet margins

Unused An uncancelled stamp, not necessarily 'mint'

Used A stamp which has been postally used and appropriately postmarked

Used abroad Stamps of one country used and postmarked in another

Used on piece Stamp kept on part of the original cover to preserve the complete postmark

Variety A stamp differing in some detail from the normal issue

Watermark A distinctive device or emblem in stamps, formed by 'thinning' of the paper during production. Watermarks illustrated in this catalogue are shown as if viewed through the front of the stamp

Wilding The name given to British definitive stamps, first issued in 1952, bearing the Queen's head from a photographic portrait by Dorothy Wilding

Wing margin Wide margin on one side of a stamp caused by central perforation of the sheet gutter margin

For other and fuller definitions, see the Stanley Gibbons book *Philatelic Terms Illustrated* by James Mackay.

How can Stanley Gibbons help you to build your collection?

Our History

Stanley Gibbons started trading in 1856 and we have been at the forefront of stamp collecting for more than 160 years, making us the world's oldest philatelic company. We can help you build your collection in a wide variety of ways – all with the backing of our unrivalled expertise.

When building a collection it helps to know what you have. You can use Collect British Stamps as a checklist to highlight all the items you currently own. You can then easily see where the gaps are that you need to fill.

Visit 399 Strand, London, UK

Our world famous stamp shop is a collector's paradise which aims to keep a full range of Great Britain stamps to sell at current catalogue price — so if there are any changes via a different catalogue, then prices will be adjusted accordingly. As well as stamps, the shop stocks albums, accessories and specialist philatelic books. Plan a visit now!

GB Specialist Department

When purchasing high value items you should definitely contact our specialist department for advice and guarantees on the items purchased. We can explain what to look for and where, and help you plan your future collection.

Auctions and Valuations

Stanley Gibbons Auctions have been running since the 1900's. They offer a range of auctions to suit all levels of collectors and dealers. You can of course also sell your collection or individual rare items through our public auctions and regular postal auctions. You can check out charges with the auction department directly.

Stanley Gibbons Publications

Our catalogues are trusted worldwide as the industry standard To keep up to date with new issues you can follow the additions to this listing in our magazine Gibbons Stamp Monthly. This is a must-read for all collectors and dealers. It contains news, views and insights into all things philatelic, from beginner to specialist.

Completing the set

When is it cheaper to complete your collection by buying a whole set rather than item by item? You can use the prices in Collect British Stamps, which lists single item values and a complete set value, to check if it is better to buy the odd items missing, or a complete set. Some of the definitive sets can be built up over time. The current definitive set is regularly augmented by Royal Mail.

Condition

Condition can make a big difference to the price you can pay for an item (see 'The Stanley Gibbons Guide to Stamp Pricing on p xiv). The prices in this catalogue are for items in very fine condition. When building your collection you do need to keep condition in mind and always buy the best condition you can find and afford. Collectors are reminded that for issues from 1936 to date, prices in the unused column are for unmounted mint. This means that the condition of the gum is the same as issued from the Post Office. If the gum is disturbed or has had an adhesion it can be classed as mounted. When buying issues prior to 1936 you should always look for the least amount of disturbance and adhesion. You do have to keep in mind the age of the issue when looking at the condition.

When buying philatelic items listed you need to make sure they are in the same condition as issued by the Post Office. This applies to Presentation Packs, were the stamps are issued on a stock card with an information card and held together in a plastic wallet and also to Year Books, which should be in a slip case with a stock card of stamps. The prices quoted are for a complete item in good condition so make sure you check this – and of course that they are complete. You will find some items may appear in different formats (e.g. language cards, different bindings, etc) which will be listed under the normal listing within this catalogue.

Ask the Experts

While you are building your collection, if you need help or guidance, you are welcome to come along to Stanley Gibbons in the Strand and ask for assistance. If you would like to have your collection appraised, you can arrange for a verbal evaluation Monday to Friday 9.00am – 4.30pm. We also provide insurance valuations should you require. Of course this up-to-date catalogue listing can assist with the valuation and may be presented to an insurance agent or company.

Guide to Entries

(A) Accession to the Throne

(B) Illustration – Generally all stamps illustrated. To comply with Post Office regulations illustrations are reduced to 75%, with overprints shown actual size.

(C) Illustration or Type Number – These numbers are used to help identify stamps, in the type column.

(D) Date of Issue – When a set of definitive stamps have been issued over several years the Year Date given is for the earliest issue, commemorative sets are set in chronological order.

(E) Phosphor Description – Phosphorised paper is activated by ultraviolet light.

(F) Perforations – The 'perforation' is the number of holes in a length of 2 cm, as measured by the Stanley Gibbons *Instanta* gauge. From 1992 certain stamps occur with a large elliptical (oval) hole inserted in each line of vertical perforations. From 2009 certain stamps have U-shaped die-cut slits.

(G) Stanley Gibbons Catalogue Number – This is a unique number for each stamp to help the collector identify stamps in the listing. The Stanley Gibbons numbering system is universally recognized as definitive, where insufficient numbers have been left to provide for additional stamps listings, some stamps will have a suffix letter after the catalogue number.

(H) Catalogue Price – Mint/Unused. Prices quoted for pre-1945 stamps are for lightly hinged examples. Prices quoted of unused King Edward VIII to Queen Elizabeth issues are for unmounted mint.

(I) Catalogue Price – Used. Prices generally refer to very fine postally used examples.

Prices

Before February 1971 British currency was:

£1 = 20s. One pound = twenty shillings *and*
1s = 12d. One Shilling = 12 pence

Under decimalisation this became:

£1 = 100p One pound = one hundred (new) pence

Shown in Catalogue as	Explanation
10	10 pence
1·75	£1·75
15·00	£15
£150	£150
£2300	£2300

(J) Face Value – This refers to the value of the stamp and is sold at the Post Office when issued. Some modern stamps do not have their values in figures but instead indicate the service which they cover.

(K) Type Number – Indicates a design type on which stamp is based. These are bold figures found below each illustration. The type numbers are also given in bold in the second column of figures alongside the stamp description to indicate the design of each stamp.

(L) Colour – Colour of stamps (if fewer than four colours, otherwise noted as 'multicoloured').

(M) Sets of Stamps – Two or more stamps with a common theme or subject.

(N) First Day Covers – Prices for first day covers are for complete sets used on plain covers or on special covers.

(O) Presentation Packs – Special packs consisting of the issue and slip-in cards with printed information inside a protective covering.

(P) PHQ Cards – Each card shows a large reproduction of a current British stamp.

(Q) Sets of Gutters – The term is used for a pair of stamps separated by part of the blank gutter margin or with Traffic Lights on the gutter margin.

(R) Footnote – Further information on background or key facts on issues.

(S) Other Types of Stamps – Postage Dues, Officials and Regional Issues

(T) Number Prefix – Stamps other than definitives and commemoratives have a prefix letter before the catalogue number.

QUEEN ELIZABETH II

(A) Accession to the Throne ———— ●6 February, 1952

(B) Illustration ————

(C) Illustration or Type Number ———— ● **1862** *The Very Hungry Caterpillar* (Eric Carle)

E ———— **1526** Butterfly Hat by Dai Rees

(J) Face Value

Nos. 2589/90, 2591/2, 2593/4 and 2595/6 were printed together, *se-tenant*, as horizontal pairs in sheets of 60(2 panes 6 × 5).

Animal Tales

(D) Date of Issue ———— ● **2006** (10 Jan.) One side phosphor band (2nd) or two ● phosphor bands (others). Perf 14½ ●

(E) Phosphor Description
(F) Perforations

SG No.	Type	Description	Unused	Used		
2589	**1856**	(2nd) multicoloured	30	35	☐	☐
		a. Horiz pair. Nos. 2589/90	70	70	☐	☐
2590	**1857**	(2nd) multicoloured	30	35	☐	☐
2591	**1858**	(1st) multicoloured	45	50	☐	☐
		a. Horiz pair. Nos. 2591/2	1·50	1·50	☐	☐
2592	**1859**	(1st) multicoloured	45	50	☐	☐
2593	**1860**	42p multicoloured	65	70	☐	☐
		a. Horiz pair. Nos. 2593/4	3·75	3·75	☐	☐
2594	**1861**	42p multicoloured	65	70	☐	☐
2595	**1862**	68p multicoloured	1·00	1·10	☐	☐
		a. Horiz pair. Nos. 2595/6	4·75	4·75	☐	☐
2596	**1863**	68p multicoloured	1·00	1·10	☐	☐
		Set of 8	8·50	8·50	☐	☐
		First Day Cover		8·00		
		Presentation Pack	12·00			
		PHQ Cards (set of 8)	4·50	12·00	☐	☐
		Set of 4 Gutter Blocks of 4	13·00		☐	
		Set of 4 Traffic Light Gutter Blocks of 8	28·00		☐	

(G) Stanley Gibbons Catalogue Number

(J) Face Value

(K) Type Number

(M) Sets

(O) Special Packs

(Q) Gutter Combinations

(H) Catalogue Value – Unused

(I) Catalogue Value – Used

(L) Colour

(N) FDC for Complete Sets

(P) PHQ Cards

No. 2595 contains two die-cut holes.

(R) Footnotes ———— A design as No. 2592 but self-adhesive was also issued in sheets of 20 with each stamp accompanied by a *se-tenant* label.

(S) Postage Due ———— ● D **1**

POSTAGE DUE STAMPS ●

(S) Other Types of Stamps

1968–69 Design size 21½ × 17½ mm. No wmk

No.	Type	Description	Unused	Used		
(T) Number Prefix ● D75	D **1**	4d blue	7·00	6·75	☐	☐
D76		8d red	50	1·00	☐	☐

QUEEN VICTORIA

1837 (20 June)–1901 (22 January)

5   8   6

IDENTIFICATION. In this checklist Victorian stamps are classified firstly according to which printing method was used –line-engraving, embossing or surface-printing.

Corner letters. Numerous stamps also have letters in all four, or just the lower corners. These were an anti-forgery device and the letters differ from stamp to stamp. If present in all four corners the upper pair are the reverse of the lower. Note the importance of these corner letters in the way the checklist is arranged.

Watermarks. Further classification depends on watermarks: these are illustrated in normal position, with stamps priced accordingly.

9 Watermark extending over three stamps

Letters in all four corners

Plate numbers. Stamps included a 'plate number' in their design and this affects valuation. The cheapest plates are priced here; see complete list of plate numbers overleaf.

1 Line-engraved Issues

1   **1a**   **1b**

3 White lines added above and below head   **2** Small Crown watermark   **4** Large Crown watermark

Letters in lower corners

1840 Wmk Small Crown T **2** Imperforate

2	**1**	1d.	black	£12500	£375	☐ ☐
5	**1a**	2d.	blue	£38000	£975	☐ ☐

1841

8	**1b**	1d.	red-brown	£600	35·00	☐ ☐
14	**3**	2d.	blue	£5000	90·00	☐ ☐

1854–57

(i) Wmk Small Crown T **2** Perf 16

17	**1b**	1d.	red-brown	£375	35·00	☐ ☐
19	**3**	2d.	blue	£4700	£100	☐ ☐

(ii) Wmk Small Crown T **2** Perf 14

24	**1b**	1d.	red-brown	£700	70·00	☐ ☐
23	**3**	2d.	blue	£13000	£225	☐ ☐

(iii) Wmk Large Crown T **4** Perf 16

26	**1b**	1d.	red	£2500	£130	☐ ☐
36a	**3**	2d.	blue	£14500	£325	☐ ☐

(iv) Wmk Large Crown T **4** Perf 14

40	**1b**	1d.	red	40·00	8·00	☐ ☐
34	**3**	2d.	blue	£2800	70·00	☐ ☐

7

1858–70

		(i) Wmk T **9** Perf 14				
48	**7**	½d.	red	£110	30·00	☐ ☐
		(ii) Wmk Large Crown T **4** Perf 14				
43	**5**	1d.	red	27·00	2·75	☐ ☐
51	**8**	1½d.	red	£500	75·00	☐ ☐
45	**6**	2d.	blue	£350	15·00	☐ ☐

Plate numbers on stamps 1858–1870 having letters in all four corners

Showing position of the plate number on the 1d. and 2d. values. (Plate 170 shown)   Showing the plate number (9) on the ½d. value   Position of plate Number (3) on the 1 ½d. value

HALFPENNY VALUE (SG 48)

48	*Plate 1*	£325	£100	☐ ☐
48	*Plate 3*	£250	55·00	☐ ☐
48	*Plate 4*	£150	50·00	☐ ☐
48	*Plate 5*	£110	30·00	☐ ☐
48	*Plate 6*	£120	30·00	☐ ☐
48	*Plate 8*	£600	£120	☐ ☐
48	*Plate 9*	£5000	£700	☐ ☐
48	*Plate 10*	£130	30·00	☐ ☐
48	*Plate 11*	£120	30·00	☐ ☐
48	*Plate 12*	£120	30·00	☐ ☐
48	*Plate 13*	£120	30·00	☐ ☐
48	*Plate 14*	£120	30·00	☐ ☐
48	*Plate 15*	£175	50·00	☐ ☐
48	*Plate 19*	£300	65·00	☐ ☐
48	*Plate 20*	£350	85·00	☐ ☐

PENNY VALUE (SG 43)

43	*Plate 71*	55·00	4·00	☐ ☐
43	*Plate 72*	60·00	5·00	☐ ☐
43	*Plate 73*	60·00	4·00	☐ ☐
43	*Plate 74*	60·00	2·75	☐ ☐
43	*Plate 76*	55·00	2·75	☐ ☐
43	*Plate 77*	—	£600000	☐ ☐
43	*Plate 78*	£130	2·75	☐ ☐
43	*Plate 79*	48·00	2·75	☐ ☐
43	*Plate 80*	65·00	2·75	☐ ☐

43	Plate 81	65·00	3·00	☐	☑	43	Plate 155	70·00	3·00	☐	☐
43	Plate 82	£130	5·00	☐	☐	43	Plate 156	65·00	2·75	☐	☑
43	Plate 83	£155	9·00	☐	☐	43	Plate 157	70·00	2·75	☐	☑
43	Plate 84	80·00	3·00	☐	☑	43	Plate 158	48·00	2·75	☐	☑
43	Plate 85	60·00	4·00	☐	☑	43	Plate 159	48·00	2·75	☐	☑
43	Plate 86	70·00	5·00	☐	☐	43	Plate 160	48·00	2·75	☐	☑
43	Plate 87	48·00	2·75	☐	☑	43	Plate 161	80·00	9·00	☐	☐
43	Plate 88	£190	9·50	☐	☐	43	Plate 162	70·00	9·00	☐	☑
43	Plate 89	60·00	2·75	☐	☑	43	Plate 163	70·00	4·00	☐	☑
43	Plate 90	60·00	2·75	☐	☐	43	Plate 164	70·00	4·00	☐	☑
43	Plate 91	75·00	7·00	☐	☑	43	Plate 165	65·00	2·75	☐	☐
43	Plate 92	55·00	2·75	☐	☑	43	Plate 166	65·00	7·00	☐	☑
43	Plate 93	70·00	2·75	☐	☑	43	Plate 167	65·00	2·75	☐	☑
43	Plate 94	65·00	6·00	☐	☐	43	Plate 168	70·00	10·00	☐	☐
43	Plate 95	60·00	2·75	☐	☑	43	Plate 169	80·00	9·00	☐	☐
43	Plate 96	65·00	2·75	☐	☐	43	Plate 170	55·00	2·75	☐	☐
43	Plate 97	60·00	4·50	☐	☑	43	Plate 171	27·00	2·75	☐	☐
43	Plate 98	70·00	7·00	☐	☐	43	Plate 172	48·00	2·75	☐	☐
43	Plate 99	75·00	6·00	☐	☐	43	Plate 173	95·00	11·00	☐	☐
43	Plate 100	80·00	3·00	☐	☐	43	Plate 174	48·00	2·75	☐	☐
43	Plate 101	80·00	11·00	☐	☐	43	Plate 175	80·00	4·50	☐	☐
43	Plate 102	65·00	2·75	☐	☑	43	Plate 176	80·00	3·00	☐	☐
43	Plate 103	70·00	4·50	☐	☑	43	Plate 177	60·00	2·75	☐	☐
43	Plate 104	£100	6·00	☐	☑	43	Plate 178	80·00	4·50	☐	☐
43	Plate 105	£130	9·00	☐	☑	43	Plate 179	70·00	3·00	☐	☐
43	Plate 106	75·00	2·75	☐	☐	43	Plate 180	80·00	6·50	☐	☐
43	Plate 107	80·00	9·00	☐	☑	43	Plate 181	65·00	2·75	☐	☐
43	Plate 108	£110	9·00	☐	☐	43	Plate 182	£130	6·50	☐	☐
43	Plate 109	£120	4·50	☑	☑	43	Plate 183	75·00	4·00	☐	☐
43	Plate 110	80·00	11·00	☐	☑	43	Plate 184	48·00	3·00	☐	☐
43	Plate 111	70·00	3·00	☐	☐	43	Plate 185	70·00	4·00	☐	☑
43	Plate 112	90·00	3·00	☐	☐	43	Plate 186	90·00	3·00	☐	☐
43	Plate 113	70·00	15·00	☐	☐	43	Plate 187	70·00	2·75	☐	☐
43	Plate 114	£325	15·00	☐	☐	43	Plate 188	95·00	12·00	☐	☐
43	Plate 115	£130	3·00	☐	☐	43	Plate 189	95·00	8·50	☐	☐
43	Plate 116	£100	11·00	☐	☐	43	Plate 190	70·00	7·00	☐	☐
43	Plate 117	65·00	2·75	☐	☐	43	Plate 191	48·00	9·00	☐	☐
43	Plate 118	70·00	2·75	☐	☐	43	Plate 192	70·00	2·75	☐	☐
43	Plate 119	65·00	2·75	☐	☐	43	Plate 193	48·00	2·75	☐	☐
43	Plate 120	27·00	2·75	☐	☐	43	Plate 194	70·00	10·00	☐	☐
43	Plate 121	60·00	11·00	☐	☐	43	Plate 195	70·00	10·00	☐	☐
43	Plate 122	27·00	2·75	☐	☑	43	Plate 196	70·00	6·50	☐	☐
43	Plate 123	60·00	2·75	☐	☐	43	Plate 197	75·00	11·00	☐	☐
43	Plate 124	42·00	2·75	☐	☑	43	Plate 198	60·00	7·00	☐	☑
43	Plate 125	60·00	2·75	☐	☐	43	Plate 199	75·00	7·00	☐	☐
43	Plate 127	75·00	3·00	☐	☐	43	Plate 200	80·00	2·75	☐	☐
43	Plate 129	60·00	10·00	☐	☐	43	Plate 201	48·00	6·00	☐	☐
43	Plate 130	75·00	3·00	☐	☐	43	Plate 202	80·00	10·00	☐	☐
43	Plate 131	85·00	20·00	☐	☐	43	Plate 203	48·00	20·00	☐	☐
43	Plate 132	£190	27·00	☐	☐	43	Plate 204	75·00	3·00	☐	☐
43	Plate 133	£160	11·00	☐	☑	43	Plate 205	75·00	4·00	☐	☐
43	Plate 134	27·00	2·75	☐	☐	43	Plate 206	75·00	11·00	☐	☐
43	Plate 135	£130	30·00	☐	☑	43	Plate 207	80·00	11·00	☐	☐
43	Plate 136	£130	24·00	☐	☐	43	Plate 208	75·00	18·00	☐	☐
43	Plate 137	42·00	3·00	☐	☐	43	Plate 209	65·00	10·00	☐	☐
43	Plate 138	32·00	2·75	☐	☐	43	Plate 210	90·00	15·00	☐	☐
43	Plate 139	80·00	20·00	☐	☑	43	Plate 211	95·00	25·00	☐	☐
43	Plate 140	32·00	2·75	☐	☑	43	Plate 212	80·00	13·00	☐	☐
43	Plate 141	£160	11·00	☐	☐	43	Plate 213	80·00	13·00	☐	☐
43	Plate 142	95·00	30·00	☐	☑	43	Plate 214	90·00	23·00	☐	☐
43	Plate 143	80·00	17·00	☐	☑	43	Plate 215	90·00	23·00	☐	☐
43	Plate 144	£130	25·00	☐	☑	43	Plate 216	95·00	23·00	☐	☐
43	Plate 145	48·00	3·00	☐	☐	43	Plate 217	95·00	9·00	☐	☐
43	Plate 146	60·00	7·00	☐	☑	43	Plate 218	90·00	10·00	☐	☐
43	Plate 147	70·00	4·00	☐	☑	43	Plate 219	£130	85·00	☐	☐
43	Plate 148	60·00	4·00	☐	☑	43	Plate 220	60·00	9·00	☐	☐
43	Plate 149	60·00	7·00	☐	☑	43	Plate 221	95·00	20·00	☐	☐
43	Plate 150	27·00	2·75	☐	☑	43	Plate 222	£110	50·00	☐	☐
43	Plate 151	80·00	11·00	☐	☐	43	Plate 223	£130	75·00	☐	☐
43	Plate 152	80·00	7·50	☐	☑	43	Plate 224	£165	65·00	☐	☐
43	Plate 153	£140	11·00	☐	☐	43	Plate 225	£3000	£700	☐	☐
43	Plate 154	70·00	2·75	☐	☑						

Plates 69, 70, 75, 77, 126 and 128 were prepared but rejected. No stamps therefore exist, except for a very few from Plate 77 which somehow reached the public. Plate 177 stamps, by accident or design, are sometimes passed off as the rare Plate 77.

THREE-HALFPENNY VALUE (SG 52)

52	*Plate (1)*	£725	£110	☐	☐
52	*Plate 3*	£500	75·00	☐	☐

Plate 1 did not have the plate number in the design. Plate 2 was not completed and no stamps exist.

TWOPENNY VALUE (SG 45)

45	*Plate 7*	£2000	65·00	☑	☐
45	*Plate 8*	£1850	45·00	☐	☐
45	*Plate 9*	£350	15·00	☐	☐
45	*Plate 12*	£3000	£140	☐	☐
46	*Plate 13*	£375	30·00	☐	☐
46	*Plate 14*	£500	38·00	☐	☐
46	*Plate 15*	£525	38·00	☐	☑

Plates 10 and 11 were prepared but rejected.

2 Embossed Issues

Prices are for stamps cut square and with average to fine embossing. Stamps with exceptionally clear embossing are worth more.

12 11 10

13

1847–54 Wmk **13** (6d), no wmk (others) Imperforate

59	**12**	6d.	lilac	£19500	£1000	☐	☐
57	**11**	10d.	brown	£11500	£1500	☐	☐
54	**10**	1s.	green	£24000	£1000	☐	☐

Collectors are reminded that Types **10/12** were also used to print postal stationery. 6d. stamps without watermark and 10d. and 1s. values without 'silk' threads embedded in the paper come from this source and should not be confused with the listed stamps.

3 Surface-printed Issues

IDENTIFICATION. Check first whether the design includes corner letters or not, as mentioned for 'Line-engraved Issues'. The checklist is divided up according to whether any letters are small or large, also whether they are white (uncoloured) or printed in the colour of the stamp. Further identification then depends on watermark.

PERFORATION. Except for Nos. 126/129 all the following issues of Queen Victoria are perf 14.

14

15 16 17

18 19 20 Emblems

No corner letters

1855–57

(i) Wmk Small Garter T **15**							
62	**14**	4d.	red		£8500	£450	☐ ☐
(ii) Wmk Medium Garter T **16**							
64	**14**	4d.	red		£13000	£500	☐ ☐
(iii) Wmk Large Garter T **17**							
66a	**14**	4d.	red		£1750	£150	☐ ☐
(iv) Wmk Emblems T **20**							
68	**18**	6d.	lilac		£1350	£120	☐ ☐
72	**19**	1s.	green		£3250	£350	☐ ☐

Plate numbers. Stamps Nos. 90/163 should be checked for the 'plate numbers' indicated, as this affects valuation (the cheapest plates are priced here). The mark 'Pl.' shows that several numbers exist, priced in separate list overleaf.

Plate numbers are the small numerals appearing in duplicate in some part of the frame design or adjacent to the lower corner letters (in the 5s value a single numeral above the lower inscription).

21 22 23

24 **25**

Small white corner letters

1862–64 Wmk Emblems T **20**, except 4d (Large Garter T **17**)

76	**21**	3d.	red	£2700	£350	☐	☐
80	**22**	4d.	red	£2000	£140	☐	☐
84	**23**	6d.	lilac	£2250	£140	☐	☑
87	**24**	9d.	straw	£4000	£475	☐	☑
90	**25**	1s.	green Pl.	£3200	£300	☐	☑

26 **27** **28** Hyphen in SIX-PENCE

29 **30** **31**

Large white corner letters

1865–67 Wmk Emblems T **20** except 4d (Large Garter T **17**)

92	**26**	3d.	red (Plate 4)	£2500	£250	☐	☑
94	**27**	4d.	vermilion Pl.	£575	75·00	☐	☑
97	**28**	6d.	lilac Pl.	£1200	£140	☐	☐
98	**29**	9d.	straw Pl.	£4800	£600	☐	☑
99	**30**	10d.	brown (Plate 1)	* £55000		☐	
101	**31**	1s.	green (Plate 4)	£2850	£275	☐	☑

32 **33** Spray of Rose **34**

1867–80 Wmk Spray of Rose T **33**

103	**26**	3d.	red Pl.	£525	60·00	☐	☐
105	**28**	6d.	lilac (with (hyphen) (Plate 6)	£1900	£150	☐	☐
109		6d.	mauve (without hyphen) Pl.	£700	90·00	☐	☑
111	**29**	9d.	pale straw (Plate 4)	£2400	£300	☐	☑
112	**30**	10d.	brown Pl.	£3600	£400	☐	☑
117	**31**	1s.	green Pl.	£800	45·00	☐	☑
118	**32**	2s.	blue Pl.	£4500	£225	☐	☑
121		2s.	brown (Plate 1)	£30000	£4250	☐	☐

1872–73 Wmk Spray of Rose T **33**

122b	**34**	6d.	brown Pl.	£700	65·00	☐	☐
125		6d.	grey (Plate 12)	£1900	£300	☐	☐

PLATE NUMBERS ON STAMPS OF 1862–83

Small White Corner Letters (1862–64)

90	*Plate 2*	1s. green	£3200	£300	☐	☐
91	*Plate 3*		£35000		☐	

Plate 2 is actually numbered as '1' and Plate 3 as '2' on the stamps.

Large White Corner Letters (1865–83)

103	*Plate 4*	3d. red	£1850	£300	☐	☑
103	*Plate 5*		£525	70·00	☐	☑
103	*Plate 6*		£550	70·00	☐	☑
103	*Plate 7*		£650	70·00	☐	☑
103	*Plate 8*		£625	60·00	☐	☑
103	*Plate 9*		£625	70·00	☐	☑
103	*Plate 10*		£875	£150	☐	☑
94	*Plate 7*	4d. vermilion	£650	£130	☐	☑
94	*Plate 8*		£600	90·00	☐	☑
94	*Plate 9*		£600	90·00	☐	☐
94	*Plate 10*		£825	£150	☐	☐
94	*Plate 11*		£625	90·00	☐	☐
94	*Plate 12*		£575	75·00	☐	☑
94	*Plate 13*		£650	75·00	☐	☐
94	*Plate 14*		£775	£110	☐	☐
97	*Plate 5*	6d. lilac	£1150	£140	☐	☑
97	*Plate 6*		£3800	£275	☐	☐
109	*Plate 8*	6d. mauve	£800	£140	☐	☐
109	*Plate 9*		£700	90·00	☐	☑
109	*Plate 10*		* £37500		☐	
123	*Plate 11*	6d. buff	£1100	£125	☐	☑
123	*Plate 12*		£3400	£350	☐	☐
111	*Plate 4*	9d. pale straw	£2400	£300	☐	☐
114	*Plate 1*	10d. brown	£3600	£400	☐	☐
114	*Plate 2*		£50000	£15000	☐	☐
117	*Plate 4*	1s. green	£975	65·00	☐	☑
117	*Plate 5*		£800	45·00	☐	☐
117	*Plate 6*		£1200	45·00	☐	☐
117	*Plate 7*		£1400	90·00	☐	☑
118	*Plate 1*	2s. blue	£4500	£225	☐	☑
118	*Plate 3*		* £16500		☐	
127	*Plate 1*	5s. red	£9500	£675	☐	☐
127	*Plate 2*		£15000	£1500	☐	☐

Large Coloured Corner Letters (1873–83)

139	*Plate 1*	2½d. mauve	£650	£120	☐	☐
139	*Plate 2*		£650	£120	☐	☐
139	*Plate 3*		£1000	£175	☐	☐
141	*Plate 3*	2½d. mauve	£1350	£150	☐	☐
141	*Plate 4*		£525	85·00	☐	☑
141	*Plate 5*		£525	85·00	☐	☑
141	*Plate 6*		£525	85·00	☐	☑
141	*Plate 7*		£525	85·00	☐	☐
141	*Plate 8*		£525	85·00	☐	☐
141	*Plate 9*		£525	85·00	☐	☐
141	*Plate 10*		£550	85·00	☐	☐
141	*Plate 11*		£525	85·00	☐	☐
141	*Plate 12*		£525	85·00	☐	☑
141	*Plate 13*		£525	85·00	☐	☑
141	*Plate 14*		£525	85·00	☐	☑
141	*Plate 15*		£525	85·00	☐	☐
141	*Plate 16*		£525	85·00	☐	☐
141	*Plate 17*		£1700	£300	☐	☐
142	*Plate 17*	2½d. blue	£575	75·00	☐	☐
142	*Plate 18*		£575	55·00	☐	☐
142	*Plate 19*		£575	55·00	☐	☐
142	*Plate 20*		£575	55·00	☐	☑
157	*Plate 21*	2½d. blue	£500	45·00	☐	☐
157	*Plate 22*		£450	45·00	☐	☐
157	*Plate 23*		£450	35·00	☐	☐
143	*Plate 11*	3d. red	£450	80·00	☐	☑
143	*Plate 12*		£525	80·00	☐	☐
143	*Plate 14*		£525	80·00	☐	☑
143	*Plate 15*		£450	80·00	☐	☑
143	*Plate 16*		£450	80·00	☐	☑
143	*Plate 17*		£525	80·00	☐	☐

143	Plate 18		£525	80·00	
143	Plate 19		£450	80·00	
143	Plate 20		£850	£140	
158	Plate 20	3d. red	£900	£150	
158	Plate 21		£500	£100	
152	Plate 15	4d. vermilion	£3000	£475	
152	Plate 16		*£35000		
153	Plate 15	4d. green	£1600	£325	
153	Plate 16		£1400	£300	
153	Plate 17		*£20000		
160	Plate 17	4d. brown	£475	80·00	
160	Plate 18		£450	75·00	
147	Plate 13	6d. grey	£500	90·00	
147	Plate 14		£500	90·00	
147	Plate 15		£500	90·00	
147	Plate 16		£500	90·00	
147	Plate 17		£950	£180	
161	Plate 17	6d. grey	£425	80·00	
161	Plate 18		£400	80·00	
150	Plate 8	1s. green	£825	£175	
150	Plate 9		£825	£175	
150	Plate 10		£775	£200	
150	Plate 11		£775	£175	
150	Plate 12		£650	£160	
150	Plate 13		£650	£160	
150	Plate 14		*£40000		
163	Plate 13	1s. brown	£875	£170	
163	Plate 14		£750	£170	

35   **36**   **37**

38

39 Maltese Cross   **40** Large Anchor

1867–83

		(i) Wmk Maltese Cross T **39** Perf 15½ × 15		
126	**35**	5s. red Pl.	£9500	£675
128	**36**	10s. grey (Plate 1)	£50000	£3200
129	**37**	£1 brown (Plate 1)	£75000	£4500
		(ii) Wmk Large Anchor T **40** Perf 14		
134	**35**	5s. red (Plate 4)	£28000	£3800
131	**36**	10s. grey (Plate 1)	£110000	£4500
132	**37**	£1 brown (Plate 1)	£140000	£7500
137	**38**	£5 orange (Plate 1)	£12500	£3500

41   **42**   **43**

44   **45**   **46**

47 Small anchor   **48** Orb   **49** Imperial Crown

Large coloured corner letters

1873–80

		(i) Wmk Small Anchor T **47**			
139	**41**	2½d. mauve Pl.	£675	£120	
		(ii) Wmk Orb T **48**			
141	**41**	2½d. mauve Pl.	£525	85·00	
142		2½d. blue Pl.	£575	55·00	
		(iii) Wmk Spray of Rose T **33**			
143	**42**	3d. red Pl.	£450	80·00	
145	**43**	6d. pale buff (Plate 13)	*£25000		
147		6d. grey Pl.	£500	90·00	
150	**44**	1s. green Pl.	£650	£160	
151		1s. brown (Plate 13)	£4750	£550	
		(iv) Wmk Large Garter T **17**			
152	**45**	4d. vermilion Pl.	£3000	£475	
153		4d. green Pl.	£1400	£300	
154		4d. brown (Plate 17)	£2800	£500	
156	**46**	8d. orange (Plate 1)	£1850	£350	

3d (**50**)   6d (**51**)

Surcharges in red

		1880–83 Wmk Imperial Crown T **49**			
157	**41**	2½d. blue Pl.	£450	35·00	
158	**42**	3d. red Pl.	£500	£100	
159		3d. on 3d. lilac (surch Type **50**)	£650	£160	
160	**45**	4d. brown Pl.	£450	75·00	
161	**43**	6d. grey Pl.	£400	80·00	
162		6d. on 6d. lilac (surch Type **51**)	£675	£150	
163	**44**	1s. brown Pl.	£750	£170	

52   **53**   **54**

55   56

1880–81 Wmk Imperial Crown T **49**

164	**52**	½d. green	55·00	22·00
166	**53**	1d. brown	35·00	15·00
167	**54**	1½d. brown	£250	60·00
168	**55**	2d. red	£350	£120
169	**56**	5d. indigo	£725	£175

57   Die I   Die II

1881 Wmk Imperial Crown T **49**

		(a) 14 dots in each corner, Die I		
171	**57**	1d. lilac	£225	45·00
		(b) 16 dots in each corner, Die II		
174	**57**	1d. mauve	2·75	1·75

58   59   60

Coloured letters in the corners

1883–84 Wmk Anchor T **40**

178	**58**	2s.6d. lilac	£600	£160
181	**59**	5s. red	£975	£250
183	**60**	10s. blue	£2250	£525

61

1884 Wmk 3 Imperial Crowns T **49**

185	**61**	£1 brown	£28000	£3000

1888 Wmk 3 Orbs T **48**

186	**61**	£1 brown	£60000	£4500

1891 Wmk 3 Imperial Crowns T **49**

212	**61**	£1 green	£3500	£800

62   63   64

65   66

1883–84 Wmk Imperial Crown T **49** (sideways on horiz designs)

187	**52**	½d. blue	35·00	10·00
188	**62**	1½d. lilac	£125	45·00
189	**63**	2d. lilac	£230	80·00
190	**64**	2½d. lilac	95·00	20·00
191	**65**	3d. lilac	£280	£100
192	**66**	4d. dull green	£580	£210
193	**62**	5d. dull green	£580	£210
194	**63**	6d. dull green	£625	£240
195	**64**	9d. dull green	£1250	£480
196	**65**	1s. dull green	£1600	£325

The above prices are for stamps in the true dull green colour. Stamps which have been soaked, causing the colour to run are virtually worthless.

71   72   73

74   75   76

77   78   79

80   81   82

'Jubilee' Issue

1887–1900 The bicoloured stamps have the value tablets, or the frames including the value tablets, in the second colour. Wmk Imperial Crown T **49**

197	**71**	½d. vermilion	1·75	1·25
213		½d. green*	2·00	2·25
198	**72**	1½d. purple and green	18·00	8·00
200	**73**	2d. green and red	35·00	15·00
201	**74**	2½d. purple on blue	25·00	5·00
202	**75**	3d. purple on yellow	25·00	5·00
205	**76**	4d. green and brown	40·00	18·00
206	**77**	4½d. green and red	11·00	45·00
207a	**78**	5d. purple and blue	42·00	15·00
208	**79**	6d. purple on red	40·00	15·00
209	**80**	9d. purple and blue	75·00	48·00
210	**81**	10d. purple and red	60·00	45·00
211	**82**	1s. green	£275	80·00
214		1s. green and red	65·00	£140
Set of 14			£650	£380

* The ½d. No. 213 in blue is a colour changeling.

KING EDWARD VII

1901 (22 January)–1910 (6 May)

 83
 84
 85
 86
 87
 88
 89
 90
 91
 92
 93

 94
 95
 96
 97

314	**93**	1s. green and red	60·00	35·00
260	**94**	2s.6d. purple	£275	£150
263	**95**	5s. red	£450	£220
265	**96**	10s. blue	£1000	£500
320	**97**	£1 green	£2000	£700
Set of 15 (to 1s.)			£400	£275

(b) Perf 15 × 14

279	**83**	½d. green	40·00	45·00
281		1d. red	15·00	15·00
283	**86**	2½d. blue	22·00	15·00
285	**87**	3d. purple on yellow	45·00	15·00
286	**88**	4d. orange	30·00	15·00
Set of 5			£130	90·00

1902–13 Wmks Imperial Crown T **49** (½d. to 1s.), Anchor T **40** (2s.6d. to 10s.), Three Crowns T **49** (£1)

(a) Perf 14

215	**83**	½d. blue-green	2·00	1·50
217		½d. yellow-green	2·00	1·50
219		1d. red	2·00	1·50
224	**84**	1½d. purple and green	45·00	22·00
291	**85**	2d. green and red	28·00	22·00
231	**86**	2½d. blue	20·00	15·00
232	**87**	3d. purple on yellow	50·00	18·00
238	**88**	4d. green and brown	40·00	20·00
240		4d. orange	20·00	18·00
294	**89**	5d. purple and blue	30·00	22·00
297	**83**	6d. purple	30·00	22·00
249	**90**	7d. grey	15·00	22·00
307	**91**	9d. purple and blue	60·00	60·00
311	**92**	10d. purple and red	80·00	60·00

KING GEORGE V

1910 (6 May)–1936 (20 January)

PERFORATION. All the following issues are Perf 15×14 except vertical commemorative stamps which are 14×15, unless otherwise stated.

98 (Hair dark)   **99** (Lion unshaded)   **100**

1911–12 Wmk Imperial Crown T **49**

322	**98**	½d.	green	4·00	4·00	☐ ☐
327	**99**	1d.	red	4·50	2·50	☐ ☐

1912 Wmk Royal Cypher ('Simple') T **100**

335	**98**	½d.	green	45·00	40·00	☐ ☐
336	**99**	1d.	red	30·00	30·00	☐ ☑

101 (Hair light)   **102** (Lion shaded)   **103**

1912 Wmk Imperial Crown T **49**

339	**101**	½d.	green	8·00	4·00	☐ ☐
341	**102**	1d.	red	5·00	2·00	☐ ☐

1912 Wmk Royal Cypher ('Simple') T **100**

344	**101**	½d.	green	7·00	3·00	☐ ☐
345	**102**	1d.	red	8·00	4·50	☐ ☐

1912 Wmk Royal Cypher ('Multiple') T **103**

346	**101**	½d.	green	12·00	8·00	☐ ☐
350	**102**	1d.	red	18·00	10·00	☐ ☐

104   **105**   **106**

107   **108**

1912–24 Wmk Royal Cypher T **100**

351	**105**	½d.	green	1·00	1·00	☐ ☐
357	**104**	1d.	red	1·00	1·00	☐ ☐
364	**105**	1½d.	brown	3·00	1·00	☐ ☐
368	**106**	2d.	orange	4·00	3·00	☐ ☐
371	**104**	2½d.	blue	12·00	4·00	☐ ☐
375	**106**	3d.	violet	8·00	3·00	☐ ☐

379		4d.	grey-green	15·00	2·00	☐ ☐
381	**107**	5d.	brown	15·00	5·00	☐ ☐
385		6d.	purple	15·00	7·00	☐ ☐
		a.	Perf 14	90·00	£110	☐ ☐
387		7d.	olive-green	20·00	10·00	☐ ☐
390		8d.	black on yellow	32·00	11·00	☐ ☐
392	**108**	9d.	black	15·00	6·00	☐ ☐
393a		9d.	olive-green	£110	30·00	☐ ☐
394		10d.	blue	22·00	20·00	☐ ☐
395		1s.	brown	20·00	4·00	☐ ☐
Set of 15				£250	95·00	☐ ☐

1913 Wmk Royal Cypher ('Multiple') T **103**

397	**105**	½d.	green	£150	£180	☐ ☐
398	**104**	1d.	red	£225	£225	☐ ☐

See also Nos. 418/429.

109

110

1913–18 Wmk Single Cypher T **110** Perf 11×12

414	**109**	2s.6d.	brown	£160	75·00	☐ ☐
416		5s.	red	£325	£135	☐ ☐
417		10s.	blue	£475	£175	☐ ☐
403		£1	green	£2800	£1400	☐ ☐
Set of 4				£3400	£1500	☐ ☐

T **109**. Background around portrait consists of horizontal lines
See also Nos. 450/452.

111

1924–26 Wmk Block Cypher T **111**

418	**105**	½d.	green	1·00	1·00	☐ ☐
419	**104**	1d.	red	1·00	1·00	☐ ☐
420	**105**	1½d.	brown	1·00	1·00	☐ ☐
421	**106**	2d.	orange	2·50	2·50	☐ ☐
422	**104**	2½d.	blue	5·00	3·00	☐ ☐
423	**106**	3d.	violet	10·00	2·50	☐ ☐
424		4d.	grey-green	12·00	2·50	☐ ☐
425	**107**	5d.	brown	20·00	3·00	☐ ☐
426a		6d.	purple	4·00	1·50	☐ ☐
427	**108**	9d.	olive-green	12·00	3·50	☐ ☐
428		10d.	blue	40·00	40·00	☐ ☐
429		1s.	brown	22·00	3·00	☐ ☐
Set of 12				£110	60·00	☐ ☐

112

112a

118

119

120

121

122

British Empire Exhibition

1924–25 Wmk **111** Perf 14

(a) 23.4.24. Dated '1924'

430	**112**	1d. red		10·00	11·00	☐ ☐
431	**112a**	1½d. brown		15·00	15·00	☐ ☐
First Day Cover					£450	☐

(b) 9.5.25. Dated '1925'

432	**112**	1d. red		15·00	30·00	☐ ☐
433	**112a**	1½d. brown		40·00	70·00	☐ ☐
First Day Cover					£1700	☐

1934–36 Wmk **111**

439	**118**	½d. green	50	50	☐ ☐
440	**119**	1d. red	50	50	☐ ☐
441	**118**	1½d. brown	50	50	☐ ☐
442	**120**	2d. orange	75	75	☐ ☐
443	**119**	2½d. blue	1·50	1·25	☐ ☐
444	**120**	3d. violet	1·50	1·25	☐ ☐
445		4d. grey-green	2·00	1·25	☐ ☐
446	**121**	5d. brown	6·50	2·75	☐ ☐
447	**122**	9d. olive-green	12·00	2·25	☐ ☐
448		10d. blue	15·00	10·00	☐ ☐
449		1s. brown	15·00	1·25	☐ ☐
Set of 11			50·00	20·00	☐ ☐

113

114

115

T **109** (re-engraved). Background around portrait consists of horizontal and diagonal lines

1934 Wmk **110** Perf 11×12

450	**109**	2s.6d. brown	80·00	40·00	☐ ☐
451		5s. red	£175	85·00	☐ ☐
452		10s. blue	£350	80·00	☐ ☐
Set of 3			£575	£190	☐ ☐

116 St George and the Dragon

123

123a

123b

123c

117

Ninth Universal Postal Union Congress

1929 (10 May)

(a) Wmk **111**

434	**113**	½d. green	2·25	2·25	☐ ☐
435	**114**	1d. red	2·25	2·25	☐ ☐
436		1½d. brown	2·25	1·75	☐ ☐
437	**115**	2½d. blue	10·00	10·00	☐ ☐

(b) Wmk **117** Perf 12

438	**116**	£1 black	£750	£550	☐ ☐
434/437 *Set of* 4			15·00	14·50	☐ ☐
434/437 *First Day Cover* (4 vals.)				£675	☐
434/438 *First Day Cover* (5 vals.)				£14000	☐

Silver Jubilee

1935 (7 May) Wmk **111**

453	**123**	½d. green	1·00	1·00	☐ ☐
454	**123a**	1d. red	1·50	2·00	☐ ☐
455	**123b**	1½d. brown	1·00	1·00	☐ ☐
456	**123c**	2½d. blue	5·00	6·50	☐ ☐
Set of 4			7·50	9·50	☐ ☐
First Day Cover				£650	☐

KING EDWARD VIII

1936 (20 January–10 December)

KING GEORGE VI

1936 (11 December)–1952 (6 February)

124   **125**

126 King George VI and
Queen Elizabeth   **127**

1936 Wmk **125**

457	**124**	½d. green	30	30	☐ ☐
458		1d. red	60	50	☐ ☐
459		1½d. brown	30	30	☐ ☐
460		2½d. blue	30	85	☐ ☐
Set of 4			1·25	1·75	☐ ☐

First Day Covers

1 Sept. 1936 Nos. 457, 459/460	£175	☐
14 Sept. 1936 No. 458	£200	☐

> Collectors are reminded that for issues from 1936 to date, prices in the unused column are for unmounted mint.

Coronation

1937 (13 May) Wmk **127**

461	**126**	1½d. brown	30	30	☐ ☐
First Day Cover				35·00	☐

128   **129**   **130**

King George VI and National Emblems

1937–47 Wmk **127**

462	**128**	½d. green	30	25	☐ ☐
463		1d. scarlet	30	25	☐ ☐
464		1½d. brown	30	25	☐ ☐
465		2d. orange	1·25	50	☐ ☐
466		2½d. blue	40	25	☐ ☐
467		3d. violet	5·00	1·00	☐ ☐
468	**129**	4d. green	60	75	☐ ☐
469		5d. brown	3·50	85	☐ ☐
470		6d. purple	1·50	60	☐ ☐
471	**130**	7d. green	5·00	60	☐ ☐
472		8d. red	7·50	80	☐ ☐
473		9d. deep green	6·50	1·00	☐ ☐
474		10d. blue	7·00	1·00	☐ ☐
474a		11d. plum	3·00	2·75	☐ ☐
475		1s. brown	9·00	75	☐ ☐
Set of 15			45·00	10·00	☐ ☐

First Day Covers

10 May 1937	Nos. 462/463, 466	45·00	☐
30 July 1937	No. 464	45·00	☐
31 Jan. 1938	Nos. 465, 467	£100	☐
21 Nov. 1938	Nos. 468/469	65·00	☐
30 Jan. 1939	No. 470	60·00	☐
27 Feb. 1939	Nos. 471/472	85·00	☐
1 May 1939	Nos. 473/474, 475	£500	☐
29 Dec. 1947	No. 474a	55·00	☐

For later printings of the lower values in apparently lighter shades and different colours, see Nos. 485/490 and 503/508.

130a King George VI   **131**   **132**

132a   **133**

1939–48 Wmk **133** Perf 14

476	**130a**	2s.6d. brown	£100	8·00	☐ ☐
476b		2s.6d. green	15·00	1·50	☐ ☐
477	**131**	5s. red	20·00	2·00	☐ ☐
478	**132**	10s. dark blue	£260	22·00	☐ ☐
478b		10s. bright blue	45·00	5·00	☐ ☐
478c	**132a**	£1 brown	25·00	26·00	☐ ☐
Set of 6			£425	60·00	☐ ☐

First Day Covers

21 Aug. 1939	No. 477	£850	☐
4 Sept. 1939	No. 476	£1800	☐
30 Oct. 1939	No. 478	£3250	☐
9 Mar. 1942	No. 476b	£1750	☐
30 Nov. 1942	No. 478b	£3750	☐
1 Oct. 1948	No. 478c	£325	☐

134 Queen Victoria and King George VI

Centenary of First Adhesive Postage Stamps

1940 (6 May) Wmk **127** Perf 14½ × 14

479	**134**	½d. green	30	75	☐ ☐
480		1d. red	1·00	75	☐ ☐
481		1½d. brown	50	1·50	☐ ☐
482		2d. orange	1·00	75	☐ ☐
483		2½d. blue	2·25	50	☐ ☐
484		3d. violet	3·00	3·50	☐ ☐
Set of 6			8·75	5·25	☐ ☐
First Day Cover				55·00	☐

Head as Nos. 462–467, but with lighter background

1941–42 Wmk **127**

485	**128**	½d. pale green	30	30	☐ ☐
486		1d. pale red	30	30	☐ ☐
487		1½d. pale brown	60	80	☐ ☐
488		2d. pale orange	50	50	☐ ☐
489		2½d. light blue	30	30	☐ ☐
490		3d. pale violet	2·50	1·00	☐ ☐
Set of 6			3·50	2·75	☐ ☐

First Day Covers

21 July 1941	No. 489	45·00	☐
11 Aug. 1941	No. 486	22·00	☐
1 Sept. 1941	No. 485	22·00	☐
6 Oct. 1941	No. 488	60·00	☐
3 Nov. 1941	No. 490	£110	☐
28 Sept. 1942	No. 487	55·00	☐

135 Symbols of Peace and Reconstruction   **136** Symbols of Peace and Reconstruction

Victory

1946 (11 June) Wmk **127**

491	**135**	2½d. blue	20	20	☐ ☐
492	**136**	3d. violet	20	50	☐ ☐
Set of 2			40	50	☐ ☐
First Day Cover				65·00	☐

137 King George VI and Queen Elizabeth   **138** King George VI and Queen Elizabeth

Royal Silver Wedding

1948 (26 Apr.) Wmk **127**

493	**137**	2½d. blue	35	20	☐ ☐
494	**138**	£1 blue	40·00	40·00	☐ ☐
Set of 2			40·00	40·00	☐ ☐
First Day Cover				£425	☐

1948 (10 May)

Stamps of 1d. and 2½d. showing seaweed-gathering were on sale at eight Head Post Offices elsewhere in Great Britain, but were primarily for use in the Channel Islands and are listed there (see after Regional Issues).

139 Globe and Laurel Wreath   **140** Speed

141 Olympic Symbol   **142** Winged Victory

Olympic Games

1948 (29 July) Wmk **127**

495	**139**	2½d. blue	50	10	☐ ☐
496	**140**	3d. violet	50	50	☐ ☐
497	**141**	6d. purple	3·25	75	☐ ☐
498	**142**	1s. brown	4·50	2·00	☐ ☐
Set of 4			8·00	3·00	☐ ☐
First Day Cover				45·00	☐

143 Two Hemispheres

144 UPU Monument, Bern

147 HMS *Victory*

148 White Cliffs of Dover

145 Goddess Concordia, Globe and Points of Compass

146 Posthorn and Globe

149 St George and the Dragon

150 Royal Coat of Arms

75th Anniversary of Universal Postal Union

1949 (10 Oct.) Wmk **127**

499	**143**	2½d. blue	25	10		
500	**144**	3d. violet	25	50		
501	**145**	6d. purple	50	75		
502	**146**	1s. brown	1·00	1·25		
Set of 4			1·50	2·50		
First Day Cover				80·00		

4d. as No. 468 and others as Nos. 485/489, but colours changed.

1950–51 Wmk **127**

503	**128**	½d. pale orange	30	30		
504		1d. light blue	30	30		
505		1½d. pale green	65	60		
506		2d. pale brown	75	40		
507		2½d. pale red	60	40		
508	**129**	4d. light blue	2·00	1·75		
Set of 6			4·00	3·25		
First Day Covers						
2 Oct. 1950 No. 508				£120		
3 May 1951 Nos. 503/507				55·00		

1951 (3 May) Wmk **133** Perf 11 × 12

509	**147**	2s.6d. green	7·50	1·00		
510	**148**	5s. red	35·00	1·00		
511	**149**	10s. blue	15·00	7·50		
512	**150**	£1 brown	45·00	18·00		
Set of 4			£100	25·00		
First Day Cover				£950		

151 Commerce and Prosperity

152 Festival Symbol

Festival of Britain

1951 (3 May) Wmk **127**

513	**151**	2½d. red	20	15		
514	**152**	4d. blue	30	35		
Set of 2			40	40		
First Day Cover				38·00		

QUEEN ELIZABETH II

1952 (6 February)

153 Tudor Crown

154

155

156

157

158

159

160

161

162

163

164

Coronation

1953 (3 June) Wmk **153**

532	**161**	2½d. red	20	20
533	**162**	4d. blue	80	40
534	**163**	1s.3d. green	3·00	1·00
535	**164**	1s.6d. blue	7·50	2·00
Set of 4			10·00	3·50
First Day Cover				75·00

For £1 values as T **163** see Nos. **MS**2147 and 2380.

1952–54 Wmk **153**

515	**154**	½d. orange	25	15
516		1d. ultramarine	30	20
517		1½d. green	25	20
518		2d. red-brown	30	20
519	**155**	2½d. carmine-red	30	15
520		3d. deep lilac	1·50	90
521	**156**	4d. ultramarine	3·25	1·25
		4½d. (See Nos. 577, 594, 609 and 616*b*)		
522	**157**	5d. brown	1·00	3·50
523		6d. reddish purple	4·00	1·00
524		7d. bright green	9·50	5·50
525	**158**	8d. magenta	1·25	85
526		9d. bronze-green	23·00	4·75
527		10d. Prussian blue	18·00	4·75
528		11d. brown-purple	35·00	15·00
529	**159**	1s. bistre-brown	80	50
530	**160**	1s.3d. green	4·50	3·25
531	**159**	1s.6d. grey-blue	14·00	3·75
Set of 17			£100	40·00

First Day Covers

5 Dec. 1952	Nos. 517, 519	28·00	
6 July 1953	Nos. 522, 525, 529	60·00	
31 Aug. 1953	Nos. 515/516, 518	60·00	
2 Nov. 1953	Nos. 521, 530/531	£200	
18 Jan. 1954	Nos. 520, 523/524	£125	
8 Feb. 1954	Nos. 526/528	£250	

See also Nos. 540/556, 561/566, 570/594 and 599/618*a* and for stamps as Types **154/160** with face values in decimal currency see Nos. 2031/2033, 2258/2259, **MS**2326, **MS**2367, 2378/2379 and 3329.

165 St Edward's Crown

166 Carrickfergus Castle

167 Caernarvon Castle

168 Edinburgh Castle

169 Windsor Castle

1955 (1–23 Sept.) Wmk **165** Perf 11×12

536	**166**	2s.6d. brown	15·00	2·00
537	**167**	5s. red	40·00	4·00
538	**168**	10s. blue	90·00	14·00
539	**169**	£1 black	£140	35·00
Set of 4			£250	50·00
First Day Cover (Nos. 538/539) (1 Sept.)				£850
First Day Cover (Nos. 536/537) (23 Sept.)				£650

See also Nos. 595*a*/598*a* and 759/762. For stamps as Types **166/169** with face values in decimal currency see Nos. **MS**2530 and 3221.

1955–58 Wmk **165**

540	**154**	½d. orange	20	15	☐ ☐
541		1d. blue	30	15	☐ ☐
542		1½d. green	25	30	☐ ☐
543		2d. red-brown	25	35	☐ ☐
543*b*		2d. light red-brown	30	20	☐ ☐
544	**155**	2½d. red	30	25	☐ ☐
545		3d. lilac	40	25	☐ ☐
546	**156**	4d. blue	1·25	45	☐ ☐
547	**157**	5d. brown	6·00	6·00	☐ ☐
548		6d. purple	4·50	1·25	☐ ☐
549		7d. green	50·00	10·00	☐ ☐
550	**158**	8d. magenta	7·00	1·25	☐ ☐
551		9d. bronze-green	20·00	2·75	☐ ☐
552		10d. blue	20·00	2·75	☐ ☐
553		11d. plum	1·00	1·10	☐ ☐
554	**159**	1s. bistre	22·00	65	☐ ☐
555	**160**	1s.3d. green	30·00	1·60	☐ ☐
556	**159**	1s.6d. indigo	23·00	1·60	☐ ☐
Set of 18			£160	27·00	☐ ☐

170 Scout Badge and 'Rolling Hitch'

171 'Scouts coming to Britain'

172 Globe within a Compass

173

World Scout Jubilee Jamboree

1957 (1 Aug.) Wmk **165**

557	**170**	2½d. red	20	20	☐ ☐
558	**171**	4d. blue	50	50	☐ ☐
559	**172**	1s.3d. green	3·00	2·00	☐ ☐
Set of 3			3·50	2·50	☐ ☐
First Day Cover				25·00	☐

46th Inter Parliamentary Union Conference

1957 (12 Sept.) Wmk **165**

560	**173**	4d. blue	40	40	☐ ☐
First Day Cover				£150	☐

Graphite-lined and Phosphor Issues

These are used in connection with automatic sorting machinery, originally experimentally at Southampton but now also operating elsewhere. In such areas these stamps were the normal issue, but from mid 1967 all low-value stamps bear phosphor markings.

The graphite lines were printed in black on the back, beneath the gum; two lines per stamp except for the 2d. (see below).

½d. to 1½d., 2½d., 3d.   2d.
Graphite-line arrangements
(Stamps viewed from back)

In November 1959, phosphor bands, printed on the front, replaced the graphite. They are wider than the graphite, not easy to see, but show as broad vertical bands at certain angles to the light.

Values representing the rate for printed papers (and second class mail from 1968) have one band and others have two, three or four bands according to size and format. From 1972 onwards some commemorative stamps were printed with 'all-over' phosphor.

In the small stamps the bands are on each side with the single band at left (except where otherwise stated). In the large-size commemorative stamps the single band may be at left, centre or right varying in different issues. The bands are vertical on both horizontal and vertical designs except where otherwise stated.

See also notes above No. 881.

Graphite-lined issue

1957 (19 Nov.) Two graphite lines on the back, except 2d. value, which has one line. Wmk **165**

561	**154**	½d. orange	50	40	☐ ☐
562		1d. blue	70	60	☐ ☐
563		1½d. green	2·00	1·75	☐ ☐
564		2d. light red-brown	2·50	2·50	☐ ☐
565	**155**	2½d. red	8·50	7·00	☐ ☐
566		3d. lilac	1·40	1·25	☐ ☐
Set of 6			14·00	12·00	☐ ☐
First Day Cover				90·00	☐

See also Nos. 587/594.

176 Welsh Dragon

177 Flag and Games Emblem

178 Welsh Dragon

Sixth British Empire and Commonwealth Games, Cardiff

1958 (18 July) Wmk **165**

567	**176**	3d. lilac	10	10	☐ ☐
568	**177**	6d. mauve	30	30	☐ ☐
569	**178**	1s.3d. green	1·00	1·00	☐ ☐
Set of 3			1·20	1·20	☐ ☐
First Day Cover				75·00	☐

179 Multiple Crowns

WATERMARK. All the following issues to No. 755 are Watermark **179** (sideways on the vertical commemorative stamps) unless otherwise stated.

1958–65 Wmk **179**

570	**154**	½d. orange	10	10	☐ ☐
571		1d. blue	10	10	☐ ☐
572		1½d. green	10	15	☐ ☐
573		2d. light red-brown	10	10	☐ ☐
574	**155**	2½d. red	10	20	☐ ☐
575		3d. lilac	20	15	☐ ☐

576a	156	4d. blue	15	15	□ □
577		4½d. brown	10	25	□ □
578	157	5d. brown	30	40	□ □
579		6d. purple	30	25	□ □
580		7d. green	50	45	□ □
581	158	8d. magenta	60	40	□ □
582		9d. bronze-green	60	40	□ □
583		10d. blue	1·00	50	□ □
584	159	1s. bistre	75	30	□ □
585	160	1s.3d. green	75	30	□ □
586	159	1s.6d. indigo	5·00	40	□ □
Set of 17			9·00	4·25	□ □
First Day Cover (No. 577) (9 Feb. 1959)				£250	□

Graphite-lined issue

1958–59 Two graphite lines on the back, except 2d. value, which has one line. Wmk **179**

587Wi	154	½d. orange	3·25	4·00	□ □
588		1d. blue	2·00	1·50	□ □
589Wi		1½d. green	75·00	60·00	□ □
590		2d. light red-brown	10·00	3·50	□ □
591	155	2½d. red	12·00	10·00	□ □
592		3d. lilac	90	65	□ □
593	156	4d. blue	5·50	5·00	□ □
594		4½d. brown	6·50	5·00	□ □
Set of 8			£110	70·00	□ □

The prices quoted for Nos. 587 and 589 are for examples with inverted watermark. Stamps with upright watermark are priced at: ½d. £9 mint, £9 used and 1½d. £90 mint, £80 used.

1959–63 Wmk **179** Perf 11×12

595a	166	2s.6d. brown	35	40	□ □
596a	167	5s. red	1·25	50	□ □
597a	168	10s. blue	4·50	4·50	□ □
598a	169	£1 black	13·00	8·00	□ □
Set of 4			15·00	11·00	□ □

Phosphor-Graphite issue

1959 (18 Nov.) Two phosphor bands on front and two graphite lines on back, except 2d. value, which has one band on front and one line on back

(a) Wmk **165**

599	154	½d. orange	4·25	4·25	□ □
600		1d. blue	11·00	11·00	□ □
601		1½d. green	4·50	4·50	□ □

(b) Wmk **179**

605	154	2d. light red-brown (1 band)	6·00	4·25	□ □
606	155	2½d. red	22·00	18·00	□ □
607		3d. lilac	12·00	8·00	□ □
608	156	4d. blue	20·00	16·00	□ □
609		4½d. brown	30·00	20·00	□ □
Set of 8			£100	80·00	□ □

Phosphor issue

1960–67 Two phosphor bands on front, except where otherwise stated. Wmk **179**

610	154	½d. orange	10	15	□ □
611		1d. blue	10	10	□ □
612		1½d. green	15	15	□ □
613		2d. light red-brown (1 band)	22·00	22·00	□ □
613a		2d. light red-brown (2 bands)	10	15	□ □
614	155	2½d. red (2 bands)	40	30	□ □
614a		2½d. red (1 band)	60	75	□ □
615		3d. lilac (2 bands)	60	55	□ □
615c		3d. lilac (1 side band)	60	55	□ □

615e		3d. lilac (1 centre band)	40	45	□ □
616a	156	4d. blue	25	25	□ □
616b		4½d. brown	55	30	□ □
616c	157	5d. brown	55	35	□ □
617		6d. purple	55	30	□ □
617a		7d. green	70	50	□ □
617b	158	8d. magenta	70	55	□ □
617c		9d. bronze-green	70	65	□ □
617d		10d. blue	1·00	1·00	□ □
617e	159	1s. bistre	1·00	35	□ □
618	160	1s.3d. green	1·90	2·50	□ □
618a	159	1s.6d. indigo	2·00	2·00	□ □
Set of 17 (one of each value)			10·50	8·00	□ □

No. 615c exists with the phosphor band at the left or right of the stamp.

180 Postboy of 1660   **181** Posthorn of 1660

Tercentenary of Establishment of 'General Letter Office'

1960 (7 July)

619	180	3d. lilac	20	20	□ □
620	181	1s.3d. green	1·60	1·75	□ □
Set of 2			1·60	1·75	□ □
First Day Cover				50·00	□

182 Conference Emblem

First Anniversary of European Postal and Telecommunications Conference

1960 (19 Sept.)

621	182	6d. green and purple	1·00	20	□ □
622		1s.6d. brown and blue	5·50	2·25	□ □
Set of 2			6·00	2·25	□ □
First Day Cover				50·00	□

183 Thrift Plant

184 'Growth of Savings'   **185** Thrift Plant

Centenary of Post Office Savings Bank

1961 (28 Aug.)

623A	**183**	2½d. black and red	10	10	☐	☐
624A	**184**	3d. orange-brown and				
		violet	10	10	☐	☐
625A	**185**	1s.6d. red and blue	1·00	1·25	☐	☐
Set of 3			1·00	1·25	☐	
First Day Cover				45·00	☐	

186 CEPT Emblem   **187** Doves and Emblem

188 Doves and Emblem

European Postal and Telecommunications (CEPT) Conference, Torquay

1961 (18 Sept.)

626	**186**	2d. orange, pink and				
		brown	10	10	☐	☐
627	**187**	4d. buff, mauve and				
		ultramarine	10	10	☐	☐
628	**188**	10d. turquoise, green				
		and blue	20	20	☐	☐
Set of 3			30	30	☐	☐
First Day Cover				4·00	☐	

189 Hammer Beam Roof,   **190** Palace of
Westminster Hall   Westminster

Seventh Commonwealth Parliamentary Conference

1961 (25 Sept.)

629	**189**	6d. purple and gold	10	10	☐	☐
630	**190**	1s.3d. green and blue	1·25	1·25	☐	☐
Set of 2			1·25	1·25	☐	☐
First Day Cover				25·00	☐	

191 'Units of Productivity'   **192** 'National Productivity'

193 'Unified Productivity'

National Productivity Year

1962 (14 Nov.) Wmk **179** (inverted on 2½d. and 3d.)

631	**191**	2½d. green and red	10	10	☐	☐
		p. Phosphor	60	50	☐	☐
632	**192**	3d. blue and violet	25	25	☐	☐
		p. Phosphor	1·50	80	☐	☐
633	**193**	1s.3d. red, blue and green	80	80	☐	☐
		p. Phosphor	35·00	22·00	☐	☐
Set of 3 (Ordinary)			1·00	1·00	☐	
Set of 3 (Phosphor)			35·00	22·00	☐	
First Day Cover (Ordinary)				45·00	☐	
First Day Cover (Phosphor)				£125	☐	

194 Campaign Emblem and Family   **195** Children of Three Races

Freedom from Hunger

1963 (21 Mar.) Wmk **179** (inverted)

634	**194**	2½d. crimson and pink	10	10	☐	☐
		p. Phosphor	3·00	1·25	☐	☐
635	**195**	1s.3d. brown and yellow	1·00	1·00	☐	☐
		p. Phosphor	30·00	23·00	☐	☐
Set of 2 (Ordinary)			1·00	1·00	☐	
Set of 2 (Phosphor)			30·00	23·00	☐	
First Day Cover (Ordinary)				25·00	☐	
First Day Cover (Phosphor)				40·00	☐	

196 'Paris Conference'

Paris Postal Conference Centenary

1963 (7 May) Wmk **179** (inverted)

636	**196**	6d. green and mauve	20	20	☐	☐
		p. Phosphor	3·00	2·75	☐	☐
First Day Cover (Ordinary)				7·50	☐	
First Day Cover (Phosphor)				30·00	☐	

197 Posy of Flowers   **198** Woodland Life

National Nature Week

1963 (16 May)

637	**197**	3d. multicoloured	10	10	☐	☐
		p. Phosphor	30	30	☐	☐
638	**198**	4½d. multicoloured	15	15	☐	☐
		p. Phosphor	1·40	1·40	☐	☐
Set of 2 (Ordinary)			20	20	☐	
Set of 2 (Phosphor)			1·50	1·50	☐	
First Day Cover (Ordinary)				12·00	☐	
First Day Cover (Phosphor)				35·00	☐	

199 Rescue at Sea

200 19th-century Lifeboat

201 Lifeboatmen

Ninth International Lifeboat Conference, Edinburgh

1963 (31 May)

639	**199**	2½d. blue, black and red	10	10	☐ ☐
		p. Phosphor	50	60	☐ ☐
640	**200**	4d. multicoloured	20	20	☐ ☐
		p. Phosphor	50	60	☐ ☐
641	**201**	1s.6d. sepia, yellow and blue	1·50	1·50	☐ ☐
		p. Phosphor	48·00	28·00	☐ ☐
Set of 3 (Ordinary)			1·50	1·50	☐ ☐
Set of 3 (Phosphor)			48·00	28·00	☐ ☐
First Day Cover (Ordinary)				20·00	☐
First Day Cover (Phosphor)				55·00	☐

202 Red Cross

203

204

Red Cross Centenary Congress

1963 (15 Aug.)

642	**202**	3d. red and lilac	25	25	☐ ☐
		p. Phosphor	1·10	1·00	☐ ☐
643	**203**	1s.3d. red, blue and grey	1·25	1·25	☐ ☐
		p. Phosphor	35·00	30·00	☐ ☐
644	**204**	1s.6d. red, blue and bistre	1·25	1·25	☐ ☐
		p. Phosphor	35·00	27·00	☐ ☐
Set of 3 (Ordinary)			2·50	2·50	☐ ☐
Set of 3 (Phosphor)			65·00	55·00	☐ ☐
First Day Cover (Ordinary)				20·00	☐
First Day Cover (Phosphor)				60·00	☐

205 'Commonwealth Cable'

Opening of COMPAC (Trans-Pacific Telephone Cable)

1963 (3 Dec.)

645	**205**	1s.6d. blue and black	1·25	1·25	☐ ☐
		p. Phosphor	7·25	7·00	☐ ☐
First Day Cover (Ordinary)				12·00	☐
First Day Cover (Phosphor)				35·00	☐

206 Puck and Bottom
(*A Midsummer Nights Dream*)

207 Feste
(*Twelfth Night*)

208 Balcony Scene
(*Romeo and Juliet*)

209 'Eve of Agincourt'
(*Henry V*)

210 Hamlet contemplating
Yorick's skull (*Hamlet*)
and Queen Elizabeth II

Shakespeare Festival

1964 (23 Apr.) Perf 11×12 (2s.6d.) or 15×14 (others)

646	**206**	3d. bistre, black and violet-blue	10	10	☐ ☐
		p. Phosphor	25	25	☐ ☐
647	**207**	6d. multicoloured	20	20	☐ ☐
		p. Phosphor	75	75	☐ ☐
648	**208**	1s.3d. multicoloured	40	40	☐ ☐
		p. Phosphor	2·00	2·00	☐ ☐
649	**209**	1s.6d. multicoloured	60	60	☐ ☐
		p. Phosphor	2·50	2·50	☐ ☐
650	**210**	2s.6d. deep slate-purple	1·25	1·25	☐ ☐
Set of 5 (Ordinary)			2·00	2·00	☐ ☐
Set of 4 (Phosphor)			5·00	5·00	☐ ☐
First Day Cover (Ordinary)				5·00	☐
First Day Cover (Phosphor)				9·00	☐
Presentation Pack (Ordinary)			12·00		☐

PRESENTATION PACKS were first introduced by the GPO for the Shakespeare Festival issue. The packs include one set of stamps and details of the designs, the designer and the stamp printer. They were issued for almost all later definitive and special issues.

211 Flats near Richmond
Park ('Urban Development')

212 Shipbuilding Yards,
Belfast. ('Industrial Activity')

213 Beddgelert Forest. Park,
Snowdonia ('Forestry')

214 Nuclear Reactor, Dounreay
('Technological Development')

20th International Geographical Congress, London

1964 (1 July)

651	**211**	2½d. multicoloured	10	10	☐ ☐
		p. Phosphor	40	50	☐ ☐
652	**212**	4d. multicoloured	30	30	☐ ☐
		p. Phosphor	1·25	1·25	☐ ☐

653	**213**	8d. multicoloured	80	80	☐	☐
		p. Phosphor	2·50	3·50	☐	☐
654	**214**	1s.6d. multicoloured	1·40	1·40	☐	☐
		p. Phosphor	28·00	22·00	☐	☐
Set of 4 (Ordinary)			2·00	2·00	☐	☐
Set of 4 (Phosphor)			30·00	25·00	☐	☐
First Day Cover (Ordinary)				10·00	☐	
First Day Cover (Phosphor)				35·00	☐	
Presentation Pack (Ordinary)			£100		☐	

215 Spring Gentian

216 Dog Rose

217 Honeysuckle

218 Fringed Water Lily

Tenth International Botanical Congress, Edinburgh

1964 (5 Aug.)

655	**215**	3d. violet, blue and green	25	25	☐	☐
		p. Phosphor	40	40	☐	☐
656	**216**	6d. multicoloured	30	30	☐	☐
		p. Phosphor	2·50	2·75	☐	☐
657	**217**	9d. multicoloured	80	80	☐	☐
		p. Phosphor	4·50	4·50	☐	☐
658	**218**	1s.3d. multicoloured	1·25	1·25	☐	☐
		p. Phosphor	25·00	20·00	☐	☐
Set of 4 (Ordinary)			2·00	2·00	☐	☐
Set of 4 (Phosphor)			30·00	25·00	☐	☐
First Day Cover (Ordinary)				10·00	☐	
First Day Cover (Phosphor)				35·00	☐	
Presentation Pack (Ordinary)			£125		☐	

219 Forth Road Bridge

220 Forth Road and Railway Bridges

Opening of Forth Road Bridge

1964 (4 Sept.)

659	**219**	3d. black, blue and violet	10	10	☐	☐
		p. Phosphor	50	50	☐	☐
660	**220**	6d. blackish lilac, blue and red	20	20	☐	☐
		p. Phosphor	2·25	2·25	☐	☐
Set of 2 (Ordinary)			25	25	☐	☐
Set of 2 (Phosphor)			2·50	2·50	☐	☐
First Day Cover (Ordinary)				3·00	☐	
First Day Cover (Phosphor)				10·00	☐	
Presentation Pack (Ordinary)			£325		☐	

221 Sir Winston Churchill

221a Sir Winston Churchill

Churchill Commemoration

1965 (8 July)

661	**221**	4d. black and drab	15	10	☐	☐
		p. Phosphor	20	20	☐	☐
662	**221a**	1s.3d. black and grey	45	45	☐	☐
		p. Phosphor	1·00	1·00	☐	☐
Set of 2 (Ordinary)			60	60	☐	☐
Set of 2 (Phosphor)			1·10	1·10	☐	☐
First Day Cover (Ordinary)				4·75	☐	
First Day Cover (Phosphor)				5·00	☐	
Presentation Pack (Ordinary)			40·00		☐	

700th Anniversary of Parliament
222 Simon de Montfort's Seal

223 Parliament Buildings (after engraving by Hollar, 1647)

700th Anniversary of Simon de Montfort's Parliament

1965 (19 July)

663	**222**	6d. green	10	10	☐	☐
		p. Phosphor	50	50	☐	☐
664	**223**	2s.6d. black, grey and drab	40	40	☐	☐
Set of 2 (Ordinary)			40	40	☐	☐
First Day Cover (Ordinary)				6·00	☐	
First Day Cover (Phosphor)				15·00	☐	
Presentation Pack (Ordinary)			65·00		☐	

224 Bandsmen and Banner

225 Three Salvationists

Salvation Army Centenary

1965 (9 Aug.)

665	**224**	3d. multicoloured	10	10	☐	☐
		p. Phosphor	20	20	☐	☐
666	**225**	1s.6d. multicoloured	60	60	☐	☐
		p. Phosphor	90	90	☐	☐
Set of 2 (Ordinary)			60	60	☐	☐
Set of 2 (Phosphor)			1·00	1·00	☐	☐
First Day Cover (Ordinary)				10·00	☐	
First Day Cover (Phosphor)				22·00	☐	

226 Lister's Carbolic Spray

227 Lister and Chemical Symbols

Centenary of Joseph Lister's Discovery of Antiseptic Surgery

1965 (1 Sept.)

667	**226**	4d. indigo, chestnut and grey	10	10	☐	☐
		p. Phosphor	25	25	☐	☐

668	**227**	1s. black, purple and			
		blue	40	40	☐☐
		p. Phosphor	1·00	1·00	☐☐
Set of 2 (Ordinary)			45	45	☐☐
Set of 2 (Phosphor)			1·10	1·10	☐☐
First Day Cover (Ordinary)				5·00	☐
First Day Cover (Phosphor)				9·00	☐

228 Trinidad Carnival Dancers   **229** Canadian Folk Dancers

Commonwealth Arts Festival

1965 (1 Sept.)

669	**228**	6d. black and orange	10	10	☐☐
		p. Phosphor	40	40	☐☐
670	**229**	1s.6d. black and violet	40	40	☐☐
		p. Phosphor	1·25	1·25	☐☐
Set of 2 (Ordinary)			1·25	1·25	☐☐
Set of 2 (Phosphor)			1·50	1·50	☐☐
First Day Cover (Ordinary)				7·00	☐
First Day Cover (Phosphor)				14·00	☐

230 Flight of Supermarine Spitfires   **231** Pilot in Hawker Hurricane Mk I

232 Wing-tips of Supermarine Spitfire and Messerschmitt Bf 109   **233** Supermarine Spitfires attacking Heinkel He 111H Bomber

234 Supermarine Spitfire attacking Junkers Ju 87B 'Stuka' Dive Bomber   **235** Hawker Hurricanes Mk I over Wreck of Dornier Do-17Z Bomber

236 Anti-aircraft Artillery in Action   **237** Air Battle over St Paul's Cathedral

25th Anniversary of Battle of Britain

1965 (13 Sept.)

671	**230**	4d. olive and black	25	25	☐☐
		a. Block of 6.			
		Nos. 671/676	2·50	2·50	☐☐
		p. Phosphor	40	40	☐☐
		pa. Block of 6.			
		Nos. 671p/676p	3·75	3·75	☐☐
672	**231**	4d. olive, blackish olive			
		and black	25	25	☐☐
		p. Phosphor	40	40	☐☐
673	**232**	4d. multicoloured	25	25	☐☐

		p. Phosphor	40	40	☐☐
674	**233**	4d. olive and black	25	25	☐☐
		p. Phosphor	40	40	☐☐
675	**234**	4d. olive and black	25	25	☐☐
		p. Phosphor	40	40	☐☐
676	**235**	4d. multicoloured	25	25	☐☐
		p. Phosphor	40	40	☐☐
677	**236**	9d. violet, orange and			
		purple	1·75	1·75	☐☐
		p. Phosphor	2·00	2·00	☐☐
678	**237**	1s.3d. multicoloured	1·75	1·75	☐☐
		p. Phosphor	2·00	2·00	☐☐
Set of 8 (Ordinary)			5·50	5·50	☐☐
Set of 8 (Phosphor)			7·00	7·00	☐☐
First Day Cover (Ordinary)				10·00	☐
First Day Cover (Phosphor)				15·00	☐
Presentation Pack (Ordinary)			40·00		☐

Nos. 671/676 were issued together *se-tenant* in blocks of six (3 ×2) within the sheet.

238 Tower and Georgian Buildings   **239** Tower and Nash Terrace, Regent's Park

Opening of Post Office Tower

1965 (8 Oct.)

679	**238**	3d. yellow, blue and			
		green	10	10	☐☐
		p. Phosphor	15	15	☐☐
680	**239**	1s.3d. green and blue	20	20	☐☐
		p. Phosphor	30	30	☐☐
Set of 2 (Ordinary)			25	25	☐☐
Set of 2 (Phosphor)			40	40	☐☐
First Day Cover (Ordinary)				2·50	☐
First Day Cover (Phosphor)				4·75	☐
Presentation Pack (Ordinary)			12·50		☐
Presentation Pack (Phosphor)			12·50		☐

240 UN Emblem   **241** ICY Emblem

20th Anniversary of UNO and International Co-operation Year

1965 (25 Oct.)

681	**240**	3d. black, orange and			
		blue	10	10	☐☐
		p. Phosphor	25	25	☐☐
682	**241**	1s.6d. black, purple and			
		blue	35	35	☐☐
		p. Phosphor	1·00	1·00	☐☐
Set of 2 (Ordinary)			40	40	☐☐
Set of 2 (Phosphor)			1·10	1·10	☐☐
First Day Cover (Ordinary)				5·00	☐
First Day Cover (Phosphor)				9·00	☐

242 Telecommunications Network

243 Radio Waves and Switchboard

ITU Centenary

1965 (15 Nov.)

683	**242**	9d. multicoloured	20	20	☐	☐
		p. Phosphor	75	75	☐	☐
684	**243**	1s.6d. multicoloured	40	40	☐	☐
		p. Phosphor	2·00	2·00	☐	☐
Set of 2 (Ordinary)			50	50	☐	☐
Set of 2 (Phosphor)			2·50	2·50	☐	☐
First Day Cover (Ordinary)				8·00	☐	
First Day Cover (Phosphor)				13·00	☐	

244 Robert Burns (after Skirving chalk drawing)

245 Robert Burns (after Nasmyth portrait)

Burns Commemoration

1966 (25 Jan.)

685	**244**	4d. black, indigo and blue	10	10	☐	☐
		p. Phosphor	20	20	☐	☐
686	**245**	1s.3d. black, blue and orange	20	20	☐	☐
		p. Phosphor	90	90	☐	☐
Set of 2 (Ordinary)			25	25	☐	☐
Set of 2 (Phosphor)			1·00	1·00	☐	☐
First Day Cover (Ordinary)				1·25	☐	
First Day Cover (Phosphor)				3·50	☐	
Presentation Pack (Ordinary)			40·00		☐	

246 Westminster Abbey

247 Fan Vaulting, Henry VII Chapel

900th Anniversary of Westminster Abbey

1966 (28 Feb.) Perf 15×14 (3d.) or 11×12 (2s.6d.)

687	**246**	3d. black, brown and blue	10	10	☐	☐
		p. Phosphor	10	10	☐	☐
688	**247**	2s.6d. black	30	30	☐	☐
Set of 2			30	30	☐	☐
First Day Cover (Ordinary)				2·50	☐	
First Day Cover (Phosphor)				8·00	☐	
Presentation Pack (Ordinary)			40·00		☐	

248 View near Hassocks, Sussex

249 Antrim, Northern Ireland

250 Harlech Castle, Wales

251 Cairngorm Mountains, Scotland

Landscapes

1966 (2 May)

689	**248**	4d. black, yellow-green and blue	10	10	☐	☐
		p. Phosphor	10	10	☐	☐
690	**249**	6d. black, green and blue	10	10	☐	☐
		p. Phosphor	10	10	☐	☐
691	**250**	1s.3d. black, yellow and blue	15	15	☐	☐
		p. Phosphor	15	15	☐	☐
692	**251**	1s.6d. black, orange and blue	15	15	☐	☐
		p. Phosphor	15	15	☐	☐
Set of 4 (Ordinary)			40	40	☐	☐
Set of 4 (Phosphor)			40	40	☐	☐
First Day Cover (Ordinary)				3·50	☐	
First Day Cover (Phosphor)				4·50	☐	

252 Players with Ball

253 Goalmouth Mêlée

254 Goalkeeper saving Goal

World Cup Football Championship

1966 (1 June)

693	**252**	4d. multicoloured	10	10	☐	☐
		p. Phosphor	10	10	☐	☐
694	**253**	6d. multicoloured	10	10	☐	☐
		p. Phosphor	15	15	☐	☐
695	**254**	1s.3d. multicoloured	15	15	☐	☐
		p. Phosphor	30	30	☐	☐
Set of 3 (Ordinary)			30	30	☐	☐
Set of 3 (Phosphor)			30	30	☐	☐
First Day Cover (Ordinary)				9·00	☐	
First Day Cover (Phosphor)				11·50	☐	
Presentation Pack (Ordinary)			30·00		☐	

255 Black-headed Gull

256 Blue Tit

257 European Robin

258 Blackbird

British Birds

1966 (8 Aug.)

696	**255**	4d. multicoloured	10	10
		a. Block of 4.		
		Nos. 696/699	40	40
		p. Phosphor	10	10
		pa. Block of 4.		
		Nos. 696p/699p	40	40
697	**256**	4d. multicoloured	10	10
		p. Phosphor	10	10
698	**257**	4d. multicoloured	10	10
		p. Phosphor	10	10
699	**258**	4d. multicoloured	10	10
		p. Phosphor	10	10
Set of 4 (Ordinary)			40	40
Set of 4 (Phosphor)			40	40
First Day Cover (Ordinary)				3·50
First Day Cover (Phosphor)				4·50
Presentation Pack (Ordinary)			15·00	

Nos. 696/699 were issued *se-tenant* in blocks of four within the sheet.

259 Cup Winners

England's World Cup Football Victory

1966 (18 Aug.)

700	**259**	4d. multicoloured	10	10
First Day Cover				7·50

260 Jodrell Bank Radio Telescope

261 British Motor cars

262 SR N6 Hovercraft

263 Windscale Reactor

British Technology

1966 (19 Sept.)

701	**260**	4d. black and lemon	10	10
		p. Phosphor	10	10
702	**261**	6d. red, blue and		
		orange	10	10
		p. Phosphor	10	10
703	**262**	1s.3d. multicoloured	15	15
		p. Phosphor	20	20

704	**263**	1s.6d. multicoloured	15	15
		p. Phosphor	20	20
Set of 4 (Ordinary)			40	40
Set of 4 (Phosphor)			50	50
First Day Cover (Ordinary)				2·50
First Day Cover (Phosphor)				2·50
Presentation Pack (Ordinary)			20·00	

264

265

266

267

268

269

270 Norman Ship

271 Norman Horsemen attacking Harold's Troops

900th Anniversary of Battle of Hastings

1966 (14 Oct.) Designs show scenes from Bayeux Tapestry Wmk **179** (sideways on 1s.3d.)

705	**264**	4d. multicoloured	10	10
		a. Strip of 6.		
		Nos. 705/710	60	60
		p. Phosphor	10	10
		pa. Strip of 6. Nos.		
		705p/710p	60	60
706	**265**	4d. multicoloured	10	10
		p. Phosphor	10	10
707	**266**	4d. multicoloured	10	10
		p. Phosphor	10	10
708	**267**	4d. multicoloured	10	10
		p. Phosphor	10	10
709	**268**	4d. multicoloured	10	10
		p. Phosphor	10	10
710	**269**	4d. multicoloured	10	10
		p. Phosphor	10	10
711	**270**	6d. multicoloured	10	10
		p. Phosphor	10	10
712	**271**	1s.3d. multicoloured	20	30
		p. Phosphor	20	40
Set of 8 (Ordinary)			85	1·00
Set of 8 (Phosphor)			85	1·00
First Day Cover (Ordinary)				2·00

First Day Cover (Phosphor)   3·25 ☐

Presentation Pack (Ordinary)   8·50 ☐

Nos. 705/710 show battle scenes, they were issued together *se-tenant* in horizontal strips of six within the sheet.

272 King Wenceslas   **273** Snowman

Christmas

1966 (1 Dec.) Wmk **179** (upright on 1s.6d.)

713	**272**	3d. multicoloured	10	10	☐	☐
		p. Phosphor	10	10	☐	☐
714	**273**	1s.6d. multicoloured	10	10	☐	☐
		p. Phosphor	10	10	☐	☐
Set of 2 (Ordinary)			20	20	☐	☐
Set of 2 (Phosphor)			20	20	☐	☐
First Day Cover (Ordinary)			70		☐	
First Day Cover (Phosphor)			70		☐	
Presentation Pack (Ordinary)			10·00		☐	

No. 713p exists with phosphor band at left or right.

274 Sea Freight   **275** Air Freight

European Free Trade Association (EFTA)

1967 (20 Feb.)

715	**274**	9d. multicoloured	10	10	☐	☐
		p. Phosphor	10	10	☐	☐
716	**275**	1s.6d. multicoloured	10	10	☐	☐
		p. Phosphor	10	10	☐	☐
Set of 2 (Ordinary)			20	20	☐	☐
Set of 2 (Phosphor)			20	20	☐	☐
First Day Cover (Ordinary)			5·00		☐	
First Day Cover (Phosphor)			5·00		☐	
Presentation Pack (Ordinary)			20·00		☐	

276 Hawthorn and Bramble   **277** Larger Bindweed and Viper's Bugloss

278 Ox-eye Daisy, Coltsfoot and Buttercup   **279** Bluebell, Red Campion and Wood Anemone

280 Dog Violet   **281** Primroses

British Wild Flowers

1967 (24 Apr.)

717	**276**	4d. multicoloured	10	10	☐	☐
		a. Block of 4.				
		Nos. 717/720	40	40	☐	☐
		p. Phosphor	10	10	☐	☐
		pa. Block of 4.				
		Nos. 717p/720p	40	40	☐	☐
718	**277**	4d. multicoloured	10	10	☐	☐
		p. Phosphor	10	10	☐	☐
719	**278**	4d. multicoloured	10	10	☐	☐
		p. Phosphor	10	10	☐	☐
720	**279**	4d. multicoloured	10	10	☐	☐
		p. Phosphor	10	10	☐	☐
721	**280**	9d. multicoloured	15	15	☐	☐
		p. Phosphor	15	15	☐	☐
722	**281**	1s.9d. multicoloured	15	15	☐	☐
		p. Phosphor	15	15	☐	☐
Set of 6 (Ordinary)			50	50	☐	☐
Set of 6 (Phosphor)			50	50	☐	☐
First Day Cover (Ordinary)			1·25		☐	
First Day Cover (Phosphor)			7·00		☐	
Presentation Pack (Ordinary)			20·00		☐	
Presentation Pack (Phosphor)			20·00		☐	

Nos. 717/720 were issued together *se-tenant* in blocks of four within the sheet.

282 (value at left)   **282a** (value at right)

I   II

Two types of the 2d.

I.   Value spaced away from left side of stamp.

II.   Value close to left side from new multi-positive. This results in the portrait appearing in the centre, thus conforming with the other values.

1967 (5 June)–**69** Two phosphor bands, except where otherwise stated. No wmk

723	**282**	½d. orange-brown				
		(5.2.68)	10	10	☐	☐
724		1d. light olive				
		(2 bands) (5.2.68)	10	10	☐	☐
725		1d. yellowish olive				
		(1 centre band)				
		(16.9.68)	45	45	☐	☐
726		2d. lake-brown (Type I)				
		(2 bands) (5.2.68)	10	10	☐	☐
727		2d. lake-brown (Type II)				
		(2 bands) (1969)	10	10	☐	☐
728		2d. lake-brown (Type II) 1 centre band) (27.8.69)	35	40	☐	☐
729		3d. violet (1 centre band) (8.8.67)	10	10	☐	☐
730		3d. violet (2 bands) (6.4.68)	10	15	☐	☐

731		4d. deep sepia (2 bands)	10	10	☐ ☐
732		4d. deep olive-brown (1 centre band) *(16.9.68)*	10	10	☐ ☐
733		4d. bright vermilion (1 centre band) *(6.1.69)*	10	10	☐ ☐
734		4d. vermilion (1 side band) *(6.1.69)*	65	75	☐ ☐
735		5d. blue *(1.7.68)*	10	10	☐ ☐
736		6d. purple *(5.2.68)*	10	10	☐ ☐
737	**282a**	7d. bright emerald *(1.7.68)*	25	25	☐ ☐
738		8d. bright vermilion *(1.7.68)*	10	10	☐ ☐
739		8d. turquoise-blue *(6.1.69)*	25	25	☐ ☐
740		9d. green *(8.8.67)*	25	25	☐ ☐
741	**282**	10d. drab *(1.7.68)*	25	25	☐ ☐
742		1s. light bluish violet	20	20	☐ ☐
743		1s.6d. blue and deep blue *(8.8.67)*	25	25	☐ ☐
		c. Phosphorised paper *(10.12.69)*	30	35	☐ ☐
744		1s.9d. orange and black	25	25	☐ ☐
Set of 16 (one of each value and colour)			2·00	2·25	☐ ☐
Presentation Pack (one of each value)			7·00		☐
Presentation Pack (German)			90·00		☐

First Day Covers

5 June 1967	Nos. 731, 742, 744	2·00	☐
8 Aug. 1967	Nos. 729, 740, 743	2·00	☐
5 Feb. 1968	Nos. 723/724, 726, 736	2·25	☐
1 July 1968	Nos. 735, 737/738, 741	3·00	☐

No. 734 exists with phosphor band at the left or right.

283 *Master Lambton*
(Sir Thomas Lawrence)

284 *Mares and Foals in a Landscape* (George Stubbs)

285 *Children Coming Out of School* (L. S. Lowry)

British Paintings

1967 (10 July) Two phosphor bands. No wmk

748	**283**	4d. multicoloured	10	10	☐ ☐
749	**284**	9d. multicoloured	10	10	☐ ☐
750	**285**	1s.6d. multicoloured	10	10	☐ ☐
Set of 3			30	30	☐ ☐
First Day Cover				1·00	☐
Presentation Pack			20·00		☐

286 *Gipsy Moth IV*

Sir Francis Chichester's World Voyage

1967 (24 July) Three phosphor bands. No wmk

| 751 | **286** | 1s.9d. multicoloured | 10 | 10 | ☐ ☐ |
| *First Day Cover* | | | | 40 | ☐ |

287 Radar Screen

288 *Penicillium notatum*

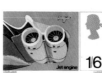

289 Vickers VC-10 Jet Engines

290 Television Equipment

British Discovery and Invention

1967 (19 Sept.) Two phosphor bands (except 4d. three bands). Wmk **179** (sideways on 1s.9d.)

752	**287**	4d. yellow, black and vermilion	10	10	☐ ☐
753	**288**	1s. multicoloured	10	10	☐ ☐
754	**289**	1s.6d. multicoloured	10	10	☐ ☐
755	**290**	1s.9d. multicoloured	10	10	☐ ☐
Set of 4			40	40	☐ ☐
First Day Cover				70	☐
Presentation Pack			9·00		☐

NO WATERMARK. All the following issues are on unwatermarked paper unless otherwise stated.

291 *The Adoration of the Shepherds* (School of Seville)

292 *Madonna and Child* (Murillo)

293 *The Adoration of the Shepherds* (Louis le Nain)

Christmas

1967 Two phosphor bands (except 3d., one phosphor band)

756	**291**	3d. multicoloured (27.11.67)	10	10	☐☐
757	**292**	4d. multicoloured (18.10.67)	10	10	☐☐
758	**293**	1s.6d. multicoloured (27.11.67)	15	15	☐☐
Set of 3			30	30	☐☐
First Day Covers (2)				3·00	☐

Gift Pack 1967

1967 (27 Nov.) Comprises Nos. 715p/722p and 748/758

GP758c	Gift Pack	2·25	☐

1967–68 No wmk. Perf 11×12

759	**166**	2s.6d. brown	10	20	☐☐
760	**167**	5s. red	50	50	☐☐
761	**168**	10s. blue	4·50	2·00	☐☐
762	**169**	£1 black	6·50	2·00	☐☐
Set of 4			10·00	4·25	☐☐

294 Tarr Steps, Exmoor

295 Aberfeldy Bridge

296 Menai Bridge

297 M4 Viaduct

British Bridges

1968 (29 Apr.) Two phosphor bands

763	**294**	4d. multicoloured	10	10	☐☐
764	**295**	9d. multicoloured	10	15	☐☐
765	**296**	1s.6d. multicoloured	15	20	☐☐
766	**297**	1s.9d. multicoloured	15	25	☐☐
Set of 4			45	65	☐☐
First Day Cover				90	☐
Presentation Pack			5·25		☐

298 'TUC' and Trades Unionists

299 Mrs Emmeline Pankhurst. (statue)

300 Sopwith Camel and English Electric Lightning Fighters

301 Captain Cook's Endeavour and Signature

British Anniversaries. Events described on stamps

1968 (29 May) Two phosphor bands

767	**298**	4d. multicoloured	10	10	☐☐
768	**299**	9d. violet, grey and black	10	10	☐☐

769	**300**	1s. multicoloured	15	20	☐☐
770	**301**	1s.9d. ochre and brown	20	25	☐☐
Set of 4			50	60	☐☐
First Day Cover				2·50	☐
Presentation Pack			5·00		☐

302 Queen Elizabeth I (Unknown Artist)

303 Pinkie (Lawrence)

304 Ruins of St Mary Le Port (John Piper)

305 The Hay Wain (John Constable)

British Paintings

1968 (12 Aug.) Two phosphor bands

771	**302**	4d. multicoloured	10	10	☐☐
772	**303**	1s. multicoloured	10	15	☐☐
773	**304**	1s.6d. multicoloured	15	20	☐☐
774	**305**	1s.9d. multicoloured	15	20	☐☐
Set of 4			45	60	☐☐
First Day Cover				1·00	☐
Presentation Pack (PO Pack No. 1)			4·50		☐
Presentation Pack (German) (PO Pack No. 1)			30·00		☐

Gift Pack 1968

1968 (16 Sept.) Comprises Nos. 763/774

GP774c	Gift Pack	3·00	☐
GP774d	Gift Pack (German)	80·00	☐

Collectors Pack 1968

1968 (16 Sept.) Comprises Nos. 752/758 and 763/774

CP774e	Collectors Pack	2·50	☐

306 Girl and Boy with Rocking Horse

307 Girl with Doll's House

308 Boy with Train Set

Christmas

1968 (25 Nov.) Two phosphor bands (except 4d., one centre phosphor band)

775	**306**	4d. multicoloured	10	10		
776	**307**	9d. multicoloured	15	15		
777	**308**	1s.6d. multicoloured	15	20		
Set of 3			35	40		
First Day Cover				1·00		
Presentation Pack (PO Pack No. 4)			9·00			
Presentation Pack (German) (PO Pack No. 4)			30·00			

309 *Queen Elizabeth 2*

310 Elizabethan Galleon

311 East Indiaman

312 *Cutty Sark*

313 *Great Britain*

314 *Mauretania*

British Ships

1969 (15 Jan.) One horiz phosphor band (5d.), two phosphor bands (9d.) or two vertical phosphor bands at right (1s.)

778	**309**	5d. multicoloured	10	10		
779	**310**	9d. multicoloured	10	10		
		a. Strip of 3. Nos. 779/781	40	50		
780	**311**	9d. multicoloured	10	10		
781	**312**	9d. multicoloured	10	10		
782	**313**	1s. multicoloured	15	15		
		a. Pair. Nos. 782/783	50	60		
783	**314**	1s. multicoloured	15	15		
Set of 6			80	1·00		
First Day Cover				1·50		
Presentation Pack (PO Pack No. 5)			3·00			
Presentation Pack (German) (PO Pack No. 5)			38·00			

The 9d. and 1s. values were arranged in horizontal strips of three and pairs respectively throughout the sheet.

315 Concorde in Flight

316 Plan and Elevation Views

317 Concorde's Nose and Tail

First Flight of Concorde

1969 (3 Mar.) Two phosphor bands

784	**315**	4d. multicoloured	10	10		
785	**316**	9d. multicoloured	15	15		
786	**317**	1s.6d. deep blue, grey and light blue	15	15		
Set of 3			35	35		
First Day Cover				4·00		
Presentation Pack (PO Pack No. 6)			7·50			
Presentation Pack (German)			75·00			

318 (See also T **357**)

1969 (5 Mar.) Perf 12

787	**318**	2s.6d. brown	20	20		
788		5s. lake	85	25		
789		10s. ultramarine	3·00	3·75		
790		£1 black	1·75	75		
Set of 4			5·00	4·50		
First Day Cover				6·50		
Presentation Pack (PO Pack No. 7)			16·00			
Presentation Pack (German)			55·00			

319 Page from the *Daily Mail*, and Vickers FB-27 Vimy Aircraft

320 Europa and CEPT Emblems

321 ILO Emblem

322 Flags of NATO Countries

323 Vickers FB-27 Vimy Aircraft and Globe showing Flight

Anniversaries. Events described on stamps

1969 (2 Apr.) Two phosphor bands

791	**319**	5d. multicoloured	10	10	☐ ☐
792	**320**	9d. multicoloured	10	15	☐ ☐
793	**321**	1s. claret, red and blue	15	20	☐ ☐
794	**322**	1s.6d. multicoloured	15	20	☐ ☐
795	**323**	1s.9d. olive, yellow and turquoise-green	25	30	☐ ☐
Set of 5			65	80	☐ ☐
First Day Cover				1·10	☐
Presentation Pack (PO Pack No. 9)			4·50		☐
Presentation Pack (German)			50·00		☐

324 Durham Cathedral   **325** York Minster

326 St Giles' Cathedral, Edinburgh   **327** Canterbury Cathedral

328 St Paul's Cathedral   **329** Liverpool Metropolitan Cathedral

British Architecture (Cathedrals)

1969 (28 May) Two phosphor bands

796	**324**	5d. multicoloured	10	10	☐ ☐
		a. Block of 4. Nos. 796/799	40	50	☐ ☐
797	**325**	5d. multicoloured	10	10	☐ ☐
798	**326**	5d. multicoloured	10	10	☐ ☐
799	**327**	5d. multicoloured	10	10	☐ ☐
800	**328**	9d. multicoloured	15	20	☐ ☐
801	**329**	1s.6d. multicoloured	20	25	☐ ☐
Set of 6			70	85	☐ ☐
First Day Cover				1·00	☐
Presentation Pack (PO Pack No. 10)			5·50		☐
Presentation Pack (German)			35·00		☐

Nos. 796/799 were issued together *se-tenant* in blocks of four within the sheet.

330 The King's Gate, Caernarvon Castle   **331** The Eagle Tower, Caernarvon Castle   **332** Queen Eleanor's Gate, Caernarvon Castle

333 Celtic Cross, Margam Abbey   **334** Prince Charles

Investiture of HRH The Prince of Wales

1969 (1 July) Two phosphor bands

802	**330**	5d. multicoloured	10	10	☐ ☐
		a. Strip of 3. Nos. 802/804	30	50	☐ ☐
803	**331**	5d. multicoloured	10	10	☐ ☐
804	**332**	5d. multicoloured	10	10	☐ ☐
805	**333**	9d. multicoloured	15	20	☐ ☐
806	**334**	1s. black and gold	15	20	☐ ☐
Set of 5			55	80	☐ ☐
First Day Cover				1·00	☐
Presentation Pack (PO Pack No. 11)			3·00		☐
Presentation Pack (German)			35·00		☐
Presentation Pack (Welsh)			40·00		☐

Nos. 802/804 were printed *se-tenant* in strips of three throughout the sheet.

335 Mahatma Gandhi

Gandhi Centenary Year

1969 (13 Aug.) Two phosphor bands

807	**335**	1s.6d. multicoloured	25	30	☐ ☐
First Day Cover				3·25	☐

Collectors Pack 1969

1969 (15 Sept.) Comprises Nos. 775/786 and 791/807

CP807*b*	Collectors Pack	10·00	☐

336 National Giro   **337** Telecommunications – International Subscriber Dialling

338 Telecommunications – Pulse Code Modulation   **339** Postal Mechanisation Automatic Sorting

British Post Office Technology

1969 (1 Oct.) Two phosphor bands. Perf 13½×14

808	**336**	5d. multicoloured	10	10	☐ ☐
809	**337**	9d. green, blue and black	10	10	☐ ☐
810	**338**	1s. green, lavender and black	15	15	☐ ☐

811	**339**	1s.6d. multicoloured	20	20	
Set of 4			50	50	
First Day Cover				75	
Presentation Pack (PO Pack No. 13)			5·00		

340 Herald Angel

341 The Three Shepherds

342 The Three Kings

Christmas

1969 (26 Nov.) Two phosphor bands (5d., 1s.6d.) or one centre band (4d.)

812	**340**	4d. multicoloured	10	10	
813	**341**	5d. multicoloured	10	10	
814	**342**	1s.6d. multicoloured	15	15	
Set of 3			30	30	
First Day Cover				70	
Presentation Pack (PO Pack No. 14)			3·00		

343 Fife Harling

344 Cotswold Limestone

345 Welsh Stucco

346 Ulster Thatch

British Rural Architecture

1970 (11 Feb.) Two phosphor bands

815	**343**	5d. multicoloured	10	10	
816	**344**	9d. multicoloured	15	15	
817	**345**	1s. multicoloured	15	15	
818	**346**	1s.6d. multicoloured	20	25	
Set of 4			55	60	
First Day Cover				85	
Presentation Pack (PO Pack No. 15)			3·00		

347 Signing the Declaration of Arbroath

348 Florence Nightingale attending Patients

349 Signing of International Co-operative Alliance

350 Pilgrims and *Mayflower*

351 Sir William Herschel, Francis Baily, Sir John Herschel and Telescope

Anniversaries. Events described on stamps

1970 (1 Apr.) Two phosphor bands

819	**347**	5d. multicoloured	10	10	
820	**348**	9d. multicoloured	10	10	
821	**349**	1s. multicoloured	15	15	
822	**350**	1s.6d. multicoloured	20	20	
823	**351**	1s.9d. multicoloured	20	20	
Set of 5			70	70	
First Day Cover				95	
Presentation Pack (PO Pack No. 16)			4·00		

352 'Mr Pickwick and Sam' (*Pickwick Papers*)

353 'Mr and Mrs Micawber' (*David Copperfield*)

354 'David Copperfield and Betsy Trotwood' (*David Copperfield*)

355 'Oliver asking for more' (*Oliver Twist*)

356 'Grasmere' (from engraving by J. Farrington, R.A.)

Literary Anniversaries. Events described on stamps

1970 (3 June) Two phosphor bands

824	**352**	5d. multicoloured	10	10	
		a. Block of 4. Nos. 824/827	40	60	
825	**353**	5d. multicoloured	10	10	
826	**354**	5d. multicoloured	10	10	
827	**355**	5d. multicoloured	10	10	
828	**356**	1s.6d. multicoloured	15	20	
Set of 5			50	70	
First Day Cover				90	
Presentation Pack (PO Pack No. 17)			4·00		

Nos. 824/827 were issued together *se-tenant* in blocks of four within the sheet.

For Nos 829/831*b* and Types 356a and 357 see Decimal Machin Definitives section.

358 Runners

359 Swimmers

360 Cyclists

Ninth British Commonwealth Games, Edinburgh

1970 (15 July) Two phosphor bands. Perf 13½×14

832	**358**	5d. pink, emerald, greenish yellow and yellow-green	10	10
833	**359**	1s.6d. greenish blue, lilac, brown and Prussian blue	15	15
834	**360**	1s.9d. yellow-orange, lilac, salmon and red-brown	15	15
Set of 3			45	45
First Day Cover				75
Presentation Pack (PO Pack No. 19)		3·00		

Collectors Pack 1970

1970 (14 Sept.) Comprises Nos. 808/828 and 832/834

CP834a	Collectors Pack	15·00	

361 1d. Black (1840)
1840 first engraved issue

362 1s. Green (1847)
1847 first embossed issue

363 4d. Carmine (1855)
1855 first surface printed issue

Philympia 70 Stamp Exhibition

1970 (18 Sept.) Two phosphor bands. Perf 14×14½

835	**361**	5d. multicoloured	10	10
836	**362**	9d. multicoloured	15	15
837	**363**	1s.6d. multicoloured	15	20
Set of 3			40	40
First Day Cover				75
Presentation Pack (PO Pack No. 21)		3·00		

364 Shepherds and Apparition of the Angel

365 Mary, Joseph and Christ in Manger

366 The Wise Men bearing Gifts

Christmas

1970 (25 Nov.) Two phosphor bands (5d., 1s.6d.) or one centre phosphor band (4d.)

838	**364**	4d. multicoloured	10	10
839	**365**	5d. multicoloured	10	10
840	**366**	1s.6d. multicoloured	15	15
Set of 3			30	30
First Day Cover				40
Presentation Pack (PO Pack No. 22)		4·00		

Nos 841/880 are no longer used.

For 1971–1996 definitives in decimal currency with standard perforations on all sides, Nos. X841/X1058, Type **367**, see Decimal Machin Definitives section.

368 *A Mountain Road* (T. P. Flanagan)

369 *Deer's Meadow* (Tom Carr)

370 *Slieve na brock* (Colin Middleton)

Ulster '71 Paintings

1971 (16 June) Two phosphor bands

881	**368**	3p. multicoloured	10	10
882	**369**	7½p. multicoloured	15	20
883	**370**	9p. multicoloured	20	20
Set of 3			40	45
First Day Cover				75
Presentation Pack (PO Pack No. 26a)		3·00		

371 John Keats (150th Death Anniversary)

372 Thomas Gray (Death Bicentenary)

373 Sir Walter Scott
(Birth Bicentenary)

Literary Anniversaries. Events described above

1971 (28 July) Two phosphor bands

884	**371**	3p. black, gold and blue	10	10	☐ ☐
885	**372**	5p. black, gold and olive	15	20	☐ ☐
886	**373**	7½p. black, gold and brown	20	20	☐ ☐
Set of 3			40	45	☐
First Day Cover				75	☐
Presentation Pack (PO Pack No. 32)		3·00			☐

374 Servicemen and Nurse of 1921   **375** Roman Centurion

376 Rugby Football, 1871

British Anniversaries. Events described on stamps

1971 (25 Aug.) Two phosphor bands

887	**374**	3p. multicoloured	10	10	☐ ☐
888	**375**	7½p. multicoloured	15	20	☐ ☐
889	**376**	9p. multicoloured	20	20	☐ ☐
Set of 3			40	45	☐
First Day Cover				1·00	☐
Presentation Pack (PO Pack No. 32A)		3·00			☐

377 Physical Sciences Building,
University College of Wales,
Aberystwyth

378 Faraday Building,
Southampton University

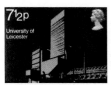

379 Engineering Department,
Leicester University

380 Hexagon Restaurant,
Essex University

British Architecture (Modern University Buildings)

1971 (22 Sept.) Two phosphor bands

890	**377**	3p. multicoloured	10	10	☐ ☐
891	**378**	5p. multicoloured	25	20	☐ ☐
892	**379**	7½p. ochre, black and purple-brown	20	30	☐ ☐
893	**380**	9p. multicoloured	30	40	☐ ☐
Set of 4			55	75	☐
First Day Cover				80	☐
Presentation Pack (PO Pack No. 33)		5·00			☐

Collectors Pack 1971

1971 (29 Sept.) Comprises Nos. 835/840 and 881/893

CP893a	Collectors Pack	20·00	☐

381 Dream of the Wise Men

382 Adoration of the Magi

383 Ride of the Magi

Christmas

1971 (13 Oct.) Two phosphor bands (3p., 7½p.) or one centre phosphor band (2½p.)

894	**381**	2½p. multicoloured	10	10	☐ ☐
895	**382**	3p. multicoloured	10	10	☐ ☐
896	**383**	7½p. multicoloured	20	20	☐ ☐
Set of 3			35	35	☐
First Day Cover				80	☐
Presentation Pack (PO Pack No. 35)		2·25			☐

384 Sir James Clark Ross

385 Sir Martin Frobisher

386 Henry Hudson

387 Captain Robert F. Scott

British Polar Explorers

1972 (16 Feb.) Two phosphor bands

897	**384**	3p. multicoloured	10	10	☐	☐
898	**385**	5p. multicoloured	10	15	☐	☐
899	**386**	7½p. multicoloured	10	15	☐	☐
900	**387**	9p. multicoloured	20	25	☐	☐
Set of 4			45	60	☐	☐
First Day Cover				85		☐
Presentation Pack (PO Pack No. 39)			4·00		☐	

388 Statuette of Tutankhamun

389 19th-century Coastguard

390 Ralph Vaughan Williams and Score

Anniversaries. Events described on stamps

1972 (26 Apr.) Two phosphor bands

901	**388**	3p. multicoloured	10	10	☐	☐
902	**389**	7½p. multicoloured	20	20	☐	☐
903	**390**	9p. multicoloured	20	25	☐	☐
Set of 3			45	50	☐	☐
First Day Cover				85		☐
Presentation Pack (PO Pack No. 40)			2·25		☐	

391 St Andrew's, Greensted - juxta-Ongar, Essex

392 All Saints, Earls Barton, Northants

393 St Andrew's, Letheringsett, Norfolk

394 St Andrew's, Helpringham, Lincs

395 St Mary the Virgin, Huish Episcopi, Somerset

British Architecture (Village Churches)

1972 (21 June) Two phosphor bands

904	**391**	3p. multicoloured	10	10	☐	☐
905	**392**	4p. multicoloured	10	10	☐	☐
906	**393**	5p. multicoloured	10	20	☐	☐
907	**394**	7½p. multicoloured	15	20	☐	☐
908	**395**	9p. multicoloured	15	20	☐	☐
Set of 5			55	80	☐	☐
First Day Cover				1·25		☐
Presentation Pack (PO Pack No. 41)			4·75		☐	

Belgica '72 Souvenir Pack

1972 (24 June) Comprises Nos. 894/896 and 904/908

CP908b	Souvenir Pack		3·75	☐

396 Microphones, 1924–1969

397 Horn Loudspeaker

398 TV Camera, 1972

399 Oscillator and Spark Transmitter, 1897

Broadcasting Anniversaries. Events described on stamps

1972 (13 Sept.) Two phosphor bands

909	**396**	3p. multicoloured	10	10	☐	☐
910	**397**	5p. multicoloured	10	10	☐	☐
911	**398**	7½p. multicoloured	15	20	☐	☐
912	**399**	9p. multicoloured	15	20	☐	☐
Set of 4			45	55	☐	☐
First Day Cover				1·25		☐
Presentation Pack (PO Pack No. 43)			3·25		☐	

400 Angel holding Trumpet

401 Angel playing Lute

402 Angel playing Harp

Christmas

1972 (18 Oct.) Two phosphor bands (3p., 7½p.) or one centre phosphor band (2½p.)

913	**400**	2½p. multicoloured	10	10
914	**401**	3p. multicoloured	10	10
915	**402**	7½p. multicoloured	20	20
Set of 3			35	35
First Day Cover				85
Presentation Pack (PO Pack No. 44)			2·00	

403 Queen Elizabeth II and Prince Philip

404 Europe

Royal Silver Wedding

1972 (20 Nov.) 3p. 'all-over' phosphor, 20p. without phosphor

916	**403**	3p. brownish black, deep blue and silver	20	20
917		20p. brownish black, reddish purple and silver	60	60
Set of 2			75	75
First Day Cover				60
Presentation Pack (PO Pack No. 45)			2·00	
Presentation Pack (Japanese)			3·00	
Souvenir Book (PO Pack No. 46)			1·25	
Gutter Pair (3p.)			1·50	
Traffic Light Gutter Pair (3p.)			20·00	

Collectors Pack 1972

1972 (20 Nov.) Comprises Nos. 897/917

CP918*a*	Collectors Pack	12·00	

Britain's Entry into European Communities

1973 (3 Jan.) Two phosphor bands

919	**404**	3p. multicoloured	10	10
920		5p. multicoloured (blue jigsaw)	15	20
		a. Pair. Nos. 920/921	35	45
921		5p. multicoloured (green jigsaw)	15	20
Set of 3			40	45
First Day Cover				70
Presentation Pack (PO Pack No. 48)			4·00	

Nos. 920/921 were issued horizontally *se-tenant* throughout the sheet.

Oak. Quercus robur
405 Oak Tree

British Trees (1st Issue)

1973 (28 Feb.) Two phosphor bands

922	**405**	9p. multicoloured	15	15
First Day Cover				40
Presentation Pack (PO Pack No. 49)			1·25	

See also No. 949.

406 David Livingstone

407 H. M. Stanley

408 Sir Francis Drake

409 Sir Walter Raleigh

410 Charles Sturt

British Explorers

1973 (18 Apr.) 'All-over' phosphor

923	**406**	3p. multicoloured	10	10
		a. Pair. Nos. 923/924	20	20
924	**407**	3p. multicoloured	10	10
925	**408**	5p. multicoloured	20	20
926	**409**	7½p. multicoloured	20	20
927	**410**	9p. multicoloured	20	20
Set of 5			75	75
First Day Cover				90
Presentation Pack (PO Pack No. 50)			2·25	

Nos. 923/924 were issued horizontally *se-tenant* throughout the sheet.

8^P Airmail blue van and postbox 1930
438 Airmail-blue Van and Post box, 1930

10^P Imperial Airways flyingboat 1937
439 Imperial Airways Short S.21 Flying Boat *Maia*, 1937

Centenary of Universal Postal Union

1974 (12 June) 'All-over' phosphor

954	**436**	3½p. multicoloured	10	10	
955	**437**	5½p. multicoloured	10	10	
956	**438**	8p. multicoloured	10	10	
957	**439**	10p. multicoloured	15	15	
Set of 4			40	40	
First Day Cover				60	
Presentation Pack (PO Pack No. 64)			2·00		
Set of 4 Gutter Pairs			80		
Set of 4 Traffic Light Gutter Pairs			28·00		

440 Robert the Bruce

441 Owain Glyndŵr

442 Henry V

443 The Black Prince

Medieval Warriors

1974 (10 July) 'All-over' phosphor

958	**440**	4½p. multicoloured	10	10	
959	**441**	5½p. multicoloured	15	15	
960	**442**	8p. multicoloured	15	15	
961	**443**	10p. multicoloured	15	15	
Set of 4			50	50	
First Day Cover				1·25	
Presentation Pack (PO Pack No. 65)			1·60		
PHQ Cards (*set of 4*) (7)			12·00	30·00	
Set of 4 Gutter Pairs			1·00		
Set of 4 Traffic Light Gutter Pairs			40·00		

444 Churchill in Royal yacht Squadron Uniform

445 Prime Minister, 1940

446 Secretary for War and Air, 1919

447 War Correspondent, South Africa, 1899

Birth Centenary of Sir Winston Churchill

1974 (9 Oct.) Queen's head and inscription in silver. 'All-over' phosphor

962	**444**	4½p. green and blue	10	10		
963	**445**	5½p. grey and black	20	15		
964	**446**	8p. rose and lake	30	30		
965	**447**	10p. stone and brown	30	30		
Set of 4			80	75		
First Day Cover				80		
Presentation Pack (PO Pack No. 66)			1·75			
Souvenir Book			1·50			
PHQ Card (No. 963) (8)			2·75	15·00		
Set of 4 Gutter Pairs			1·60			
Set of 4 Traffic Light Gutter Pairs			22·00			

448 *Adoration of the Magi* (York Minister, *c* 1355)

449 *The Nativity* (St Helen's Church, Norwich, *c* 1480)

450 *Virgin and Child* (Ottery St Mary Church, *c* 1350)

451 *Virgin and Child* (Worcester Cathedral, *c* 1224)

Christmas

1974 (27 Nov.) Designs show church roof bosses. One phosphor band (3½p.) or 'all-over' phosphor (others)

966	**448**	3½p. multicoloured	10	10		
967	**449**	4½p. multicoloured	10	10		
968	**450**	8p. multicoloured	10	10		
969	**451**	10p. multicoloured	15	15		
Set of 4			40	40		
First Day Cover				70		
Presentation Pack (PO Pack No. 67)			1·50			
Set of 4 Gutter Pairs			80			
Set of 4 Traffic Light Gutter Pairs			24·00			

Collectors Pack 1974

1974 (27 Nov.) Comprises Nos. 949/969

CP969*a*	Collectors Pack	4·75	

452 Invalid in Wheelchair

Health and Handicap Funds

1975 (22 Jan.) 'All-over' phosphor

970	**452**	4½p. +1½p. azure and blue	15	15	
First Day Cover				30	
Gutter Pair			30		
Traffic Light Gutter Pair			2·25		

Turner 1775-1851
453 Peace – Burial at Sea

Turner 1775-1851
454 Snowstorm – Steamer off a Harbour's Mouth

Turner 1775-1851
455 The Arsenal, Venice

Turner 1775-1851
456 St Laurent

Birth Bicentenary of J. M. W. Turner (painter)

1975 (19 Feb.) 'All-over' phosphor

971	**453**	4½p. multicoloured	10	10	
972	**454**	5½p. multicoloured	10	10	
973	**455**	8p. multicoloured	10	10	
974	**456**	10p. multicoloured	15	15	
Set of 4			40	40	
First Day Cover				50	
Presentation Pack (PO Pack No. 69)			1·50		
PHQ Card (No. 972) (9)			18·00	20·00	
Set of 4 Gutter Pairs			80		
Set of 4 Traffic Light Gutter Pairs			5·50		

7ᴰ Charlotte Square Edinburgh
457 Charlotte Square, Edinburgh

7ᴰ The Rows Chester
458 The Rows, Chester

8ᴰ The Royal Observatory Greenwich
459 Royal Observatory, Greenwich

10ᴰ St George's Chapel Windsor
460 St George's Chapel, Windsor

The National Theatre London
461 National Theatre, London

European Architectural Heritage Year

1975 (23 Apr.) 'All-over' phosphor

975	**457**	7p. multicoloured	10	10	
		a. Pair. Nos. 975/976	20	20	
976	**458**	7p. multicoloured	10	10	
977	**459**	8p. multicoloured	10	10	
978	**460**	10p. multicoloured	15	15	
979	**461**	12p. multicoloured	20	20	
Set of 5			60	60	
First Day Cover				80	
Presentation Pack (PO Pack No. 70)			1·50		
PHQ Cards (Nos. 975/977) (10)			4·75	10·00	
Set of 5 Gutter Pairs			1·25		
Set of 5 Traffic Light Gutter Pairs			14·00		

Nos. 975/976 were printed horizontally se-tenant throughout the sheet.

462 Sailing Dinghies

463 Racing Keel Boats

464 Cruising Yachts

465 Multihulls

Sailing

1975 (11 June) 'All-over' phosphor

980	**462**	7p. multicoloured	10	10	
981	**463**	8p. multicoloured	10	10	
982	**464**	10p. multicoloured	15	15	
983	**465**	12p. multicoloured	20	20	
Set of 4			50	50	
First Day Cover				70	
Presentation Pack (PO Pack No. 71)			1·25		
PHQ Card (No. 981) (11)			2·75	8·00	
Set of 4 Gutter Pairs			1·00		
Set of 4 Traffic Light Gutter Pairs			18·00		

Stephenson's Locomotion 7ᴾ
1825 Stockton and Darlington Railway
466 Stephenson's Locomotion, 1825

Waverley Class 8ᴾ
1876 North British Railway Drummond
467 Abbotsford, 1876

Caerphilly Castle 10ᵖ

1923 Great Western Railway Castle Class
468 *Caerphilly Castle*, 1923

High-Speed Train 12ᵖ

1975 British Rail Inter-City Service HST
469 High Speed Train, 1975

150th Anniversary of Public Railways

1975 (13 Aug.) 'All-over' phosphor

984	**466**	7p. multicoloured	10	10		
985	**467**	8p. multicoloured	20	20		
986	**468**	10p. multicoloured	20	20		
987	**469**	12p. multicoloured	30	30		
Set of 4			70	70		
First Day Cover				90		
Presentation Pack (PO Pack No. 72)			2·00			
Souvenir Book (PO Pack No. 73)			1·60			
PHQ Cards (set of 4) (12)			30·00	30·00		
Set of 4 Gutter Pairs			1·40			
Set of 4 Traffic Light Gutter Pairs			7·50			

470 Palace of Westminster

62nd Inter-Parliamentary Union Conference

1975 (3 Sept.) 'All-over' phosphor

988	**470**	12p. multicoloured	20	20		
First Day Cover				30		
Presentation Pack (PO Pack No. 74)			85			
Gutter Pair			40			
Traffic Light Gutter Pair			2·25			

471 Emma and
Mr Woodhouse (*Emma*)

472 Catherine Morland
(*Northanger Abbey*)

473 Mr Darcy (*Pride
and Prejudice*)

474 Mary and Henry
Crawford (*Mansfield Park*)

Birth Bicentenary of Jane Austen (novelist)

1975 (22 Oct.) 'All-over' phosphor

989	**471**	8½p. multicoloured	10	10		
990	**472**	10p. multicoloured	15	15		
991	**473**	11p. multicoloured	15	15		

992	**474**	13p. multicoloured	25	20		
Set of 4			60	55		
First Day Cover				75		
Presentation Pack (PO Pack No. 75)			7·00			
PHQ Cards (set of 4) (13)			9·50	15·00		
Set of 4 Gutter Pairs			1·25			
Set of 4 Traffic Light Gutter Pairs			7·00			

475 Angels with Harp and Lute

476 Angel with Mandolin

477 Angel with Horn

478 Angel with Trumpet

Christmas

1975 (26 Nov.) One phosphor band (6½p.), phosphor-inked (8½p.) (background) or 'all-over' phosphor (others)

993	**475**	6½p. multicoloured	10	10		
994	**476**	8½p. multicoloured	10	10		
995	**477**	11p. multicoloured	20	15		
996	**478**	13p. multicoloured	20	20		
Set of 4			45	50		
First Day Cover				75		
Presentation Pack (PO Pack No. 76)			1·50			
Set of 4 Gutter Pairs			1·10			
Set of 4 Traffic Light Gutter Pairs			5·00			

Collectors Pack 1975

1975 (26 Nov.) Comprises Nos. 970/996

CP996a	Collectors Pack		4·25	

479 Housewife

480 Policeman

481 District Nurse

482 Industrialist

Telephone Centenary

1976 (10 Mar.) 'All-over' phosphor

997	**479**	8½p. multicoloured	10	10		
998	**480**	10p. multicoloured	15	15		
999	**481**	11p. multicoloured	15	15		
1000	**482**	13p. multicoloured	25	20		
Set of 4			60	55		
First Day Cover				60		
Presentation Pack (PO Pack No. 78)			1·40			
Set of 4 Gutter Pairs			1·25			
Set of 4 Traffic Light Gutter Pairs			11·00			

483 Hewing Coal
(Thomas Hepburn)

484 Machinery
(Robert Owen)

485 Chimney Cleaning
(Lord Shaftesbury)

486 Hands clutching Prison Bars
(Elizabeth Fry)

Social Reformers

1976 (28 Apr.) 'All-over' phosphor

1001	**483**	8½p. multicoloured	10	10	☐	☐
1002	**484**	10p. multicoloured	15	15	☐	☐
1003	**485**	11p. black, slate-grey and drab	15	15	☐	☐
1004	**486**	13p. slate-grey, black and green	25	20	☐	☐
Set of 4			60	55	☐	☐
First Day Cover				60	☐	
Presentation Pack (PO Pack No. 79)			1·25		☐	
PHQ Card (No. 1001) (14)			2·75	9·00	☐	☐
Set of 4 Gutter Pairs			1·25		☐	
Set of 4 Traffic Light Gutter Pairs			5·00		☐	

487 Benjamin Franklin
(bust. by Jean-Jacques Caffieri)

Bicentenary of American Revolution

1976 (2 June) 'All-over' phosphor

1005	**487**	11p. multicoloured	20	20	☐	☐
First Day Cover				50	☐	
Presentation Pack (PO Pack No. 80)			65		☐	
PHQ Card (15)			2·25	8·00	☐	☐
Gutter Pair			40		☐	
Traffic Light Gutter Pair			2·25		☐	

488 'Elizabeth of Glamis'

489 'Grandpa Dickson'

490 'Rosa Mundi'

491 'Sweet Briar'

Centenary of Royal National Rose Society

1976 (30 June) 'All-over' phosphor

1006	**488**	8½p. multicoloured	10	10	☐	☐
1007	**489**	10p. multicoloured	15	15	☐	☐
1008	**490**	11p. multicoloured	15	15	☐	☐
1009	**491**	13p. multicoloured	25	20	☐	☐
Set of 4			60	55	☐	☐
First Day Cover				60	☐	
Presentation Pack (PO Pack No. 81)			1·50		☐	
PHQ Cards (*set of 4*) (16)			14·00	15·00	☐	☐
Set of 4 Gutter Pairs			1·25		☐	
Set of 4 Traffic Light Gutter Pairs			6·00		☐	

492 Archdruid

493 Morris Dancing

494 Scots Piper

495 Welsh Harpist

British Cultural Traditions

1976 (4 Aug.) 'All-over' phosphor

1010	**492**	8½p. multicoloured	10	10	☐	☐
1011	**493**	10p. multicoloured	15	15	☐	☐
1012	**494**	11p. multicoloured	15	15	☐	☐
1013	**495**	13p. multicoloured	25	20	☐	☐
Set of 4			60	55	☐	☐
First Day Cover				60	☐	
Presentation Pack (PO Pack No. 82)			1·25		☐	
PHQ Cards (*set of 4*) (17)			7·50	12·00	☐	☐
Set of 4 Gutter Pairs			1·25		☐	
Set of 4 Traffic Light Gutter Pairs			6·00		☐	

496 *The Canterbury Tales* William Caxton 1476 8½P

497 *The Tretyse of Love* William Caxton 1476 10P

498 *Game and Playe of Chesse* William Caxton 1476 11P

499 *Early Printing Press* William Caxton 1476 13P

500th Anniversary of British Printing

1976 (29 Sept.) 'All-over' phosphor

1014	**496**	8½p. black, blue and gold	10	10	☐	☐
1015	**497**	10p. black, olive-green and gold	15	15	☐	☐
1016	**498**	11p. black, grey and gold	15	15	☐	☐
1017	**499**	13p. brown, ochre and gold	25	25	☐	☐
Set of 4			60	60	☐	☐
First Day Cover				65		☐
Presentation Pack (PO Pack No. 83)			1·25			☐
PHQ Cards (*set of 4*) (18)			6·00	9·00	☐	☐
Set of 4 Gutter Pairs			1·25			☐
Set of 4 Traffic Light Gutter Pairs			6·00			☐

500 Virgin and Child English Embroidery c.1272 6½P

501 Angel with Crown English Embroidery c.1340 8½P

502 Angel appearing to Shepherds English Embroidery c.1320 11P

503 The Three Kings English Embroidery c.1390 13P

Christmas

1976 (24 Nov.) Designs show English medieval embroidery. One phosphor band (6½p.) or 'all-over' phosphor (others)

1018	**500**	6½p. multicoloured	10	10	☐	
1019	**501**	8½p. multicoloured	15	15	☐	
1020	**502**	11p. multicoloured	15	15	☐	
1021	**503**	13p. multicoloured	20	20	☐	
Set of 4			55	55	☐	
First Day Cover				60		☐
Presentation Pack (PO Pack No. 87)			1·40			☐
PHQ Cards (*set of 4*) (19)			1·75	5·00	☐	
Set of 4 Gutter Pairs			1·10			☐
Set of 4 Traffic Light Gutter Pairs			4·50			☐

Collectors Pack 1976

1976 (24 Nov.) Comprises Nos. 997/1021

CP1021*a*	Collectors Pack		5·50	☐

504 Lawn Tennis 8½p

505 Table Tennis 10p

506 Squash 11p

507 Badminton 13p

Racket Sports

1977 (12 Jan.) Phosphorised paper

1022	**504**	8½p. multicoloured	10	10	☐	
1023	**505**	10p. multicoloured	15	15	☐	
1024	**506**	11p. multicoloured	15	15	☐	
1025	**507**	13p. multicoloured	20	20	☐	
Set of 4			55	55	☐	
First Day Cover				60		☐
Presentation Pack (PO Pack No. 89)			1·50			☐
PHQ Cards (*set of 4*) (20)			3·50	8·00	☐	☐
Set of 4 Gutter Pairs			1·10			☐
Set of 4 Traffic Light Gutter Pairs			5·50			☐

> For Nos. 1026/1028, Type **508**, see Decimal Machin Definitives section.

509 Steroids — Conformational Analysis 8½p

510 Vitamin C — Synthesis 10p

511 Starch — Chromatography 11p

512 Salt — Crystallography 13p

Centenary of Royal Institute of Chemistry

1977 (2 Mar.) 'All-over' phosphor

1029	**509**	8½p. multicoloured	10	10	☐	
1030	**510**	10p. multicoloured	15	15	☐	
1031	**511**	11p. multicoloured	15	15	☐	
1032	**512**	13p. multicoloured	20	20	☐	
Set of 4			55	55	☐	
First Day Cover				60		☐
Presentation Pack (PO Pack No. 92)			1·50			☐
PHQ Cards (*set of 4*) (21)			3·50	8·00	☐	☐
Set of 4 Gutter Pairs			1·10			☐
Set of 4 Traffic Light Gutter Pairs			5·50			☐

513

Silver Jubilee

1977 (11 May–15 June) 'All-over' phosphor

1033	**513**	8½p. multicoloured	10	10	☐ ☐
1034		9p. multicoloured			
		(15.6.77)	20	20	☐ ☐
1035		10p. multicoloured	10	10	☐ ☐
1036		11p. multicoloured	25	30	☐ ☐
1037		13p. multicoloured	25	30	☐ ☐
Set of 5			80	85	☐
First Day Covers (2)				90	☐
Presentation Pack (ex 9p.)					
(PO Pack No. 94)			1·00		☐
Souvenir Book (ex 9p.) (PO Pack No. 93)			1·25		☐
PHQ Cards (*set of 5*) (22)			5·50	10·00	☐ ☐
Set of 5 Gutter Pairs			1·60		☐
Set of 5 Traffic Light Gutter Pairs			8·00		☐

517 'Gathering of Nations'

Commonwealth Heads of Government Meeting, London

1977 (8 June) 'All-over' phosphor

1038	**517**	13p. black, deep green,			
		rose and silver	20	20	☐ ☐
First Day Cover				40	☐
Presentation Pack (PO Pack No. 95)			45		☐
PHQ Card (23)			1·25	1·50	☐ ☐
Gutter Pair			40		☐
Traffic Light Gutter Pair			1·75		☐

518 Hedgehog **519** Brown Hare **520** Red Squirrel

521 Otter **522** Badger

British Wildlife

1977 (5 Oct.) 'All-over' phosphor

1039	**518**	9p. multicoloured	15	20	☐ ☐
		a. Strip of 5.			
		Nos.1039/1043	70	95	☐ ☐
1040	**519**	9p. multicoloured	15	20	☐ ☐
1041	**520**	9p. multicoloured	15	20	☐ ☐
1042	**521**	9p. multicoloured	15	20	☐ ☐
1043	**522**	9p. multicoloured	15	20	☐ ☐
Set of 5			70	95	☐
First Day Cover				1·00	☐
Presentation Pack (PO Pack No. 96)			1·00		☐
PHQ Cards (*set of 5*) (25)			1·50	2·50	☐ ☐
Set of 10 Gutter Strip			1·40		☐
Set of 10 Traffic Light Gutter Strip			5·00		☐

Nos. 1039/1043 were printed together, *se-tenant*, throughout the sheet.

523 Three French Hens, Two Turtle Doves and a Partridge in a Pear Tree

524 Six Geese a laying, Five Gold Rings, Four Colly Birds

525 Eight Maids a-milking, Seven Swans a-swimming

526 Ten Pipers piping, Nine Drummers drumming

527 Twelve Lords a-leaping, Eleven Ladies Dancing

528 A Partridge in a Pear Tree

Christmas

1977 (23 Nov.) One centre phosphor band (7p.) or 'all-over' phosphor (9p.)

1044	**523**	7p. multicoloured	10	10	☐ ☐
		a. Strip of 5. Nos.			
		1044/1048	50	50	☐ ☐
1045	**524**	7p. multicoloured	10	10	☐ ☐
1046	**525**	7p. multicoloured	10	10	☐ ☐
1047	**526**	7p. multicoloured	10	10	☐ ☐
1048	**527**	7p. multicoloured	10	10	☐ ☐
1049	**528**	9p. multicoloured	10	20	☐ ☐
Set of 6			60	70	☐
First Day Cover				75	☐
Presentation Pack (PO Pack No. 97)			90		☐
PHQ Cards (*set of 6*) (26)			1·50	2·50	☐ ☐
Set of 6 Gutter Pairs			1·25		☐
Set of 6 Traffic Light Gutter Pairs			3·75		☐

Nos. 1044/1049 depict the carol *The Twelve Days of Christmas*. Nos. 1044/1048 were printed horizontally *se-tenant* throughout the sheet.

Collectors Pack 1977

1977 (23 Nov.) Comprises Nos. 1022/1025, 1029/1049
CP1049*b*   Collectors Pack   3·75

529 Oil — North Sea
Production Platform

530 Coal — Modern
Pithead

531 Natural Gas —
Flame Rising from Sea

532 Electricity —
Nuclear Power Station
and Uranium Atom

Energy Resources

1978 (25 Jan.) 'All-over' phosphor

1050	**529**	9p. multicoloured	10	10
1051	**530**	10½p. multicoloured	15	15
1052	**531**	11p. multicoloured	15	15
1053	**532**	13p. multicoloured	20	20
Set of 4			55	55
First Day Cover				60
Presentation Pack (PO Pack No. 99)			85	
PHQ Cards (set of 4) (27)			1·50	2·50
Set of 4 Gutter Pairs			1·10	
Set of 4 Traffic Light Gutter Pairs			4·50	

533 Tower of London

534 Holyroodhouse

535 Caernarvon Castle

536 Hampton Court Palace

British Architecture (Historic Buildings)

1978 (1 Mar.) 'All-over' phosphor

1054	**533**	9p. multicoloured	10	10
1055	**534**	10½p. multicoloured	15	15
1056	**535**	11p. multicoloured	15	15
1057	**536**	13p. multicoloured	20	20
Set of 4			55	55
First Day Cover				60
Presentation Pack (PO Pack No. 100)			75	

PHQ Cards (set of 4) (28)		1·50	2·50
Set of 4 Gutter Pairs		1·10	
Set of 4 Traffic Light Gutter Pairs		4·25	
MS1058 121×90 mm. Nos. 1054/1057		70	70
First Day Cover			85

No. **MS**1058 was sold at 53½p., the premium being used for the
London 1980 Stamp Exhibition.

537 State Coach

538 St Edward's Crown

539 The Sovereign's Orb

540 Imperial State Crown

25th Anniversary of Coronation

1978 (31 May) 'All-over' phosphor

1059	**537**	9p. gold and blue	15	20
1060	**538**	10½p. gold and red	20	20
1061	**539**	11p. gold and green	20	20
1062	**540**	13p. gold and violet	25	25
Set of 4			75	75
First Day Cover				80
Presentation Pack (PO Pack No. 101)			85	
Souvenir Book			1·25	
PHQ Cards (set of 4) (29)			1·50	2·25
Set of 4 Gutter Pairs			1·40	
Set of 4 Traffic Light Gutter Pairs			4·25	

541 Shire Horse

542 Shetland Pony

543 Welsh Pony

544 Thoroughbred

Horses

1978 (5 July) 'All-over' phosphor

1063	**541**	9p. multicoloured	10	10
1064	**542**	10½p. multicoloured	15	15
1065	**543**	11p. multicoloured	15	15
1066	**544**	13p. multicoloured	20	20
Set of 4			55	55
First Day Cover				60
Presentation Pack (PO Pack No. 102)			75	

PHQ Cards (*set of 4*) (30)	1·00	1·75 ☐ ☐
Set of 4 Gutter Pairs	1·10	☐
Set of 4 Traffic Light Gutter Pairs	4·50	☐

545 Penny-farthing and 1884 Safety Bicycle   **546** 1920 Touring Bicycles

547 Modern Small-wheel Bicycles   **548** 1978 Road-racers

Centenaries of Cyclists Touring Club and British Cycling Federation

1978 (2 Aug.) 'All-over' phosphor

1067	**545**	9p. multicoloured	10	10	☐ ☐
1068	**546**	10½p. multicoloured	15	15	☐ ☐
1069	**547**	11p. multicoloured	15	15	☐ ☐
1070	**548**	13p. multicoloured	20	20	☐ ☐
Set of 4			55	55	☐ ☐
First Day Cover				60	☐
Presentation Pack (PO Pack No. 103)			75		☐
PHQ Cards (set of 4) (31)			1·00	1·75	☐ ☐
Set of 4 Gutter Pairs			1·10		☐
Set of 4 Traffic Light Gutter Pairs			4·25		☐

549 Singing Carols round the Christmas Tree   **550** The Waits

551 18th-century Carol Singers   **552** *The Boar's Head Carol*

Christmas

1978 (22 Nov.) One centre phosphor band (7p.) or 'all-over' phosphor (others)

1071	**549**	7p. multicoloured	10	10	☐ ☐
1072	**550**	9p. multicoloured	15	15	☐ ☐
1073	**551**	11p. multicoloured	15	15	☐ ☐
1074	**552**	13p. multicoloured	20	20	☐ ☐
Set of 4			55	55	☐ ☐
First Day Cover				60	☐
Presentation Pack (PO Pack No. 104)			75		☐
PHQ Cards (set of 4) (32)			1·00	1·75	☐ ☐
Set of 4 Gutter Pairs			1·10		☐
Set of 4 Traffic Light Gutter Pairs			4·00		☐

Collectors Pack 1978

1978 (22 Nov.) Comprises Nos. 1050/1057, 1059/1074

CP1074*a*	Collectors Pack	3·75	☐

553 Old English Sheepdog   **554** Welsh Springer Spaniel

555 West Highland Terrier   **556** Irish Setter

Dogs

1979 (7 Feb.) 'All-over' phosphor

1075	**553**	9p. multicoloured	10	10	☐ ☐
1076	**554**	10½p. multicoloured	15	15	☐ ☐
1077	**555**	11p. multicoloured	15	15	☐ ☐
1078	**556**	13p. multicoloured	20	20	☐ ☐
Set of 4			55	55	☐ ☐
First Day Cover				60	☐
Presentation Pack (PO Pack No. 106)			70		☐
PHQ Cards (set of 4) (33)			80	1·50	☐ ☐
Set of 4 Gutter Pairs			1·10		
Set of 4 Traffic Light Gutter Pairs			4·00		☐

557 Primrose   **558** Daffodil

559 Bluebell   **560** Snowdrop

Spring Wild Flowers

1979 (21 Mar.) 'All-over' phosphor

1079	**557**	9p. multicoloured	10	10	☐ ☐
1080	**558**	10½p. multicoloured	15	15	☐ ☐
1081	**559**	11p. multicoloured	15	15	☐ ☐
1082	**560**	13p. multicoloured	20	20	☐ ☐
Set of 4			55	55	☐ ☐
First Day Cover				60	☐
Presentation Pack (PO Pack No. 107)			70		☐
PHQ Cards (set of 4) (34)			80	1·25	☐ ☐

Set of 4 Gutter Pairs	1·10	
Set of 4 Traffic Light Gutter Pairs	4·00	

561

562

563

564

First Direct Elections to European Assembly

1979 (9 May) Phosphorised paper

1083	**561**	9p. multicoloured	10	10	
1084	**562**	10½p. multicoloured	15	15	
1085	**563**	1.1p. multicoloured	15	15	
1086	**564**	13p. multicoloured	20	20	
Set of 4			55	55	
First Day Cover				60	
Presentation Pack (PO Pack No. 108)			70		
PHQ Cards (set of 4) (35)			80	1·25	
Set of 4 Gutter Pairs			1·10		
Set of 4 Traffic Light Gutter Pairs			4·00		

Nos. 1083/1086 show hands placing the flags of the member nations into ballot boxes.

565 Saddling Mahmoud for the Derby, 1936 (Sir Alfred Munnings)

566 The Liverpool Great National Steeple Chase, 1839 (aquatint by F. C. Turner)

567 The First. Spring Meeting, Newmarket, 1793 (J. N. Sartorius)

568 Racing at Dorsett Ferry, Windsor, 1684 (Francis Barlow)

Horseracing Paintings and Bicentenary of The Derby (9p.)

1979 (6 June) 'All-over' phosphor

1087	**565**	9p. multicoloured	10	10	
1088	**566**	10½p. multicoloured	15	15	
1089	**567**	11p. multicoloured	15	15	
1090	**568**	13p. multicoloured	20	20	
Set of 4			55	55	
First Day Cover				60	
Presentation Pack (PO Pack No. 109)			70		
PHQ Cards (set of 4) (36)			80	1·25	
Set of 4 Gutter Pairs			1·10		
Set of 4 Traffic Light Gutter Pairs			4·50		

569 The Tale of Peter Rabbit (Beatrix Potter)

570 The Wind in the Willows (Kenneth Grahame)

571 Winnie-the-Pooh (A. A. Milne)

572 Alice's Adventures in Wonderland (Lewis Carroll)

International Year of the Child

1979 (11 July) 'All-over' phosphor

1091	**569**	9p. multicoloured	15	15	
1092	**570**	10½p. multicoloured	20	20	
1093	**571**	11p. multicoloured	20	20	
1094	**572**	13p. multicoloured	25	25	
Set of 4			75	75	
First Day Cover				80	
Presentation Pack (PO Pack No. 110)			1·00		
PHQ Cards (set of 4) (37)			80	1·40	
Set of 4 Gutter Pairs			1·50		
Set of 4 Traffic Light Gutter Pairs			3·75		

Nos. 1091/1094 depict original illustrations from the four books.

573 Sir Rowland Hill, 1795–1879

574 General Post, c 1839

575 London Post, c 1839

576 Uniform Postage, 1840

Death Centenary of Sir Rowland Hill (postal reformer)

1979 (22 Aug.–24 Oct.) 'All-over' phosphor

1095	**573**	10p. multicoloured	15	15	
1096	**574**	11½p. multicoloured	15	15	
1097	**575**	13p. multicoloured	20	20	
1098	**576**	15p. multicoloured	25	25	

Set of 4		70	70	☐ ☐
First Day Cover			75	☐
Presentation Pack (PO Pack No. 111)		80		☐
PHQ Cards *(set of 4)* (38)		50	1·25	☐ ☐
Set of 4 Gutter Pairs		1·40		☐
Set of 4 Traffic Light Gutter Pairs		3·75		☐
MS1099 89×121 mm. Nos. 1095/1098		70	75	☐ ☐
First Day Cover (24.10.79)			80	☐

No. **MS**1099 was sold at 59½p., the premium being used for the London 1980 Stamp Exhibition.

577 Policeman on the Beat

578 Policeman directing Traffic

579 Mounted Policewoman

580 River Patrol Boat

150th Anniversary of Metropolitan Police

1979

1100	**577**	10p. multicoloured	15	15	☐ ☐
1101	**578**	11½p. multicoloured	15	15	☐ ☐
1102	**579**	13p. multicoloured	20	20	☐ ☐
1103	**580**	15p. multicoloured	25	25	☐ ☐
Set of 4			70	70	☐ ☐
First Day Cover				75	☐
Presentation Pack (PO Pack No. 112)			80		☐
PHQ Cards *(set of 4)* (39)			50	1·25	☐ ☐
Set of 4 Gutter Pairs			1·40		☐
Set of 4 Traffic Light Gutter Pairs			3·75		☐

581 The Three Kings

582 Angel appearing to the Shepherds

583 The Nativity

584 Mary and Joseph travelling to Bethlehem

585 The Annunciation

Christmas

1979 (21 Nov.) One centre phosphor band (8p.) or phosphorised paper (others)

1104	**581**	8p. multicoloured	10	10	☐ ☐
1105	**582**	10p. multicoloured	15	15	☐ ☐
1106	**583**	11½p. multicoloured	15	15	☐ ☐
1107	**584**	13p. multicoloured	20	20	☐ ☐
1108	**585**	15p. multicoloured	20	20	☐ ☐
Set of 5			75	75	☐ ☐
First Day Cover				80	☐
Presentation Pack (PO Pack No. 113)			80		☐
PHQ Cards *(set of 5)* (40)			50	1·25	☐ ☐
Set of 5 Gutter Pairs			1·50		☐
Set of 5 Traffic Light Gutter Pairs			4·50		☐

Collectors Pack 1979

1979 (21 Nov.) Comprises Nos. 1075/1098, 1100/1108

CP1108*a*	Collectors Pack	4·50	☐

586 Common Kingfisher

587 Dipper

588 Moorhen

589 Yellow Wagtails

Centenary of Wild Bird Protection Act

1980 (16 Jan.) Phosphorised paper

1109	**586**	10p. multicoloured	15	15	☐ ☐
1110	**587**	11½p. multicoloured	15	15	☐ ☐
1111	**588**	13p. multicoloured	20	20	☐ ☐
1112	**589**	15p. multicoloured	20	20	☐ ☐
Set of 4			60	60	☐ ☐
First Day Cover				65	☐
Presentation Pack (PO Pack No. 115)			70		☐
PHQ Cards *(set of 4)* (41)			50	1·00	☐ ☐
Set of 4 Gutter Pairs			1·25		☐

590 *Rocket* approaching Moorish Arch, Liverpool

591 First. and Second Class Carriages passing through Olive Mount Cutting

592 Third Class Carriage and Sheep Truck crossing Chat Moss

593 Horsebox and Carriage Truck near Bridgewater Canal

594 Goods Truck and Mailcoach at Manchester

596 Buckingham Palace

597 The Albert Memorial

598 Royal Opera House

599 Hampton Court

600 Kensington Palace

150th Anniversary of Liverpool and Manchester Railway

1980 (12 Mar.) Phosphorised paper

1113	**590**	12p. multicoloured	15	10
		a. Strip of 5. Nos. 1113/1117	75	60
1114	**591**	12p. multicoloured	15	10
1115	**592**	12p. multicoloured	15	10
1116	**593**	12p. multicoloured	15	10
1117	**594**	12p. multicoloured	15	10
Set of 5			75	60
First Day Cover				70
Presentation Pack (PO Pack No. 116)			85	
PHQ Cards (set of 5) (42)			50	1·25
Gutter Block of 10			1·50	

Nos. 1113/1117 were printed together, *se-tenant*, in horizontal strips of five throughout the sheet.

INTERNATIONAL STAMP EXHIBITION
595 Montage of London Buildings

London 1980 International Stamp Exhibition

1980 (9 Apr.–7 May) Phosphorised paper. Perf 14½×14

1118	**595**	50p. agate	75	70
First Day Cover				75
Presentation Pack (PO Pack No. 117)			85	
PHQ Card (43)			20	80
Gutter Pair			1·50	
MS1119 90×123 mm. No. 1118			75	95
First Day Cover (7.5.80)				95

No. **MS**1119 was sold at 75p., the premium being used for the exhibition.

London Landmarks

1980 (7 May) Phosphorised paper

1120	**596**	10½p. multicoloured	10	10
1121	**597**	12p. multicoloured	15	15
1122	**598**	13½p. multicoloured	20	15
1123	**599**	15p. multicoloured	20	20
1124	**600**	17½p. multicoloured	25	20
Set of 5			85	75
First Day Cover				80
Presentation Pack (PO Pack No. 118)			90	
PHQ Cards (set of 5) (43)			60	1·10
Set of 5 Gutter Pairs			4·25	

601 Charlotte Brontë (*Jane Eyre*)

602 George Eliot (*The Mill on the Floss*)

603 Emily Brontë (*Wuthering Heights*)

604 Mrs Gaskell (*North and South*)

Famous Authoresses

1980 (9 July) Phosphorised paper

1125	**601**	12p. multicoloured	15	15
1126	**602**	13½p. multicoloured	15	15
1127	**603**	15p. multicoloured	25	25
1128	**604**	17½p. multicoloured	30	30
Set of 4			75	75
First Day Cover				80
Presentation Pack (PO Pack No. 119)			80	
PHQ Cards (set of 4) (44)			50	1·00
Set of 4 Gutter Pairs			1·50	

Nos. 1125/1128 show authoresses and scenes from their novels. Nos. 1125/1126 also include the Europa CEPT emblem.

605 Queen Elizabeth
the Queen Mother

80th Birthday of Queen Elizabeth the Queen Mother

1980 (4 Aug.) Phosphorised paper

1129	**605**	12p. multicoloured	25	25	
First Day Cover				50	
PHQ Card (45)			20	40	
Gutter Pair				50	

606 Sir Henry Wood   **607** Sir Thomas
Beecham

608 Sir Malcolm   **609** Sir John Barbirolli
Sargent

British Conductors

1980 (10 Sept.) Phosphorised paper

1130	**606**	12p. multicoloured	15	15	
1131	**607**	13½p. multicoloured	15	15	
1132	**608**	15p. multicoloured	25	25	
1133	**609**	17½p. multicoloured	30	30	
Set of 4			75	75	
First Day Cover				80	
Presentation Pack (PO Pack No. 120)			80		
PHQ Cards (*set of 4*) (46)			60	1·00	
Set of 4 Gutter Pairs			1·50		

610 Running   **611** Rugby

612 Boxing

613 Cricket

Sports Centenaries

1980 (10 Oct.) Phosphorised paper. Perf 14×14½

1134	**610**	12p. multicoloured	15	15	
1135	**611**	13½p. multicoloured	15	15	
1136	**612**	15p. multicoloured	25	25	
1137	**613**	17½p. multicoloured	30	30	
Set of 4			75	75	
First Day Cover				80	
Presentation Pack (PO Pack No. 121)			80		
PHQ Cards (*set of 4*) (47)			60	1·00	
Set of 4 Gutter Pairs			1·50		

Centenaries: 12p. Amateur Athletics Association; 13½p. Welsh Rugby Union; 15p. Amateur Boxing Association; 17½p. First England v Australia Test Match.

614 Christmas Tree   **615** Candles

616 Apples and Mistletoe   **617** Crown, Chains and Bell

618 Holly

Christmas

1980 (19 Nov.) One centre phosphor band (10p.) or phosphorised paper (others)

1138	**614**	10p. multicoloured	10	10	
1139	**615**	12p. multicoloured	15	15	
1140	**616**	13½p. multicoloured	15	15	
1141	**617**	15p. multicoloured	25	25	
1142	**618**	17½p. multicoloured	25	25	
Set of 5			80	80	
First Day Cover				85	
Presentation Pack (PO Pack No. 122)			85		
PHQ Cards (*set of 5*) (48)			75	1·00	
Set of 5 Gutter Pairs			1·60		

Collectors Pack 1980

1980 (19 Nov.) Comprises Nos. 1109/1118, 1120/1142
CP1142a   Collectors Pack   5·50   ☐

619 St Valentine's Day

620 Morris Dancers

621 Lammastide

622 Medieval Mummers

Folklore

1981 (6 Feb.) Phosphorised paper

1143	**619**	14p. multicoloured	20	20	☐	☐
1144	**620**	18p. multicoloured	20	20	☐	☐
1145	**621**	22p. multicoloured	30	35	☐	☐
1146	**622**	25p. multicoloured	40	45	☐	☐
Set of 4			1·00	1·10	☐	
First Day Cover				1·25	☐	
Presentation Pack (PO Pack No. 124)			1·25		☐	
PHQ Cards (*set of 4*) (49)			60	1·25	☐	☐
Set of 4 Gutter Pairs			2·00		☐	

Nos. 1143/1144 also include the Europa CEPT emblem.

623 Blind Man with Guide Dog

624 Hands spelling 'Deaf' in Sign Language

625 Disabled Man in Wheelchair

626 Disabled Artist painting with Foot

International Year of the Disabled

1981 (25 Mar.) Phosphorised paper

1147	**623**	14p. multicoloured	20	20	☐	☐
1148	**624**	18p. multicoloured	20	20	☐	☐
1149	**625**	22p. multicoloured	35	35	☐	☐
1150	**626**	25p. multicoloured	45	45	☐	☐
Set of 4			1·10	1·10	☐	
First Day Cover				1·25	☐	
Presentation Pack (PO Pack No. 125)			1·25		☐	
PHQ Cards (*set of 4*) (50)			60	1·25	☐	☐
Set of 4 Gutter Pairs			2·25		☐	

Small Tortoiseshell
627 *Aglais urticae*

Large Blue
628 *Maculinea arion*

Peacock
629 *Inachis io*

Chequered Skipper
630 *Carterocephalus palaemon*

Butterflies

1981 (13 May) Phosphorised paper

1151	**627**	14p. multicoloured	20	20	☐	☐
1152	**628**	18p. multicoloured	20	20	☐	☐
1153	**629**	22p. multicoloured	35	35	☐	☐
1154	**630**	25p. multicoloured	45	45	☐	☐
Set of 4			1·10	1·10	☐	
First Day Cover				1·25	☐	
Presentation Pack (PO Pack No. 126)			1·25		☐	
PHQ Cards (*set of 4*) (51)			60	1·25	☐	☐
Set of 4 Gutter Pairs			2·25		☐	

631 Glenfinnan, Scotland

632 Derwentwater, England

633 Stackpole Head, Wales

634 Giant's Causeway, N. Ireland

635 St Kilda, Scotland

50th Anniversary of National Trust for Scotland (British landscapes)

1981 (24 June) Phosphorised paper

1155	**631**	14p. multicoloured	20	20	☐	☐
1156	**632**	18p. multicoloured	20	20	☐	☐
1157	**633**	20p. multicoloured	25	25	☐	☐
1158	**634**	22p. multicoloured	35	35	☐	☐
1159	**635**	25p. multicoloured	45	45	☐	☐

Set of 5		1·25	1·25	☐ ☐
First Day Cover			1·40	☐
Presentation Pack (PO Pack No. 127)		1·40		☐
PHQ Cards (set of 5) (52)		75	1·40	☐ ☐
Set of 5 Gutter Pairs		2·50		☐

636 Prince Charles and Lady Diana Spencer

Royal Wedding

1981 (22 July) Phosphorised paper

1160	**636**	14p. multicoloured	25	20	☐ ☐
1161		25p. multicoloured	40	35	☐ ☐
Set of 2			60	50	☐ ☐
First Day Cover				1·25	☐
Presentation Pack (PO Pack No. 127a)			1·10		☐
Souvenir Book			1·25		☐
PHQ Cards (set of 2) (53)			30	70	☐ ☐
Set of 2 Gutter Pairs			1·25		☐

637 'Expeditions'   **638** 'Skills'

639 'Service'   **640** 'Recreation'

25th Anniversary of Duke of Edinburgh's Award Scheme

1981 (12 Aug.) Phosphorised paper. Perf 14

1162	**637**	14p. multicoloured	20	20	☐ ☐
1163	**638**	18p. multicoloured	20	20	☐ ☐
1164	**639**	22p. multicoloured	35	35	☐ ☐
1165	**640**	25p. multicoloured	45	45	☐ ☐
Set of 4			1·10	1·10	☐ ☐
First Day Cover				1·25	☐
Presentation Pack (PO Pack No. 128)			1·25		☐
PHQ Cards (set of 4) (54)			60	1·25	☐ ☐
Set of 4 Gutter Pairs			2·25		☐

641 Cockle-dredging from Lindsey II   **642** Hauling Trawl Net

643 Lobster Potting   **644** Hoisting Seine Net

Fishing Industry

1981 (23 Sept.) Phosphorised paper

1166	**641**	14p. multicoloured	20	20	☐ ☐
1167	**642**	18p. multicoloured	20	20	☐ ☐
1168	**643**	22p. multicoloured	35	35	☐ ☐
1169	**644**	25p. multicoloured	45	45	☐ ☐
Set of 4			1·10	1·10	☐ ☐
First Day Cover				1·25	☐
Presentation Pack (PO Pack No. 129)			1·25		☐
PHQ Cards (set of 4) (55)			60	1·25	☐ ☐
Set of 4 Gutter Pairs			2·25		☐

Nos. 1166/1169 were issued on the occasion of the centenary of Royal National Mission to Deep Sea Fishermen.

645 Father Christmas   **646** Jesus Christ

647 Flying Angel   **648** Joseph and Mary arriving at Bethlehem

649 Three Kings approaching Bethlehem

Christmas. Children's Pictures

1981 (18 Nov.) One phosphor band (11½p.) or phosphorised paper (others)

1170	**645**	11½p. multicoloured	20	20	☐ ☐
1171	**646**	14p. multicoloured	20	20	☐ ☐
1172	**647**	18p. multicoloured	20	20	☐ ☐
1173	**648**	22p. multicoloured	30	30	☐ ☐
1174	**649**	25p. multicoloured	40	40	☐ ☐
Set of 5			1·25	1·25	☐ ☐
First Day Cover				1·40	☐
Presentation Pack (PO Pack No. 130)			1·40		☐
PHQ Cards (set of 5) (56)			75	1·40	☐ ☐
Set of 5 Gutter Pairs			2·50		☐

Collectors Pack 1981

1981 (18 Nov.) Comprises Nos. 1143/1174

CP1174a	Collectors Pack	7·25	☐

650 Charles Darwin and Giant Tortoises

651 Darwin and Marine Iguanas

652 Darwin, Cactus Ground Finch and Large Ground Finch

653 Darwin and Prehistoric Skulls

Death Centenary of Charles Darwin

1982 (10 Feb.) Phosphorised paper

1175	**650**	15½p. multicoloured	20	20		
1176	**651**	19½p. multicoloured	25	25		
1177	**652**	26p. multicoloured	35	35		
1178	**653**	29p. multicoloured	50	50		
Set of 4			1·25	1·25		
First Day Cover				1·40		
Presentation Pack (PO Pack No. 132)			1·40			
PHQ Cards (set of 4) (57)			60	1·40		
Set of 4 Gutter Pairs			2·50			

654 Boys' Brigade

655 Girls' Brigade

656 Boy Scout Movement

657 Girl Guide Movement

Youth Organisations

1982 (24 Mar.) Phosphorised paper

1179	**654**	15½p. multicoloured	20	20		
1180	**655**	19½p. multicoloured	25	25		
1181	**656**	26p. multicoloured	35	35		
1182	**657**	29p. multicoloured	50	50		
Set of 4			1·25	1·25		
First Day Cover				1·40		
Presentation Pack (PO Pack No. 133)			1·40			
PHQ Cards (set of 4) (58)			60	1·40		
Set of 4 Gutter Pairs			2·50			

Nos. 1179/1182 were issued on the occasion of the 75th anniversary of the Boy Scout Movement, the 125th birth anniversary of Lord Baden-Powell and the centenary of the Boys' Brigade (1983).

658 Ballerina

659 Harlequin

660 Hamlet

661 Opera Singer

Europa. British Theatre

1982 (28 Apr.) Phosphorised paper

1183	**658**	15½p. multicoloured	20	20		
1184	**659**	19½p. multicoloured	25	25		
1185	**660**	26p. multicoloured	35	35		
1186	**661**	29p. multicoloured	50	50		
Set of 4			1·25	1·25		
First Day Cover				1·40		
Presentation Pack (PO Pack No. 134)			1·40			
PHQ Cards (set of 4) (59)			60	1·40		
Set of 4 Gutter Pairs			2·50			

662 Henry VIII and *Mary Rose*

663 Admiral Blake and *Triumph*

664 Lord Nelson and HMS *Victory*

665 Lord Fisher and HMS *Dreadnought*

666 Viscount Cunningham and HMS *Warspite*

Maritime Heritage

1982 (16 June) Phosphorised paper

1187	**662**	15½p. multicoloured	20	20		
1188	**663**	19½p. multicoloured	25	25		
1189	**664**	24p. multicoloured	35	35		
1190	**665**	26p. multicoloured	40	40		
1191	**666**	29p. multicoloured	50	50		

Set of 5		1·60	1·60 ☐☐
First Day Cover			1·75 ☐
Presentation Pack (PO Pack No. 136)		1·75	☐
PHQ Cards (set of 5) (60)		75	1·75 ☐☐
Set of 5 Gutter Pairs		3·25	☐

667 Strawberry Thief
(William Morris)

668 Untitled
(Steiner and Co)

669 Cherry Orchard
(Paul Nash)

670 Chevron
(Andrew Foster)

British Textiles

1982 (23 July) Phosphorised paper

1192	**667**	15½p. multicoloured	20	20 ☐☐
1193	**668**	19½p. multicoloured	25	25 ☐☐
1194	**669**	26p. multicoloured	35	35 ☐☐
1195	**670**	29p. multicoloured	50	50 ☐☐
Set of 4			1·25	1·25 ☐☐
First Day Cover				1·40 ☐
Presentation Pack (PO Pack No. 137)			1·40	☐
PHQ Cards (set of 4) (61)			60	1·40 ☐☐
Set of 4 Gutter Pairs			2·50	☐

Nos 1192/1195 were issued on the occasion of the 250th birth anniversary of Sir Richard Arkwright (inventor of spinning machine).

671 Development of Communications

672 Modern Technological Aids

Information Technology

1982 (8 Sept.) Phosphorised paper. Perf 14×15

1196	**671**	15½p. multicoloured	25	25 ☐☐
1197	**672**	26p. multicoloured	35	35 ☐☐
Set of 2			55	55 ☐☐
First Day Cover				60 ☐
Presentation Pack (PO Pack No. 138)			60	☐
PHQ Cards (set of 2) (62)			30	60 ☐☐
Set of 2 Gutter Pairs			1·10	☐

673 Austin Seven and Metro

674 Ford Model T and Escort

675 Jaguar SS1 and XJ6

676 Rolls-Royce Silver Ghost and Silver Spirit

British Motor Industry

1982 (13 Oct.) Phosphorised paper. Perf 14½×14

1198	**673**	15½p. multicoloured	20	20 ☐☐
1199	**674**	19½p. multicoloured	25	25 ☐☐
1200	**675**	26p. multicoloured	35	35 ☐☐
1201	**676**	29p. multicoloured	50	50 ☐☐
Set of 4			1·25	1·25 ☐☐
First Day Cover				1·40 ☐
Presentation Pack (PO Pack No. 139)			1·40	☐
PHQ Cards (set of 4) (63)			60	1·40 ☐☐
Set of 4 Gutter Pairs			2·50	☐

677 While Shepherds Watched

678 The Holly and the Ivy

679 I Saw Three Ships

680 We Three Kings

681 Good King Wenceslas

Christmas. Carols

1982 (17 Nov.) One phosphor band (12½p.) or phosphorised paper (others)

1202	**677**	12½p. multicoloured	20	20 ☐☐
1203	**678**	15½p. multicoloured	20	20 ☐☐
1204	**679**	19½p. multicoloured	25	25 ☐☐
1205	**680**	26p. multicoloured	35	35 ☐☐
1206	**681**	29p. multicoloured	50	50 ☐☐
Set of 5			1·40	1·40 ☐☐
First Day Cover				1·50 ☐
Presentation Pack (PO Pack No. 140)			1·50	☐
PHQ Cards (set of 5) (64)			75	1·50 ☐☐
Set of 5 Gutter Pairs			2·75	☐

Collectors Pack 1982

1982 (17 Nov.) Comprises Nos. 1175/1206
CP1206a   Collectors Pack   12·00

682 Atlantic Salmon   **683** Northern Pike

684 Brown Trout   **685** Eurasian Perch

British River Fish

1983 (26 Jan.) Phosphorised paper

1207	**682**	15½p. multicoloured	20	20
1208	**683**	19½p. multicoloured	25	25
1209	**684**	26p. multicoloured	35	35
1210	**685**	29p. multicoloured	50	50
Set of 4			1·25	1·25
First Day Cover				1·40
Presentation Pack (PO Pack No. 142)			1·40	
PHQ Cards (set of 4) (65)			60	1·40
Set of 4 Gutter Pairs			2·50	

686 Tropical Island   **687** Desert

688 Temperate Farmland   **689** Mountain Range

Commonwealth Day. Geographical Regions

1983 (9 Mar.) Phosphorised paper

1211	**686**	15½p. multicoloured	20	20
1212	**687**	19½p. multicoloured	25	25
1213	**688**	26p. multicoloured	35	35
1214	**689**	29p. multicoloured	50	50
Set of 4			1·25	1·25
First Day Cover				1·40
Presentation Pack (PO Pack No. 143)			1·40	
PHQ Cards (set of 4) (66)			60	1·40
Set of 4 Gutter Pairs			2·50	

690 Humber Bridge   **691** Thames Flood Barrier

692 Iolair (oilfield emergency
support vessel)

Europa. Engineering Achievements

1983 (25 May) Phosphorised paper

1215	**690**	16p. multicoloured	20	20
1216	**691**	20½p. multicoloured	30	30
1217	**692**	28p. multicoloured	50	50
Set of 3			90	90
First Day Cover				1·00
Presentation Pack (PO Pack No. 144)			1·00	
PHQ Cards (set of 3) (67)			40	1·00
Set of 3 Gutter Pairs			1·75	

693 Musketeer and   **694** Fusilier and Ensign,
Pikeman, The Royal   The Royal Welch Fusiliers
Scots (1633)   (mid-18th-century)

695 Riflemen, 95th Rifles   **696** Sergeant (khaki
(The Royal Green Jackets)   service uniform) and Guardsman
(1805)   full dress), The Irish Guards (1900).

697 Paratroopers,
The Parachute Regiment (1983)

British Army Uniforms

1983 (6 July) Phosphorised paper

1218	**693**	16p. multicoloured	20	20	☐	☐
1219	**694**	20½p. multicoloured	25	25	☐	☐
1220	**695**	26p. multicoloured	35	35	☐	☐
1221	**696**	28p. multicoloured	40	40	☐	☐
1222	**697**	31p. multicoloured	50	50	☐	☐
Set of 5			1·60	1·60	☐	☐
First Day Cover				1·75		☐
Presentation Pack (PO Pack No. 145)			1·75			☐
PHQ Cards (*set of 5*) (68)			75	1·75	☐	☐
Set of 5 Gutter Pairs			3·25			☐

Nos. 1218/1222 were issued on the occasion of the 350th anniversary of The Royal Scots, the senior line regiment of the British Army.

20th CENTURY GARDEN
SISSINGHURST
698 20th-century Garden, Sissinghurst

19th CENTURY GARDEN
BIDDULPH GRANGE
699 19th-century Garden, Biddulph Grange

18th CENTURY GARDEN
BLENHEIM
700 18th-century Garden, Blenheim

17th CENTURY GARDEN
PITMEDDEN
701 17th-century Garden, Pitmedden

British Gardens

1983 (24 Aug.) Phosphorised paper. Perf 14

1223	**698**	16p. multicoloured	20	20	☐	☐
1224	**699**	20½p. multicoloured	25	25	☐	☐
1225	**700**	28p. multicoloured	35	35	☐	☐
1226	**701**	31p. multicoloured	50	50	☐	☐
Set of 4			1·25	1·25	☐	☐
First Day Cover				1·40		☐
Presentation Pack (PO Pack No. 146)			1·40			☐
PHQ Cards (*set of 4*) (69)			60	1·40	☐	☐
Set of 4 Gutter Pairs			2·50			☐

702 Merry-go-round

703 Big Wheel, Helter-skelter and Performing Animals

704 Side-shows

705 Early Produce Fair

British Fairs

1983 (5 Oct.) Phosphorised paper

1227	**702**	16p. multicoloured	20	20	☐	☐
1228	**703**	20½p. multicoloured	25	25	☐	☐
1229	**704**	28p. multicoloured	35	35	☐	☐
1230	**705**	31p. multicoloured	50	50	☐	☐
Set of 4			1·25	1·25	☐	☐
First Day Cover				1·40		☐
Presentation Pack (PO Pack No. 147)			1·40			☐
PHQ Cards (*set of 4*) (70)			60	1·40	☐	☐
Set of 4 Gutter Pairs			2·50			☐

Nos. 1227/1230 were issued to mark the 850th anniversary of St Bartholomew's Fair, Smithfield, London.

706 Christmas Post (Pillar box)

707 The Three Kings (chimney pots)

708 World at Peace (Dove and Blackbird)

709 Light of Christmas (street lamp)

710 Christmas Dove (hedge sculpture)

Christmas

1983 (16 Nov.) One phosphor band (12½p.) or phosphorised paper (others)

1231	**706**	12½p. multicoloured	20	20	☐	☐
1232	**707**	16p. multicoloured	20	20	☐	☐
1233	**708**	20½p. multicoloured	25	25	☐	☐
1234	**709**	28p. multicoloured	35	35	☐	☐
1235	**710**	31p. multicoloured	50	50	☐	☐
Set of 5			1·50	1·50	☐	☐
First Day Cover				1·50		☐
Presentation Pack (PO Pack No. 148)			1·50			☐
PHQ Cards (*set of 5*) (71)			75	1·50	☐	☐
Set of 5 Gutter Pairs			3·00			☐

Collectors Pack 1983

1983 (16 Nov.) Comprises Nos. 1207/1235

CP1235*a*	Collectors Pack	13·50	☐

711 Arms of the College of Arms

712 Arms of King Richard III (founder)

713 Arms of the Earl Marshal of England

714 Arms of the City of London

500th Anniversary of College of Arms

1984 (17 Jan.) Phosphorised paper. Perf 14½

1236	**711**	16p. multicoloured	25	25		
1237	**712**	20½p. multicoloured	30	30		
1238	**713**	28p. multicoloured	40	40		
1239	**714**	31p. multicoloured	50	50		
Set of 4			1·25	1·25		
First Day Cover				1·50		
Presentation Pack (PO Pack No. 150)			1·50			
PHQ Cards (set of 4) (72)			60	1·50		
Set of 4 Gutter Pairs			2·50			

715 Highland Cow

717 Hereford Bull   **718** Welsh Black Bull

719 Irish Moiled Cow

British Cattle

1984 (6 Mar.) Phosphorised paper

1240	**715**	16p. multicoloured	25	25		
1241	**716**	20½p. multicoloured	30	30		
1242	**717**	26p. multicoloured	35	35		
1243	**718**	28p. multicoloured	40	40		
1244	**719**	31p. multicoloured	50	50		
Set of 5			1·60	1·60		
First Day Cover				1·75		
Presentation Pack (PO Pack No. 151)			1·75			

PHQ Cards (set of 5) (73)		75	1·75
Set of 5 Gutter Pairs		3·25	

Nos. 1240/1244 marked the centenary of the Highland Cattle Society and the bicentenary of the Royal Highland and Agricultural Society of Scotland.

720 Festival Hall, Liverpool

721 Milburngate Shopping Centre, Durham

722 Bush House, Bristol

723 Commercial Street Housing Scheme, Perth

Urban Renewal

1984 (10 Apr.) Phosphorised paper

1245	**720**	16p. multicoloured	25	25		
1246	**721**	20½p. multicoloured	30	30		
1247	**722**	28p. multicoloured	40	40		
1248	**723**	31p. multicoloured	50	50		
Set of 4			1·25	1·25		
First Day Cover				1·50		
Presentation Pack (PO Pack No. 152)			1·50			
PHQ Cards (set of 4) (74)			60	1·50		
Set of 4 Gutter Pairs			2·50			

Nos. 1245/1248 marked the opening of the International Gardens Festival, Liverpool, and the 150th anniversaries of the Royal Institute of British Architects and the Chartered Institute of Building.

724 CEPT 25th Anniversary Logo

725 Abduction of Europa

Europa. 25th Anniversary of CEPT and 2nd European Parliamentary Elections

1984 (15 May) Phosphorised paper

1249	**724**	16p. greenish slate, deep blue and gold	30	30		
		a. Horiz pair. Nos. 1249/1250	60	60		
1250	**725**	16p. greenish slate, deep blue, black and gold	30	30		
1251	**724**	20½p. Venetian red, deep magenta and gold	35	35		
		a. Horiz pair. Nos. 1251/1252	70	70		
1252	**725**	20½p. Venetian red, deep magenta, black and gold	35	35		
Set of 4			1·25	1·25		
First Day Cover				1·40		
Presentation Pack (PO Pack No. 153)			1·40			

| PHQ Cards (*set of 4*) (75) | 60 | 1·40 | ☐ ☐ |
| *Set of 2 Gutter Blocks of 4* | | 2·50 | ☐ |

Nos. 1249/1250 and 1251/1252 were each printed together, *se-tenant*, in horizontal pairs throughout the sheets.

726 Lancaster House

London Economic Summit Conference

1984 (5 June) Phosphorised paper

1253	**726**	31p. multicoloured	50	50	☐ ☐
First Day Cover				60	☐
PHQ Card (76)			20	60	☐ ☐
Gutter Pair				1·00	☐

727 View of Earth
from *Apollo 11*

728 Navigational Chart
of English Channel

729 Greenwich
Observatory

730 Sir George Airey's
Transit Telescope

Centenary of Greenwich Meridian

1984 (26 June) Phosphorised paper. Perf 14 × 14½

1254	**727**	16p. multicoloured	25	25	☐ ☐
1255	**728**	20½p. multicoloured	30	30	☐ ☐
1256	**729**	28p. multicoloured	40	40	☐ ☐
1257	**730**	31p. multicoloured	50	50	☐ ☐
Set of 4			1·25	1·25	☐ ☐
First Day Cover				1·50	☐
Presentation Pack (PO Pack No. 154)			1·50		☐
PHQ Cards (*set of 4*) (77)			60	1·50	☐ ☐
Set of 4 Gutter Pairs			2·50		☐

731 Bath Mail Coach, 1784

732 Attack on Exeter Mail, 1816

733 Norwich Mail in Thunderstorm,
1827

734 Holyhead and Liverpool Mails
leaving London, 1828

735 Edinburgh Mail
Snowbound, 1831

Bicentenary of First Mail Coach Run, Bath and Bristol to London

1984 (31 July) Phosphorised paper

1258	**731**	16p. multicoloured	25	25	☐ ☐
		a. Horiz strip of 5.			
		Nos. 1258/1262	1·25	1·25	☐ ☐
1259	**732**	16p. multicoloured	25	25	☐ ☐
1260	**733**	16p. multicoloured	25	25	☐ ☐
1261	**734**	16p. multicoloured	25	25	☐ ☐
1262	**735**	16p. multicoloured	25	25	☐ ☐
Set of 5			1·25	1·25	☐ ☐
First Day Cover				1·40	☐
Presentation Pack (PO Pack No. 155)			1·40		☐
Souvenir Book			3·25		☐
PHQ Cards (*set of 5*) (78)			75	1·40	☐ ☐
Gutter Block of 10			2·50		☐

Nos. 1285/1262 were printed together, *se-tenant*, in horizontal strips of five throughout the sheet.

736 Nigerian Clinic

737 Violinist and Acropolis, Athens

738 Building Project, Sri Lanka

739 British Council Library

50th Anniversary of The British Council

1984 (25 Sept.) Phosphorised paper

1263	**736**	17p. multicoloured	25	25	☐ ☐
1264	**737**	22p. multicoloured	30	30	☐ ☐
1265	**738**	31p. multicoloured	40	40	☐ ☐
1266	**739**	34p. multicoloured	50	50	☐ ☐
Set of 4			1·40	1·40	☐ ☐
First Day Cover				1·50	☐
Presentation Pack (PO Pack No. 156)			1·50		☐
PHQ Cards (*set of 4*) (79)			60	1·50	☐ ☐
Set of 4 Gutter Pairs			2·75		☐

740 The Holy Family

741 Arrival in Bethlehem

742 Shepherd and Lamb

743 Virgin and Child

744 Offering of Frankincense

Christmas

1984 (20 Nov.) One phosphor band (13p.) or phosphorised paper (others)

1267	**740**	13p. multicoloured	25	25	☐	☐
1268	**741**	17p. multicoloured	25	25	☐	☐
1269	**742**	22p. multicoloured	30	30	☐	☐
1270	**743**	31p. multicoloured	40	40	☐	☐
1271	**744**	34p. multicoloured	50	50	☐	☐
Set of 5			1·60	1·60	☐	
First Day Cover				1·75	☐	
Presentation Pack (PO Pack No. 157)			1·75		☐	
PHQ Cards (*set of 5*) (80)			75	1·75	☐	☐
Set of 5 Gutter Pairs			3·25		☐	

Collectors Pack 1984

1984 (20 Nov.) Comprises Nos. 1236/1271

CP1271a	Collectors Pack	16·00	☐

Post Office Yearbook

1984 Comprises Nos. 1236/1271 in hardbound book with slip case

YB1271a	Yearbook	42·00	☐

745 'Flying Scotsman'

746 'Golden Arrow'

747 'Cheltenham Flyer'

748 'Royal Scot'

749 'Cornish Riviera'

Famous Trains

1985 (22 Jan.) Phosphorised paper

1272	**745**	17p. multicoloured	25	25	☐	☐
1273	**746**	22p. multicoloured	30	30	☐	☐
1274	**747**	29p. multicoloured	40	40	☐	☐
1275	**748**	31p. multicoloured	40	40	☐	☐
1276	**749**	34p. multicoloured	50	50	☐	☐
Set of 5			1·75	1·75	☐	
First Day Cover				1·90	☐	
Presentation Pack (PO Pack No. 159)			1·90		☐	
PHQ Cards (*set of 5*) (81)			75	1·90	☐	☐
Set of 5 Gutter Pairs			3·50		☐	

Nos. 1272/1276 were issued on the occasion of the 150th anniversary of the Great Western Railway Company.

750 *Bombus terrestris* (Bee)
Buff Tailed Bumble Bee

751 *Coccinella septempunctata* (Ladybird)
Seven Spotted Ladybird

752 *Decticus verrucivorus* (Bush-cricket)
Wart-Biter Bush-Cricket

753 *Lucanus cervus* (Stag Beetle)
Stag Beetle

754 *Anax imperator* (Dragonfly)
Emperor Dragonfly

Insects

1985 (12 Mar.) Phosphorised paper

1277	**750**	17p. multicoloured	25	25	☐	☐
1278	**751**	22p. multicoloured	30	30	☐	☐
1279	**752**	29p. multicoloured	40	40	☐	☐
1280	**753**	31p. multicoloured	40	40	☐	☐
1281	**754**	34p. multicoloured	50	50	☐	☐
Set of 5			1·75	1·75	☐	
First Day Cover				1·90	☐	
Presentation Pack (PO Pack No. 160)			1·90		☐	
PHQ Cards (*set of 5*) (82)			75	1·90	☐	☐
Set of 5 Gutter Pairs			3·50		☐	

Nos. 1277/1281 were issued on the occasion of the centenaries of the Royal Entomological Society of London's Royal Charter and of the Selborne Society.

755 *Water Music*, by Handel

756 *The Planets*, by Holst

757 *The First Cuckoo*, by Delius

758 *Sea Pictures*, by Elgar

Europa. European Music Year

1985 (14 May) Phosphorised paper. Perf 14½

1282	**755**	17p. multicoloured	25	25		
1283	**756**	22p. multicoloured	30	30		
1284	**757**	31p. multicoloured	45	45		
1285	**758**	34p. multicoloured	55	55		
Set of 4			1·40	1·40		
First Day Cover				1·50		
Presentation Pack (PO Pack No. 161)			1·50			
PHQ Cards (*set of 4*) (83)			60	1·50		
Set of 4 Gutter Pairs			2·75			

Nos. 1282/1285 were issued on the occasion of the 300th birth anniversary of Handel.

759 RNLI Lifeboat and Signal Flags

760 Beachy Head Lighthouse and Chart

761 *Marecs A* Communications Satellite and Dish Aerials

762 Buoys

Safety at Sea

1985 (18 June) Phosphorised paper. Perf 14

1286	**759**	17p. multicoloured	25	25		
1287	**760**	22p. multicoloured	30	30		
1288	**761**	31p. multicoloured	45	45		
1289	**762**	34p. multicoloured	55	55		
Set of 4			1·40	1·40		
First Day Cover				1·50		
Presentation Pack (PO Pack No. 162)			1·50			
PHQ Cards (*set of 4*) (84)			60	1·50		
Set of 4 Gutter Pairs			2·75			

Nos. 1286/1289 were issued to mark the bicentenary of the unimmersible lifeboat and the 50th anniversary of Radar.

763 Datapost Motorcyclist, City of London

764 Rural Postbus

765 Parcel Delivery in Winter

766 Town Letter Delivery

350 Years of Royal Mail Public Postal Service

1985 (30 July) Phosphorised paper

1290	**763**	17p. multicoloured	25	25		
1291	**764**	22p. multicoloured	30	30		
1292	**765**	31p. multicoloured	45	45		
1293	**766**	34p. multicoloured	55	55		
Set of 4			1·40	1·40		
First Day Cover				1·50		
Presentation Pack (PO Pack No. 163)			1·50			
PHQ Cards (*set of 4*) (85)			60	1·50		
Set of 4 Gutter Pairs			2·75			

767 King Arthur and Merlin

768 The Lady of the Lake

769 Queen Guinevere and Sir Lancelot

770 Sir Galahad

Arthurian Legends

1985 (3 Sept.) Phosphorised paper

1294	**767**	17p. multicoloured	25	25		
1295	**768**	22p. multicoloured	30	30		
1296	**769**	31p. multicoloured	45	45		
1297	**770**	34p. multicoloured	55	55		
Set of 4			1·40	1·40		
First Day Cover				1·50		
Presentation Pack (PO Pack No.164)			1·50			
PHQ Cards (*set of 4*) (86)			60	1·50		
Set of 4 Gutter Pairs			2·75			

Nos. 1294/1297 were issued to mark the 500th anniversary of the printing of Sir Thomas Malory's *Morte d'Arthur*.

771 Peter Sellers (from photo by Bill Brandt)

772 David Niven (from photo by Cornell Lucas)

773 Charlie Chaplin (from photo by Lord Snowdon)

774 Vivien Leigh (from photo by Angus McBean)

775 Alfred Hitchcock (from photo by Howard Coster)

British Film Year

1985 (8 Oct.) Phosphorised paper. Perf 14½

1298	**771**	17p. multicoloured	25	25
1299	**772**	22p. multicoloured	30	30
1300	**773**	29p. multicoloured	45	45
1301	**774**	31p. multicoloured	50	50
1302	**775**	34p. multicoloured	55	55
Set of 5			1·90	1·90
First Day Cover				2·10
Presentation Pack (PO Pack No. 165)			2·10	
Souvenir Book			4·75	
PHQ Cards (set of 5) (87)			75	2·10
Set of 5 Gutter Pairs			3·75	

The souvenir book is a 24-page illustrated booklet with a set of stamps in a sachet attached to the front cover

776 Principal Boy

777 Genie

778 Dame

779 Good Fairy

780 Pantomime Cat

Christmas. Pantomime Characters

1985 (19 Nov.) One phosphor band (12p.) or phosphorised paper (others)

1303	**776**	12p. multicoloured	20	20
1304	**777**	17p. multicoloured	25	25
1305	**778**	22p. multicoloured	30	30
1306	**779**	31p. multicoloured	40	40
1307	**780**	34p. multicoloured	50	50
Set of 5			1·40	1·40
First Day Cover				1·60
Presentation Pack (PO Pack No. 166)			1·60	
PHQ Cards (set of 5) (88)			75	1·60
Set of 5 Gutter Pairs			2·75	

Collectors Pack 1985

1985 (19 Nov.) Comprises Nos. 1272/1307

CP1307a	Collectors Pack	16·00	

Post Office Yearbook

1985 Comprises Nos. 1272/1307 in hardbound book with slip case

YB1307a	Yearbook	30·00	

781 Light Bulb and North Sea Oil Drilling Rig (Energy)

782 Thermometer and Pharmaceutical Laboratory (Health)

783 Garden Hoe and Steel Works (Steel)

784 Loaf of Bread and Cornfield (Agriculture)

Industry Year

1986 (14 Jan.) Phosphorised paper. Perf 14½ × 14

1308	**781**	17p. multicoloured	25	25
1309	**782**	22p. multicoloured	30	30
1310	**783**	31p. multicoloured	45	45
1311	**784**	34p. multicoloured	55	55
Set of 4			1·40	1·40
First Day Cover				1·60
Presentation Pack (PO Pack No. 168)			1·60	
PHQ Cards (set of 4) (89)			60	1·60
Set of 4 Gutter Pairs			2·75	

785 Dr Edmond Halley as Comet

786 *Giotto* Spacecraft approaching Comet

787 'Twice in a Lifetime'

788 Comet orbiting Sun and Planets

791 Barn Owl

792 Pine Marten

793 Wild Cat

794 Natterjack Toad

Appearance of Halley's Comet

1986 (18 Feb.) Phosphorised paper

1312	**785**	17p. multicoloured	25	25	
1313	**786**	22p. multicoloured	30	30	
1314	**787**	31p. multicoloured	45	45	
1315	**788**	34p. multicoloured	55	55	
Set of 4			1·40	1·40	
First Day Cover				1·60	
Presentation Pack (PO Pack No. 168)*			1·60		
PHQ Cards (*set of 4*) (90)			60	1·60	
Set of 4 Gutter Pairs			2·75		

* The presentation pack was incorrectly numbered '168'.

Europa. Nature Conservation. Endangered Species

1986 (20 May) Phosphorised paper. Perf 14½ × 14

1320	**791**	17p. multicoloured	25	25	
1321	**792**	22p. multicoloured	30	30	
1322	**793**	31p. multicoloured	45	45	
1323	**794**	34p. multicoloured	55	55	
Set of 4			1·50	1·50	
First Day Cover				1·60	
Presentation Pack (PO Pack No. 171)			1·60		
PHQ Cards (*set of 4*) (92)			60	1·60	
Set of 4 Gutter Pairs			3·00		

789 Queen Elizabeth II in 1928, 1942 and 1952

790 Queen Elizabeth II in 1958, 1973 and 1982

795 Peasants Working in Fields

796 Freemen working at Town Trades

60th Birthday of Queen Elizabeth II

1986 (21 Apr.) Phosphorised paper

1316	**789**	17p. multicoloured	30	40	
		a. Horiz. pair. Nos. 1316/1317	80	1·00	
1317	**790**	17p. multicoloured	30	40	
1318	**789**	34p. multicoloured	60	75	
		a. Horiz. pair. Nos. 1318/1319	1·40	1·75	
1319	**790**	34p. multicoloured	60	75	
Set of 4			2·00	2·50	
First Day Cover				2·60	
Presentation Pack (PO Pack No. 170)			2·10		
Souvenir Book			3·75		
PHQ Cards (*set of 4*) (91)			60	2·60	
Set of 2 Gutter Blocks of 4			4·00		

Nos. 1316/1317 and 1318/1319 were each printed together, *se-tenant*, in horizontal pairs throughout the sheets.

The souvenir book is a special booklet, fully illustrated and containing a complete set of stamps.

797 Knight and Retainers

798 Lord at Banquet

900th Anniversary of Domesday Book

1986 (17 June) Phosphorised paper

1324	**795**	17p. multicoloured	25	25	
1325	**796**	22p. multicoloured	30	30	
1326	**797**	31p. multicoloured	45	45	
1327	**798**	34p. multicoloured	55	55	
Set of 4			1·50	1·50	
First Day Cover				1·60	
Presentation Pack (PO Pack No. 172)			1·60		
PHQ Cards (*set of 4*) (93)			60	1·60	
Set of 4 Gutter Pairs			3·00		

799 Athletics

800 Rowing

801 Weightlifting

802 Rifle-shooting

803 Hockey

13th Commonwealth Games, Edinburgh (Nos. 1328/1331) and World Men's Hockey Cup, London (No. 1332)

1986 (15 July) Phosphorised paper

1328	**799**	17p. multicoloured	25	25
1329	**800**	22p. multicoloured	30	30
1330	**801**	29p. multicoloured	45	45
1331	**802**	31p. multicoloured	45	45
1332	**803**	34p. multicoloured	55	55
Set of 5			1·75	1·75
First Day Cover				1·90
Presentation Pack (PO Pack No. 173)			1·90	
PHQ Cards (*set of 5*) (94)			75	1·90
Set of 5 Gutter Pairs			3·50	

No. 1332 also marked the centenary of the Hockey Association.

804 Prince Andrew and Miss Sarah Ferguson

805 Prince Andrew and Miss Sarah Ferguson

Royal Wedding

1986 (22 July) One side band (12p.) or phosphorised paper (17p.)

1333	**804**	12p. multicoloured	25	25
1334	**805**	17p. multicoloured	40	40
Set of 2			60	60
First Day Cover				70
Presentation Pack (PO Pack No. 174)			75	
PHQ Cards (*set of 2*) (95)			30	75
Set of 2 Gutter Pairs			1·25	

806 Stylised Cross on Ballot Paper

32nd Commonwealth Parliamentary Conference, London

1986 (19 Aug.) Phosphorised paper. Perf 14 × 14½

1335	**806**	34p. multicoloured	50	50
First Day Cover				55
PHQ Card (96)			15	55
Gutter Pair			1·00	

807 Lord Dowding and Hawker Hurricane I

808 Lord Tedder and Hawker Typhoon 1B

809 Lord Trenchard and de Havilland DH.9A

810 Sir Arthur Harris and Avro Lancaster

811 Lord Portal and de Havilland DH.98 Mosquito

History of the Royal Air Force

1986 (16th Sept.) Phosphorised paper. Perf 14½ × 14

1336	**807**	17p. multicoloured	25	25
1337	**808**	22p. multicoloured	35	35
1338	**809**	29p. multicoloured	45	45
1339	**810**	31p. multicoloured	50	50
1340	**811**	34p. multicoloured	55	55
Set of 5			2·00	2·00
First Day Cover				2·10
Presentation Pack (PO Pack No. 175)			2·10	
PHQ Cards (*set of 5*) (97)			75	2·10
Set of 5 Gutter Pairs			4·00	

Nos. 1336/1340 were issued to celebrate the 50th anniversary of the first RAF Commands.

812 The Glastonbury Thorn

813 The Tanad Valley Plygain

814 The Hebrides Tribute

815 The Dewsbury Church Knell

816 The Hereford Boy Bishop

Christmas. Folk Customs

1986 (18 Nov.–2 Dec.) One phosphor band (12p., 13p.) or phosphorised paper (others)

1341	**812**	12p. multicoloured (2.12.86)	25	25	☐ ☐
1342		13p. multicoloured	25	25	☐ ☐
1343	**813**	18p. multicoloured	30	30	☐ ☐
1344	**814**	22p. multicoloured	40	40	☐ ☐
1345	**815**	31p. multicoloured	45	45	☐ ☐
1346	**816**	34p. multicoloured	50	50	☐ ☐
Set of 6			1·90	1·90	☐
First Day Covers (2)				2·40	☐
Presentation Pack (Nos. 1342/1346) (PO Pack No. 176)			2·00		☐
PHQ Cards (*set of 5*) (Nos. 1342/1346) (98)			75	1·75	☐ ☐
Set of 6 Gutter Pairs			3·75		☐

Collectors Pack 1986

1986 (18 Nov.) Comprises Nos. 1308/1340, 1342/1346

CP1346a	Collectors Pack	16·00	☐

Post Office Yearbook

1986 Comprises Nos. 1308/1340, 1342/1346 in hardbound book with slip case

YB1346a	Yearbook	23·00	☐

817 North American Blanket Flower

818 Globe Thistle

819 Echeveria

820 Autumn Crocus

Flower Photographs by Alfred Lammer

1987 (20 Jan.) Phosphorised paper. Perf 14½ × 14

1347	**817**	18p. multicoloured	25	25	☐ ☐
1348	**818**	22p. multicoloured	30	30	☐ ☐
1349	**819**	31p. multicoloured	45	45	☐ ☐
1350	**820**	34p. multicoloured	55	55	☐ ☐
Set of 4			1·50	1·50	☐ ☐
First Day Cover				1·60	☐
Presentation Pack (PO Pack No. 178)			1·60		☐
PHQ Cards (*set of 4*) (99)			60	1·60	☐ ☐
Set of 4 Gutter Pairs			3·00		☐

821 The Principia Mathematica

822 Motion of Bodies in Ellipses

823 Optick Treatise

824 The System of the World

300th Anniversary of The Principia Mathematica by Sir Isaac Newton

1987 (24 Mar.) Phosphorised paper

1351	**821**	18p. multicoloured	25	25	☐ ☐
1352	**822**	22p. multicoloured	30	30	☐ ☐
1353	**823**	31p. multicoloured	45	45	☐ ☐
1354	**824**	34p. multicoloured	55	55	☐ ☐
Set of 4			1·50	1·50	☐ ☐
First Day Cover				1·60	☐
Presentation Pack (PO Pack No. 179)			1·60		☐
PHQ Cards (*set of 4*) (100)			60	1·60	☐ ☐
Set of 4 Gutter Pairs			3·00		☐

825 Willis Faber and Dumas Building, Ipswich

826 Pompidou Centre, Paris

827 Staatsgalerie, Stuttgart

828 European Investment Bank, Luxembourg

Europa. British Architects in Europe

1987 (12 May) Phosphorised paper

1355	825	18p. multicoloured	25	25	☐	☐
1356	826	22p. multicoloured	30	30	☐	☐
1357	827	31p. multicoloured	45	45	☐	☐
1358	828	34p. multicoloured	55	55	☐	☐
Set of 4			1·50	1·50	☐	☐
First Day Cover				1·60	☐	
Presentation Pack (PO Pack No. 180)			1·60		☐	
PHQ Cards (set of 4) (101)			60	1·60	☐	☐
Set of 4 Gutter Pairs			3·00		☐	

829 Brigade Members with Ashford Litter, 1887

830 Bandaging Blitz Victim, 1940

831 Volunteer with fainting Girl, 1965

832 Transport of Transplant Organ by Air Wing, 1987

Centenary of St John Ambulance Brigade

1987 (16 June) Phosphorised paper. Perf 14 × 14½

1359	829	18p. multicoloured	25	25	☐	☐
1360	830	22p. multicoloured	30	30	☐	☐
1361	831	31p. multicoloured	45	45	☐	☐
1362	832	34p. multicoloured	55	55	☐	☐
Set of 4			1·50	1·50	☐	☐
First Day Cover				1·60	☐	
Presentation Pack (PO Pack No. 181)			1·60		☐	
PHQ Cards (set of 4) (102)			60	1·60	☐	☐
Set of 4 Gutter Pairs			3·00		☐	

833 Arms of the Lord Lyon King of Arms

834 Scottish Heraldic Banner of Prince Charles

835 Arms of Royal Scottish Academy of Painting, Sculpture and Architecture

836 Arms of Royal Society of Edinburgh

300th Anniversary of Revival of Order of the Thistle

1987 (21 July) Phosphorised paper. Perf 14½

1363	833	18p. multicoloured	25	25	☐	☐
1364	834	22p. multicoloured	30	30	☐	☐
1365	835	31p. multicoloured	45	45	☐	☐
1366	836	34p. multicoloured	55	55	☐	☐
Set of 4			1·50	1·50	☐	☐
First Day Cover				1·60	☐	
Presentation Pack (PO Pack No.182)			1·60		☐	
PHQ Cards (set of 4) (103)			60	1·60	☐	☐
Set of 4 Gutter Pairs			3·00		☐	

837 Crystal Palace, Monarch of the Glen (Landseer) and Grace Darling

838 Great Eastern, Beeton's Book of Household Management and Prince Albert

839 Albert Memorial, Ballot Box and Disraeli

840 Diamond Jubilee Emblem, Morse Key and Newspaper Placard for Relief of Mafeking

150th Anniversary of Queen Victoria's Accession

1987 (8 Sept.) Phosphorised paper

1367	837	18p. multicoloured	25	25	☐	☐
1368	838	22p. multicoloured	30	30	☐	☐
1369	839	31p. multicoloured	45	45	☐	☐
1370	840	34p. multicoloured	55	55	☐	☐
Set of 4			1·50	1·50	☐	☐
First Day Cover				1·60	☐	
Presentation Pack (PO Pack No. 183)			1·60		☐	
PHQ Cards (set of 4) (104)			60	1·60	☐	☐
Set of 4 Gutter Pairs			3·00		☐	

841 Pot by Bernard Leach

842 Pot by Elizabeth Fritsch

843 Pot by Lucie Rie **844** Pot by Hans Coper

Studio Pottery

1987 (13 Oct.) Phosphorised paper. Perf 14½ × 14

1371	**841**	18p. multicoloured	25	25	☐	☐
1372	**842**	26p. multicoloured	30	30	☐	☐
1373	**843**	31p. multicoloured	45	45	☐	☐
1374	**844**	34p. multicoloured	55	55	☐	☐
Set of 4			1·50	1·50	☐	☐
First Day Cover				1·60	☐	
Presentation Pack (PO Pack No. 184)			1·60		☐	
PHQ Cards (*set of 4*) (105)			60	1·60	☐	☐
Set of 4 Gutter Pairs			3·00		☐	

Nos. 1371/1374 also mark the birth centenary of Bernard Leach, the potter.

845 Decorating the Christmas Tree **846** Waiting for Father Christmas

847 Sleeping Child and Father Christmas in Sleigh **848** Child reading

849 Child playing Flute and Snowman

Christmas

1987 (17 Nov.) One phosphor band (13p.) or phosphorised paper (others)

1375	**845**	13p. multicoloured	20	20	☐	☐
1376	**846**	18p. multicoloured	25	25	☐	☐
1377	**847**	26p. multicoloured	30	30	☐	☐
1378	**848**	31p. multicoloured	40	40	☐	☐
1379	**849**	34p. multicoloured	50	50	☐	☐
Set of 5			1·50	1·50	☐	☐
First Day Cover				1·60	☐	
Presentation Pack (PO Pack No. 185)			1·60		☐	
PHQ Cards (*set of 5*) (106)			75	1·60	☐	☐
Set of 5 Gutter Pairs			3·00		☐	

Collectors Pack 1987

1987 (17 Nov.) Comprises Nos. 1347/1379

CP1379a	Collectors Pack	16·00		☐

Post Office Yearbook

1987 Comprises Nos. 1347/1379 in hardbound book with slip case

YB1379a	Yearbook	13·00	☐

Bull-rout *Myoxocephalus scorpius*
THE LINNEAN SOCIETY 1788/1988

Yellow Waterlily *Nuphar lutea*
THE LINNEAN SOCIETY 1788/1988

850 Short-spined Seascorpion ('Bull-rout') (Jonathan Couch) **851** Yellow Waterlily (Major Joshua Swatkin)

Bewick's Swan *Cygnus columbianus*
THE LINNEAN SOCIETY 1788/1988

Morel *Morchella esculenta*
THE LINNEAN SOCIETY 1788/1988

852 Whistling ('Bewick's') Swan (Edward Lear) **853** *Morchella esculenta* (James Sowerby)

Bicentenary of Linnean Society. Archive Illustrations

1988 (19 Jan.) Phosphorised paper

1380	**850**	18p. multicoloured	25	25	☐	☐
1381	**851**	26p. multicoloured	35	35	☐	☐
1382	**852**	31p. multicoloured	45	45	☐	☐
1383	**853**	34p. multicoloured	60	60	☐	☐
Set of 4			1·50	1·50	☐	☐
First Day Cover				1·60	☐	
Presentation Pack (PO Pack No. 187)			1·60		☐	
PHQ Cards (*set of 4*) (107)			60	1·60	☐	☐
Set of 4 Gutter Pairs			3·00		☐	

854 Revd William Morgan (Bible translator, 1588) **855** William Salesbury (New Testament translator, 1567)

856 Bishop Richard Davies (New Testament translator, 1567) **857** Bishop Richard Parry (editor of Revised Welsh Bible, 1620)

400th Anniversary of Welsh Bible

1988 (1 Mar.) Phosphorised paper. Perf 14½ × 14

1384	**854**	18p. multicoloured	25	25	☐	☐
1385	**855**	26p. multicoloured	35	35	☐	☐
1386	**856**	31p. multicoloured	45	45	☐	☐
1387	**857**	34p. multicoloured	60	60	☐	☐
Set of 4			1·50	1·50	☐	☐
First Day Cover				1·60	☐	
Presentation Pack (PO Pack No. 188)			1·60		☐	

PHQ Cards (set of 4) (108)	60	1·60	
Set of 4 Gutter Pairs	3·00		

18p
858 Gymnastics (Centenary of British Amateur Gymnastics Association)

26p
859 Downhill Skiing (Ski Club of Great Britain)

31p
860 Tennis (Centenary of Lawn Tennis Association)

34p
861 Football (Centenary of Football League)

Sports Organisations

1988 (22 Mar.) Phosphorised paper. Perf 14½

1388	**858**	18p. multicoloured	25	25		
1389	**859**	26p. multicoloured	35	35		
1390	**860**	31p. multicoloured	45	45		
1391	**861**	34p. multicoloured	60	60		
Set of 4			1·50	1·50		
First Day Cover				1·60		
Presentation Pack (PO Pack No. 189)			1·60			
PHQ Cards (set of 4) (109)			60	1·60		
Set of 4 Gutter Pairs			3·00			

18p
862 *Mallard* and Mailbags on Pick-up Arms

26p
863 Loading Transatlantic Mail on Liner *Queen Elizabeth*

31p
864 Glasgow Tram No. 1173 and Pillar Box

34p
865 Imperial Airways Handley Page HP.45 *Horatius* and Airmail Van

Europa. Transport and Mail Services in 1930's

1988 (10 May) Phosphorised paper

1392	**862**	18p. multicoloured	25	25		
1393	**863**	26p. multicoloured	35	35		
1394	**864**	31p. multicoloured	45	45		
1395	**865**	34p. multicoloured	60	60		
Set of 4			1·50	1·50		
First Day Cover				1·60		
Presentation Pack (PO Pack No.190)			1·60			
PHQ Cards (set of 4) (110)			60	1·60		
Set of 4 Gutter Pairs			3·00			

 as shown

866 Early Settler and Sailing Clipper

867 Queen Elizabeth II with British and Australian Parliament Buildings

868 W. G. Grace (cricketer) and Tennis Racquet

869 Shakespeare, John Lennon (entertainer) and Sydney Landmarks

Bicentenary of Australian Settlement

1988 (21 June) Phosphorised paper. Perf 14½

1396	**866**	18p. multicoloured	25	25		
		a. Horiz pair. Nos. 1396/1397	55	55		
1397	**867**	18p. multicoloured	25	25		
1398	**868**	34p. multicoloured	50	50		
		a. Horiz pair. Nos. 1398/1399	1·10	1·10		
1399	**869**	34p. multicoloured	50	50		
Set of 4			1·50	1·50		
First Day Cover				1·60		
Presentation Pack (PO Pack No. 191)			1·60			
Souvenir Book			6·00			
PHQ Cards (set of 4) (111)			60	1·60		
Set of 2 Gutter Blocks of 4			3·00			

Nos. 1396/1397 and 1398/1399 were each printed together, *se-tenant*, in horizontal pairs throughout the sheets, each pair showing a background design of the Australian flag.

Stamps in similar designs were also issued by Australia. These are included in the Souvenir Book.

870 Spanish Galeasse off The Lizard

871 English Fleet leaving Plymouth

872 Engagement off Isle of Wight

873 Attack of English Fire-ships, Calais

874 Armada in Storm, North Sea

400th Anniversary of Spanish Armada

1988 (19 July) Phosphorised paper

1400	**870**	18p. multicoloured	25	25	
		a. Horiz strip of 5. Nos. 1400/1404	1·40	1·40	
1401	**871**	18p. multicoloured	25	25	
1402	**872**	18p. multicoloured	25	25	
1403	**873**	18p. multicoloured	25	25	
1404	**874**	18p. multicoloured	25	25	
Set of 5			1·40	1·40	
First Day Cover				1·50	
Presentation Pack (PO Pack No.192)			1·50		
PHQ Cards (set of 5) (112)			75	1·50	
Gutter Block of 10			2·75		

Nos. 1400/1404 were printed together, *se-tenant*, in horizontal strips of five throughout the sheet, forming a composite design.

875 'The Owl and the pussy-cat'

876 'Edward Lear as a Bird' (self-portrait)

877 'Cat' (from alphabet book)

878 'There was a Young Lady whose Bonnet ...' (limerick)

Death Centenary of Edward Lear (artist and author)

1988 (6–27 Sept.) Phosphorised paper

1405	**875**	19p. black, pale cream and carmine	25	25	
1406	**876**	27p. black, pale cream and yellow	35	35	
1407	**877**	32p. black, pale cream and emerald	45	45	
1408	**878**	35p. black, pale cream and blue	60	60	
Set of 4			1·50	1·50	
First Day Cover				1·60	
Presentation Pack (PO Pack No. 193)			1·60		
PHQ Cards (set of 4) (113)			60	1·60	
Set of 4 Gutter Pairs			3·00		
MS1409 122 × 90 mm. Nos. 1405/1408			3·25	3·50	
First Day Cover (27.9.88)				3·75	

No. **MS**1409 was sold at £1·35, the premium being used for the Stamp World London 90 International Stamp Exhibition.

879 Carrickfergus Castle

880 Caernarfon Castle

881 Edinburgh Castle

882 Windsor Castle

1988 (18 Oct.) Ordinary paper

1410	**879**	£1 deep green	3·50	25	
1411	**880**	£1·50 maroon	3·75	50	
1412	**881**	£2 indigo	6·50	75	
1413	**882**	£5 deep brown	17·00	1·50	
Set of 4			28·00	2·75	
First Day Cover				16·00	
Presentation Pack (PO Pack No. 18)			30·00		
Set of 4 Gutter pairs			60·00		

For similar designs, but with silhouette of Queen's head see Nos. 1611/1614 and 1993/1996.

883 Journey to Bethlehem

884 Shepherds and Star

885 Three Wise Men

886 Nativity

887 The Annunciation

Christmas

1988 (15 Nov.) One phosphor band (14p.) or phosphorised paper (others)

1414	**883**	14p. multicoloured	25	25	
1415	**884**	19p. multicoloured	25	25	
1416	**885**	27p. multicoloured	35	35	
1417	**886**	32p. multicoloured	40	40	
1418	**887**	35p. multicoloured	55	55	
Set of 5			1·60	1·60	
First Day Cover				1·75	
Presentation Pack (PO Pack No. 194)			1·75		
PHQ Cards (set of 5) (114)			75	1·75	
Set of 5 Gutter Pairs			3·25		

Collectors Pack 1988

1988 (15 Nov.) Comprises Nos. 1380/1408, 1414/1418
CP1418*a*   Collectors Pack   16·00   ☐

Post Office Yearbook

1988 Comprises Nos. 1380/1404, **MS**1409, 1414/1418 in hardbound book with slip case
YB1418*a*   Yearbook   13·00   ☐

888 Atlantic Puffin   889 Avocet

890 Oystercatcher   891 Northern Gannet

Centenary of Royal Society for the Protection of Birds

1989 (17 Jan.) Phosphorised paper

1419	**888**	19p. multicoloured	25	25	☐	☐
1420	**889**	27p. multicoloured	35	35	☐	☐
1421	**890**	32p. multicoloured	45	45	☐	☐
1422	**891**	35p. multicoloured	60	60	☐	☐
Set of 4			1·50	1·50	☐	☐
First Day Cover				1·60	☐	
Presentation Pack (PO Pack No. 196)			1·60		☐	
PHQ Cards (*set of 4*) (115)			60	1·60	☐	☐
Set of 4 Gutter Pairs			3·00		☐	

892 Rose   893 Cupid

894 Yachts   895 Fruit

896 Teddy Bear

Greetings (1st series). Booklet Stamps

1989 (31 Jan.) Phosphorised paper

1423	**892**	19p. multicoloured	50	60	☐	☐
		a. Booklet pane. Nos. 1423/1427×2	24·00		☐	
		b. Horiz strip of 5. Nos. 1423/1427	10·00	12·00	☐	☐
1424	**893**	19p. multicoloured	50	60	☐	☐
1425	**894**	19p. multicoloured	50	60	☐	☐
1426	**895**	19p. multicoloured	50	60	☐	☐
1427	**896**	19p. multicoloured	50	60	☐	☐
Set of 5			10·00	12·00	☐	☐
First Day Cover				12·00	☐	

Nos. 1423/1427 were printed together, *se-tenant*, in horizontal strips of five, two such strips forming the booklet pane with twelve half stamp-size labels.

897 Fruit and Vegetables   898 Meat Products

899 Dairy Produce   900 Cereal Products

Food and Farming Year

1989 (7 Mar.) Phosphorised paper. Perf 14×14½

1428	**897**	19p. multicoloured	25	25	☐	☐
1429	**898**	27p. multicoloured	35	35	☐	☐
1430	**899**	32p. multicoloured	45	45	☐	☐
1431	**900**	35p. multicoloured	60	60	☐	☐
Set of 4			1·50	1·50	☐	☐
First Day Cover				1·60	☐	
Presentation Pack (PO Pack No. 197)			1·60		☐	
PHQ Cards (*set of 4*) (116)			60	1·60	☐	☐
Set of 4 Gutter Pairs			3·00		☐	

901 Mortar Board (150th Anniversary of Public Education in England)

902 Cross on Ballot Paper (3rd Direct Elections to European Parliament)

903 Posthorn (26th Postal, Telegraph and Telephone International Congress, Brighton)

904 Globe (Inter-Parliamentary Union Centenary Conference, London)

Anniversaries

1989 (11 Apr.) Phosphorised paper. Perf 14 × 14½

1432	**901**	19p. multicoloured	25	25	☐	☐
		a. Horiz pair.				
		Nos. 1432/1433	60	60	☐	☐
1433	**902**	19p. multicoloured	25	25	☐	☐
1434	**903**	35p. multicoloured	50	50	☐	☐
		a. Horiz pair.				
		Nos. 1434/1435	1·10	1·10	☐	☐
1435	**904**	35p. multicoloured	50	50	☐	☐
Set of 4			1·50	1·50	☐	☐
First Day Cover				1·60		☐
Presentation Pack (PO Pack No. 198)			1·60		☐	
PHQ Cards (set of 4) (117)			60	1·60	☐	☐
Set of 2 Gutter Strips of 4			3·00		☐	

Nos. 1432/1433 and 1434/1435 were each printed together, se-tenant, in horizontal pairs throughout the sheets.

905 Toy Train and Aeroplanes

906 Building Bricks

907 Dice and Board Games

908 Toy Robot, Boat and Doll's House

Europa. Games and Toys

1989 (16 May) Phosphorised paper

1436	**905**	19p. multicoloured	25	25	☐	☐
1437	**906**	27p. multicoloured	35	35	☐	☐
1438	**907**	32p. multicoloured	45	45	☐	☐
1439	**908**	35p. multicoloured	60	60	☐	☐

Set of 4		1·50	1·50	☐ ☐
First Day Cover			1·60	☐
Presentation Pack (PO Pack No. 199)		1·60		☐
PHQ Cards (set of 4) (118)		60	1·60	☐ ☐
Set of 4 Gutter Pairs		3·00		☐

909 Ironbridge, Shropshire

910 Tin Mine, St Agnes Head, Cornwall

911 Cotton Mills, New Lanark, Strathclyde

912 Pontcysylite Aqueduct, Clwyd

912a

Industrial Archaeology

1989 (4–25 July) Phosphorised paper

1440	**909**	19p. multicoloured	25	25	☐	☐
1441	**910**	27p. multicoloured	35	35	☐	☐
1442	**911**	32p. multicoloured	45	45	☐	☐
1443	**912**	35p. multicoloured	60	60	☐	☐
Set of 4			1·50	1·50	☐	☐
First Day Cover				1·60		☐
Presentation Pack (PO Pack No. 200)			1·60		☐	
PHQ Cards (set of 4) (119)			60	1·60	☐	☐
Set of 4 Gutter Pairs			3·00		☐	
MS1444 122 × 90 mm. **912a** As Nos.						
1440/1443 but designs horizontal			3·00	3·00	☐	☐
First Day Cover (25.7.89)				3·00		☐

No. **MS**1444 was sold at £1·40, the premium being used for the Stamp World London 90 International Stamp Exhibition.

For Nos. 1445/1452, Types **913/914**, see Decimal Machin Definitives section.

915 Snowflake (×10)

916 *Calliphora erythrocephala* (fly) (×5)

917 Blood Cells (×500)

918 Microchip (×600)

150th Anniversary of Royal Microscopical Society

1989 (5 Sept.) Phosphorised paper. Perf 14½ × 14

1453	**915**	19p. multicoloured	25	25
1454	**916**	27p. multicoloured	35	35
1455	**917**	32p. multicoloured	45	45
1456	**918**	35p. multicoloured	60	60
Set of 4			1·50	1·50
First Day Cover				1·60
Presentation Pack (PO Pack No. 201)			1·60	
PHQ Cards (set of 4) (120)			60	1·60
Set of 4 Gutter Pairs			3·00	

919 Royal Mail Coach

920 Escort of Blues and Royals

921 Lord Mayor's Coach

922 Coach Team passing St Paul's

923 Blues and Royals Drum Horse

Lord Mayor's Show, London

1989 (17 Oct.) Phosphorised paper

1457	**919**	20p. multicoloured	25	25
		a. Horiz strip of 5.		
		Nos. 1457/1461	1·40	1·40
1458	**920**	20p. multicoloured	25	25
1459	**921**	20p. multicoloured	25	25
1460	**922**	20p. multicoloured	25	25
1461	**923**	20p. multicoloured	25	25
Set of 5			1·40	1·40
First Day Cover				1·50
Presentation Pack (PO Pack No. 202)			1·50	
PHQ Cards (set of 5) (121)			75	1·50
Gutter Strip of 10			2·75	

Nos. 1457/1461 commemorate the 800th anniversary of the installation of the first Lord Mayor of London.

Nos. 1457/1461 were printed together, *se-tenant*, in horizontal strips of five throughout the sheet, forming a composite design.

See also No. 2957.

924 14th-century Peasants from Stained-glass Window

925 Arches and Roundels, West Front

926 Octagon Tower

927 Arcade from West Transept

928 Triple Arch from West Front

Christmas. 800th Anniversary of Ely Cathedral

1989 (14 Nov.) One phosphor band (Nos. 1462/1463) or phosphorised paper (others)

1462	**924**	15p. gold, silver and blue	25	25
1463	**925**	15p. +1p. gold, silver and blue	25	35
1464	**926**	20p. +1p. gold, silver and rosine	35	35

1465	**927**	34p. +1p. gold, silver and emerald	45	45	☐ ☐
1466	**928**	37p. +1p. gold, silver and yellow-olive	60	60	☐ ☐
Set of 5			1·75	1·75	☐ ☐
First Day Cover				1·90	☐
Presentation Pack (PO Pack No. 203)			1·90		☐
PHQ Cards (set of 5) (122)			75	1·90	☐ ☐
Set of 5 Gutter Pairs			3·50		☐

Collectors Pack 1989

1989 (14 Nov.) Comprises Nos. 1419/1422, 1428/1443 and 1453/1466

| CP1466a | Collectors Pack | 16·00 | ☐ |

Post Office Yearbook

1989 (14 Nov.) Comprises Nos. 1419/1422, 1428/1444 and 1453/1466 in hardback book with slip case

| YB1466a | Yearbook | 14·00 | ☐ |

929 Queen Victoria and Queen Elizabeth II

150th Anniversary of the Penny Black

1990 (10 Jan.–17 Apr.)

(a) Printed in photogravure by Harrison and Sons (Nos. 1468, 1470, 1472 from booklets only). Perf 15 × 14

1467	**929**	15p. bright blue (1 centre band)	30	30	☐ ☐
1468a		15p. bright blue (1 side band) *(30.1.90)*	1·75	1·75	☐ ☐
1469		20p. brownish black and cream (phosphorised paper)	40	40	☐ ☐
1470		20p. brownish black and cream (2 bands) *(30.1.90)*	80	80	☐ ☐
1471		29p. deep mauve (phosphorised paper)	55	55	☐ ☐
1472		29p. deep mauve (2 bands) *(20.3.90)*	3·75	3·75	☐ ☐
1473		34p. deep bluish grey (phosphorised paper)	70	70	☐ ☐
1474		37p. rosine (phosphorised paper)	75	75	☐ ☐
Set of 5 (Nos. 1467, 1469, 1471, 1473/1474)			2·50	2·50	☐ ☐
First Day Cover (Nos. 1467, 1469, 1471, 1473/1474)				2·75	☐
Presentation Pack (Nos. 1467, 1469, 1471, 1473/1474) (PO Pack No. 21)			2·90		☐

(b) Litho Walsall (booklets). Perf 14 (30 Jan.)

| 1475 | **929** | 15p. bright blue (1 centre band) *(30.1.90)* | 50 | 50 | ☐ ☐ |
| 1476 | | 20p. brownish black and cream (phosphorised paper) *(30.1.90)* | 50 | 50 | ☐ ☐ |

(c) Litho Questa (booklets). Perf 15 × 14 (17 Apr.)

| 1477 | **929** | 15p. bright blue (1 centre band) *(17.4.90)* | 85 | 85 | ☐ ☐ |
| 1478 | | 20p. brownish black (phosphorised paper) *(17.4.90)* | 85 | 85 | ☐ ☐ |

No. 1468 exists with the phosphor band at the left or right of the stamp.

See also **MS**1501, 2133, 2955 and **MS**3965.

For T **929** redrawn with '1st' face value see Nos. 2133a and 2956.

1840·RSPCA·1990
930 Kitten

1840·RSPCA·1990
931 Rabbit

1840·RSPCA·1990
932 Duckling

1840·RSPCA·1990
933 Puppy

150th Anniversary of Royal Society for Prevention of Cruelty to Animals

1990 (23 Jan.) Phosphorised paper. Perf 14 × 14½

1479	**930**	20p. multicoloured	30	30	☐ ☐
1480	**931**	29p. multicoloured	45	45	☐ ☐
1481	**932**	34p. multicoloured	55	55	☐ ☐
1482	**933**	37p. multicoloured	65	65	☐ ☐
Set of 4			1·75	1·75	☐ ☐
First Day Cover				1·90	☐
Presentation Pack (PO Pack No. 205)			1·90		☐
PHQ Cards (set of 4) (123)			80	1·90	☐ ☐
Set of 4 Gutter Pairs			3·50		☐

934 Teddy Bear

935 Dennis the Menace

936 Punch

937 Cheshire Cat

938 The Man in the Moon

939 The Laughing Policeman

940 Clown

941 Mona Lisa

942 Queen of Hearts

943 Stan Laurel (comedian)

Greetings (2nd series) Smiles. Booklet Stamps

1990 (6 Feb.) Two phosphor bands

1483	**934**	20p. multicoloured	60	70	
		a. Booklet pane.			
		Nos. 1483/1492	11·50	12·50	
1484	**935**	20p. multicoloured	60	70	
1485	**936**	20p. multicoloured	60	70	
1486	**937**	20p. multicoloured	60	70	
1487	**938**	20p. multicoloured	60	70	
1488	**939**	20p. multicoloured	60	70	
1489	**940**	20p. multicoloured	60	70	
1490	**941**	20p. multicoloured	60	70	
1491	**942**	20p. multicoloured	60	70	
1492	**943**	20p. gold and grey-black	60	70	
Set of 10			11·50	12·50	
First Day Cover				13·00	

Nos. 1483/1492 were printed together, *se-tenant*, in booklet panes of ten.

For these designs with the face value expressed as '1st' see Nos. 1550/1559.

SET PRICES. Please note that set prices for booklet greetings stamps are for complete panes. Sets of single stamps are worth considerably less.

---

944 Alexandra Palace
(Stamp World London
90 Exhibition)

945 Glasgow School
of Art

946 British Philatelic
Bureau, Edinburgh

947 Templeton
Carpet Factory,
Glasgow

Europa (Nos. 1493 and 1495) and Glasgow 1990 European City of Culture (Nos. 1494 and 1496)

1990 (6 Mar.) Phosphorised paper

1493	**944**	20p. multicoloured	25	25	
1494	**945**	20p. multicoloured	35	35	
1495	**946**	29p. multicoloured	45	45	
1496	**947**	37p. multicoloured	60	60	
Set of 4			1·50	1·50	
First Day Cover				1·60	
Presentation Pack (PO Pack No. 206)			1·60		
PHQ Cards (*set of 4*) (124)			80	1·60	
Set of 4 Gutter Pairs			3·00		

948 Export
Achievement Award

949 Technological
Achievement Award

25th Anniversary of Queen's Awards for Export and Technology

1990 (10 Apr.) Phosphorised paper. Perf 14 × 14½

1497	**948**	20p. multicoloured	25	25	
		a. Horiz pair.			
		Nos. 1497/1498	60	60	
1498	**949**	20p. multicoloured	25	25	
1499	**948**	37p. multicoloured	50	50	
		a. Horiz pair.			
		Nos. 1499/1500	1·10	1·10	
1500	**949**	37p. multicoloured	50	50	
Set of 4			1·50	1·50	
First Day Cover				1·60	
Presentation Pack (PO Pack No. 207)			1·60		
PHQ Cards (*set of 4*) (125)			80	1·60	
Set of 2 Gutter Strips of 4			3·00		

Nos. 1497/1498 and 1499/1500 were each printed together, *se-tenant*, in horizontal pairs throughout the sheets.

949a

Stamp World London 90 International Stamp Exhibition, London. Minature sheet

1990 (3 May) Sheet 122 × 90 mm. Phosphorised paper

MS1501 **949a** 20p. brownish black and cream		2·40	2·40	☐ ☐
First Day Cover			2·50	☐
Souvenir Book (Nos. 1467, 1469, 1471, 1473/1474 and **MS**1501			8·50	☐

No. **MS**1501 was sold at £1, the premium being used for the exhibition.

KEW GARDENS 1840-1990
950 Cycad and Sir Joseph Banks Building

KEW GARDENS 1840-1990
951 Stone Pine and Princess of Wales Conservatory

KEW GARDENS 1840-1990
952 Willow Tree and Palm House

KEW GARDENS 1840-1990
953 Cedar Tree and Pagoda

150th Anniversary of Kew Gardens

1990 (5 June) Phosphorised paper

1502	**950**	20p. multicoloured	25	25	☐ ☐
1503	**951**	29p. multicoloured	35	35	☐ ☐
1504	**952**	34p. multicoloured	45	45	☐ ☐
1505	**953**	37p. multicoloured	60	60	☐ ☐
Set of 4			1·50	1·50	☐ ☐
First Day Cover				1·60	☐
Presentation Pack (PO Pack No. 208)			1·60		☐
PHQ Cards (*set of 4*) (126)			80	1·60	☐ ☐
Set of 4 Gutter Pairs			3·00		☐

954 Thomas Hardy and Clyffe Clump, Dorset

150th Birth Anniversary of Thomas Hardy (author)

1990 (10 July) Phosphorised paper

1506	**954**	20p. multicoloured	30	30	☐ ☐
First Day Cover				40	☐
Presentation Pack (PO Pack No. 209)			55		☐
PHQ Card (127)			20	40	☐ ☐
Gutter Pair			60		☐

955 Queen Elizabeth the Queen Mother

956 Queen Elizabeth

957 Elizabeth, Duchess of York

958 Lady Elizabeth Bowes-Lyon

90th Birthday of Queen Elizabeth the Queen Mother

1990 (2 Aug.) Phosphorised paper

1507	**955**	20p. multicoloured	40	40	☐ ☐
1508	**956**	29p. silver, indigo and grey-blue	60	60	☐ ☐
1509	**957**	34p. multicoloured	90	90	☐ ☐
1510	**958**	37p. silver, sepia and stone	1·10	1·10	☐ ☐
Set of 4			2·75	2·75	☐ ☐
First Day Cover				2·90	☐
Presentation Pack (PO Pack No. 210)			2·90		☐
PHQ Cards (*set of 4*) (128)			80	2·90	☐ ☐
Set of 4 Gutter Pairs			5·50		☐

For these designs with Queen mother's head and frame in black see Nos. 2280/2283.

For Nos. 1511/1516 see Decimal Machin Definitives section.

959 Victoria Cross

960 George Cross

961 Distinguished Service Cross and Distinguished Service Medal

962 Military Cross and Military Medal

963 Distinguished Flying Cross and Distinguished Flying Medal

Gallantry Awards

1990 (11 Sept.) Phosphorised paper

1517	**959**	20p. multicoloured	35	35
1518	**960**	20p. multicoloured	35	35
1519	**961**	20p. multicoloured	35	35
1520	**962**	20p. multicoloured	35	35
1521	**963**	20p. multicoloured	35	35
Set of 5			1·50	1·50
First Day Cover				1·60
Presentation Pack (PO Pack No. 211)			1·60	
PHQ Cards (*set of 5*) (129)			1·00	1·60
Set of 5 Gutter Pairs			3·00	

For **T 959** with 'all-over' phosphor and perf 14 × 14½ see No. 2666.

964 Armagh Observatory, Jodrell Bank Radio Telescope and La Palma Telescope

965 Newton's Moon and Tides Diagram with Early Telescopes

966 Greenwich Old Observatory and Early Astronomical Equipment

967 Stonehenge, Gyroscope and Navigating by Stars

Astronomy

1990 (16 Oct.) Phosphorised paper. Perf 14 × 14½

1522	**964**	22p. multicoloured	25	25
1523	**965**	26p. multicoloured	35	35
1524	**966**	31p. multicoloured	45	45
1525	**967**	37p. multicoloured	60	60
Set of 4			1·50	1·50
First Day Cover				1·60
Presentation Pack (PO Pack No. 212)			1·60	
PHQ Cards (*set of 4*) (130)			80	1·60
Set of 4 Gutter Pairs			3·00	

Nos. 1522/1525 commemorate the centenary of the British Astronomical Association and the bicentenary of the Armagh Observatory.

968 Building a Snowman

969 Fetching the Christmas Tree

970 Carol Singing

971 Tobogganing

972 Ice skating

Christmas Scenes

1990 (13 Nov.) One phosphor band (17p.) or phosphorised paper (others)

1526	**968**	17p. multicoloured	25	25
1527	**969**	22p. multicoloured	25	25
1528	**970**	26p. multicoloured	35	35
1529	**971**	31p. multicoloured	45	45
1530	**972**	37p. multicoloured	60	60
Set of 5			1·75	1·75
First Day Cover				1·90
Presentation Pack (PO Pack No. 213)			1·90	
PHQ Cards (*set of 5*) (131)			1·00	1·90
Set of 5 Gutter Pairs			3·50	

Collectors Pack 1990

1990 (13 Nov.) Comprises Nos. 1479/1482, 1493/1510 and 1517/1530

CP1530*a*	Collectors Pack	18·00	

Post Office Yearbook

1990 Comprises Nos. 1479/1482, 1493/1500, 1502/1510 and 1517/1530 in hardback book with slip case

YB1530*a*	Yearbook	18·00	

973 *King Charles Spaniel*

974 *A Pointer*

975 *Two Hounds in a Landscape*

976 *A Rough Dog*

977 *Fino and Tiny*

Dogs. Paintings by George Stubbs

1991 (8 Jan.) Phosphorised paper. Perf 14 × 14½

1531	**973**	22p. multicoloured	25	25	
1532	**974**	26p. multicoloured	30	30	
1533	**975**	31p. multicoloured	40	40	
1534	**976**	33p. multicoloured	45	45	
1535	**977**	37p. multicoloured	60	60	
Set of 5			1·75	1·75	
First Day Cover				2·00	
Presentation Pack (PO Pack No. 215)			2·00		
PHQ Cards (*set of 5*) (132)			1·00	2·00	
Set of 5 Gutter Pairs			3·50		

978 Thrush's Nest

979 Shooting Star and Rainbow

980 Magpies and Charm Bracelet

981 Black Cat

982 Common Kingfisher with Key

983 Mallard and Frog

984 Four-leaf Clover in Boot and Match Box

985 Pot of Gold at End of Rainbow

986 Heart-shaped Butterflies

987 Wishing Well and Sixpence

Greetings Good Luck (3rd series). Booklet Stamps

1991 (5 Feb.) Two phosphor bands

1536	**978**	(1st) multicoloured	80	80	
		a. Booklet pane.			
		Nos. 1536/1545	9·00	9·00	
1537	**979**	(1st) multicoloured	80	80	
1538	**980**	(1st) multicoloured	80	80	
1539	**981**	(1st) multicoloured	80	80	
1540	**982**	(1st) multicoloured	80	80	
1541	**983**	(1st) multicoloured	80	80	
1542	**984**	(1st) multicoloured	80	80	
1543	**985**	(1st) multicoloured	80	80	
1544	**986**	(1st) multicoloured	80	80	
1545	**987**	(1st) multicoloured	80	80	
Set of 10			9·00	9·00	
First Day Cover				9·25	

Nos. 1536/1545 were printed together, *se-tenant*, in booklet panes of ten stamps and 12 half stamp-size labels, the backgrounds of the stamps forming a composite design.

SET PRICES. Please note that set prices for booklet greetings stamps are for complete panes. Sets of single stamps are worth considerably less.

---

988 Michael Faraday (inventor of electric motor) (Birth Bicentenary)

989 Charles Babbage (computer science pioneer) (Birth Bicentenary)

990 Radar Sweep of East Anglia (50th Anniversary of Discovery by Sir Robert Watson-Watt)

991 Gloster Whittle E28/39 Aircraft over East Anglia (50th Anniversary of First Flight of Sir Frank Whittle's Jet Engine)

1106 Horse Chestnut

1107 Blackberry

1108 Hazel

1109 Rowan

1110 Pear

The Four Seasons. (2nd series) Autumn.
Fruits and Leaves

1993 (14 Sept.) One phosphor band (18p.) or phosphorised paper (others)

1779	**1106**	18p. multicoloured	30	30
1780	**1107**	24p. multicoloured	35	35
1781	**1108**	28p. multicoloured	45	45
1782	**1109**	33p. multicoloured	50	50
1783	**1110**	39p. multicoloured	60	60
Set of 5			2·00	2·00
First Day Cover				2·25
Presentation Pack (PO Pack No. 240)			2·25	
PHQ Cards (set of 5) (155)			1·00	2·25
Set of 5 Gutter Pairs			4·00	

SHERLOCK HOLMES & DR WATSON
"THE REIGATE SQUIRE"
1111 The Reigate Squire

SHERLOCK HOLMES & SIR HENRY
"THE HOUND OF THE BASKERVILLES"
1112 The Hound of the Baskervilles

SHERLOCK HOLMES & LESTRADE
"THE SIX NAPOLEONS"
1113 The Six Napoleons

SHERLOCK HOLMES & MYCROFT
"THE GREEK INTERPRETER"
1114 The Greek Interpreter

SHERLOCK HOLMES & MORIARTY
"THE FINAL PROBLEM"
1115 The Final Problem

Sherlock Holmes.
Centenary of the Publication of *The Final Problem*

1993 (12 Oct.) Phosphorised paper. Perf 14 × 14½

1784	**1111**	24p. multicoloured	30	30
		a. Horiz strip of 5. Nos. 1784/1788	1·90	2·40
1785	**1112**	24p. multicoloured	30	30
1786	**1113**	24p. multicoloured	30	30
1787	**1114**	24p. multicoloured	30	30
1788	**1115**	24p. multicoloured	30	30
Set of 5			1·90	2·40
First Day Cover				2·50
Presentation Pack (PO Pack No. 241)			2·50	
PHQ Cards (set of 5) (156)			1·00	2·50
Gutter Strip of 10			3·75	

Nos. 1784/1788 were printed together, *se-tenant*, in horizontal strips of five throughout the sheet.

For Nos. 1789, Type **1116** see Decimal Machin Definitives section.

1117 Bob Cratchit and Tiny Tim

1118 Mr and Mrs Fezziwig

1119 Scrooge

1120 The Prize Turkey

1121 Mr Scrooge's Nephew

Christmas.
150th Anniversary of Publication of *A Christmas Carol*

1993 (9 Nov.) One phosphor band (19p.) or phosphorised paper (others)

1790	**1117**	19p. multicoloured	30	30
1791	**1118**	25p. multicoloured	40	40
1792	**1119**	30p. multicoloured	50	50
1793	**1120**	35p. multicoloured	55	55

1794 **1121**	41p. multicoloured	65	65	☐	☐
Set of 5		2·10	2·10	☐	☐
First Day Cover			2·25	☐	
Presentation Pack (PO Pack No. 242)		2·75			☐
PHQ Cards (set of 5) (157)		1·00	2·25	☐	☐
Set of 5 Gutter Pairs		4·25			☐

Collectors Pack 1993

1993 (9 Nov.) Comprises Nos. 1639/1643, 1654/1657, 1659/1663, 1767/1788 and 1790/1794
CP1794a Collectors Pack   22·00   ☐

Post Office Yearbook

1993 (9 Nov.) Comprises Nos. 1639/1643, 1654/1657, 1659/1663, 1767/1788 and 1790/1794 in hardback book with slip case
YB1794a Yearbook   20·00   ☐

1122 Class 5 No. 44957 and Class B1 No. 61342 on West Highland Line

1123 Class A1 No. 60149 *Amadis* at Kings Cross

1124 Class 4 No. 43000 on Turntable at Blythe North

1125 Class 4 No. 42455 near Wigan Central

1126 Castle Class No. 7002 *Devizes Castle* on Bridge crossing Worcester and Birmingham Canal

The Age of Steam.
Railway Photographs by Colin Gifford

1994 (18 Jan.) One phosphor band (19p.) or phosphorised paper with two bands (others). Perf 14½

1795 **1122**	19p. deep blue-green, grey-black and black	30	30	☐	☐
1796 **1123**	25p. slate-lilac, grey-black and black	40	40	☐	☐
1797 **1124**	30p. lake-brown, grey-black and black	50	50	☐	☐
1798 **1125**	35p. deep claret, grey-black and black	60	60	☐	☐
1799 **1126**	41p. indigo, grey-black and black	70	70	☐	☐
Set of 5		2·25	2·25	☐	☐
First Day Cover			2·50	☐	
Presentation Pack (PO Pack No. 244)		3·00			☐
PHQ Cards (set of 5) (158)		1·00	2·50	☐	☐
Set of 5 Gutter Pairs		4·50			☐

1127 Dan Dare and the Mekon

1128 The Three Bears

1129 Rupert Bear

1130 Alice (*Alice in Wonderland*)

1131 Noggin and the Ice Dragon

1132 Peter Rabbit posting Letter

1133 Red Riding Hood and Wolf

1134 Orlando the Marmalade Cat

1135 Biggles

1136 Paddington Bear on Station

Greetings Stamps. Messages (7th series).
Booklet Stamps

1994 (1 Feb.) Two phosphor bands. Perf 15×14 (with one elliptical hole in each vertical side)

1800 **1127**	(1st) multicoloured	1·00	50	☐	☐
	a. Booklet pane. Nos. 1800/1809	9·00	9·00	☐	☐
1801 **1128**	(1st) multicoloured	1·00	50	☐	☐
1802 **1129**	(1st) multicoloured	1·00	50	☐	☐
1803 **1130**	(1st) gold, bistre-yellow and black	1·00	50	☐	☐
1804 **1131**	(1st) multicoloured	1·00	50	☐	☐
1805 **1132**	(1st) multicoloured	1·00	50	☐	☐
1806 **1133**	(1st) multicoloured	1·00	50	☐	☐
1807 **1134**	(1st) multicoloured	1·00	50	☐	☐
1808 **1135**	(1st) multicoloured	1·00	50	☐	☐
1809 **1136**	(1st) multicoloured	1·00	50	☐	☐
Set of 10		9·00	9·00	☐	☐
First Day Cover			9·25	☐	
Presentation Pack (PO Pack No. G3)		11·00			☐
PHQ Cards (set of 10) (GS2)		2·00	9·25	☐	☐

Nos. 1800/1809 were printed together, *se-tenant*, in booklet panes of ten stamps and 20 half stamp-size labels.

SET PRICES. Please note that set prices for booklet greetings stamps are for complete panes. Sets of single stamps are worth considerably less.

1137 Castell Y Waun (Chirk Castle), Clwyd, Wales

1138 Ben Arkle, Sutherland, Scotland

1139 Mourne Mountains, County Down, Northern Ireland

1140 Dersingham, Norfolk, England

1141 Dolwyddelan, Gwynedd, Wales

25th Anniversary of Investiture of the Prince of Wales. Paintings by Prince Charles

1994 (1 Mar.) One phosphor band (19p.) or phosphorised paper (others)

1810	**1137**	19p. multicoloured	30	30
1811	**1138**	25p. multicoloured	35	35
1812	**1139**	30p. multicoloured	45	45
1813	**1140**	35p. multicoloured	60	60
1814	**1141**	41p. multicoloured	70	70
Set of 5			2·25	2·25
First Day Cover				2·40
Presentation Pack (PO Pack No. 245)			2·40	
PHQ Cards (*set of 5*) (159)			1·00	2·40
Set of 5 Gutter Pairs			4·50	

1142 Bather at Blackpool

1143 'Where's my Little Lad?'

1144 'Wish You were Here!'

1145 Punch and Judy Show

1146 'The Tower Crane' Machine

Centenary of Picture Postcards

1994 (12 Apr.) One side band (19p.) or two phosphor bands (others). Perf 14 × 14½

1815	**1142**	19p. multicoloured	30	30
1816	**1143**	25p. multicoloured	35	35
1817	**1144**	30p. multicoloured	45	45
1818	**1145**	35p. multicoloured	60	60
1819	**1146**	41p. multicoloured	70	70
Set of 5			2·25	2·25
First Day Cover				2·40
Presentation Pack (PO Pack No. 246)			2·40	
PHQ Cards (*set of 5*) (160)			1·00	2·40
Set of 5 Gutter Pairs			4·50	

1147 British Lion and French Cockerel over Tunnel

1148 Symbolic Hands over Train

Opening of Channel Tunnel

1994 (3 May) Phosphorised paper. Perf 14 × 14½

1820	**1147**	25p. multicoloured	30	35
		a. Horiz pair.		
		Nos. 1820/1821	1·00	1·10
1821	**1148**	25p. multicoloured	30	35
1822	**1147**	41p. multicoloured	50	60
		a. Horiz pair.		
		Nos. 1822/1823	1·50	1·70
1823	**1148**	41p. multicoloured	50	60
Set of 4			2·25	2·50
First Day Cover				2·75
First Day Covers (2) (UK and French stamps)				6·00
Presentation Pack (PO Pack No. 247)			2·75	
Presentation Pack (UK and French stamps)			15·00	
Souvenir Book			32·00	
PHQ Cards (*set of 4*) (161)			60	2·50

Stamps in similar designs were also issued by France and these are included in the joint Presentation Pack and Souvenir Book.

Nos. 1820/1821 and 1822/1823 were printed together, *se-tenant*, in horizontal pairs throughout the sheets.

1149 Groundcrew replacing Smoke Canisters on Douglas Boston of 88 Sqn

1150 HMS *Warspite* (battleship) shelling Enemy Positions

1151 Commandos Landing on Gold Beach

1152 Infantry regrouping on Sword Beach

1153 Tank and Infantry advancing, Ouistreham

50th Anniversary of D-Day

1994 (6 June) Two phosphor bands. Perf 14½ × 14

1824	**1149**	25p. multicoloured	35	30	□	□
		a. Horiz strip of 5.				
		Nos. 1824/1828	2·10	1·75	□	□
1825	**1150**	25p. multicoloured	35	30	□	□
1826	**1151**	25p. multicoloured	35	30	□	□
1827	**1152**	25p. multicoloured	35	30	□	□
1828	**1153**	25p. multicoloured	35	30	□	□
Set of 5			2·10	1·75	□	□
First Day Cover				1·90		□
Presentation Pack (PO Pack No. 248)			2·40			□
PHQ Cards (*set of 5*) (162)			1·00	1·90	□	□
Gutter Block of 10			4·25		□	

Nos. 1824/1828 were printed together, *se-tenant*, in horizontal strips of five throughout the sheet.

1154 The Old Course, St Andrews

1155 The 18th Hole, Muirfield

1156 The 15th Hole ('Luckyslap'), Carnoustie

1157 The 8th Hole ('The Postage Stamp'), Royal Troon

1158 The 9th Hole, Turnberry

Scottish Golf Courses

1994 (5 July) One phosphor band (19p.) or phosphorised paper (others). Perf 14½ × 14

1829	**1154**	19p. multicoloured	30	30	□	□
1830	**1155**	25p. multicoloured	35	35	□	□
1831	**1156**	30p. multicoloured	45	45	□	□
1832	**1157**	35p. multicoloured	60	60	□	□
1833	**1158**	41p. multicoloured	70	70	□	□
Set of 5			2·10	2·10	□	□
First Day Cover				2·25		□
Presentation Pack (PO Pack No. 249)			2·40			□
PHQ Cards (*set of 5*) (163)			1·00	2·25	□	□
Set of 5 Gutter Pairs			4·25		□	

Nos. 1829/1833 commemorate the 250th anniversary of golf's first set of rules produced by the Honourable Company of Edinburgh Golfers.

AMSER HAF/SUMMERTIME *Llanelwedd*
1159 Royal Welsh Show, Llanelwedd

SUMMERTIME *Wimbledon*
1160 All England Tennis Championships, Wimbledon

SUMMERTIME *Cowes*
1161 Cowes Week

SUMMERTIME *Lord's*
1162 Test Match, Lord's

SUMMERTIME *Braemar*
1163 Braemar Gathering

BY APPOINTMENT TO
HER MAJESTY THE QUEEN
PHILATELISTS
STANLEY GIBBONS LTD
LONDON

STANLEY GIBBONS

THE HOME OF STAMP COLLECTING

Kensington

A binder for the refined collector,
soft touch red or navy faux leathers
accompanied by a sumptuous padding
to give you a luxurious feel.

Size 275x300mm

Sandringham

The quintessential stamp binder,
designed for the everyday
collector looking to bring an
element of prestige to their
collection with red or navy
faux leather casings adding a
premium feel.

Size 275x300mm

To order, call **01425 472 363** email **orders@stanleygibbons.com**
or visit **stanleygibbons.com**

Binders

Our new binder range allows for complete customisation and flexibility, with interchangeable leaves, a choice of colours and finishes, available in 22-ring or Springback variations. You can now keep your entire collection in one type of binder, allowing for a more consistent look to your collection whilst making no sacrifice on quality, feel or prestige. Handmade exclusively for Stanley Gibbons and our customers.

Leaves and Pages for these binders can be found on our website

Binder Type	Binder Colour	product code	price
Sandringham	●	RSAN-BLU	£19.95
Sandringham	●	RSAN-RED	£19.95
Kensington	●	RKEN-BLU	£27.95
Kensington	●	RKEN-RED	£27.95

The **Kensington** Binder features a sumptuous 3mm padding for a luxurious feel

The **Sandringham** Binder features a faux leather lining and gold foiling along the spine

STANLEY GIBBONS | 399 Strand | London | WC2R 0LX
www.stanleygibbons.com

 @StanleyGibbons   /StanleyGibbonsGroup   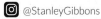 @StanleyGibbons

The Four Seasons (3rd series). Summertime. Events

1994 (2 Aug.) One phosphor band (19p.) or phosphorised paper (others)

1834	**1159**	19p. multicoloured	30	30	☐	☐
1835	**1160**	25p. multicoloured	35	35	☐	☐
1836	**1161**	30p. multicoloured	45	45	☐	☐
1837	**1162**	35p. multicoloured	60	60	☐	☐
1838	**1163**	41p. multicoloured	70	70	☐	☐
Set of 5			2·10	2·10	☐	☐
First Day Cover				2·25		☐
Presentation Pack (PO Pack No. 250)			2·40		☐	
PHQ Cards (set of 5) (164)			1·00	2·25	☐	☐
Set of 5 Gutter Pairs			4·25		☐	

1164 Ultrasonic Imaging

1165 Scanning Electron Microscopy

1166 Magnetic Resonance Imaging

1167 Computed Tomography

Europa. Medical Discoveries

1994 (27 Sept.) Phosphorised paper. Perf 14 × 14½

1839	**1164**	25p. multicoloured	40	40	☐	☐
1840	**1165**	30p. multicoloured	50	50	☐	☐
1841	**1166**	35p. multicoloured	60	60	☐	☐
1842	**1167**	41p. multicoloured	70	70	☐	☐
Set of 4			2·00	2·00	☐	☐
First Day Cover				2·25		☐
Presentation Pack (PO Pack No. 251)			2·40		☐	
PHQ Cards (set of 4) (165)			80	2·25	☐	☐
Set of 4 Gutter Pairs			4·00		☐	

1168 Virgin Mary and Joseph

1169 Three Wise Men

1170 Virgin and Child

1171 Shepherds

1172 Angels

Christmas. Children's Nativity Plays

1994 (1 Nov.) One phosphor band (19p.) or phosphorised paper (others)

1843	**1168**	19p. multicoloured	30	30	☐	☐
1844	**1169**	25p. multicoloured	35	35	☐	☐
1845	**1170**	30p. multicoloured	45	45	☐	☐
1846	**1171**	35p. multicoloured	55	60	☐	☐
1847	**1172**	41p. multicoloured	65	70	☐	☐
Set of 5			2·00	2·10	☐	☐
First Day Cover				2·25		☐
Presentation Pack (PO Pack No. 252)			2·25		☐	
PHQ Cards (set of 5) (166)			1·00	2·25	☐	☐
Set of 5 Gutter Pairs			4·00		☐	

Year Pack 1994

1994 (14 Nov.) Comprises Nos. 1795/1847

CP1847a	Year Pack	27·00	☐

Post Office Yearbook

1994 (14 Nov.) Comprises Nos. 1795/1799 and 1810/1847 in hardback book with slip case

YB1847a	Yearbook	20·00	☐

1173 Sophie (black cat)

1174 Puskas (Siamese) and Tigger (tabby)

1175 Chloe (ginger cat)

1176 Kikko (tortoiseshell) and Rosie (Abyssinian)

1177 Fred (black and white cat)

Cats

1995 (17 Jan.) One phosphor band (19p.) or two phosphor bands (others). Perf 14½ × 14

1848	**1173**	19p. multicoloured	30	30	☐	☐
1849	**1174**	25p. multicoloured	40	40	☐	☐

1850	**1175**	30p. multicoloured	50	50	
1851	**1176**	35p. multicoloured	60	60	
1852	**1177**	41p. multicoloured	70	70	
Set of 5			2·25	2·25	
First Day Cover				2·50	
Presentation Pack (PO Pack No. 254)			2·50		
PHQ Cards (set of 5) (167)			1·00	2·50	
Set of 5 Gutter Pairs			4·50		

1178 Dandelions

1179 Sweet Chestnut Leaves

1180 Garlic Leaves

1181 Hazel Leaves

1182 Spring Grass

The Four Seasons (4th series). Springtime.
Plant Sculptures by Andy Goldsworthy

1995 (14 Mar.) One phosphor band (19p.) or two phosphor bands (others)

1853	**1178**	19p. multicoloured	30	30	
1854	**1179**	25p. multicoloured	35	35	
1855	**1180**	30p. multicoloured	45	45	
1856	**1181**	35p. multicoloured	55	55	
1857	**1182**	41p. multicoloured	65	65	
Set of 5			2·00	2·00	
First Day Cover				2·25	
Presentation Pack (PO Pack No. 255)			2·40		
PHQ Cards (set of 5) (168)			1·00	2·25	
Set of 5 Gutter Pairs			4·00		

1183 La Danse à la Campagne (Renoir)

1184 Troilus and Criseyde (Peter Brookes)

1185 The Kiss (Rodin)

1186 Girls on the Town (Beryl Cook)

1187 Jazz (Andrew Mockett)

1188 Girls performing a Kathal Dance (Aurangzeb period)

1189 Alice Keppel with her Daughter (Alice Hughes)

1190 Children Playing (L. S. Lowry)

1191 Circus Clowns (Emily Firmin and Justin Mitchell)

1192 Decoration from All the Love Poems of Shakespeare (Eric Gill)

Greetings. (8th series) Greetings in Art.
Booklet stamps

1995 (21 Mar.) Two phosphor bands. Perf 14½ × 14 (with one elliptical hole in each vertical side)

1858	**1183**	(1st) multicoloured	1·00	50	
		a. Booklet pane. Nos. 1858/1867	9·00	9·00	
1859	**1184**	(1st) multicoloured	1·00	50	
1860	**1185**	(1st) multicoloured	1·00	50	
1861	**1186**	(1st) multicoloured	1·00	50	
1862	**1187**	(1st) multicoloured	1·00	50	
1863	**1188**	(1st) multicoloured	1·00	50	
1864	**1189**	(1st) purple-brown and silver	1·00	50	
1865	**1190**	(1st) multicoloured	1·00	50	
1866	**1191**	(1st) multicoloured	1·00	50	
1867	**1192**	(1st) black, greenish yellow and silver	1·00	50	
Set of 10			9·00	9·00	
First Day Cover				9·25	
Presentation Pack (PO Pack No. G4)			10·00		
PHQ Cards (set of 10) (GS3)			2·00	9·25	

Nos. 1858/1867 were printed together, se-tenant, in booklet panes of ten stamps and 20 half stamp-size labels.

The National Trust Celebrating 100 Years 19

1193 Fireplace Decoration, Attingham Park, Shropshire

The National Trust Protecting Land 25

1194 Oak Seedling

The National Trust
Conserving Art 30

1195 Carved Table Leg, Attingham Park

The National Trust
Saving Coast 35

1196 St David's Head, Dyfed, Wales

The National Trust
Repairing Buildings 41

1197 Elizabethan Window, Little Moreton Hall, Cheshire

Centenary of The National Trust

1995 (11 Apr.) One phosphor band (19p.), two phosphor bands (25p., 35p.) or phosphorised paper (30p., 41p.)

1868	**1193**	19p. multicoloured	30	30
1869	**1194**	25p. multicoloured	35	35
1870	**1195**	30p. multicoloured	45	45
1871	**1196**	35p. multicoloured	55	55
1872	**1197**	41p. multicoloured	65	65
Set of 5			2·00	2·00
First Day Cover				2·25
Presentation Pack (PO Pack No. 256)			2·40	
PHQ Cards (*set of 5*) (169)			1·00	2·25
Set of 5 Gutter Pairs			4·00	

1198 British Troops and French Civilians celebrating

1199 Symbolic Hands and Red Cross

1200 St Paul's Cathedral and Searchlights

1201 Symbolic Hand releasing Peace Dove

1202 Symbolic Hands

Europa. Peace and Freedom

1995 (2 May) One phosphor band (Nos. 1873/1874) or two phosphor bands (others). Perf 14½ × 14

1873	**1198**	19p. silver, bistre-brown and grey-black	35	35
1874	**1199**	19p. multicoloured	35	35
1875	**1200**	25p. silver, blue and grey-black	45	45
1876	**1201**	25p. multicoloured	45	45
1877	**1202**	30p. multicoloured	60	60
Set of 5			2·00	2·00
First Day Cover				2·25
Presentation Pack (PO Pack No. 257)			2·40	
PHQ Cards (*set of 5*) (170)			1·00	2·25
Set of 5 Gutter Pairs			4·00	

Nos. 1873 and 1875 commemorate the 50th anniversary of the end of the Second World War, No. 1874 the 125th anniversary of the British Red Cross Society and Nos. 1876/1877 the 50th anniversary of the United Nations.

Nos. 1876/1877 include the EUROPA emblem.

For T **1200** with the face value expressed as '1st' see No. **MS**2547.

1203 The Time Machine

1204 The First Men in the Moon

1205 The War of the Worlds

1206 The Shape of Things to Come

Science Fiction. Novels by H. G. Wells

1995 (6 June) Two phosphor bands. Perf 14½ × 14

1878	**1203**	25p. multicoloured	40	40
1879	**1204**	30p. multicoloured	50	50
1880	**1205**	35p. multicoloured	60	60
1881	**1206**	41p. multicoloured	70	70
Set of 4			2·00	2·00
First Day Cover				2·25
Presentation Pack (PO Pack No. 258)			2·40	
PHQ Cards (*set of 4*) (171)			80	2·25
Set of 4 Gutter Pairs			4·00	

Nos. 1878/1881 commemorate the centenary of publication of Wells's *The Time Machine.*

1207 The Swan, 1595

1208 The Rose, 1592

1209 The Globe, 1599

1210 The Hope, 1613

1211 The Globe, 1614

Reconstruction of Shakespeare's Globe Theatre

1995 (8 Aug.) Two phosphor bands. Perf 14½

1882	**1207**	25p. multicoloured	40	30	☐ ☐
		a. Horiz strip of 5.			
		Nos. 1882/1886	2·00	2·25	☐ ☐
1883	**1208**	25p. multicoloured	40	30	☐ ☐
1884	**1209**	25p. multicoloured	40	30	☐ ☐
1885	**1210**	25p. multicoloured	40	30	☐ ☐
1886	**1211**	25p. multicoloured	40	30	☐ ☐
Set of 5			2·00	2·25	☐ ☐
First Day Cover				2·40	☐
Presentation Pack (PO Pack No. 259)			2·40		☐
PHQ Cards (*set of 5*) (172)			1·00	2·40	☐ ☐
Gutter Strip of 10			4·00		☐

Nos. 1882/1886 were printed together, *se-tenant*, in horizontal strips of five throughout the sheet, the backgrounds forming a composite design.

1212 Sir Rowland Hill and Uniform Penny Postage Petition

1213 Hill and Penny Black

1214 Guglielmo Marconi and Early Wireless

1215 Marconi and Sinking of *Titanic* (liner)

Pioneers of Communications

1995 (5 Sept.) One phosphor band (19p.) or phosphorised paper (others). Perf 14½ × 14

1887	**1212**	19p. silver, red and black	40	40	☐ ☐
1888	**1213**	25p. silver, brown and black	50	50	☐ ☐
1889	**1214**	41p. silver, grey-green and black	65	65	☐ ☐
1890	**1215**	60p. silver, deep ultramarine and black	75	75	☐ ☐
Set of 4			2·10	2·10	☐ ☐
First Day Cover				2·25	☐
Presentation Pack (PO Pack No. 260)			2·50		☐
PHQ Cards (*set of 4*) (173)			80	2·25	☐ ☐
Set of 4 Gutter Pairs			4·25		☐

Nos. 1887/1888 mark the birth bicentenary of Sir Rowland Hill and Nos. 1889/1890 the centenary of the first radio transmissions.

1216 Harold Wagstaff

1217 Gus Risman

1218 Jim Sullivan

1219 Billy Batten

1220 Brian Bevan

Centenary of Rugby League

1995 (3 Oct.) One phosphor band (19p.) or two phosphor bands (others). Perf 14 × 14½

1891	**1216**	19p. multicoloured	30	30	☐ ☐
1892	**1217**	25p. multicoloured	35	35	☐ ☐
1893	**1218**	30p. multicoloured	45	45	☐ ☐
1894	**1219**	35p. multicoloured	55	55	☐ ☐

1895	**1220**	41p. multicoloured	65	65	☐ ☐
Set of 5			2·10	2·10	☐ ☐
First Day Cover				2·25	☐
Presentation Pack (PO Pack No. 261)			2·40		☐
PHQ Cards (*set of 5*) (174)			1·00	2·25	☐ ☐
Set of 5 Gutter Pairs			4·25		☐

1221 European Robin in Mouth of Pillar Box

1222 European Robin on Railings and Holly

1223 European Robin on Snow-covered Milk Bottles

1224 European Robin on Road Sign

1225 European Robin on Door Knob and Christmas Wreath

Christmas. Christmas Robins

1995 (30 Oct.) One phosphor band (19p.) or two phosphor bands (others)

1896	**1221**	19p. multicoloured	30	30	☐ ☐
1897	**1222**	25p. multicoloured	35	40	☐ ☐
1898	**1223**	30p. multicoloured	50	55	☐ ☐
1899	**1224**	41p. multicoloured	60	65	☐ ☐
1900	**1225**	60p. multicoloured	75	80	☐ ☐
Set of 5			2·25	2·50	☐ ☐
First Day Cover				2·75	☐
Presentation Pack (PO Pack No. 262)			2·50		☐
PHQ Cards (*set of 5*) (175)			1·00	2·75	☐ ☐
Set of 5 Gutter Pairs			4·50		☐

The 19p value was re-issued on 3 October 2000 and 9 October 2001 in sheets of 20 each with *se-tenant* label, in connection with 'customised' stamps available from the Philatelic Bureau. The labels show either Christmas greetings or a personal photograph.

Year Pack 1995

1995 (30 Oct.) Comprises Nos. 1848/1900

CP1900*a*	Year Pack	25·00	☐

Post Office Yearbook

1995 (30 Oct.) Comprises Nos. 1848/1857 and 1868/1900 in hardback book with slip case

YB1900*a*	Yearbook	20·00	☐

1226 Opening Lines of *To a Mouse* and Fieldmouse

1227 *O my Luve's like a red, red rose* and Wild Rose

1228 *Scots, wha hae wi Wallace bled* and Sir William Wallace

1229 *Auld Lang Syne* and Highland Dancers

Death Bicentenary of Robert Burns (Scottish poet)

1996 (25 Jan.) One phosphor band (19p.) or two phosphor bands (others). Perf 14½

1901	**1226**	19p. cream, bistre-brown and black	40	40	☐ ☐
1902	**1227**	25p. multicoloured	50	50	☐ ☐
1903	**1228**	41p. multicoloured	65	70	☐ ☐
1904	**1229**	60p. multicoloured	75	80	☐ ☐
Set of 4			2·00	2·25	☐ ☐
First Day Cover				2·40	☐
Presentation Pack (PO Pack No. 264)			2·40		☐
PHQ Cards (*set of 4*) (176)			80	2·40	☐ ☐
Set of 4 Gutter Pairs			4·00		☐

1230 'MORE! LOVE' (Mel Calman)

1231 'Sincerely' (Charles Barsotti)

1232 'Do you have something for the HUMAN CONDITION?' (Mel Calman)

1233 'MENTAL FLOSS' (Leo Cullum)

1234 '4.55 P.M.' (Charles Barsotti)

1235 'Dear lottery prize winner' (Larry)

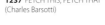

1236 'I'm writing to you because...' (Mel Calman)

1237 'FETCH THIS, FETCH THAT' (Charles Barsotti)

1238 'My day starts before I'm ready for it' (Mel Calman)

1239 'THE CHEQUE IN THE POST' (Jack Ziegler)

Greetings (9th series) Cartoons. Booklet Stamps

1996 (26 Feb.–11 Nov.) '2' phosphor. Perf 14½ × 14 (with one elliptical hole in each vertical side)

1905	**1230**	(1st) black and bright mauve	1·00	50	
		a. Booklet pane. Nos. 1905/1914	9·00	9·00	
		p. Two phosphor bands	1·00	1·00	
		pa. Booklet pane. Nos. 1905p/1914p *(11.11.96)*	24·00	25·00	
1906	**1231**	(1st) black and blue-green	1·00	50	
		p. Two phosphor bands	1·00	1·00	
1907	**1232**	(1st) black and new blue	1·00	50	
		p. Two phosphor bands	1·00	1·00	
1908	**1233**	(1st) black and bright violet	1·00	50	
		p. Two phosphor bands	1·00	1·00	
1909	**1234**	(1st) black and vermilion	1·00	50	
		p. Two phosphor bands	1·00	1·00	
1910	**1235**	(1st) black and new blue	1·00	50	
		p. Two phosphor bands	1·00	1·00	
1911	**1236**	(1st) black and vermilion	1·00	50	
		p. Two phosphor bands	1·00	1·00	
1912	**1237**	(1st) black and bright violet	1·00	50	
		p. Two phosphor bands	1·00	1·00	
1913	**1238**	(1st) black and blue-green	1·00	50	
		p. Two phosphor bands	1·00	1·00	
1914	**1239**	(1st) black and bright mauve	1·00	50	
		p. Two phosphor bands	1·00	1·00	
Set of 10 (Nos. 1905/1914)			9·00	9·00	
Set of 10 (Nos. 1905p/1914p)			24·00	25·00	
First Day Cover (Nos. 1905/1914)				9·50	
Presentation Pack (Nos. 1905/1914) (PO Pack No. G5)			10·00		
PHQ Cards (*set of 10*) (GS4)			2·00	9·50	

Nos. 1905/1914 were printed together, *se-tenant*, in booklet panes of ten stamps and 20 half stamp-size labels.

Nos. 1905/1914 were re-issued on 18 December 2001 in sheets of ten, each stamp with a *se-tenant* label showing cartoon titles. They were again issued on 29 July 2003 in sheets of 20 containing two of each design, each stamp accompanied by a half stamp size label showing a crossword grid or personal photograph. Such sheets are perforated without elliptical holes.

> **SET PRICES.** Please note that set prices for booklet greetings stamps are for complete panes. Sets of single stamps are worth considerably less.

1240 'Muscovy Duck'

1241 'Lapwing'

1242 'White-fronted Goose'

1243 'Bittern'

1244 'Whooper Swan'

50th Anniversary of the Wildfowl and Wetlands Trust. Bird Paintings by C. F. Tunnicliffe

1996 (12 Mar.) One phosphor band (19p.) or phosphorised paper (others). Perf 14 × 14½

1915	**1240**	19p. multicoloured	30	30	
1916	**1241**	25p. multicoloured	35	35	
1917	**1242**	30p. multicoloured	45	45	
1918	**1243**	35p. multicoloured	55	55	
1919	**1244**	41p. multicoloured	65	65	
Set of 5			2·10	2·10	
First Day Cover				2·40	
Presentation Pack (PO Pack No. 265)			2·50		
PHQ Cards (*set of 5*) (177)			1·00	2·40	
Set of 5 Gutter Pairs			4·25		

1245 The Odeon, Harrogate

1246 Laurence Olivier and Vivien Leigh in *Lady Hamilton* (film)

1247 Old Cinema Ticket

1248 Pathé News Still

1249 Cinema Sign,
The Odeon, Manchester

Centenary of Cinema

1996 (16 Apr.) One phosphor band (19p.) or two phosphor bands (others). Perf 14×14½

1920	**1245**	19p. multicoloured	30	30	☐☐
1921	**1246**	25p. multicoloured	35	35	☐☐
1922	**1247**	30p. multicoloured	45	45	☐☐
1923	**1248**	35p. black, red and silver	60	60	☐☐
1924	**1249**	41p. multicoloured	70	70	☐☐
Set of 5			2·25	2·25	☐☐
First Day Cover				2·40	☐
Presentation Pack (PO Pack No. 266)			2·50		☐
PHQ Cards (*set of* 5) (178)			1·00	2·40	☐☐
Set of 5 Gutter Pairs			4·50		☐

1250 Dixie Dean

1251 Bobby Moore

1252 Duncan Edwards

1253 Billy Wright

1254 Danny Blanchflower

European Football Championship

1996 (14 May) One phosphor band (19p.) or two phosphor bands (others). Perf 14½×14

1925	**1250**	19p. multicoloured	30	30	☐☐
1926	**1251**	25p. multicoloured	40	40	☐☐

1927	**1252**	35p. multicoloured	50	50	☐☐
1928	**1253**	41p. multicoloured	60	60	☐☐
1929	**1254**	60p. multicoloured	90	90	☐☐
Set of 5			2·50	2·50	☐☐
First Day Cover				2·75	☐
Presentation Pack (PO Pack No. 267)			2·75		☐
PHQ Cards (*set of* 5) (179)			1·00	2·75	☐☐
Set of 5 Gutter Pairs			5·00		☐

1255 Athlete on Starting Blocks

1256 Throwing the Javelin

1257 Basketball

1258 Swimming

1259 Athlete celebrating and
Olympic Rings

Olympic and Paralympic Games, Atlanta

1996 (9 July) Two phosphor bands. Perf 14½×14

1930	**1255**	26p. multicoloured	30	30	☐☐
		a. Horiz strip of 5.			
		Nos. 1930/1934	2·00	2·10	☐☐
1931	**1256**	26p. multicoloured	30	30	☐☐
1932	**1257**	26p. multicoloured	30	30	☐☐
1933	**1258**	26p. multicoloured	30	30	☐☐
1934	**1259**	26p. multicoloured	30	30	☐☐
Set of 5			2·00	2·10	☐☐
First Day Cover				2·50	☐
Presentation Pack (PO Pack No. 268)			2·50		☐
PHQ Cards (*set of* 5) (180)			1·00	2·50	☐☐
Gutter Strip of 10			4·00		☐

Nos. 1930/1934 were printed together, *se-tenant*, in horizontal strips of five throughout the sheet.

For these designs with the face value expressed as '1st' see No. **MS**2554.

1260 Professor Dorothy
Hodgkin (scientist)

1261 Dame Margot
Fonteyn (ballerina)

1262 Dame Elisabeth Frink (sculptress)

1263 Dame Daphne du Maurier (novelist)

1264 Dame Marea Hartman (sports administrator)

Europa. Famous Women

1996 (6 Aug.) One phosphor band (20p.) or two phosphor bands (others). Perf 14½

1935	**1260**	20p. dull blue-green, brownish grey and black	30	30	☐	☐
1936	**1261**	26p. dull mauve, brownish grey and black	35	35	☐	☐
1937	**1262**	31p. bronze, brownish grey and black	50	50	☐	☐
1938	**1263**	37p. silver, brownish grey and black	60	60	☐	☐
1939	**1264**	43p. gold, brownish grey and black	70	70	☐	☐
Set of 5			2·25	2·25	☐	
First Day Cover				2·50	☐	
Presentation Pack (PO Pack No. 269)			2·75		☐	
PHQ Cards (set of 5) (181)			1·00	2·50	☐	☐
Set of 5 Gutter Pairs			4·50		☐	

Nos. 1936/1937 include the EUROPA emblem.

1265 Muffin the Mule

1266 Sooty

1267 Stingray

1268 The Clangers

1269 Dangermouse

50th Anniversary of Children's Television

1996 (3 Sept.)–**97** One phosphor band (20p.) or two phosphor bands (others). Perf 14½ × 14

1940	**1265**	20p. multicoloured	30	30	☐	☐
		a. Perf 15 × 14				
		(23.9.97)	65	65	☐	☐
1941	**1266**	26p. multicoloured	35	35	☐	☐
1942	**1267**	31p. multicoloured	50	50	☐	☐
1943	**1268**	37p. multicoloured	60	60	☐	☐
1944	**1269**	43p. multicoloured	70	70	☐	☐
Set of 5			2·25	2·25	☐	
First Day Cover				2·75	☐	
Presentation Pack (PO Pack No. 270)			3·00		☐	
PHQ Cards (set of 5) (182)			1·00	2·75	☐	☐
Set of 5 Gutter Pairs			4·50		☐	

No. 1940a was only issued in the £6·15 Celebrating 75 years of the BBC stamp booklet, No. DX19.

1270 Triumph TR3

1271 MG TD

1272 Austin-Healey 100

1273 Jaguar XK120

1274 Morgan Plus 4

Classic Sports Cars

1996 (1 Oct.) One phosphor band (20p.) or two phosphor bands (others). Perf 14½

1945	**1270**	20p. multicoloured	30	30	☐	☐
1946	**1271**	26p. multicoloured	50	50	☐	☐
1947	**1272**	37p. multicoloured	60	65	☐	☐
1948	**1273**	43p. multicoloured	70	75	☐	☐
1949	**1274**	63p. multicoloured	90	95	☐	☐
Set of 5			2·75	3·00	☐	
First Day Cover				3·25	☐	
Presentation Pack (PO Pack No. 271)			3·00		☐	
PHQ Cards (set of 5) (183)			1·00	3·25	☐	☐
Set of 5 Gutter Pairs			5·50		☐	

1275 The Three Kings

1276 The Annunciation

1277 The Journey to
Bethlehem

1278 The Nativity

1279 The Shepherds

Christmas. Biblical Scenes

1996 (28 Oct.) One phosphor band (2nd) or two phosphor
bands (others)

1950	**1275**	(2nd) multicoloured	60	35
1951	**1276**	(1st) multicoloured	70	55
1952	**1277**	31p. multicoloured	50	65
1953	**1278**	43p. multicoloured	50	75
1954	**1279**	63p. multicoloured	70	95
Set of 5			2·75	3·00
First Day Cover				3·25
Presentation Pack (PO Pack No. 272)			3·25	
PHQ Cards (*set of* 5) (184)			1·00	3·25
Set of 5 Gutter Pairs			5·50	

Year Pack 1996

1996 (28 Oct.) Comprises Nos. 1901/1954

CP1954*a*	Year Pack	27·00	

Post Office Yearbook

1996 (28 Oct.) Comprises Nos. 1901/1904 and 1915/1954 in
hardback book with slip case

YB1954*a*	Yearbook	21·00	

1280 *Gentiana acaulis*
(Georg Ehret)

1281 *Magnolia grandiflora* (Ehret)

1282 *Camellia japonica*
(Alfred Chandler)

1283 *Tulipa* (Ehret)

1284 *Fuchsia* 'Princess of
Wales' (Augusta Sowerby)

1285 *Tulipa gesneriana* (Ehret)

1286 *Gazania splendens* (Charlotte
Sowerby)

1287 *Iris latifolia* (Ehret)

1288 *Hippeastrum rutilum* (Pierre-
Joseph Redouté)

1289 *Passiflora coerulea*
(Ehret)

Greetings Stamps (10th series)
19th-century Flower Paintings. Booklet Stamps

1997 (6 Jan.) Two phosphor bands. Perf 14½×14 (with one
elliptical hole in each vertical side)

1955	**1280**	(1st) multicoloured	1·00	50
		a. Booklet pane.		
		Nos. 1955/1964	9·00	9·00
1956	**1281**	(1st) multicoloured	1·00	50
1957	**1282**	(1st) multicoloured	1·00	50
1958	**1283**	(1st) multicoloured	1·00	50
1959	**1284**	(1st) multicoloured	1·00	50
1960	**1285**	(1st) multicoloured	1·00	50
1961	**1286**	(1st) multicoloured	1·00	50
1962	**1287**	(1st) multicoloured	1·00	50
1963	**1288**	(1st) multicoloured	1·00	50
1964	**1289**	(1st) multicoloured	1·00	50
Set of 10			9·00	9·00
First Day Cover				9·50
Presentation Pack (PO Pack No. G6)			10·00	
PHQ Cards (*set of* 10) (GS5)			2·00	9·50

Nos. 1955/1964 were printed together, *se-tenant*, in booklet
panes of ten stamps and 20 half stamp-size labels.

Nos. 1955/1964 were re-issued on 21 January 2003 in *se-
tenant* sheets of 20, each accompanied by a label showing
flowers or personal photograph. Such sheets are perforated
without elliptical holes.

For Types **1280**, **1283** and **1287** perf 15×14 see Nos.
2463/2465.

For Types **1283** and **1287** printed in photogravure and perf
14, see Nos. 2942/2943.

1290 King Henry VIII

1291 Catherine of Aragon   **1292** Anne Boleyn   **1293** Jane Seymour

1294 Anne of Cleves   **1295** Catherine Howard   **1296** Catherine Parr

450th Death Anniversary of King Henry VIII

1997 (21 Jan.) Two phosphor bands. Perf 15 (No. 1965) or 14×15 (others)

1965	**1290**	26p. multicoloured	50	50		
1966	**1291**	26p. multicoloured	50	50		
		a. Horiz strip of 6. Nos. 1966/1971	3·00	3·00		
1967	**1292**	26p. multicoloured	50	50		
1968	**1293**	26p. multicoloured	50	50		
1969	**1294**	26p. multicoloured	50	50		
1970	**1295**	26p. multicoloured	50	50		
1971	**1296**	26p. multicoloured	50	50		
Set of 7			3·25	3·25		
First Day Cover				3·75		
Presentation Pack (PO Pack No. 274)			4·75			
PHQ Cards (*set of 7*) (185)			1·40	3·75		
Gutter Pair and *Gutter Block of* 12			6·50			

Nos. 1966/1971 were printed together, *se-tenant*, in horizontal strips of six throughout the sheet.

1297 St Columba in Boat

1298 St Columba on Iona

1299 St Augustine with King Ethelbert

1300 St Augustine with Model of Cathedral

Religious Anniversaries

1997 (11 Mar.) Two phosphor bands. Perf 14½

1972	**1297**	26p. multicoloured	40	40		
1973	**1298**	37p. multicoloured	60	60		
1974	**1299**	43p. multicoloured	80	85		
1975	**1300**	63p. multicoloured	90	95		
Set of 4			2·50	2·50		
First Day Cover				3·00		
Presentation Pack (PO Pack No. 275)			3·25			
PHQ Cards (*set of 4*) (186)			80	3·00		
Set of 4 Gutter Pairs			5·00			

Nos. 1972/1973 commemorate the 1400th death anniversary of St Columba and Nos. 1974/1975 the 1400th anniversary of the arrival of St Augustine of Canterbury in Kent.

For Nos. 1976/1977, Types **1301/1302** see Decimal Machin Definitives section.

Nos. 1978/1979 are vacant.

Dracula
1303 Dracula

Frankenstein
1304 Frankenstein

Dr Jekyll and Mr Hyde
1305 Dr Jekyll and Mr Hyde

The Hound of the Baskervilles
1306 The Hound of the Baskervilles

Europa. Tales and Legends. Horror Stories

1997 (13 May) Two phosphor bands. Perf 14×15

1980	**1303**	26p. multicoloured	40	40		
1981	**1304**	31p. multicoloured	55	60		
1982	**1305**	37p. multicoloured	70	75		
1983	**1306**	43p. multicoloured	80	85		
Set of 4			2·25	2·40		
First Day Cover				2·75		
Presentation Pack (PO Pack No. 276)			3·00			
PHQ Cards (*set of 4*) (187)			80	2·75		
Set of 4 Gutter Pairs			4·50			

Nos. 1980/1983 commemorate the birth bicentenary of Mary Shelley (creator of Frankenstein) with the 26p. and 31p. values incorporating the EUROPA emblem.

1307 Reginald Mitchell and Supermarine Spitfire IIA

1308 Roy Chadwick and Avro Lancaster I

1309 Ronald Bishop and de Havilland Mosquito B XVI

1310 George Carter and Gloster Meteor T7

1311 Sir Sidney Camm and Hawker Hunter FGA9

British Aircraft Designers

1997 (10 June) One phosphor band (20p.) or two phosphor bands (others)

1984	**1307**	20p. multicoloured	40	40
1985	**1308**	26p. multicoloured	50	50
1986	**1309**	37p. multicoloured	60	60
1987	**1310**	43p. multicoloured	80	80
1988	**1311**	63p. multicoloured	90	90
Set of 5			3·00	3·00
First Day Cover				3·25
Presentation Pack (PO Pack No. 277)			3·50	
PHQ Cards (set of 5) (188)			1·00	3·25
Set of 5 Gutter Pairs			6·00	

For T **1307** printed in lithography and perf 14, see No. 2868.

1312 Carriage Horse and Coachman

1313 Lifeguards Horse and Trooper

1314 Household Cavalry Drum Horse and Drummer

1315 Duke of Edinburgh's Horse and Groom

50th Anniversary of the British Horse Society All The Queen's Horses.

1997 (8 July) One phosphor band (20p.) or two phosphor bands (others). Perf 14½

1989	**1312**	20p. multicoloured	40	40
1990	**1313**	26p. multicoloured	55	60
1991	**1314**	43p. multicoloured	70	75
1992	**1315**	63p. multicoloured	85	85
Set of 4			2·25	2·50

First Day Cover		2·75
Presentation Pack (PO Pack No. 278)	3·00	
PHQ Cards (set of 4) (189)	80	2·75
Set of 4 Gutter Pairs	4·50	

1315a Caernarfon Castle

CASTLE
Harrison printing (Nos. 1611/1614)

CASTLE
Enschedé printing (Nos. 1993/1996)

Differences between Harrison and Enschedé printings:

Harrison – 'C' has top serif and tail of letter points to right. 'A' has flat top. 'S' has top and bottom serifs.

Enschedé – 'C' has no top serif and tail of letter points upwards. 'A' has pointed top. 'S' has no serifs.

1997 (29 July) Designs as Nos. 1611/1614 with Queen's head in silhouette as T **1044**, but re-engraved as above. Perf 15 × 14 (with one elliptical hole in each vertical side)

1993	**1315a**	£1·50 deep claret and gold†	12·00	6·00
1994	**1315b**	£2 indigo and gold†	14·00	2·25
1995	**1315c**	£3 violet and gold†	30·00	3·50
1996	**1315d**	£5 deep brown and gold†	35·00	10·00
Set of 4			80·00	18·00
Presentation Pack (PO Pack No. 40)		£150	
Set of 4 Gutter Pairs		£175	

† The Queen's head on these stamps is printed in optically variable ink which changes colour from gold to green when viewed from different angles.

There was no official Royal Mail first day cover service provided for Nos. 1993/1996.

See also Nos. 1410/1413 and 1611/1614.

1316 Haroldswick, Shetland

1317 Painswick, Gloucestershire

1318 Beddgelert, Gwynedd

1319 Ballyroney, County Down

Sub-Post Offices

1997 (12 Aug.) One phosphor band (20p.) or two phosphor bands (others). Perf 14½

1997	**1316**	20p. multicoloured	40	40	☐ ☐
1998	**1317**	26p. multicoloured	55	60	☐ ☐
1999	**1318**	43p. multicoloured	70	75	☐ ☐
2000	**1319**	63p. multicoloured	85	85	☐ ☐
Set of 4			2·25	2·40	☐ ☐
First Day Cover				2·75	☐
Presentation Pack (PO Pack No. 279)			3·00		☐
PHQ Cards (*set of 4*) (190)			80	2·75	☐ ☐
Set of 4 Gutter Pairs			4·50		☐

Nos. 1997/2000 also mark the centenary of the National Federation of Sub-Postmasters.

Enid Blyton's *Noddy*
1320 *Noddy*

Enid Blyton's *Famous Five*
1321 *Famous Five*

Enid Blyton's *Secret Seven*
1322 *Secret Seven*

Enid Blyton's *Faraway Tree*
1323 *Faraway Tree*

Enid Blyton's *Malory Towers*
1324 *Malory Towers*

Birth Centenary of Enid Blyton (children's author)

1997 (9 Sept.) One phosphor band (20p.) or two phosphor bands (others). Perf 14 × 14½

2001	**1320**	20p. multicoloured	30	30	☐ ☐
2002	**1321**	26p. multicoloured	50	50	☐ ☐
2003	**1322**	37p. multicoloured	55	60	☐ ☐
2004	**1323**	43p. multicoloured	65	70	☐ ☐
2005	**1324**	63p. multicoloured	75	80	☐ ☐
Set of 5			2·50	2·75	☐ ☐
First Day Cover				3·00	☐
Presentation Pack (PO Pack No. 280)			3·00		☐
PHQ Cards (*set of 5*) (191)			1·00	3·00	☐ ☐
Set of 5 Gutter Pairs			5·00		☐

1325 Children and Father Christmas pulling Cracker

1326 Father Christmas with Traditional Cracker

1327 Father Christmas riding Cracker

1328 Father Christmas on Snowball

1329 Father Christmas and Chimney

Christmas. 150th Anniversary of the Christmas Cracker

1997 (27 Oct.) One phosphor band (2nd) or two phosphor bands (others)

2006	**1325**	(2nd) multicoloured	90	35	☐ ☐
2007	**1326**	(1st) multicoloured	1·00	55	☐ ☐
2008	**1327**	31p. multicoloured	50	60	☐ ☐
2009	**1328**	43p. multicoloured	50	70	☐ ☐
2010	**1329**	63p. multicoloured	70	80	☐ ☐
Set of 5			3·25	2·75	☐ ☐
First Day Cover				3·00	☐
Presentation Pack (PO Pack No. 282)			4·00		☐
PHQ Cards (*set of 5*) (192)			1·00	3·00	☐ ☐
Set of 5 Gutter Pairs			6·50		☐

The 1st value was re-issued on 3 October 2000 and 9 October 2001, in sheets of ten in photogravure, each stamp with a *se-tenant* label, in connection with 'customised' service available from the Philatelic Bureau. On 1 October 2002 in sheet size of 20 in lithography the 1st value was again issued but perforated 14½ × 14. The labels show either Christmas greetings or a personal photograph.

1330 Wedding Photograph, 1947

1331 Queen Elizabeth II and Prince Philip, 1997

Royal Golden Wedding

1997 (13 Nov.) One phosphor band (20p.) or two phosphor bands (others). Perf 15

2011	**1330**	20p. gold, yellow-brown and grey-black	40	40	☐ ☐
2012	**1331**	26p. multicoloured	60	60	☐ ☐
2013	**1330**	43p. gold, bluish green and grey-black	1·10	1·10	☐ ☐

2014 **1331**	63p. multicoloured	1·50	1·50	☐ ☐
Set of 4		3·25	3·25	☐ ☐
First Day Cover			3·50	☐
Presentation Pack (PO Pack No. 281)		3·75		☐
Souvenir Book (contains Nos. 1668, 1989/1992 and 2011/2014)		22·00		☐
PHQ Cards (*set of 4*) (192)		80	3·50	☐ ☐
Set of 4 Gutter Pairs		6·50		☐

Year Pack 1997

1997 (13 Nov.) Comprises Nos. 1965/1975, 1980/1992 and 1997/2014

CP2014*a* Year Pack		32·00	☐

Post Office Yearbook

1997 (13 Nov.) Comprises Nos. 1965/1975, 1980/1992 and 1997/2014 in hardback book with slip case

YB2014*a* Yearbook		26·00	☐

20 ENDANGERED SPECIES
Common dormouse
Muscardinus avellanarius
1332 Common Doormouse

26 ENDANGERED SPECIES
Lady's slipper orchid
Cypripedium calceolus
1333 Lady's Slipper Orchid

31 ENDANGERED SPECIES
Song thrush
Turdus philomelos
1334 Song Thrush

37 ENDANGERED SPECIES
Shining ram's-horn snail
Segmentina nitida
1335 Shining Ram's-horn Snail

43 ENDANGERED SPECIES
Mole cricket
Gryllotalpa gryllotalpa
1336 Mole Cricket

63 ENDANGERED SPECIES
Devil's bolete
Boletus satanas
1337 Devil's Bolete

Endangered Species

1998 (20 Jan.) One side phosphor band (20p.) or two phosphor bands (others). Perf 14 × 14½

2015 **1332**	20p. multicoloured	40	40	☐ ☐
2016 **1333**	26p. multicoloured	50	50	☐ ☐
2017 **1334**	31p. multicoloured	60	60	☐ ☐
2018 **1335**	37p. multicoloured	70	70	☐ ☐
2019 **1336**	43p. multicoloured	85	85	☐ ☐
2020 **1337**	63p. multicoloured	1·00	1·00	☐ ☐
Set of 6		3·75	3·75	☐ ☐
First Day Cover			4·00	☐
Presentation Pack (PO Pack No. 284)		4·25		☐
PHQ Cards (*Set of 6*) (194)		1·25	4·00	☐ ☐
Set of 6 Gutter Pairs		7·50		☐

1338 Diana, Princess of Wales (photo by Lord Snowdon)

1339 At British Lung Foundation Function, April 1997 (photo by John Stillwell)

1340 Wearing Tiara, 1991 (photo by Lord Snowdon)

1341 On Visit to Birmingham, October 1995 (photo by Tim Graham)

1342 In Evening Dress, 1987 (photo by Terence Donovan)

Diana, Princess of Wales Commemoration

1998 (3 Feb.) Two phosphor bands

2021 **1338**	26p. multicoloured	50	30	☐ ☐
	a. Horiz strip of 5. Nos. 2021/2025	2·00	2·00	☐ ☐
2022 **1339**	26p. multicoloured	50	30	☐ ☐
2023 **1340**	26p. multicoloured	50	30	☐ ☐
2024 **1341**	26p. multicoloured	50	30	☐ ☐
2025 **1342**	26p. multicoloured	50	30	☐ ☐
Set of 5		2·00	2·00	☐ ☐
First Day Cover			3·00	☐
Presentation Pack (Unnumbered)		8·00		☐
Presentation Pack (Welsh)		60·00		☐
Gutter Strip of 10		4·00		☐

Nos. 2021/2025 were printed together, *se-tenant*, in horizontal strips of five throughout the sheet.

1343 Lion of England and Griffin of Edward III

1344 Falcon of Plantagenet and Bull of Clarence

1345 Lion of Mortimer and Yale of Beaufort

1346 Greyhound of Richmond and Dragon of Wales

1347 Unicorn of Scotland and Horse of Hanover

650th Anniversary of the Order of the Garter. The Queen's Beasts

1998 (24 Feb.) Two phosphor bands

2026	**1343**	26p. multicoloured	50	30	☐	☐
		a. Horiz strip of 5.				
		Nos. 2026/2030	2·25	2·25	☐	☐
2027	**1344**	26p. multicoloured	50	30	☐	☐
2028	**1345**	26p. multicoloured	50	30	☐	☐
2029	**1346**	26p. multicoloured	50	30	☐	☐
2030	**1347**	26p. multicoloured	50	30	☐	☐
Set of 5			2·25	2·25	☐	
First Day Cover				2·75	☐	
Presentation Pack (PO Pack No. 285)			2·50		☐	
PHQ Cards (set of 5) (195)			1·00	2·75	☐	☐
Gutter Block of 10			4·50		☐	

Nos. 2026/2030 were printed together, *se-tenant*, in horizontal strips of five throughout the sheet.

The phosphor bands on Nos. 2026/2030 are only half the height of the stamps and do not cover the silver parts of the designs.

1348

Wilding definitives. The Definitive Portrait. Booklet Stamps

1998 (10 Mar.) Design as T **157** (issued 1952–1954), but with face values in decimal currency as T **1348**. One side phosphor band (20p.) or two phosphor bands (others). Perf 14 (with one elliptical hole in each vertical side)

2031	**1348**	20p. light green	40	40	☐	☐
2032		26p. red-brown	50	50	☐	☐
2033		37p. light purple	1·10	1·10	☐	☐
Set of 3			1·90	1·90	☐	☐
First Day Cover				4·75	☐	

Nos. 2031/2033 were only issued in the £7·49 The Definitive Portrait booklet, No. DX20.

For further Wilding designs in decimal currency see Nos. 2258/2259, **MS**2326, **MS**2367, 2378/2380 and 3329.

1349 St John's Point Lighthouse, County Down

1350 Smalls Lighthouse, Pembrokeshire

1351 Needles Rock Lighthouse, Isle of Wight, *c* 1900

1352 Bell Rock Lighthouse, Arbroath, mid 19th-century

1353 Eddystone Lighthouse, Plymouth, 1698

Lighthouses

1998 (24 Mar.) One side phosphor band (20p.) or two phosphor bands (others). Perf 14½ × 14

2034	**1349**	20p. multicoloured	40	40	☐	☐
2035	**1350**	26p. multicoloured	50	50	☐	☐
2036	**1351**	37p. multicoloured	60	60	☐	☐
2037	**1352**	43p. multicoloured	80	80	☐	☐
2038	**1353**	63p. multicoloured	90	90	☐	☐
Set of 5			3·00	3·00	☐	☐
First Day Cover				3·25	☐	
Presentation Pack (PO Pack No. 286)			3·50		☐	
PHQ Cards (set of 5) (196)			1·00	3·25	☐	☐
Set of 5 Gutter Pairs			6·00		☐	

Nos. 2034/2038 commemorate the 300th anniversary of the first Eddystone Lighthouse and the final year of manned lighthouses.

For Nos. 2039/2040 see Decimal Machin Definitives section

1354 Tommy Cooper

1355 Eric Morecambe

1356 Joyce Grenfell

1357 Les Dawson

1358 Peter Cook

Comedians

1998 (23 Apr.) One phosphor band (20p.) or two phosphor bands (others). Perf 14½ × 14

2041	**1354**	20p. multicoloured	40	40	☐ ☐
2042	**1355**	26p. multicoloured	50	50	☐ ☐
2043	**1356**	37p. multicoloured	60	60	☐ ☐
2044	**1357**	43p. multicoloured	80	80	☐ ☐
2045	**1358**	63p. multicoloured	90	90	☐ ☐
Set of 5			3·00	3·00	☐ ☐
First Day Cover				3·25	☐
Presentation Pack (PO Pack No. 287)			3·50		☐
PHQ Cards (*set of 5*) (197)			1·00	3·25	☐ ☐
Set of 5 Gutter Pairs			6·00		☐

1359 Hands forming Heart

1360 Adult and Child holding Hands

1361 Hands forming Cradle

1362 Hands taking Pulse

50th Anniversary of National Health Service

1998 (23 June) One side phosphor band (20p.) or two phosphor bands (others). Perf 14 × 14½

2046	**1359**	20p. multicoloured	40	40	☐ ☐
2047	**1360**	26p. multicoloured	50	50	☐ ☐
2048	**1361**	43p. multicoloured	80	80	☐ ☐
2049	**1362**	63p. multicoloured	90	90	☐ ☐
Set of 4			2·25	2·25	☐ ☐
First Day Cover				2·75	☐
Presentation Pack (PO Pack No. 288)			2·75		☐
PHQ Cards (*set of 4*) (198)			80	2·75	☐ ☐
Set of 4 Gutter Pairs			4·50		☐

1363 *The Hobbit* (J. R. R. Tolkien)

1364 *The Lion, The Witch and the Wardrobe* (C. S. Lewis)

1365 *The Phoenix and the Carpet* (E. Nesbit)

1366 *The Borrowers* (Mary Norton)

1367 *Through the Looking Glass* (Lewis Carroll)

Famous Children's Fantasy Novels

1998 (21 July) One phosphor band (20p.) or two phosphor bands (others)

2050	**1363**	20p. multicoloured	35	35	☐ ☐
2051	**1364**	26p. multicoloured	45	45	☐ ☐
2052	**1365**	37p. multicoloured	60	60	☐ ☐
2053	**1366**	43p. multicoloured	80	80	☐ ☐
2054	**1367**	63p. multicoloured	90	90	☐ ☐
Set of 5			3·00	3·00	☐ ☐
First Day Cover				3·25	☐
Presentation Pack (PO Pack No. 289)			3·25		☐
PHQ Cards (*set of 5*) (199)			1·00	3·25	☐ ☐
Set of 5 Gutter Pairs			6·00		☐

Nos. 2050/2054 commemorate the birth centenary of C. S. Lewis and the death centenary of Lewis Carroll.

1368 Woman in Yellow Feathered Costume

1369 Woman in Blue Costume and Headdress

1370 Group of Children in White and Gold Robes

1371 Child in 'Tree' Costume

Europa. Festivals. Notting Hill Carnival

1998 (25 Aug.) One centre phosphor band (20p.) or two phosphor bands (others). Perf 14 × 14½

2055	**1368**	20p. multicoloured	40	40	☐ ☐
2056	**1369**	26p. multicoloured	60	60	☐ ☐
2057	**1370**	43p. multicoloured	75	75	☐ ☐
2058	**1371**	63p. multicoloured	1·00	1·00	☐ ☐
Set of 4			2·50	2·50	☐ ☐
First Day Cover				3·00	☐
Presentation Pack (PO Pack No. 290)			2·75		☐
PHQ Cards (*set of 4*) (200)			80	3·00	☐ ☐
Set of 4 Gutter Pairs			5·00		☐

Nos. 2055/2056 include the EUROPA emblem.

1372 Sir Malcolm Campbell's Bluebird, 1925

1373 Sir Henry Segrave's Sunbeam, 1926

1374 John G. Parry Thomas's Babs, 1926

1375 John R. Cobb's Railton Mobil Special, 1947

1376 Donald Campbell's Bluebird CN7, 1964

British Land Speed Record Holders

1998 (29 Sept.–13 Oct.) One phosphor band (20p.) or two phosphor bands (others). Perf 15 × 14

2059	**1372**	20p. multicoloured (centre band)	30	30	☐ ☐
		a. Perf 14½ × 13½ (side band) *(13.10.98)*	75	75	☐ ☐
2060	**1373**	26p. multicoloured	40	40	☐ ☐
2061	**1374**	30p. multicoloured	60	60	☐ ☐
2062	**1375**	43p. multicoloured	80	80	☐ ☐
2063	**1376**	63p. multicoloured	90	90	☐ ☐
Set of 5			2·75	2·75	☐ ☐
First Day Cover				3·00	☐
Presentation Pack (PO Pack No. 291)			3·25		☐
PHQ Cards (*set of 5*) (201)			1·00	3·00	☐ ☐
Set of 5 Gutter Pairs			5·50		☐

No. 2059a, which occurs with the phosphor band at the left or right of the stamp, was only issued in the £6·16 Breaking Barriers booklet, No. DX21. There are minor differences of design between No. 2059 and No. 2059a, which also omits the copyright symbol and date.

Nos. 2059/2063 commemorate the 50th death anniversary of Sir Malcolm Campbell.

1377 Angel with Hands raised in Blessing

1378 Angel praying

1379 Angel playing Flute

1380 Angel playing Lute

1381 Angel praying

Christmas. Angels

1998 (2 Nov.) One phosphor band (20p.) or two phosphor bands (others)

2064	**1377**	20p. multicoloured	35	35	☐ ☐
2065	**1378**	26p. multicoloured	45	45	☐ ☐
2066	**1379**	30p. multicoloured	60	60	☐ ☐
2067	**1380**	43p. multicoloured	80	80	☐ ☐
2068	**1381**	63p. multicoloured	90	90	☐ ☐
Set of 5			2·75	2·75	☐ ☐
First Day Cover				3·00	☐
Presentation Pack (PO Pack No. 292)			3·25		☐
PHQ Cards (*set of 5*) (202)			1·00	3·00	☐ ☐
Set of 5 Gutter Pairs			5·50		☐

Year Pack 1998

1998 (2 Nov.) Comprises Nos. 2015/2030, 2034/2038 and 2041/2068

CP2068*a*	Year Pack	40·00	☐

Post Office Yearbook

1998 (2 Nov.) Comprises Nos. 2015/2030, 2034/2038 and 2041/2068 in hardback book with slip case

YB2068*a*	Yearbook	35·00	☐

1382 Greenwich Meridian and Clock (John Harrison's Chronometer)

1383 Industrial Worker and Blast Furnace (James Watt's discovery of steam power)

1384 Early Photos of Leaves (Henry Fox-Talbot's photographic experiments)

1385 Computer inside Human Head (Alan Turing's work on computers)

Millennium Series. The Inventors' Tale

1999 (12 Jan.–21 Sept.) One centre phosphor band (20p.) or two phosphor bands (others). Perf 14 × 14½

2069	**1382**	20p. multicoloured	40	40	☐ ☐
2070	**1383**	26p. multicoloured	60	60	☐ ☐
2071	**1384**	43p. multicoloured	80	80	☐ ☐
2072	**1385**	63p. multicoloured	1·00	1·00	☐ ☐
		a. Perf 13½ × 14 *(21.9.99.)*	1·75	1·75	☐ ☐
Set of 4			2·50	2·50	☐ ☐
First Day Cover				4·25	☐
Presentation Pack (PO Pack No. 294)			3·25		☐

| PHQ Cards (set of 4) (203) | 80 | 2·75 | ☐ ☐ |
| Set of 4 Gutter Pairs | 5·00 | | ☐ |

No. 2072a was only issued in the £6·99 World Changers booklet, No. DX23.

1386 Airliner hugging Globe (International air travel)

1387 Woman on Bicycle (Development of the bicycle)

1388 Victorian Railway Station (Growth of public transport)

1389 Captain Cook and Maori (Captain James Cook's voyages)

Millennium Series. The Travellers' Tale

1999 (2 Feb.) One centre phosphor band (20p.) or two phosphor bands (others). Perf 14 × 14½

2073	**1386**	20p. multicoloured	40	40	☐ ☐
2074	**1387**	26p. multicoloured	60	60	☐ ☐
2075	**1388**	43p. grey-black, stone and bronze	80	80	☐ ☐
2076	**1389**	63p. multicoloured	1·00	1·00	☐ ☐
Set of 4			2·50	2·50	☐ ☐
First Day Cover				3·25	☐
Presentation Pack (PO Pack No. 295)			3·25		☐
PHQ Cards (set of 4) (204)			80	3·25	☐ ☐
Set of 4 Gutter Pairs			5·00		☐

For Nos. 2077/2079, Type **1390**, see Decimal Machin Definitives section.

1391 Vaccinating Child (pattern in cow markings) (Jenner's development of smallpox vaccine)

1392 Patient on Trolley (nursing care)

1393 Penicillin Mould (Fleming's discovery of Penicillin)

1394 Sculpture of Test-tube Baby (development of in vitro fertilisation)

Millennium Series. The Patients' Tale

1999 (2 Mar.) One centre phosphor band (20p.) or two phosphor bands (others). Perf 13½ × 14

2080	**1391**	20p. multicoloured	40	40	☐ ☐
2081	**1392**	26p. multicoloured	60	60	☐ ☐
2082	**1393**	43p. multicoloured	80	80	☐ ☐
2083	**1394**	63p. multicoloured	1·00	1·00	☐ ☐
Set of 4			2·50	2·50	☐ ☐
First Day Cover				3·25	☐
Presentation Pack (PO Pack No. 296)			3·25		☐
PHQ Cards (set of 4) (205)			80	3·25	☐ ☐
Set of 4 Gutter Pairs			5·00		☐

1395 Dove and Norman Settler (medieval migration to Scotland)

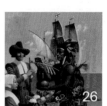

1396 Pilgrim Fathers and Red Indian (17th-century migration to America)

1397 Sailing Ship and Aspects of Settlement (19th-century migration to Australia)

1398 Hummingbird and Superimposed Stylised Face (20th-century migration to Great Britain)

Millennium Series. The Settlers' Tale

1999 (6 Apr.) One centre phosphor band (20p.) or two phosphor bands (others). Perf 14 × 14½

2084	**1395**	20p. multicoloured	40	40	☐ ☐
2085	**1396**	26p. multicoloured	60	60	☐ ☐
2086	**1397**	43p. multicoloured	80	80	☐ ☐
2087	**1398**	63p. multicoloured	1·00	1·00	☐ ☐
Set of 4			2·50	2·50	☐ ☐
First Day Cover				3·25	☐
Presentation Pack (PO Pack No. 297)			3·25		☐
PHQ Cards (set of 4) (206)			80	3·25	☐ ☐
Set of 4 Gutter Pairs			5·00		☐

1399 Woven Threads (woollen industry)

1400 Salts Mill, Saltaire (worsted cloth industry)

1401 Hull on Slipway (shipbuilding)

1402 Lloyd's Building (City of London finance centre)

Millennium Series. The Workers' Tale

1999 (4 May) One centre phosphor band (19p.) or two phosphor bands (others). Perf 14×14½

2088	**1399**	19p. multicoloured	40	40		
2089	**1400**	26p. multicoloured	60	60		
2090	**1401**	44p. multicoloured	80	80		
2091	**1402**	64p. multicoloured	1·00	1·00		
Set of 4			2·50	2·50		
First Day Cover				3·25		
Presentation Pack (PO Pack No. 298)			3·25			
PHQ Cards (set of 4) (207)			80	3·25		
Set of 4 Gutter Pairs			5·00			

1403 Freddie Mercury (lead singer of Queen) (Popular Music)

1404 Bobby Moore with World Cup, 1966 (Sport)

1405 Dalek from *Dr Who* (science-fiction series) (Television)

1406 Charlie Chaplin (film star) (Cinema)

Millennium Series. The Entertainers' Tale

1999 (1 June) One centre phosphor band (19p.) or two phosphor bands (others). Perf 14×14½

2092	**1403**	19p. multicoloured	40	40		
2093	**1404**	26p. multicoloured	60	60		
2094	**1405**	44p. multicoloured	80	80		
2095	**1406**	64p. multicoloured	1·00	1·00		
Set of 4			2·50	2·50		
First Day Cover				3·25		
Presentation Pack (PO Pack No. 299)			3·25			
PHQ Cards (set of 4) (208)			80	3·25		
Set of 4 Gutter Pairs			5·00			

1407 Prince Edward and Miss Sophie Rhys-Jones (from photos by John Swannell)

1408 Prince Edward and Miss Sophie Rhys-Jones (from photos by John Swannell)

Royal Wedding

1999 (15 June) Two phosphor bands

2096	**1407**	26p. multicoloured	40	40		
2097	**1408**	64p. multicoloured	1·25	1·25		
Set of 2			1·30	1·30		
First Day Cover				2·00		
Presentation Pack (PO Pack No. M01)			2·00			
PHQ Cards (set of 2) (PSM1)			40	2·00		
Set of 2 Gutter Pairs			2·50			

1409 Suffragette behind Prison Window ('Equal Rights for Women')

1410 Water Tap ('Right to Health')

1411 Generations of School Children ('Right to Education')

1412 'MAGNA CARTA' ('Human Rights')

Millennium Series. The Citizens' Tale

1999 (6 July) One centre phosphor band (19p.) or two phosphor bands (others). Perf 14×14½

2098	**1409**	19p. multicoloured	40	40		
2099	**1410**	26p. multicoloured	60	60		
2100	**1411**	44p. multicoloured	80	80		
2101	**1412**	64p. multicoloured	1·00	1·00		
Set of 4			2·50	2·50		
First Day Cover				3·25		
Presentation Pack (PO Pack No. 300)			3·25			
PHQ Cards (set of 4) (209)			80	3·25		
Set of 4 Gutter Pairs			5·00			

1413 Molecular Structures (DNA decoding)

1414 Galápagos Finch and Fossilised Skeleton (Darwin's theory of evolution)

1415 Rotation of Polarised Light by Magnetism (Faraday's work on electricity)

1416 Saturn (development of astronomical telescopes)

Millennium Series. The Scientists' Tale

1999 (3 Aug.–21 Sept.) One centre phosphor band (19p.) or two phosphor bands (others). Perf 13½×14 (19p., 64p.) or 14×14½ (26p., 44p.)

2102	**1413**	19p. multicoloured	40	40	☐☐
2103	**1414**	26p. multicoloured	60	60	☐☐
		b. Perf 14½×14			
		(21.9.99)	1·50	1·50	☐☐
2104	**1415**	44p. multicoloured	80	80	☐☐
		a. Perf 14½×14			
		(21.9.99)	1·50	1·50	☐☐
2105	**1416**	64p. multicoloured	1·00	1·00	☐☐
Set of 4			2·50	2·50	☐☐
First Day Cover				3·25	☐
Presentation Pack (PO Pack No. 301)			3·25		☐
PHQ Cards (*set of 4*) (210)			80	3·25	☐☐
Set of 4 Gutter Pairs			5·00		☐

Nos. 2103b and 2104a were only issued in the £6·99 World Changers booklet, No. DX23.

1416a

Solar Eclipse miniature sheet

1999 (11 Aug.) Sheet 89×121 mm. Two phosphor bands. Perf 14×14½

MS2106	**1416a**	64p.×4 multicoloured	11·00	11·00	☐☐
First Day Cover				11·50	☐

1417 Upland Landscape (Strip farming)

1418 Horse-drawn Rotary Seed Drill (Mechanical farming)

1419 Man peeling Potato (Food imports)

1420 Aerial View of Combine-harvester (Satellite agriculture)

Millennium Series. The Farmers' Tale

1999 (7 Sept.) One centre phosphor band (19p.) or two phosphor bands (others). Perf 14×14½

2107	**1417**	19p. multicoloured	40	40	☐☐
2108	**1418**	26p. multicoloured	60	60	☐☐
2109	**1419**	44p. multicoloured	80	80	☐☐
2110	**1420**	64p. multicoloured	1·00	1·00	☐☐
Set of 4			2·50	2·50	☐☐
First Day Cover				3·25	☐
Presentation Pack (PO Pack No. 302)			3·25		☐
PHQ Cards (*set of 4*) (211)			80	3·25	☐☐
Set of 4 Gutter Pairs			5·00		☐

No. 2107 includes the EUROPA emblem.

1421 Robert the Bruce (Battle of Bannockburn, 1314)

1422 Cavalier and Horse (English Civil War)

1423 War Graves Cemetery, The Somme (World Wars)

1424 Soldiers with Boy (Peacekeeping)

Millennium Series. The Soldiers' Tale

1999 (5 Oct.) One centre phosphor band (19p.) or two phosphor bands (others). Perf 14×14½

2111	**1421**	19p. black, stone and silver	40	40	☐☐
2112	**1422**	26p. multicoloured	60	60	☐☐
2113	**1423**	44p. grey-black, black and silver	80	80	☐☐
2114	**1424**	64p. multicoloured	1·00	1·00	☐☐
Set of 4			2·50	2·50	☐☐
First Day Cover				3·25	☐
Presentation Pack (PO Pack No. 303*)			3·25		☐
PHQ Cards (*set of 4*) (212)			80	3·25	☐☐
Set of 4 Gutter Pairs			5·00		☐

* The presentation pack was numbered 302 in error.

1425 *Hark the herald angels sing* and Hymn book (John Wesley)

1426 King James I and Bible (Authorised Version of Bible)

1427 St Andrews Cathedral, Fife (Pilgrimage)

1428 Nativity (First Christmas)

Millennium Series. The Christians' Tale

1999 (2 Nov.) One centre phosphor band (19p.) or two phosphor bands (others). Perf 14 × 14½

2115	**1425**	19p. multicoloured	40	40		
2116	**1426**	26p. multicoloured	60	60		
2117	**1427**	44p. multicoloured	80	80		
2118	**1428**	64p. multicoloured	1·00	1·00		
Set of 4			2·50	2·50		
First Day Cover				3·25		
Presentation Pack (PO Pack No. 304)			3·25			
PHQ Cards (*set of 4*) (213)			80	3·25		
Set of 4 Gutter Pairs			5·00			

1429 'World of the Stage' (Allen Jones)

1430 'World of Music' (Bridget Riley)

1431 'World of Literature' (Lisa Milroy)

1432 'New Worlds' (Sir Howard Hodgkin)

Millennium Series. The Artists' Tale

1999 (7 Dec.) One centre phosphor band (19p.) or two phosphor bands (others). Perf 14 × 14½

2119	**1429**	19p. multicoloured	40	40		
2120	**1430**	26p. multicoloured	60	60		
2121	**1431**	44p. multicoloured	80	80		
2122	**1432**	64p. multicoloured	1·00	1·00		
Set of 4			2·50	2·50		
First Day Cover				3·25		
Presentation Pack (PO Pack No. 305)			3·25			
PHQ Cards (*set of 4*) (214)			80	3·25		
Set of 4 Gutter Pairs			5·00			

Year Pack 1999

1999 (7 Dec.) Comprises Nos. 2069/2076, 2080/2105 and 2107/2122

CP2122*a*	Year Pack	65·00	

Post Office Yearbook

1999 (7 Dec.) Comprises Nos. 2069/2076, 2080/2105 and 2107/2122 in hardback book with slip case

YB2122*a*	Yearbook	50·00	

1433a

Millennium Series. Millennium Timekeeper Miniature Sheet

1999 (14 Dec.) Sheet 120 × 89 mm. Multicoloured. Two phosphor bands. Perf 14 × 14½

MS2123	**1433a**	64p. Clock face and map of North America; 64p. Clock face and map of Asia; 64p. Clock face and map of Middle East; 64p. Clock face and map of Europe	11·00	11·00		
First Day Cover				11·00		
Presentation Pack (PO Pack No. M02)			11·00			
PHQ Cards (*set of* 5) (PSM02)			1·00	11·00		

No. **MS**2123 also exists overprinted 'EARLS COURT, LONDON 22–28 MAY 2000 THE STAMP SHOW 2000' from Exhibition Premium Passes, costing £10, available from 1 March 2000.

The five PHQ cards show the four individual stamps and the complete miniature sheet.

For Nos. 2014/d, Type **1437**, see Decimal Machin Definitives section.

1438 Barn Owl (World Owl Trust, Muncaster)

1439 Night Sky (National Space Science Centre, Leicester)

1440 River Goyt and Textile Mills (Torrs Walkaway, New Mills)

1441 Cape Gannets (Seabird Centre, North Berwick)

Millennium Projects (1st series). Above and Beyond

2000 (18 Jan.–26 May) One centre phosphor band (19p.) or two phosphor bands (others). Perf 14×14½ (1st, 44p.) or 13½×14 (others)

2125	**1438**	19p. multicoloured	40	40	☐ ☐
2126	**1439**	26p. multicoloured	70	70	☐ ☐
2126*a*		(1st) multicoloured			
		(26.5.2000)	2·25	2·25	☐ ☐
2127	**1440**	44p. multicoloured	1·00	1·00	☐ ☐
2128	**1441**	64p. multicoloured	1·25	1·25	☐ ☐
Set of 4 (ex No. 2126*a*)			3·00	3·00	☐ ☐
First Day Cover				4·00	☐
Presentation Pack (PO Pack No. 307)			3·75		☐
PHQ Cards (*set of* 4) (215)			80	3·50	☐ ☐
Set of 4 *Gutter Pairs*			6·00		☐

No. 2126*a* was only issued in the £2·70 Millennium booklet, No. HBA3, and, on 24 Sept 2002 in the £6·83 Across the Universe booklet, No. DX29.

1442 Millennium Beacon (Beacons across the Land)

1443 Garratt Steam Locomotive No. 143 pulling Train (Rheilffordd Eryri, Welsh Highland Railway)

1444 Lightning (Dynamic Earth Centre, Edinburgh)

1445 Multicoloured Lights (Lighting Croydon's Skyline)

Millennium Projects (2nd series). Fire and Light

2000 (1 Feb.) One centre phosphor band (19p.) or two phosphor bands (others). Perf 14×14½

2129	**1442**	19p. multicoloured	40	40	☐ ☐
2130	**1443**	26p. multicoloured	70	70	☐ ☐
2131	**1444**	44p. multicoloured	1·00	1·00	☐ ☐
2132	**1445**	64p. multicoloured	1·25	1·25	☐ ☐
Set of 4			3·00	3·00	☐ ☐
First Day Cover				4·00	☐
Presentation Pack (PO Pack No. 308)			3·75		☐
PHQ Cards (*set of* 4) (216)			1·25	3·50	☐ ☐
Set of 4 *Gutter Pairs*			6·00		☐

1446 Queen Victoria and Queen Elizabeth II

Booklet Stamps

2000 (15 Feb.)–**17** Design T **929**, but redrawn with '1st' face value as T **1446**. Two phosphor bands. Perf 14 (No. 2133) or Perf 14½×14 (both with one elliptical hole in each vertical side)

2133	**1446**	20p. brownish black			
		and cream *(5.6.17)*	1·10	1·10	☐ ☐
2133*a*		(1st) brownish black			
		and cream	1·10	1·10	☐ ☐
First Day Cover (2133*a*)				5·50	☐

No. 2133 comes from the £15·14 50th Anniversary of the Machin Prestige booklet, No. DY21, issued on 5 June 2017.

No. 2133*a* was only issued in the £7·50 Special by Design booklet. See also Nos. 2955/2956

1447 Beach Pebbles (Turning the Tide, Durham Coast)

1448 Frog's Legs and Water Lilies (National Pondlife Centre, Merseyside)

1449 Cliff Boardwalk (Parc Ardfordirol, Llanelli Coast)

1450 Reflections in Water (Portsmouth Harbour Development)

Millennium Projects (3rd series). Water and Coast

2000 (7 Mar.) One centre phosphor band (19p.) or two phosphor bands (others). Perf 14×14½

2134	**1447**	19p. multicoloured	40	40	☐ ☐
2135	**1448**	26p. multicoloured	70	70	☐ ☐
2136	**1449**	44p. black, grey and			
		silver	1·00	1·00	☐ ☐
2137	**1450**	64p. multicoloured	1·25	1·25	☐ ☐
Set of 4			3·00	3·00	☐ ☐
First Day Cover				4·00	☐
Presentation Pack (PO Pack No. 309)			3·75		☐
PHQ Cards (*set of* 4) (217)			1·25	4·50	☐ ☐
Set of 4 *Gutter Pairs*			6·00		☐

1451 Reed Beds, River Braid (ECOS, Ballymena)

1452 South American Leaf-cutter Ants (Web of Life Exhibition, London Zoo)

1453 Solar Sensors
(Earth Centre, Doncaster)

1454 Hydroponic Leaves
(Project SUZY, Teesside)

Millennium Projects (4th series). Life and Earth

2000 (4 Apr.) One centre phosphor band (2nd) or two phosphor bands (others). Perf 14 × 14½

2138	**1451**	(2nd) multicoloured	90	90		
2139	**1452**	(1st) multicoloured	1·00	1·00		
2140	**1453**	44p. multicoloured	1·00	1·00		
2141	**1454**	64p. multicoloured	1·25	1·25		
Set of 4			3·75	3·75		
First Day Cover				4·00		
Presentation Pack (PO Pack No. 310)			4·25			
PHQ Cards (*set of 4*) (218)			1·25	4·50		
Set of 4 Gutter Pairs			7·50			

1455 Pottery Glaze (Ceramic Museum, Stoke-on-Trent)

1456 Bankside Galleries (Tate Modern, London)

1457 Road Marking (Cycle Network Artworks)

1458 People of Salford (Lowry Centre, Salford)

Millennium Projects (5th series). Art and Craft

2000 (2 May) One centre phosphor band (2nd) or two phosphor bands (others). Perf 14 × 14½

2142	**1455**	(2nd) multicoloured	90	90		
2143	**1456**	(1st) multicoloured	1·00	1·00		
2144	**1457**	45p. multicoloured	1·00	1·00		
2145	**1458**	65p. multicoloured	1·25	1·25		
Set of 4			3·75	3·75		
First Day Cover				4·00		
Presentation Pack (PO Pack No. 311)			4·25			
PHQ Cards (*set of 4*) (219)			1·25	4·00		
Set of 4 Gutter Pairs			7·50			

> For Nos. **MS**2146/**MS**2147, Types **1459/1459a** see Decimal Machin Definitives section.

1460 Children playing (Millenium Greens Project)

1461 Millennium Bridge, Gateshead

1462 Daisies (Mile End Park, London)

1463 African Hut and Thatched Cottage (On the Meridian Line Project)

Millennium Projects (6th series). People and Places

2000 (6 June) One centre phosphor band (2nd) or two phosphor bands (others). Perf 14 × 14½

2148	**1460**	(2nd) multicoloured	90	90		
2149	**1461**	(1st) multicoloured	1·00	1·00		
2150	**1462**	45p. multicoloured	1·00	1·00		
2151	**1463**	65p. multicoloured	1·25	1·25		
Set of 4			3·75	3·75		
First Day Cover				4·00		
Presentation Pack (PO Pack No. 312)			4·25			
PHQ Cards (*set of 4*) (220)			1·25	4·50		
Set of 4 Gutter Pairs			7·50			

1464 Raising the Stone (Strangford Stone, Killyleagh)

1465 Horse's Hooves (Trans Pennine Trail, Derbyshire)

1466 Cyclist (Kingdom of Fife Cycle Ways, Scotland)

1467 Bluebell Wood (Groundwork's Changing Places Project)

Millennium Projects (7th series). Stone and Soil

2000 (4 July) One centre phosphor band (2nd) or two phosphor bands (others). Perf 14 × 14½

2152	**1464**	(2nd) brownish black, grey-black and silver	90	90		
2153	**1465**	(1st) multicoloured	1·00	1·00		
2154	**1466**	45p. multicoloured	90	90		
2155	**1467**	65p. multicoloured	1·10	1·10		
Set of 4			3·50	3·50		

First Day Cover		4·00	
Presentation Pack (PO Pack No. 313)	4·00		
PHQ Cards (*set of* 4) (221)	1·25	4·25	
Set of 4 Gutter Pairs		7·00	

1468 Tree Roots (Yews for the Millennium Project)

1469 Sunflower (Eden Project, St Austell)

1470 Sycamore Seeds (Millennium Seed Bank, Wakehurst Place, Surrey)

1471 Forest, Doire Dach (Forest for Scotland)

Millennium Projects (8th series). Tree and Leaf

2000 (1 Aug.) One centre phosphor band (2nd) or two phosphor bands (others). Perf 14 × 14½

2156	**1468**	(2nd) multicoloured	90	90
2157	**1469**	(1st) multicoloured	1·00	1·00
2158	**1470**	45p. multicoloured	90	90
2159	**1471**	65p. multicoloured	1·10	1·10
Set of 4			3·50	3·50
First Day Cover				4·00
Presentation Pack (PO Pack No. 314)			4·00	
PHQ Cards (*set of 4*) (222)			1·25	4·25
Set of 4 Gutter Pairs			7·00	

1472 Queen Elizabeth the Queen Mother

1472a Royal Family on Queen Mother's 100th Birthday (from photo by J. Swannell)

Queen Elizabeth the Queen Mother's 100th Birthday

2000 (4 Aug.) Phosphorised paper plus two phosphor bands. Perf 14½

2160	**1472**	27p. multicoloured	1·25	1·25
MS2161		121×89 mm. **1472a** 27p. Queen Elizabeth II; 27p. Prince William; 27p. Queen Elizabeth the Queen Mother; 27p. Prince Charles	5·00	5·00
First Day Cover (No. **MS**2161)				5·25
Presentation Pack (No. **MS**2161) (PO Pack No. M04)			11·00	
PHQ Cards (*set of 5*) (PSM04)			1·50	5·50

No. 2160 was only issued in the £7·03 Life of the Century booklet No. DX25 and in No. **MS**2161.

The complete miniature sheet is shown on one of the PHQ cards with the others depicting individual stamps.

1473 Head of *Gigantiops destructor* (Ant) (Wildscreen at Bristol)

1474 Gathering Water Lilies on Broads (Norfolk and Norwich Project)

1475 X-ray of Hand holding Computer Mouse (Millennium Point, Birmingham

1476 Tartan Wool Holder (Scottish Cultural Resources Access Network)

Millennium Projects (9th series). Mind and Matter

2000 (5 Sept.) One centre phosphor band (2nd) or two phosphor bands (others). Perf 14 × 14½

2162	**1473**	(2nd) multicoloured	90	90
2163	**1474**	(1st) multicoloured	1·00	1·00
2164	**1475**	45p. multicoloured	90	90
2165	**1476**	65p. multicoloured	1·10	1·10
Set of 4			3·50	3·50
First Day Cover				4·00
Presentation Pack (PO Pack No. 315)			4·00	
PHQ Cards (*set of 4*) (223)			1·25	4·25
Set of 4 Gutter Pairs			7·00	

1477 Acrobatic Performers (Millennium Dome)

1478 Football Players (Hampden Park, Glasgow)

1479 Bather (Bath Spa Project)

1480 Hen's Egg under Magnification (Centre for Life, Newcastle)

Millennium Projects (10th series). Body and Bone

2000 (3 Oct.) One centre phosphor band (2nd) or two phosphor bands (others). Perf 14 × 14½ (2nd) or 13½ × 14 (others)

2166	**1477**	(2nd) black, slate-blue and silver	90	90	☐	☐
2167	**1478**	(1st) multicoloured	1·00	1·00	☐	☐
2168	**1479**	45p. multicoloured	90	90	☐	☐
2169	**1480**	65p. multicoloured	1·10	1·10	☐	☐
	Set of 4		3·50	3·50	☐	☐
	First Day Cover			4·00	☐	
	Presentation Pack (PO Pack No. 316)		4·00		☐	
	PHQ Cards (*set of 4*) (224)		1·25	4·25	☐	☐
	Set of 4 Gutter Pairs		7·00		☐	

1481 Virgin and Child Stained Glass Window, St Edmundsbury Cathedral (Suffolk Cathedral Millennium Project)

1482 Floodlit Church of St Peter and St Paul, Overstowey (Church Floodlighting Trust)

1483 12th-century. Latin Gradual (St Patrick Centre, Downpatrick)

1484 Chapter House Ceiling, York Minster (York Millennium Mystery Plays)

Millennium Projects (11th series). Spirit and Faith

2000 (7 Nov.) One centre phosphor band (2nd) or two phosphor bands (others). Perf 14 × 14½

2170	**1481**	(2nd) multicoloured	90	90	☐	☐
2171	**1482**	(1st) multicoloured	1·00	1·00	☐	☐
2172	**1483**	45p. multicoloured	90	90	☐	☐
2173	**1484**	65p. multicoloured	1·10	1·10	☐	☐
	Set of 4		3·50	3·50	☐	☐
	First Day Cover			4·00	☐	
	Presentation Pack (PO Pack No. 317)		4·00		☐	
	PHQ Cards (*set of 4*) (225)		1·25	4·25	☐	☐
	Set of 4 Gutter Pairs		7·00		☐	

Post Office Yearbook

2000 (7 Nov.) Comprises Nos. 2125/2126, 2127/2132, 2134/2145, 2148/2159 and **MS**2161/2177 in hardback book with slip case

YB2177*a*	Yearbook	48·00	☐

The last two issues in the Millennium Projects Series were supplied for insertion into the above at a later date.

1485 Church Bells (Ringing in the Millennium)

1486 Eye (Year of the Artist)

1487 Top of Harp (Canolfan Mileniwn, Cardiff)

1488 Figure within Latticework (TS2K Creative Enterprise Centres, London)

Millennium Projects (12th series). Sound and Vision

2000 (5 Dec.) One centre phosphor band (2nd) or two phosphor bands (others). Perf 14 × 14½

2174	**1485**	(2nd) multicoloured	90	90	☐	☐
2175	**1486**	(1st) multicoloured	1·00	1·00	☐	☐
2176	**1487**	45p. multicoloured	90	90	☐	☐
2177	**1488**	65p. multicoloured	1·10	1·10	☐	☐
	Set of 4		3·50	3·50	☐	☐
	First Day Cover			4·00	☐	
	Presentation Pack (PO Pack No. 318)		4·00		☐	
	PHQ Cards (*set of 4*) (226)		1·25	4·25	☐	☐
	Set of 4 Gutter Pairs		7·00		☐	

Year Pack 2000

2000 (5 Dec.) Comprises Nos. 2125/2126, 2127/2132, 2134/2145, 2148/2159 and **MS**2161/2177

CP2177*a*	Year Pack	65·00	☐

1489 Flower (Nurture Children)

1490 Tiger (Listen to Children)

1491 Owl (Teach Children)

1492 Butterfly (Ensure Children's Freedom)

Year Pack 2001

2001 (6 Nov.) Comprises Nos. 2178/2200, 2202/**MS**2206, 2210/2214, 2216/2229 and 2232/2242
CP2242*a*   Year Pack   70·00   □

Post Office Yearbook

2001 (6 Nov.) Comprises Nos. 2178/2196, **MS**2201/**MS**2206, **MS**2215/2229 and 2232/2242 in hardback book with slip case
YB2242*a*   Yearbook   48·00   □

1550 *How the Whale got his Throat*

1551 *How the Camel got his Hump*

1552 *How the Rhinoceros got his Skin*

1553 *How the Leopard got his Spots*

1554 *The Elephant's Child*

1555 *The Sing-Song of Old Man Kangaroo*

1556 *The Beginning of the Armadillos*

1557 *The Crab that played with the Sea*

1558 *The Cat that walked by Himself*

1559 *The Butterfly that stamped*

Centenary of Publication of Rudyard Kipling's Just So Stories

2002 (15 Jan.) Self-adhesive. Two phosphor bands. Die-cut perf 15×14

2243	**1550**	(1st) multicoloured	1·00	1·00	□	□
		a. Sheetlet of 10.				
		Nos. 2243/2252	9·00	9·00	□	□
2244	**1551**	(1st) multicoloured	1·00	1·00	□	□
2245	**1552**	(1st) multicoloured	1·00	1·00	□	□

2246	**1553**	(1st) multicoloured	1·00	1·00	□	□
2247	**1554**	(1st) multicoloured	1·00	1·00	□	□
2248	**1555**	(1st) multicoloured	1·00	1·00	□	□
2249	**1556**	(1st) multicoloured	1·00	1·00	□	□
2250	**1557**	(1st) multicoloured	1·00	1·00	□	□
2251	**1558**	(1st) multicoloured	1·00	1·00	□	□
2252	**1559**	(1st) multicoloured	1·00	1·00	□	□
Set of 10			9·00	9·00	□	
First Day Cover				9·25		□
Presentation Pack (PO Pack No. 330)			10·00		□	
PHQ Cards (*set of* 10) (237)			3·00	11·00	□	□

Nos. 2243/2252 were printed together in sheetlets of ten (5×2), with the surplus self-adhesive paper around each stamp retained.

1560 Queen Elizabeth II, 1952 (Dorothy Wilding)

1561 Queen Elizabeth II, 1968 (Cecil Beaton)

1562 Queen Elizabeth II, 1978 (Lord Snowdon)

1563 Queen Elizabeth II, 1984 (Yousef Karsh)

1564 Queen Elizabeth II, 1996 (Tim Graham)

1565

Golden Jubilee. Studio portraits of Queen Elizabeth II by photographers named

2002 (6 Feb.) One centre phosphor band (2nd) or two phosphor bands (others). W **1565** (sideways). Perf 14½×14

2253	**1560**	(2nd) multicoloured	90	90	□	□
2254	**1561**	(1st) multicoloured	1·00	1·00	□	□
2255	**1562**	(E) multicoloured	1·75	1·50	□	□
2256	**1563**	45p. multicoloured	1·00	1·10	□	□
2257	**1564**	65p. multicoloured	1·10	1·25	□	□
Set of 5			5·25	5·00	□	□
First Day Cover				5·25		□
Presentation Pack (PO Pack No. 331)			7·00		□	
PHQ Cards (*set of* 5) (238)			1·50	5·75	□	□
Set of 5 *Gutter Pairs*			10·50		□	

Nos. 2253/2257 were also issued with watermark upright, in the £7·29 A Gracious Accession booklet, No DX28.

1566

Booklet Stamps

2002 (6 Feb.) Designs as 1952–1954 issue, but with service indicator as T **1566**. One centre phosphor band (2nd) or two phosphor bands (1st). W **1565**. Uncoated paper. Perf 15 × 14 (with one elliptical hole in each vertical side)

2258	**1566**	(2nd) carmine-red	1·10	1·10	☐	☐
2259	**154**	(1st) green	1·25	1·25	☐	☐
Set of 2			2·10	2·10	☐	☐
First Day Cover				7·50	☐	

Nos. 2258/2259 were only issued in the £7·29 The Gracious Accession stamp booklet, No. DX18.

For other Wilding designs with decimal face vace values, see Nos. 2031/2033, **MS**2326, **MS**2367, 2378/2380 and 3329.

1567 Rabbits ('a new baby')

1568 'LOVE'

1569 Aircraft Sky-writing 'hello'

1570 Bear pulling Potted Topiary Tree (Moving Home)

1571 Flowers ('best wishes')

Greetings Stamps Occasions

2002 (5 Mar.)-**03** Two phosphor bands

(a) Litho. Ordinary gum. Perf 15 × 14

2260	**1567**	(1st) multicoloured	1·10	1·10	☐	☐
2261	**1568**	(1st) multicoloured	1·10	1·10	☐	☐
2262	**1569**	(1st) multicoloured	1·10	1·10	☐	☐
2263	**1570**	(1st) multicoloured	1·10	1·10	☐	☐
2264	**1571**	(1st) multicoloured	1·10	1·10	☐	☐
Set of 5			5·00	5·00	☐	☐
First Day Cover				5·25	☐	
Presentation Pack (PO Pack No. M07)			5·25		☐	
PHQ Cards (*set of 5*) (PSM08)			1·50	6·00	☐	☐
Set of 5 Gutter Pairs			10·00		☐	

(b) Photo. Self-adhesive. Die-cut perf 15 × 14

2264a	**1569**	(1st) multicoloured				
		(4.3.03)	3·00	3·00	☐	☐

Nos. 2260/2264 were re-issued on 23 April 2002 in sheets of 20 perforated 14, either of one design or *se-tenant*, with each stamp accompanied by a half stamp-size label showing either greetings or a personal photograph.

No. 2262 was also issued in sheets of 20 with *se-tenant* labels in connection with the Hong Kong Stamp Expo on 30 January 2004. It was issued in sheets of 20 perforated 14 with *se-tenant* labels on 21 April 2005 for Pacific Explorer 2005 World Stamp Expo, on 25 May 2006 for Washington 2006 International Stamp Exhibition, on 14 November 2006 for Belgica 2006 International Stamp Exhibition, on 5 August 2008 for Beijing 2008 Olympic Expo, on 3 August 2009 for Thaipex 09 Stamp Exhibition, on 21 October 2009 for Italia 2009 International Stamp Exhibition and on 4 December 2009 for MonacoPhil International Stamp Exhibition.

No. 2264a was only issued in £1·62 stamp booklets in which the surplus self-adhesive paper around each stamp was removed.

1572 Studland Bay, Dorset

1573 Luskentyre, South Harris

1574 Cliffs, Dover, Kent

1575 Padstow Harbour, Cornwall

1576 Broadstairs, Kent

1577 St Abb's Head, Scottish Borders

1578 Dunster Beach, Somerset

1579 Newquay Beach, Cornwall

1580 Portrush, County Antrim

1581 Sand-spit, Conwy

British Coastlines

2002 (19 Mar.) Two phosphor bands. Perf 14½

2265	**1572**	27p. multicoloured	50	50	☐	☐
		a. Block of 10.				
		Nos. 2265/2274	4·50	4·50	☐	☐
2266	**1573**	27p. multicoloured	50	50	☐	☐
2267	**1574**	27p. multicoloured	50	50	☐	☐
2268	**1575**	27p. multicoloured	50	50	☐	☐
2269	**1576**	27p. multicoloured	50	50	☐	☐
2270	**1577**	27p. multicoloured	50	50	☐	☐
2271	**1578**	27p. multicoloured	50	50	☐	☐
2272	**1579**	27p. multicoloured	50	50	☐	☐
2273	**1580**	27p. multicoloured	50	50	☐	☐
2274	**1581**	27p. multicoloured	50	50	☐	☐
Set of 10			4·50	4·50	☐	
First Day Cover				4·75	☐	
Presentation Pack (PO Pack No. 332)			5·00		☐	
PHQ Cards (*set of* 10) (239)			3·00	6·00	☐	☐
Gutter Block of 20			9·00		☐	

Nos. 2265/2274 were printed together, *se-tenant*, in blocks of ten (5 × 2) throughout the sheet.

1582 Slack Wire Act

1583 Lion Tamer

1584 Trick Tri-cyclists

1585 Krazy Kar

1586 Equestrienne

Europa. Circus

2002 (10 Apr.) One centre phosphor band (2nd) or two phosphor bands (others). Perf 14½

2275	**1582**	(2nd) multicoloured	90	90	☐	☐
2276	**1583**	(1st) multicoloured	1·00	1·00	☐	☐
2277	**1584**	(E) multicoloured	1·75	1·50	☐	☐
2278	**1585**	45p. multicoloured	1·00	1·10	☐	☐
2279	**1586**	65p. multicoloured	1·10	1·25	☐	☐
Set of 5			5·25	5·00	☐	☐
First Day Cover				5·25	☐	
Presentation Pack (PO Pack No. 333)			5·75		☐	
PHQ Cards (*set of* 5) (240)			1·50	5·75	☐	☐
Set of 5 *Gutter Pairs*			10·50		☐	

The 1st and E values incorporate the EUROPA emblem.

Due to the funeral of the Queen Mother, the actual issue of Nos. 2275/2279 was delayed from 9 April which is the date that appears on first day covers.

1587 Queen Elizabeth the Queen Mother

Queen Elizabeth the Queen Mother Commemoration

2002 (25 Apr.) Vert designs as Types **955/958** with changed face values and showing both the Queen's head and frame in black as in T **1587**. Two phosphor bands. Perf 14 × 15

2280	**1587**	(1st) multicoloured	1·00	1·00	☐	☐
2281	**956**	(E) black and indigo	1·75	1·50	☐	☐
2282	**957**	45p. multicoloured	1·00	1·10	☐	☐
2283	**958**	65p. black, stone & sepia	1·10	1·25	☐	☐
Set of 4			4·50	4·25	☐	☐
First Day Cover				4·50	☐	
Presentation Pack (PO Pack No. M08)			4·75		☐	
Set of 4 *Gutter Pairs*			9·00		☐	

1588 Airbus A340-600 (2002)

1589 Concorde (1976)

1590 Trident (1964)

1591 VC 10 (1964)

1592 Comet (1952)

50th Anniversary of Passenger Jet Aviation. Airliners

2002 (2 May) One centre phosphor band (2nd) or two phosphor bands (others). Perf 14½

(a) Photo De La Rue. Ordinary gum

2284	**1588**	(2nd) multicoloured	90	90	☐	☐
2285	**1589**	(1st) multicoloured	1·00	1·00	☐	☐
2286	**1590**	(E) multicoloured	1·75	1·50	☐	☐
2287	**1591**	45p. multicoloured	1·50	1·50	☐	☐
2288	**1592**	65p. multicoloured	1·75	1·75	☐	☐
Set of 5			6·25	6·00	☐	☐
First Day Cover				6·50	☐	
Presentation Pack (PO Pack No. 334)			7·00		☐	
PHQ Cards (*set of* 6) (241)			1·75	12·00	☐	☐
Set of 5 *Gutter Pairs*			12·50		☐	

MS2289 120×105 mm. Nos. 2284/2288   3·00   3·00 ☐ ☐
First Day Cover   7·50   ☐

(b) Photo Questa. Self-adhesive
2290 **1589**   (1st) multicoloured   3·00   3·00 ☐ ☐
The complete miniature sheet is shown on one of the PHQ cards with the others depicting individual stamps.

No. 2290 was only issued in £1·62 stamp booklets. For T **1589** printed by lithography see No. 2897.

1593 Crowned Lion with Shield of St George

1594 Top Left Quarter of English Flag, and Football

1595 Top Right Quarter of English Flag, and Football

1596 Bottom Left Quarter of English Flag, and Football

1597 Bottom Right Quarter of English Flag, and Football

World Cup Football Championship, Japan and Korea

2002 (21 May) Two phosphor bands. Perf 14½×14

(a) Ordinary gum
2291 **1593**   (1st) deep turquoise-
                      blue, scarlet-
                      vermilion
                      and silver   1·25   1·25 ☐ ☐
MS2292 145×74 mm. No. 2291;
    Type **1594** (1st) multicoloured;
    Type **1595** (1st) multicoloured;
    Type **1596** (1st) multicoloured;
    Type **1597** (1st) multicoloured   5·00   5·00 ☐ ☐
First Day Cover (No. **MS**2292)   5·50   ☐
Presentation Pack (No. **MS**2292)
(PO Pack No. 335)   5·75   ☐
PHQ Cards (*set of 6*) (242)   1·75   7·50 ☐ ☐
Gutter Pair (No. 2291)   2·50   ☐

(b) Self-adhesive. Die-cut perf 15×14
2293 **1594**   (1st) multicoloured   2·50   2·50 ☐ ☐
2294 **1595**   (1st) multicoloured   2·50   2·50 ☐ ☐
The complete miniature sheet is shown on one of the PHQ cards with the others depicting individual stamps from No. **MS**2292 and No. 2291.

Nos. 2293/2294 were only issued in £1·62 stamp booklets.

Stamps as T **1597** were also issued in sheets of 20, *se-tenant* with half stamp-sized labels, printed in lithography instead of gravure. The labels show either match scenes or personal photographs.

Stamps as T **1593** but with 'WORLD CUP 2002' inscription omitted were issued on 17 May 2007 in sheets of 20 with *se-tenant* labels showing scenes from Wembley Stadium.

For Nos. **2295/2298**, see Decimal Machin Definitives section.

1598 Swimming

1599 Running

1600 Cycling

1601 Long Jumping

1602 Wheelchair Racing

17th Commonwealth Games, Manchester

2002 (16 July) One side phosphor band (2nd) or two phosphor bands (others). Perf 14½
2299 **1598**   (2nd) multicoloured   90   90 ☐ ☐
2300 **1599**   (1st) multicoloured   1·00   1·00 ☐ ☐
2301 **1600**   (E) multicoloured   1·75   1·25 ☐ ☐
2302 **1601**   47p. multicoloured   1·25   1·25 ☐ ☐
2303 **1602**   68p. multicoloured   1·40   1·50 ☐ ☐
Set of 5   5·75   5·50 ☐ ☐
First Day Cover   6·00   ☐
Presentation Pack (PO Pack No. 336)   6·00   ☐
PHQ Cards (*set of 5*) (243)   1·50   6·75 ☐ ☐
Set of 5 Gutter Pairs   11·50   ☐

1603 Tinkerbell

1604 Wendy, John and Michael Darling in front of Big Ben

1605 Crocodile and Alarm Clock

1606 Captain Hook

1607 Peter Pan

150th Anniversary of Great Ormond Street Children's Hospital. *Peter Pan* **by Sir James Barrie**

2002 (20 Aug.) One centre phosphor band (2nd) or two phosphor bands (others). Perf 15 × 14

2304	**1603**	(2nd) multicoloured	90	90	☐	☐
2305	**1604**	(1st) multicoloured	1·00	1·00	☐	☐
2306	**1605**	(E) multicoloured	1·75	1·50	☐	☐
2307	**1606**	47p. multicoloured	1·25	1·25	☐	☐
2308	**1607**	68p. multicoloured	1·40	1·50	☐	☐
Set of 5			5·75	5·50	☐	☐
First Day Cover				6·00		☐
Presentation Pack (PO Pack No. 337)			6·00		☐	
PHQ Cards (*set of 5*) (244)			1·50	6·75	☐	☐
Set of 5 Gutter Pairs			11·50		☐	

1608 Millennium Bridge, 2001   1609 Tower Bridge, 1894

1610 Westminster Bridge, 1864   1611 *Blackfriars Bridge, c 1800* (William Marlow)

1612 *London Bridge, c 1670* (Wenceslaus Hollar)

Bridges of London

2002 (10 Sept.) One centre phosphor band (2nd) or two phosphor bands (others)

(a) Litho. Ordinary gum. Perf 15 × 14

2309	**1608**	(2nd) multicoloured	90	90	☐	☐
2310	**1609**	(1st) multicoloured	1·00	1·00	☐	☐
2311	**1610**	(E) multicoloured	1·75	1·50	☐	☐
2312	**1611**	47p. multicoloured	1·60	1·60	☐	☐
2313	**1612**	68p. multicoloured	1·75	1·75	☐	☐
Set of 5			6·25	6·00	☐	☐
First Day Cover				6·25		☐
Presentation Pack (PO Pack No. 338)			30·00		☐	
PHQ Cards (*set of 5*) (245)			1·50	7·00	☐	☐
Set of 5 Gutter Pairs			12·50		☐	

(b) Gravure. Self-adhesive. Die-cut perf 15 × 14

2314	**1609**	(1st) multicoloured	3·00	3·00	☐	☐

No. 2314 was only issued in £1·62 stamp booklets.

1613 Galaxies and Nebula

Astronomy

2002 (5 Nov.) Sheet 120 × 89mm. Multicoloured. Two phosphor bands. Perf 14½ × 14

MS2315	**1613**	(1st) Planetary nebula in Aquila; (1st) Seyfert 2 galaxy in Pegasus; (1st) Planetary nebula in Norma; (1st) Seyfert 2 galaxy in Circinus	4·00	4·00	☐	☐
First Day Cover				4·75		☐
Presentation Pack (PO Pack No. 339)			11·00		☐	
PHQ Cards (*set of 5*) (246)			1·50	5·00	☐	☐

The five PHQ cards depict the four designs and the complete miniature sheet.

No. **MS**2315 was also issued the £6·83 Accross the Universe booklet, No. DX29.

1614 Green Pillar Box, 1857   1615 Horizontal Aperture Box, 1874   1616 Air Mail Box, 1934

1617 Double Aperture Box, 1939   1618 Modern Style Box, 1980

150th Anniversary of the First Pillar Box

2002 (8 Oct.) One centre phosphor band (2nd) or two phosphor bands (others). Perf 14 × 14½

2316	**1614**	(2nd) multicoloured	90	90	☐	☐
2317	**1615**	(1st) multicoloured	1·00	1·00	☐	☐
2318	**1616**	(E) multicoloured	1·75	1·50	☐	☐
2319	**1617**	47p. multicoloured	1·00	1·10	☐	☐
2320	**1618**	68p. multicoloured	1·25	1·25	☐	☐
Set of 5			5·25	5·00	☐	☐

First Day Cover		5·25	
Presentation Pack (PO Pack No. 340)	5·75		
PHQ Cards (set of 5) (247)	1·50	5·50	
Set of 5 Gutter Pairs	10·50		

1619 Blue Spruce Star

1620 Holly

1621 Ivy

1622 Mistletoe

1623 Pine Cone

Christmas. Christmas Plants

2002 (5 Nov.) Self-adhesive. One centre phosphor band (2nd) or two phosphor bands (others). Die-cut perf 14½ × 14

2321	**1619**	(2nd) multicoloured	90	90	
2322	**1620**	(1st) multicoloured	1·00	1·00	
2323	**1621**	(E) multicoloured	1·75	1·50	
2324	**1622**	47p. multicoloured	1·25	1·25	
2325	**1623**	68p. multicoloured	1·40	1·40	
Set of 5			5·25	5·00	
First Day Cover				5·25	
Presentation Pack (PO Pack No. 341)			5·25		
PHQ Cards (set of 5) (248)			1·50	5·75	

Year Pack 2002

2002 (5 Nov.) Comprises Nos. 2243/2257, 2260/2264, 2265/2288, **MS**2292, 2299/2313 and **MS**2315/2325

CP2325a	Year Pack	65·00	

Post Office Yearbook

2002 (5 Nov.) Comprises Nos. 2243/2257, 2260/2264, 2265/2288, 2291/2292, 2299/2313 and **MS**2315/2325 in hardback book with slip case

YB2325a	Yearbook	48·00	

The Wilding definitives collection I ~ 1952 - 1953

1623a

50th Anniversary of Wilding Definitives (1st series)

2002 (5 Dec.) Sheet 124×70 mm. Printed on pale cream. One centre phosphor band (2nd) or two phosphor bands (others). W **1565**. Perf 15 × 14 (with one elliptical hole in each vertical side)

MS2326 **1623a** 1p. orange-red; 2p. ultramarine; 5p. red-brown; (2nd) carmine-red; (1st) green; 33p. brown; 37p. magenta; 47p. bistre-brown; 50p. green and label showing national emblems	5·00	5·00	
First Day Cover		5·25	
Presentation Pack (PO Pack No. 59)	25·00		
PHQ Cards (set of 5) (D21)	1·50	5·25	

The PHQ cards depict the (2nd), (1st), 33p., 37p. and 47p. stamps.

For further Wilding designs with decimal face values, see Nos. 2031/2033, 2258/2259, **MS**2367 and 2378/2380.

1624 Barn Owl landing

1625 Barn Owl with folded Wings and Legs down

1626 Barn Owl with extended Wings and Legs down

1627 Barn Owl in Flight with Wings lowered

1628 Barn Owl in Flight with Wings raised

1629 Kestrel with Wings folded

1630 Kestrel with Wings fully extended upwards

1631 Kestrel with Wings horizontal

1632 Kestrel with Wings partly extended downwards

1633 Kestrel with Wings fully extended downwards

Birds of Prey

2003 (14 Jan.) Phosphor background. Perf 14½

2327	**1624**	(1st) multicoloured	1·00	1·00	☐	☐
		a. Block of 10.				
		Nos. 2327/2336	9·00	9·00	☐	☐
2328	**1625**	(1st) multicoloured	1·00	1·00	☐	☐
2329	**1626**	(1st) multicoloured	1·00	1·00	☐	☐
2330	**1627**	(1st) multicoloured	1·00	1·00	☐	☐
2331	**1628**	(1st) multicoloured	1·00	1·00	☐	☐
2332	**1629**	(1st) multicoloured	1·00	1·00	☐	☐
2333	**1630**	(1st) multicoloured	1·00	1·00	☐	☐
2334	**1631**	(1st) multicoloured	1·00	1·00	☐	☐
2335	**1632**	(1st) multicoloured	1·00	1·00	☐	☐
2336	**1633**	(1st) multicoloured	1·00	1·00	☐	☐
Set of 10			9·00	9·00	☐	☐
First Day Cover				9·25		☐
Presentation Pack (PO Pack No. 343)			9·50		☐	
PHQ Cards (*set of 10*) (249)			3·00	11·00	☐	☐
Gutter Block of 20			18·00		☐	

Nos. 2327/2336 were printed together, *se-tenant*, in blocks of ten (5 × 2) throughout the sheet.

1634 'Gold star, See me, Playtime'

1635 '1♥U, XXXX, S.W.A.L.K.'

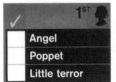

1636 'Angel, Poppet, Little terror'

1637 'Yes, No, Maybe'

1638 'Oops!, Sorry, Will try harder'

1639 'I did it!, You did it!, We did it!'

Greetings Stamps Occasions (3rd series)

2003 (4 Feb.) Two phosphor bands. Perf 14½ × 14

2337	**1634**	(1st) lemon and new blue	1·00	1·00	☐	☐
		a. Block of 6.				
		Nos. 2337/2342	5·50	5·50	☐	☐
2338	**1635**	(1st) red and deep ultramarine	1·00	1·00	☐	☐
2339	**1636**	(1st) purple and bright yellow-green	1·00	1·00	☐	☐
2340	**1637**	(1st) bright yellow-green and red	1·00	1·00	☐	☐
2341	**1638**	(1st) deep ultramarine and lemon	1·00	1·00	☐	☐
2342	**1639**	(1st) new blue and purple	1·00	1·00	☐	☐
Set of 6			5·50	5·50	☐	☐
First Day Cover				5·75		☐
Presentation Pack (PO Pack No. M09)			6·00		☐	
PHQ Cards (*set of 6*) (PSM09)			1·75	6·25	☐	☐
Gutter Block of 12			11·00		☐	

Nos. 2337/2342 were printed together, *se-tenant*, in blocks of six (3 × 2) throughout the sheet.

Nos. 2337/2342 were also available in *se-tenant* sheets of 20 containing four examples of Nos. 2338 and 2340 and three of each of the others. The stamps are accompanied by half stamp-size printed labels or a personal photograph.

1640 Completing the Genome Jigsaw

1641 Ape with Moustache and Scientist

1642 DNA Snakes and Ladders

1643 Animal Scientists

1644 Genome Crystal Ball

50th Anniversary of Discovery of DNA

2003 (25 Feb.) One centre phosphor band (2nd) or two phosphor bands (others). Perf 14½

2343	**1640**	(2nd) multicoloured	90	90	☐	☐
2344	**1641**	(1st) multicoloured	1·00	1·00	☐	☐
2345	**1642**	(E) multicoloured	1·75	1·50	☐	☐
2346	**1643**	47p. multicoloured	1·30	1·40	☐	☐
2347	**1644**	68p. multicoloured	1·50	1·60	☐	☐
Set of 5			6·00	5·75	☐	☐
First Day Cover				6·25		☐
Presentation Pack (PO Pack No. 344)			6·00		☐	
PHQ Cards (*set of 5*) (250)			1·50	6·25	☐	☐
Set of 5 Gutter Pairs			12·00		☐	

Nos. 2343/2347 were also issued in a £6·99 Microcosmos booklet.

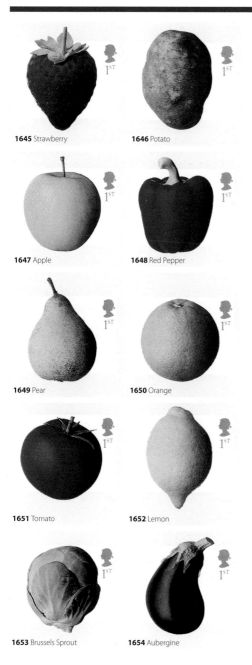

1645 Strawberry   **1646** Potato

1647 Apple   **1648** Red Pepper

1649 Pear   **1650** Orange

1651 Tomato   **1652** Lemon

1653 Brussels Sprout   **1654** Aubergine

Fruit and Vegetables

2003 (25 Mar.) Self-adhesive. Two phosphor bands. Perf
14½×14 die-cut (without teeth around protruding tops or
bottoms of the designs)

2348	**1645**	(1st) multicoloured	1·00	1·00	☐	☐
		a. Sheetlet of 10.				
		Nos. 2348/2357				
		and pane of				
		decorative labels	9·00		☐	
2349	**1646**	(1st) multicoloured	1·00	1·00	☐	☐
2350	**1647**	(1st) multicoloured	1·00	1·00	☐	☐
2351	**1648**	(1st) multicoloured	1·00	1·00	☐	☐
2352	**1649**	(1st) multicoloured	1·00	1·00	☐	☐
2353	**1650**	(1st) multicoloured	1·00	1·00	☐	☐
2354	**1651**	(1st) multicoloured	1·00	1·00	☐	☐
2355	**1652**	(1st) multicoloured	1·00	1·00	☐	☐
2356	**1653**	(1st) multicoloured	1·00	1·00	☐	☐
2357	**1654**	(1st) multicoloured	1·00	1·00	☐	☐
		Set of 10	9·00	9·00	☐	☐
		First Day Cover		9·25	☐	
		Presentation Pack (PO Pack No. 345)	12·00		☐	
		PHQ Cards (*set of* 10) (251)	3·00	10·50	☐	☐

Nos. 2348/2357 were printed together in sheets of ten with
the surplus self-adhesive paper around each stamp retained.
The stamp pane is accompanied by a similar-sized pane of self-
adhesive labels showing ears, eyes, mouths, hats, etc which are
intended for the adornment of fruit and vegetables depicted.
This pane is separated from the stamps by a line of roulettes.

Nos. 2348/2357 were re-issued on 7th March 2006 in sheets
of 20 containing two of each of the ten designs, each stamp
accompanied by a *se-tenant* speech bubble label. These sheets
were printed in lithography instead of gravure, and have
stickers showing eyes, hats, etc in the sheet margin.

For Nos. 2357a/2359, Type **1655**, see Decimal Machin
Definitives section.

1656 Amy Johnson (pilot) and Biplane

1657 Members of 1953 Everest Team

1658 Freya Stark (traveller and writer) and Desert

1659 Ernest Shackleton (Antarctic explorer)
and Wreck of *Endurance*

1660 Francis Chichester (yachtsman) and *Gipsy Moth IV*

1661 Robert Falcon Scott (Antarctic explorer)
and Norwegian Expedition at the Pole

Extreme Endeavours (British Explorers)

2003 (29 Apr.) One centre phosphor band (2nd) or two phosphor bands (others)

(a) Ordinary gum. Perf 15 × 14½

2360	**1656**	2nd) multicoloured	90	90	☐ ☐
2361	**1657**	(1st) multicoloured	1·00	1·00	☐ ☐
2362	**1658**	(E) multicoloured	1·75	1·50	☐ ☐
2363	**1659**	42p. multicoloured	1·00	1·00	☐ ☐
2364	**1660**	47p. multicoloured	1·10	1·25	☐ ☐
2365	**1661**	68p. multicoloured	1·25	1·40	☐ ☐
Set of 6			6·50	6·25	☐ ☐
First Day Cover				7·00	☐
Presentation Pack (PO Pack No. 346)			7·25		☐
PHQ Cards (*set of 6*) (252)			1·75	6·50	☐ ☐
Set of 6 Gutter Pairs			13·00		☐

(b) Self-adhesive. Die-cut perf 14½

2366	**1657**	(1st) multicoloured	3·00	3·00	☐ ☐

The phosphor bands on Nos. 2361/2365 are at the centre and right of each stamp.

No. 2366 was only issued in £1·62 stamp booklets in which the surplus self-adhesive paper around each stamp was removed.

1661a

50th Anniversary of Wilding Definitives (2nd series)

2003 (20 May) Sheet 124 × 70 mm. Printed on pale cream. One centre phosphor band (20p.) or two phosphor bands (others). W **1565**. P 15 × 14 (with one elliptical hole in each vertical side).

MS2367	**1661a** 4p. deep lilac; 8p. ultramarine; 10p. reddish purple; 20p. bright green; 28p. bronze-green; 34p. brown-purple; (E) chestnut; 42p. Prussian blue; 68p. grey-blue and label showing national emblems		4·50	4·75	☐ ☐
First Day Cover			5·50	☐
Presentation Pack (PO Pack No. 61)		9·00		☐

For further Wilding designs with decimal face values see Nos. 2031/2033, 2258/2259, **MS**2326 and 2378/2380.

1662 Guardsmen in Coronation Procession

1663 East End Children reading Coronation Party Poster

1664 Queen Elizabeth II in Coronation Chair with Bishops of Durham and Bath & Wells

1665 Children in Plymouth working on Royal Montage

1666 Queen Elizabeth II in Coronation Robes (photograph by Cecil Beaton)

1667 Children's Race at East End Street Party

1668 Coronation Coach passing through Marble Arch

1669 Children in Fancy Dress

1670 Coronation Coach outside Buckingham Palace

1671 Children eating at London Street Party

50th Anniversary of Coronation

2003 (2 June) W **1565**. Two phosphor bands. Perf 14½ × 14

2368	**1662**	(1st) multicoloured	1·00	1·00	☐ ☐
		a. Block of 10. Nos. 2368/2377	9·00	9·00	☐ ☐
2369	**1663**	(1st) black and gold	1·00	1·00	☐ ☐
2370	**1664**	(1st) multicoloured	1·00	1·00	☐ ☐
2371	**1665**	(1st) black and gold	1·00	1·00	☐ ☐
2372	**1666**	(1st) multicoloured	1·00	1·00	☐ ☐
2373	**1667**	(1st) black and gold	1·00	1·00	☐ ☐
2374	**1668**	(1st) multicoloured	1·00	1·00	☐ ☐
2375	**1669**	(1st) black and gold	1·00	1·00	☐ ☐
2376	**1670**	(1st) multicoloured	1·00	1·00	☐ ☐
2377	**1671**	(1st) black and gold	1·00	1·00	☐ ☐
Set of 10			9·00	9·00	☐ ☐
First Day Cover				9·50	☐
Presentation Pack (PO Pack No. 347)			10·00		☐
PHQ Cards (*set of 10*) (253)			3·00	10·00	☐ ☐
Gutter Block of 20			18·00		☐

Nos. 2368/2377 were printed together, *se-tenant*, as blocks of ten (5 × 2) in sheets of 60 (2 panes of 30).

No. 2372 does not show the Queen's head in gold as do the other nine designs.

50th Anniversary of Coronation. Booklet Stamps

2003 (2 June) Designs as T **160** (Wilding definitive of 1952) and T **163** (Coronation commemorative of 1953), but with values in decimal currency as T **1348**. W **1565**. Two phosphor bands. P 15 × 14 (with one elliptical hole in each vertical side for Nos. 2378/2379)

2378	**160**	47p. bistre-brown	2·00	2·00		
2379		68p. grey-blue	2·50	2·50		
2380	**163**	£1 deep yellow-green	26·00	26·00		
Set of 3			30·00	30·00		

Nos. 2378/2380 were only available in the £7·46 A Perfect Coronation stamp booklet, No. DX31. Stamps as Nos. 2378/2379, but on pale cream, were also included in the Wilding miniature sheets, Nos. **MS**2326 and **MS**2367. A £1 design as No. 2380, but on phosphorised paper, was previously included in the Stamp Show 2000 miniature sheet, No. **MS**2147.

For further Wilding designs with decimal face values see Nos. 2031/2033, 2258/2259, **MS**2326 and **MS**2367.

1672 Prince William in September 2001 (Brendan Beirne)

1673 Prince William in September 2000 (Tim Graham)

1674 Prince William in September 2001 (Camera Press)

1675 Prince William in September 2001 (Tim Graham)

21st Birthday of Prince William of Wales

2003 (17 June) Phosphor backgrounds. Perf 14½

2381	**1672**	28p. multicoloured	95	95		
2382	**1673**	(E) dull mauve, grey-black and light green	1·75	1·50		
2383	**1674**	47p. multicoloured	1·90	1·90		
2384	**1675**	68p. sage-green, black and bright green	2·25	2·25		
Set of 4			6·25	6·00		
First Day Cover				6·25		
Presentation Pack (PO Pack No. 348)			8·00			
PHQ Cards (*set of 4*) (254)			1·25	6·75		
Set of 4 Gutter Pairs			12·50			

1676 Loch Assynt, Sutherland

1677 Ben More, Isle of Mull

1678 Rothiemurchus, Cairngorms

1679 Dalveen Pass, Lowther Hills

1680 Glenfinnan Viaduct, Lochaber

1681 Papa Little, Shetland Islands

A British Journey (1st series): Scotland

2003 (15 July) One centre phosphor band (2nd) or two phosphor bands (others). Perf 14½

			(a) Ordinary gum			
2385	**1676**	(2nd) multicoloured	90	90		
2386	**1677**	(1st) multicoloured	1·00	1·00		
2387	**1678**	(E) multicoloured	1·75	1·50		
2388	**1679**	42p. multicoloured	1·00	1·00		
2389	**1680**	47p. multicoloured	1·10	1·25		
2390	**1681**	68p. multicoloured	1·25	1·40		
Set of 6			6·50	6·25		
First Day Cover				6·75		
Presentation Pack (PO Pack No. 349)			7·00			
PHQ Cards (*set of 6*) (255)			3·00	6·75		
Set of 6 Gutter Pairs			13·00			

(b) Self-adhesive. Die-cut perf 14½

2391	**1677**	(1st) multicoloured	3·00	3·00		

No. 2391 was only issued in £1·68 stamp booklets in which the surplus self-adhesive paper around each stamp was removed.

1682 'The Station' (Andrew Davidson)

1683 'Black Swan' (Stanley Chew)

1684 'The Cross Keys' (George Mackenney)

1685 'The Mayflower' (Ralph Ellis)

1686 'The Barley Sheaf' (Joy Cooper)

Europa. British Pub Signs

2003 (12 Aug.) Two phosphor bands. Perf 14 × 14½

2392	**1682**	(1st) multicoloured	1·00	1·00	☐	☐
2393	**1683**	(E) multicoloured	1·75	1·50	☐	☐
2394	**1684**	42p. multicoloured	1·00	1·00	☐	☐
2395	**1685**	47p. multicoloured	1·25	1·25	☐	☐
2396	**1686**	68p. multicoloured	1·40	1·40	☐	☐
Set of 5			5·75	5·50	☐	☐
First Day Cover				5·75	☐	
Presentation Pack (PO Pack No. 350)			5·75		☐	
PHQ Cards (*set of 5*) (256)			1·50	6·00	☐	☐
Set of 5 Gutter Pairs			11·50		☐	

The 1st and E values incorporate the EUROPA emblem.

No. 2392 was also issued in the £7·44 Letters by Night booklet, No. DX32.

1687 Meccano Constructor Biplane, *c.* 1931

1688 Wells-Brimtoy Clockwork Double-decker Omnibus, *c.* 1938

1689 Hornby M1 Clockwork Locomotive and Tender, *c.* 1948

1690 Dinky Toys Ford Zephyr, *c.* 1956

1691 Mettoy Friction Drive Space Ship Eagle, *c.* 1960

Classic Transport Toys

2003 (18 Sept.) Two phosphor bands

(a) Ordinary gum. Perf 14½ × 14

2397	**1687**	(1st) multicoloured	1·00	1·00	☐	☐
2398	**1688**	(E) multicoloured	1·75	1·50	☐	☐
2399	**1689**	42p. multicoloured	95	1·00	☐	☐
2400	**1690**	47p. multicoloured	1·25	1·25	☐	☐
2401	**1691**	68p. multicoloured	1·40	1·50	☐	☐
Set of 5			5·75	5·50	☐	☐
First Day Cover				5·75	☐	
Presentation Pack (PO Pack No. 351)			6·00		☐	
PHQ Cards (*set of 6*) (257)			1·75	6·00	☐	☐
Set of 5 Gutter Pairs			11·50		☐	
MS2402 115 × 105 mm. Nos. 2397/2401			5·50	5·50	☐	☐
First Day Cover				6·75	☐	

(b) Self-adhesive. Die-cut perf 14½ × 14

2403	**1687**	(1st) multicoloured	3·00	3·00	☐	☐

The complete miniature sheet is shown on one of the PHQ cards with the others depicting individual stamps.

No. 2403 was only issued in £1·68 stamp booklets in which the surplus self-adhesive paper around each stamp was removed.

1692 Coffin of Denytenamun, Egyptian, *c.* 900BC

1693 Alexander the Great, Greek, *c.* 200BC

1694 Sutton Hoo Helmet, Anglo-Saxon, *c.* AD600

1695 Sculpture of Parvati, South Indian, *c.* AD1550

1696 Mask of Xiutechuhtli, Mixtec-Aztec, *c.* AD1500

1697 Hoa Hakananai'a, Easter Island, *c.* AD1000

250th Anniversary of the British Museum

2003 (7 Oct.) One side phosphor band (2nd), two phosphor bands ((1st), (E), 47p.) or phosphor background at left and band at right (42p., 68p.). Perf 14 × 14½

2404	**1692**	(2nd) multicoloured	90	90	☐	☐
2405	**1693**	(1st) multicoloured	1·00	1·00	☐	☐
2406	**1694**	(E) multicoloured	1·75	1·50	☐	☐
2407	**1695**	42p. multicoloured	90	1·00	☐	☐
2408	**1696**	47p. multicoloured	1·00	1·00	☐	☐
2409	**1697**	68p. multicoloured	1·10	1·25	☐	☐
Set of 6			6·25	6·00	☐	☐
First Day Cover				6·50	☐	
Presentation Pack (PO Pack No. 352)			7·00		☐	
PHQ Cards (*set of 6*) (258)			1·75	6·50	☐	☐
Set of 6 Gutter Pairs			12·50		☐	

1698 Ice Spiral

1699 Icicle Star

1700 Wall of Ice Blocks

1701 Ice Ball

1702 Ice Hole

1703 Snow Pyramids

Christmas. Ice Sculptures by Andy Goldsworthy

2003 (4 Nov.) Self-adhesive. One side phosphor band (2nd), 'all-over' phosphor (1st) or two bands (others). Die-cut perf 14½ × 14

2410	**1698**	(2nd) multicoloured	90	90
2411	**1699**	(1st) multicoloured	1·00	1·00
2412	**1700**	(E) multicoloured	1·75	1·50
2413	**1701**	53p. multicoloured	1·25	1·25
2414	**1702**	68p. multicoloured	1·40	1·50
2415	**1703**	£1·12 multicoloured	1·50	1·60
Set of 6			7·00	6·75
First Day Cover				7·50
Presentation Pack (PO Pack No. 353)			7·25	
PHQ Cards (*set of 6*) (259)			1·75	7·50

The 2nd and 1st class were also issued in separate sheets of 20, each stamp printed in photogravure instead of photogravure and accompanied by a half stamp-size *se-tenant* label showing either animals, ice sculptures or a personal photograph.

Year Pack 2003

2003 (4 Nov.) Comprises Nos. 2327/2357, 2360/2365, 2368/2377, 2381/2390, 2392/2401 and 2404/2415

CP2415*a*	Year Pack	70·00	

Post Office Yearbook

2003 (4 Nov.) Comprises Nos. 2327/2357, 2360/2365, 2368/2377, 2381/2390, 2392/2401 and 2404/2415

YB2415*a*	Yearbook	55·00	

1704 Rugby Scenes

England's Victory in Rugby World Cup Championship, Australia. Miniature Sheet

2003 (19 Dec.) Sheet 115×85 mm. Multicoloured. Two phosphor bands. Perf 14

MS2416 **1704** (1st) England flags and fans; (1st) England team standing in circle before match; 68p. World Cup trophy; 68p. Victorious England players after match	9·00	9·00
First Day Cover		9·25
Presentation Pack (PO Pack No. M9B)	20·00	

1705 Dolgoch, Rheilffordd Talyllyn Railway, Gwynedd

1706 CR Class 439, Bo'ness and Kinneil Railway, West Lothian

1707 GCR Class 8K, Leicestershire

1708 GWR Manor Class *Bradley Manor*, Severn Valley Railway, Worcestershire

1709 SR West Country class *Blackmoor Vale*, Bluebell Railway, East Sussex

1710 BR Standard class, Keighley & Worth Valley Railway, Yorkshire

Classic Locomotives

2004 (13 Jan.) One side phosphor band (20p.) or two phosphor bands (others). Perf 14½

2417	**1705**	20p. multicoloured	65	65
2418	**1706**	28p. multicoloured	75	75
2419	**1707**	(E) multicoloured	1·75	1·50
2420	**1708**	42p. multicoloured	1·00	1·00
2421	**1709**	47p. multicoloured	1·10	1·25
2422	**1710**	68p. multicoloured	1·25	1·25
Set of 6			5·75	5·50
First Day Cover				6·00
Presentation Pack (PO Pack No. 355)			10·00	
PHQ *Cards* (*set of 7*) (260)			2·00	6·25
Set of 6 Gutter Pairs			11·50	
MS2423 190×67 mm. Nos. 2417/2422			14·50	14·50
First Day Cover				15·00

The seven PHQ cards depict the six stamps and the miniature sheet.

Nos. 2418/2420 were also issued in the £7·44 Letters by Night booklet, No. DX32.

1711 Postman

1712 Face

1713 Duck

1714 Baby

1715 Aircraft

Greetings Stamps Occasions (4th series)

2004 (3 Feb.) Two phosphor bands. Perf 14½ × 14

2424	**1711**	(1st) bright mauve and black	1·00	1·00
		a. Horiz strip of 5. Nos. 2424/2428	4·50	4·50
2425	**1712**	(1st) magenta and black	1·00	1·00
2426	**1713**	(1st) lemon and black	1·00	1·00
2427	**1714**	(1st) pale turquoise-green and black	1·00	1·00
2428	**1715**	(1st) bright new blue and black	1·00	1·00
Set of 5			4·50	4·50
First Day Cover				5·00
Presentation Pack (PO Pack No. M10)			5·75	
PHQ *Cards* (*set of 5*) (PSM10)			1·50	6·00
Gutter Block of 10			9·00	

Nos. 2424/2428 were printed together, *se-tenant*, as horizontal strips of five in sheets of 25 (5×5).

Nos. 2424/2428 were also issued in sheets of 20 containing the five designs *se-tenant* with half stamp-size printed message labels. Similar sheets containing either Nos. 2424 and 2428 or Nos. 2425/2427 came with personal photographs on the labels.

1716 Map showing Middle Earth

1717 Forest of Lothlórien in Spring

1718 Dust-jacket for
The Fellowship of the Ring

1719 Rivendell

1720 The Hall at Bag End

1721 Orthanc

1722 Doors of Durin

1723 Barad-dûr

1724 Minas Tirith

1725 Fangorn Forest

50th Anniversary of Publication of *The Fellowship of the Ring* and *The Two Towers* by J. R. R. Tolkien

2004 (26 Feb.) Two phosphor bands. Perf 14½

2429	**1716**	(1st) multicoloured	1·00	1·00
		a. Block of 10.		
		Nos. 2429/2438	9·00	9·00
2430	**1717**	(1st) multicoloured	1·00	1·00
2431	**1718**	(1st) multicoloured	1·00	1·00
2432	**1719**	(1st) multicoloured	1·00	1·00
2433	**1720**	(1st) multicoloured	1·00	1·00
2434	**1721**	(1st) multicoloured	1·00	1·00
2435	**1722**	(1st) multicoloured	1·00	1·00
2436	**1723**	(1st) multicoloured	1·00	1·00
2437	**1724**	(1st) multicoloured	1·00	1·00

2438	**1725**	(1st) multicoloured	1·00	1·00
Set of 10			9·00	9·00
First Day Cover				9·25
Presentation Pack (PO Pack No. 356)			10·50	
PHQ Cards (*set of* 10) (261)			3·00	10·50
Gutter Block of 20			18·00	

Nos. 2429/2438 were printed together, *se-tenant*, in blocks of ten (5×2) throughout the sheet.

1726 Ely Island, Lower
Lough Erne

1727 Giant's Causeway,
Antrim Coast

1728 Slemish, Antrim
Mountains

1729 Banns Road,
Mourne Mountains

1730 Glenelly Valley,
Sperrins

1731 Islandmore,
Strangford Lough

A British Journey (2nd series): Northern Ireland

2004 (16 Mar.) One side phosphor band (2nd) or two phosphor bands (others). Perf 14½

(a) Ordinary gum

2439	**1726**	(2nd) multicoloured	90	90
2440	**1727**	(1st) multicoloured	1·00	1·00
2441	**1728**	(E) multicoloured	1·75	1·50
2442	**1729**	42p. multicoloured	70	85
2443	**1730**	47p. multicoloured	85	95
2444	**1731**	68p. multicoloured	95	1·10
Set of 6			5·75	5·50
First Day Cover				5·75
Presentation Pack (PO Pack No. 357)			6·00	
PHQ Cards (*set of* 6) (262)			1·75	5·75
Set of 6 *Gutter Pairs*			11·50	

(b) Self-adhesive. Die-cut perf 14½

2445	**1727**	(1st) multicoloured	3·25	3·25

No. 2445 was only issued in £1·68 stamp booklets in which the surplus self-adhesive paper around each stamp was removed.

1732 *Lace 1 (trial proof) 1968 (Sir Terry Frost)*

1733 *Coccinelle (Sonia Delaunay)*

Centenary of the Entente Cordiale. Contemporary Paintings

2004 (6 Apr.) Two phosphor bands. Perf 14 × 14½

2446	**1732**	28p. grey, black and rosine	80	80	
2447	**1733**	57p. multicoloured	1·25	1·25	
Set of 2			1·75	1·75	
First Day Cover				1·90	
Presentation Pack (PO Pack No. 358)			8·00		
Presentation Pack (UK and French stamps)			8·00		
PHQ Cards (set of 2) (263)			60	2·00	
Set of 2 Gutter Pairs			3·50		
Set of 2 Traffic Light Gutter Blocks of 4			10·00		

Stamps in similar designs were issued by France and these are included in the joint Presentation Pack.

1734 *RMS Queen Mary 2, 2004 (Edward D. Walker)*

1735 *SS Canberra 1961 (David Cobb)*

1736 *RMS Queen Mary 1936 (Charles Pears)*

1737 *RMS Mauretania, 1907 (Thomas Henry)*

1738 *SS City of New York, 1888 (Raphael Monleaon y Torres)*

1739 *PS Great Western, 1838 (Joseph Walter)*

Ocean Liners

2004 (13 Apr.) Two phosphor bands.

(a) Gravure. Ordinary gum. Perf 14½ × 14

2448	**1734**	(1st) multicoloured	1·00	1·00	
2449	**1735**	(E) multicoloured	1·75	1·50	
2450	**1736**	42p. multicoloured	70	80	
2451	**1737**	47p. multicoloured	75	85	
2452	**1738**	57p. multicoloured	80	90	
2453	**1739**	68p. multicoloured	85	95	
Set of 6			5·25	5·00	

First Day Cover		5·50	
Presentation Pack (PO Pack No. 359)	5·50		
PHQ Cards (set of 7) (264)	2·00	5·25	
Set of 6 Gutter Pairs	10·50		
MS2454 114 × 104 mm. Nos. 2448/2453	7·25	7·25	
First Day Cover		7·50	

(b) Self-adhesive. Die-cut perf 14½ × 14

2455	**1734**	(1st) multicoloured	3·25	3·25	

Nos. 2448/2455 commemorate the introduction to service of the *Queen Mary 2*.

No. 2455 was only issued in £1·68 stamp booklets in which the surplus self-adhesive paper around each stamp was removed.

The complete miniature sheet is shown on one of the PHQ cards with the others depicting individual stamps. See also No. 2614.

For T **1739** printed in lithography, see No. 2514.

1740 *Dianthus Allwoodii Group*

1741 *Dahlia 'Garden Princess'*

1742 *Clematis 'Arabella'*

1743 *Miltonia 'French Lake'*

1744 *Lilium 'Lemon Pixie'*

1745 *Delphinium 'Clifford Sky'*

Bicentenary of the Royal Horticultural Society (1st issue)

2004 (25 May) One side phosphor band (2nd) or 'all-over' phosphor (others). Perf 14½

2456	**1740**	(2nd) multicoloured	90	90	
2457	**1741**	(1st) multicoloured	1·00	1·00	
2458	**1742**	(E) multicoloured	1·75	1·50	
2459	**1743**	42p. multicoloured	80	85	
2460	**1744**	47p. multicoloured	85	90	
2461	**1745**	68p. multicoloured	90	1·00	
Set of 6			5·75	5·50	
First Day Cover				5·75	
Presentation Pack (PO Pack No. 360)			5·75		
PHQ Cards (set of 7) (265)			2·00	6·50	
Set of 6 Gutter Pairs			11·50		
MS2462 115 × 105 mm. Nos. 2456/2461			6·50	6·50	
First Day Cover				7·25	

The complete miniature sheet is shown on one of the PHQ cards with the others depicting individual stamps.

The 1st class stamp was also issued in sheets of 20, printed in lithography instead of gravure, each stamp accompanied by a *se-tenant* stamp-size label. Nos. 2456/2461 were also, issued in the £7·23 The Glory of the Garden booklet No. DX33.

Bicentenary of the Royal Horticultural Society (2nd issue). Booklet stamps

2004 (25 May) Designs as Nos. 1955, 1958 and 1962 (1997 Greeting Stamps 19th-century Flower Paintings). Two phosphor bands. Perf 15×14 (with one elliptical hole in each vertical side)

2463	**1280**	(1st) multicoloured	2·75	2·75	☐	☐
2464	**1283**	(1st) multicoloured	1·40	1·40	☐	☐
2465	**1287**	(1st) multicoloured	2·75	2·75	☐	☐
Set of 3			6·50	6·50	☐	☐

On Nos. 2463/2465 the phosphor bands appear at the left and the centre of each stamp.

Nos. 2463/2465 were only issued in the in £7·23 The Glory of the Garden booklet, No. DX33.

1746 Barmouth Bridge

1747 Hyddgen, Plynlimon

1748 Brecon Beacons

1749 Pen-pych, Rhondda Valley

1750 Rhewl, Dee Valley

1751 Marloes Sands

A British Journey (3rd series): Wales

2004 (15 June) One centre phosphor band (2nd), 'all-over' phosphor (1st) or two phosphor bands (others)

(a) Ordinary gum. Perf 14½

2466	**1746**	(2nd) multicoloured	90	90	☐	☐
2467	**1747**	(1st) multicoloured	1·00	1·00	☐	☐
2468	**1748**	40p. multicoloured	70	70	☐	☐
2469	**1749**	43p. multicoloured	75	75	☐	☐
2470	**1750**	47p. multicoloured	80	85	☐	☐
2471	**1751**	68p. multicoloured	90	95	☐	☐
Set of 6			4·50	4·50	☐	☐
First Day Cover				4·75		☐
Presentation Pack (PO Pack No. 361)			4·75			☐
PHQ Cards (*set of 6*) (266)			1·75	5·25	☐	☐
Set of 6 Gutter Pairs			9·00			☐

(b) Self-adhesive. Die-cut perf 14½

2472	**1747**	(1st) multicoloured	3·25	3·25	☐	☐

The 1st and 40p. values include the EUROPA emblem.

No. 2472 was only issued in £1·68 stamp booklets in which the surplus self-adhesive paper around each stamp was removed.

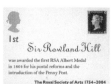

1752 Sir Rowland Hill Award

1753 William Shipley (Founder of Royal Society of Arts)

1754 'RSA' as Typewriter Keys and Shorthand

1755 Chimney Sweep

1756 Gill Typeface

1757 'Zero Waste'

250th Anniversary of the Royal Society of Arts

2004 (10 Aug.) Two phosphor bands. Perf 14

2473	**1752**	(1st) multicoloured	1·00	1·00	☐	☐
2474	**1753**	40p. multicoloured	75	75	☐	☐
2475	**1754**	43p. multicoloured	80	80	☐	☐
2476	**1755**	47p. multicoloured	1·00	1·00	☐	☐
2477	**1756**	57p. silver, vermilion and black	1·25	1·25	☐	☐
2478	**1757**	68p. silver, vermilion and black	1·50	1·50	☐	☐
Set of 6			5·50	5·50	☐	☐
First Day Cover				5·75		☐
Presentation Pack (PO Pack No. 362)			6·00			☐
PHQ Cards (*set of 6*) (267)			1·75	6·50	☐	☐
Set of 6 Gutter Pairs			11·00			☐

1758 Pine Marten

1759 Roe Deer

1760 Badger

1761 Yellow-necked Mouse

1762 Wild Cat

1763 Red Squirrel

1764 Stoat

1765 Natterer's Bat

1766 Mole

1767 Fox

1768 Private McNamara, 5th Dragoon Guards, Heavy Brigade Charge, Battle of Balaklava

1769 Piper Muir, 42nd Regt of Foot, Amphibious Assault on Kerch

1770 Sergeant Major Edwards, Scots Fusilier Guards, Gallant Action, Battle of Inkerman

1771 Sergeant Powell, 1st Regt of Foot Guards, Battles of Alma and Inkerman

1772 Sergeant Major Poole, Royal Sappers and Miners, Defensive Line, Battle of Inkerman

1773 Sergeant Glasgow, Royal Artillery, Gun Battery besieged Sevastopol

Woodland Animals

2004 (16 Sept.) Two phosphor bands. Perf 14½

2479	**1758**	(1st) multicoloured	1·00	1·00	☐ ☐
		a. Block of 10.			
		Nos. 2479/2488	9·00	9·00	☐ ☐
2480	**1759**	(1st) multicoloured	1·00	1·00	☐ ☐
2481	**1760**	(1st) multicoloured	1·00	1·00	☐ ☐
2482	**1761**	(1st) multicoloured	1·00	1·00	☐ ☐
2483	**1762**	(1st) multicoloured	1·00	1·00	☐ ☐
2484	**1763**	(1st) multicoloured	1·00	1·00	☐ ☐
2485	**1764**	(1st) multicoloured	1·00	1·00	☐ ☐
2486	**1765**	(1st) multicoloured	1·00	1·00	☐ ☐
2487	**1766**	(1st) multicoloured	1·00	1·00	☐ ☐
2488	**1767**	(1st) multicoloured	1·00	1·00	☐ ☐
Set of 10			9·00	9·00	☐ ☐
First Day Cover				9·25	☐
Presentation Pack (PO Pack No. 363)			10·00		☐
PHQ Cards (*set of 10*) (268)			3·00	10·00	☐ ☐
Gutter Block of 20			18·00		☐
Traffic Light Gutter Block of 20			40·00		☐

Nos. 2479/2488 were printed together, *se-tenant*, in blocks of ten (5×2) throughout the sheet.

For the miniature sheet celebrating the opening of the new Scottish Parliament Building, Edinburgh, issued 5 October 2004, see the Regionals section.

150th Anniversary of the Crimean War

2004 (12 Oct.) One centre phosphor band (2nd) or two phosphor bands (others). Perf 14

2489	**1768**	(2nd) multicoloured	90	90	☐ ☐
2490	**1769**	(1st) multicoloured	1·00	1·00	☐ ☐
2491	**1770**	40p. multicoloured	1·00	1·00	☐ ☐
2492	**1771**	57p. multicoloured	1·10	1·10	☐ ☐
2493	**1772**	68p. multicoloured	1·25	1·25	☐ ☐
2494	**1773**	£1·12 multicoloured	1·60	1·60	☐ ☐
Set of 6			6·00	6·00	☐ ☐
First Day Cover				6·25	☐
Presentation Pack (PO Pack No. 364)			6·25		☐
PHQ Cards (*set of 6*) (269)			1·75	7·00	☐ ☐
Set of 6 Gutter Pairs			12·00		☐
Set of 6 Traffic Light Pairs			38·00		☐

Nos. 2489/2494 show Crimean Heroes photographs taken in 1856.

1774 Father Christmas on Snowy Roof

1775 Celebrating the Sunrise

1776 On Roof in Gale

1777 With Umbrella in Rain

1782 Clydesdale Mare and Foal

1783 Dairy Shorthorn Cattle

1778 In Fog on Edge of Roof with Torch

1779 Sheltering from Hailstorm behind Chimney

1784 Border Collie Dog

1785 Light Sussex Chicks

Christmas. Father Christmas

2004 (2 Nov.) One centre phosphor band (2nd) or two phosphor bands (others). Perf 14½ × 14

		(a) Self-adhesive			
2495	**1774**	(2nd) multicoloured	90	90	☐ ☐
2496	**1775**	(1st) multicoloured	1·00	1·00	☐ ☐
2497	**1776**	40p. multicoloured	80	80	☐ ☐
2498	**1777**	57p. multicoloured	1·00	1·00	☐ ☐
2499	**1778**	68p. multicoloured	1·10	1·10	☐ ☐
2500	**1779**	£1·12 multicoloured	1·25	1·25	☐ ☐
Set of 6			5·50	5·50	☐ ☐
First Day Cover				5·75	☐
Presentation Pack (PO Pack No. 365)			5·75		☐
PHQ Cards (set of 7) (270)			2·00	6·25	☐ ☐

	(b) Ordinary gum			
MS2501 115 × 105 mm. As Nos. 2495/2500		6·00	6·00	☐ ☐
First Day Cover			6·25	☐

The seven PHQ cards depict the six individual stamps and the miniature sheet.

The 2nd and 1st class stamps were also issued in sheets of 20 printed in lithography instead of gravure containing ten 1st class and ten 2nd class stamps, each stamp accompanied by a *se-tenant* stamp-size label showing Father Christmas.

Separate sheets of either 20 1st or 20 2nd class were available with personal photographs.

1786 Suffolk Sheep

1787 Bagot Goat

Year Pack 2004

2004 (2 Nov.) Comprises Nos. 2417/2422, 2424/2444, 2446/2453, 2456/2461, 2466/2471 and 2473/2500

CP2500a	Year Pack	65·00	☐

Post Office Yearbook

2004 (2 Nov.) Comprises Nos. 2417/2422, 2424/2444, 2446/2453, 2456/2461, 2466/2471 and 2473/2500

YB2500a	Yearbook	60·00	☐

1788 Norfolk Black Turkeys

1789 Embden Geese

Farm Animals

2005 (11 Jan.) Two phosphor bands. Perf 14½

2502	**1780**	(1st) multicoloured	1·00	1·00	☐ ☐
		a. Block of 10.			
		Nos. 2502/2511	9·00	9·00	☐ ☐
2503	**1781**	(1st) multicoloured	1·00	1·00	☐ ☐
2504	**1782**	(1st) multicoloured	1·00	1·00	☐ ☐
2505	**1783**	(1st) multicoloured	1·00	1·00	☐ ☐
2506	**1784**	(1st) multicoloured	1·00	1·00	☐ ☐
2507	**1785**	(1st) multicoloured	1·00	1·00	☐ ☐
2508	**1786**	(1st) multicoloured	1·00	1·00	☐ ☐
2509	**1787**	(1st) multicoloured	1·00	1·00	☐ ☐
2510	**1788**	(1st) multicoloured	1·00	1·00	☐ ☐
2511	**1789**	(1st) multicoloured	1·00	1·00	☐ ☐
Set of 10			9·00	9·00	☐ ☐
First Day Cover				9·25	☐
Presentation Pack (PO Pack No. 367)			9·25		☐
PHQ Cards (set of 10) (271)			3·00	10·50	☐ ☐
Gutter Block of 20			18·00		☐
Traffic Light Gutter Block of 20			65·00		☐

Nos. 2502/2511 were printed together, *se-tenant*, in blocks of ten (5 × 2) throughout the sheet.

Nos. 2502/2511 were also issued in sheets of 20, printed in lithography instead of gravure, containing two of each of the ten designs, arranged in vertical strips of five alternated with printed labels.

1780 British Saddleback Pigs

1781 Khaki Campbell Ducks

1790 Old Harry Rocks,
Studland Bay

1791 Wheal Coates,
St Agnes

1792 Start Point, Start Bay

1793 Horton Down, Wiltshire

1794 Chiselcombe,
Exmoor

1795 St James's Stone,
Lundy

A British Journey (4th series): South West England

2005 (8 Feb.) One centre phosphor band (2nd) or two phosphor
bands (others). Perf 14½

2512	**1790**	(2nd) multicoloured	90	90	☐ ☐
2513	**1791**	(1st) multicoloured	1·00	1·00	☐ ☐
2514	**1792**	40p. multicoloured	75	75	☐ ☐
2515	**1793**	43p. multicoloured	85	85	☐ ☐
2516	**1794**	57p. multicoloured	1·00	1·00	☐ ☐
2517	**1795**	68p. multicoloured	1·25	1·25	☐ ☐
Set of 6			5·25	5·25	☐
First Day Cover				5·50	☐
Presentation Pack (PO Pack No. 368)			5·50		☐
PHQ Cards (*set of 6*) (272)			1·75	5·75	☐ ☐
Set of 6 Gutter Pairs			10·50		☐

1796 Mr Rochester   **1797** Come to Me   **1798** In the Comfort
of her Bonnet

1799 La Ligne des
Rats   **1800** Refectory   **1801** Inspection

150th Death Anniversary of Charlotte Brontë.
Illustrations of Scenes from *Jane Eyre* by Paula Rego

2005 (24 Feb.) One centre phosphor band (2nd) or two
phosphor bands (others). Perf 14 × 14½

2518	**1796**	(2nd) multicoloured	90	90	☐ ☐
2519	**1797**	(1st) multicoloured	1·00	1·00	☐ ☐
2520	**1798**	40p. multicoloured	1·00	1·00	☐ ☐
2521	**1799**	57p. silver, brownish			
		grey and black	1·25	1·25	☐ ☐
2522	**1800**	68p. multicoloured	1·40	1·40	☐ ☐
2523	**1801**	£1·12 silver, brownish			
		grey and black	1·60	1·60	☐ ☐
Set of 6			6·50	6·50	☐ ☐
First Day Cover				7·00	☐
Presentation Pack (PO Pack No. 369)			6.75		☐
PHQ Cards (*set of 6*) (273)			2·00	7·00	☐ ☐
Set of 6 Gutter Pairs			13·00		☐
Set of 6 Traffic Light Gutter Blocks of 4			48·00		☐
MS2524 114 × 105 mm. Nos. 2518/2523			6·50	6·50	☐ ☐
First Day Cover				7·00	☐

The complete miniature sheet is shown on one of the PHQ
cards with the others depicting individual stamps.
   Nos. 2518/2523 were also issued in the £7·43 The Brontë
Sisters booklet No. DX34.

1802 Spinning Coin

1803 Rabbit out of Hat Trick

1804 Knotted Scarf Trick

1805 Card Trick

1806 Pyramid under Fez Trick

Centenary of the Magic Circle

2005 (15 Mar.) Two phosphor bands. Perf 14½ × 14

2525	**1802**	(1st) multicoloured	1·00	1·00	☐ ☐
2526	**1803**	40p. multicoloured	1·00	1·00	☐ ☐
2527	**1804**	47p. multicoloured	1·25	1·25	☐ ☐
2528	**1805**	68p. multicoloured	1·40	1·40	☐ ☐
2529	**1806**	£1·12 multicoloured	1·75	1·75	☐ ☐
Set of 5			5·75	5·75	☐ ☐
First Day Cover				6·00	☐
Presentation Pack (PO Pack No. 370)			6·00		☐
PHQ Cards (*set of 5*) (274)			1·50	6·00	☐ ☐
Set of 5 Gutter Pairs			11·50		☐

Nos. 2525/2529 are each printed with instructions for the illusion or trick on the stamp.

No. 2525 can be rubbed with a coin to reveal the 'head' or 'tail' of a coin. The two versions, which appear identical before rubbing, are printed in alternate rows of the sheet, indicated by the letters H and T in the side margins of the sheet.

No. 2525 was also issued in sheets of 20 with *se-tenant* labels showing magic tricks, printed in lithography instead of gravure.

Nos. 2526 and 2528 each show optical illusions.

The spotted scarf on No. 2527 and the fezzes on No. 2529 are printed in thermochromic inks which fade temporarily when exposed to heat, making the pyramid under the centre fez visible.

1806a

50th Anniversary of First Castles Definitives. Miniature Sheet

2005 (22 Mar.) Sheet 127×73 mm, printed on pale cream. 'All-over' phosphor. Perf 11×11½

MS2530 **1806a** 50p. brownish-black; 50p. black; £1 dull vermilion; £1 royal blue		4·50	4·50	☐ ☐
First Day Cover			5·75	☐
Presentation Pack (PO Pack No. 69)		5·75		☐
PHQ Cards (*set of* 5) (D28)		1·50	5·75	☐ ☐

See also No. 3221

1807 Prince Charles and Mrs Camilla Parker Bowles

Royal Wedding. Miniature Sheet

2005 (9 Apr.) Sheet 85×115 mm. Multicoloured 'All-over' phosphor. Perf 13½×14

MS2531 **1807** 30p.×2 Prince Charles and Mrs Camilla Parker Bowles laughing; 68p.×2 Prince Charles and Mrs Camilla Parker Bowles smiling into camera	4·50	4·50	☐ ☐
First Day Cover		5·00	☐
Presentation Pack (PO Pack No. M10)	8·00		☐

1808 Hadrian's Wall, England

1809 Uluru-Kata Tjuta National Park, Australia

1810 Stonehenge, England

1811 Wet Tropics of Queensland, Australia

1812 Blenheim Palace, England

1813 Greater Blue Mountains Area, Australia

1814 Heart of Neolithic Orkney, Scotland

1815 Purnululu National Park, Australia

World Heritage Sites

2005 (21 Apr.) One side phosphor band (2nd) or two phosphor bands (others). Perf 14½

2532	**1808**	(2nd) multicoloured		90	90	☐ ☐
		a. Horiz pair. Nos. 2532/2533		1·75	1·75	☐ ☐
2533	**1809**	(2nd) multicoloured		90	90	☐ ☐
2534	**1810**	(1st) multicoloured		1·00	1·00	☐ ☐
		a. Horiz pair. Nos. 2534/2535		2·00	2·00	☐ ☐
2535	**1811**	(1st) multicoloured		1·00	1·00	☐ ☐
2536	**1812**	47p. multicoloured		80	80	☐ ☐
		a. Horiz pair. Nos. 2536/2537		1·60	1·60	☐ ☐
2537	**1813**	47p. multicoloured		80	80	☐ ☐
2538	**1814**	68p. multicoloured		1·00	1·00	☐ ☐
		a. Horiz pair. Nos. 2538/2539		2·00	2·00	☐ ☐

2539	**1815**	68p. multicoloured		1·00	1·00
Set of 8				6·50	6·50
First Day Cover					7·75
Presentation Pack (PO Pack No. 371)				7.50	
Presentation Pack					
(UK and Australian stamps)				11.00	
PHQ Cards (*set of 8*) (275)				2·50	7·50
Set of 4 Gutter Strips of 4				13·00	
Set of 4 Traffic Light Gutter Blocks of 8				32·00	

Nos. 2532/2533, 2534/2535, 2536/2537 and 2538/2539 were each printed together, *se-tenant*, in horizontal pairs.

Stamps in these designs were also issued by Australia and these are included in the joint Presentation Pack.

1816 Ensign of the Scots Guards, 2002

1817 Queen taking the salute as Colonel-in-Chief of the Grenadier Guards, 1983

1818 Trumpeter of the Household Cavalry, 2004

1819 Welsh Guardsman, 1990s

1820 Queen riding side-saddle, 1972

1821 Queen and Duke of Edinburgh in Carriage, 2004

Trooping the Colour

2005 (7 June) One phosphor band (2nd), two phosphor bands (others). Perf 14½

2540	**1816**	(2nd) multicoloured	90	90
2541	**1817**	(1st) multicoloured	1·00	1·00
2542	**1818**	42p. multicoloured	85	85
2543	**1819**	60p. multicoloured	1·00	1·00
2544	**1820**	68p. multicoloured	1·10	1·10
2545	**1821**	£1·12 multicoloured	1·50	1·50
Set of 6			5·75	5·75
First Day Cover				6·00
Presentation Pack (PO Pack No. 372)			5·75	
PHQ Cards (*set of 6*) (276)			2·00	11·00
Set of 6 Gutter Pairs			11·50	
MS2546 115 × 105 mm. Nos. 2540/2545			5·50	5·50
First Day Cover				5·75

The six PHQ cards show the six stamps and the miniature sheet.

1822

60th Anniversary of End of the Second World War. Miniature Sheet

2005 (5 July) Sheet 115 × 105 mm. Containing design as T **1200** (1995 Peace and Freedom) but with service indicator and No. 1668 × 5. Two phosphor bands. Perf 15 × 14 (with one elliptical hole in each vertical side) (No. 1668) or 14½ × 14 (T **1200**)

MS2547	**1822**	(1st) gold × 5; (1st) silver,		
		blue and grey-black	5·00	5·25
First Day Cover				5·50

1823 Norton F.1, Road Version of Race Winner (1991)

1824 BSA Rocket 3, Early Three Cylinder Superbike (1969)

1825 Vincent Black Shadow, Fastest Standard Motorcycle (1949)

1826 Triumph Speed Twin, Two Cylinder Innovation (1938)

1827 Brough Superior, Bespoke Luxury Motorcycle (1930)

1828 Royal Enfield, Small Engined Motor Bicycle (1914)

Motorcycles

2005 (19 July) Two phosphor bands. Perf 14 × 14½

2548	**1823**	(1st) multicoloured	90	90
2549	**1824**	40p. multicoloured	60	60
2550	**1825**	42p. multicoloured	65	65
2551	**1826**	47p. multicoloured	80	80
2552	**1827**	60p. multicoloured	1·00	1·00
2553	**1828**	68p. multicoloured	1·25	1·25
Set of 6			4·50	4·50

First Day Cover		5·75	☐
Presentation Pack (PO Pack No. 373)	5·25		☐
PHQ Cards (*set of 6*) (277)	1·75	5·75	☐ ☐
Set of 6 Gutter Pairs	9·00		☐

1829

**London's Successful Bid for Olympic Games, 2012.
Miniature Sheet**

2005 (5 Aug.) Sheet 115×105 mm. Containing designs as Types **1255/1259**, but with service indicator. Multicoloured. Two phosphor bands. Perf 14½

MS2554 **1829** (1st) Athlete celebrating ×2; (1st) Throwing the javelin; (1st) Swimming; (1st) Athlete on starting blocks; (1st) Basketball	5·00	5·00	☐ ☐
First Day Cover		5·75	☐
Presentation Pack (PO Pack No. M11)	5·25		☐

Stamps from No. **MS**2554 are all inscribed 'London 2012–Host City' and have imprint date '2005'. The design as T **1259** omits the Olympic rings.

1830 African Woman eating Rice

1831 Indian Woman drinking Tea

1832 Boy eating Sushi

1833 Woman eating Pasta

1834 Woman eating Chips

1835 Teenage Boy eating Apple

Europa. Gastronomy. Changing Tastes in Britain

2005 (23 Aug.) One side phosphor band (2nd) or two phosphor bands (others). Perf 14½

2555	**1830**	(2nd) multicoloured	90	90	☐ ☐
2556	**1831**	(1st) multicoloured	1·00	1·00	☐ ☐
2557	**1832**	42p. multicoloured	60	60	☐ ☐
2558	**1833**	47p. multicoloured	75	75	☐ ☐
2559	**1834**	60p. multicoloured	90	90	☐ ☐
2560	**1835**	68p. multicoloured	1·10	1·25	☐ ☐
Set of 6			4·75	4·75	☐ ☐
First Day Cover				5·00	☐
Presentation Pack (PO Pack No. 374)			5·00		☐
PHQ Cards (*set of 6*) (278)			1·75	5·75	☐ ☐
Set of 6 Gutter Pairs			9·50		☐

The 1st and 42p. values include the EUROPA emblem.

1836 *Inspector Morse*

1837 *Emmerdale*

1838 *Rising Damp*

1839 *The Avengers*

1840 *The South Bank Show*

1841 *Who Wants to be a Millionaire*

**50th Anniversary of Independent Television.
Classic ITV Programmes**

2005 (15 Sept.) One side phosphor band (2nd) or two phosphor bands (others). Perf 14½×14

2561	**1836**	(2nd) multicoloured	90	90	☐ ☐
2562	**1837**	(1st) multicoloured	1·00	1·00	☐ ☐
2563	**1838**	42p. multicoloured	60	60	☐ ☐
2564	**1839**	47p. multicoloured	75	75	☐ ☐
2565	**1840**	60p. multicoloured	90	90	☐ ☐
2566	**1841**	68p. multicoloured	1·10	1·10	☐ ☐
Set of 6			4·75	4·75	☐ ☐
First Day Cover				5·25	☐
Presentation Pack (PO Pack No. 375)			5·00		☐
PHQ Cards (*set of 6*) (279)			1·75	5·75	☐ ☐
Set of 6 Gutter Pairs			9·50		☐

The 1st class stamps were also issued in sheets of 20 with each stamp accompanied by a half stamp-size *se-tenant* label.

1842 Gazania Splendens
(Charlotte Sowerby)

1842a 'LOVE'

Smilers (1st series). Booklet stamps

2005 (4 Oct.) Designs as Types **992**, **1221**, **1286**, **1517** and **1568/1569** but smaller, 20×23 mm, and inscribed 1st as T **1842**. Self-adhesive. Two phosphor bands. Die-cut perf 15×14.

2567	**1842**	(1st) multicoloured	1·10	1·25	☐	☐
		a. Booklet pane.				
		Nos. 2567/2572	9·00		☐	
2568	**1569**	(1st) multicoloured	1·10	1·25	☐	☐
2569	**1842a**	(1st) multicoloured	1·10	1·25	☐	☐
2570	**1517**	(1st) multicoloured	1·10	1·25	☐	☐
2571	**992**	(1st) multicoloured	1·10	1·25	☐	☐
2572	**1221**	(1st) multicoloured	1·10	1·25	☐	☐
Set of 6			9·00	9·00	☐	☐
First Day Cover				9·25	☐	

Nos. 2567/2572 were printed together, *se-tenant*, in booklet panes of six in which the surplus self-adhesive paper around each stamp was removed.

Nos. 2567/2572 were re-issued on 4 July 2006 in sheets of 20 with *se-tenant* labels, printed in lithography instead of gravure.

Nos. 2568/2570 were re-issued on 18 January 2008 in sheets of 20 with circular *se-tenant* labels, printed in lithography.

No. 2567 was re-issued on 28 October 2008 in sheets of ten with circular *se-tenant* Flower Fairy labels, printed in lithography.

Stamps as Nos. 2569 and 2572 but perforated with one elliptical hole on each vertical side were issued, together with Nos. 2674 and 2821/2823 and four designs from No. **MS**3024, on 8 May 2010 in sheets of 20 stamps with *se-tenant* greetings labels.

See also No. 2693 and Nos. 2819/2824.

THE ASHES ENGLAND WINNERS 2005

1843 Cricket Scenes

England's Ashes Victory. Miniature Sheet

2005 (6 Oct.) Sheet 115×90 mm. Multicoloured. Two phosphor bands. Perf 14½×14.

MS2573	**1843**	(1st) England team with Ashes trophy; (1st) Kevin Pieterson, Michael Vaughan and Andrew Flintoff on opening day of First Test, Lords; 68p. Michael Vaughan, Third Test, Old Trafford; 68p. Second Test Edgbaston	4·00	4·00	☐ ☐
First Day Cover				5·00	☐
Presentation Pack (PO Pack No. M12)			4·25		☐

1844 *Entrepreante* with dismasted British *Belle Isle*

1845 Nelson wounded on Deck of HMS *Victory*

1846 British Cutter *Entrepreante* attempting to rescue crew of burning French *Achille*

1847 Cutter and HMS *Pickle* (schooner)

1848 British Fleet attacking in two columns

1849 Franco/Spanish Fleet putting to sea from Cadiz

Bicentenary of the Battle of Trafalgar (1st issue). Scenes from *Panorama of the Battle of Trafalgar* by William Heath

2005 (18 Oct.) Two phosphor bands. Perf 15×14½

2574	**1844**	(1st) multicoloured	1·00	1·00	☐	☐
		a. Horiz pair.				
		Nos. 2574/2575	2·00	2·00	☐	☐
2575	**1845**	(1st) multicoloured	1·00	1·00	☐	☐
2576	**1846**	42p. multicoloured	70	80	☐	☐
		a. Horiz pair.				
		Nos. 2576/2577	1·60	1·60	☐	☐
2577	**1847**	42p. multicoloured	70	80	☐	☐
2578	**1848**	68p. multicoloured	1·00	1·10	☐	☐
		a. Horiz pair.				
		Nos. 2578/2579	2·00	2·00	☐	☐
2579	**1849**	68p. multicoloured	1·00	1·10	☐	☐
Set of 6			5·00	5·00	☐	☐
First Day Cover				5·50	☐	
Presentation Pack (PO Pack No. 376)			5·75		☐	
PHQ Cards (*set of 7*) (280)			2·00	11·50	☐	☐
Set of 3 Gutter Strips of 4			10·00		☐	
MS2580	190×68 mm. Nos. 2574/2579		5·25	5·50	☐	☐
First Day Cover				5·75	☐	

Nos. 2574/2575, 2576/2577 and 2578/2579 were each printed together, *se-tenant*, in horizontal pairs throughout the sheets, each pair forming a composite design and were also issued in the £7·26 Bicentenary of the Battle of Trafalgar booklet, No. DX35.

The phosphor bands are at just left of centre and at right of each stamp.

The seven PHQ cards depict the six individual stamps and the miniature sheet.

**Bicentenary of the Battle of Trafalgar (2nd issue).
Booklet stamp**

2005 (18 Oct.) Design as T **1516** (White Ensign from 2001 Submarine Centenary). Litho. Two phosphor bands. Perf 14½
2581 **1516** (1st) multicoloured 1·50 1·50 ☐ ☐
No. 2581 was only issued in the £7·26 Bicentenary of the Battle of Trafalgar, No. DX41, £7·40 Ian Fleming's James Bond, No. DX35 and £7·93 Royal Navy Uniforms, No. DX47, booklets.

1850 Black Madonna and Child from Haiti

1851 *Madonna and Child* (Marianne Stokes)

1852 The Virgin Mary with the Infant Christ

1853 Choctaw Virgin Mother and Child (Fr. John Giuliani)

1854 Madonna and the Infant Jesus (from India)

1855 Come let us adore Him (Dianne Tchumut)

Christmas. Madonna and Child Paintings

2005 (1 Nov.) One side phosphor band (2nd) or two phosphor bands (others). Perf 14½ × 14

(a) Self-adhesive

2582	**1850**	(2nd) multicoloured	90	90	☐	☐
2583	**1851**	(1st) multicoloured	1·00	1·00	☐	☐
2584	**1852**	42p. multicoloured	90	90	☐	☐
2585	**1853**	60p. multicoloured	1·00	1·00	☐	☐
2586	**1854**	68p. multicoloured	1·25	1·25	☐	☐
2587	**1855**	£1·12 multicoloured	1·40	1·40	☐	☐
Set of 6			5·75	5·75	☐	☐
First Day Cover				6·00	☐	
Presentation Pack (PO Pack No. 377)			6·00		☐	
PHQ Cards (*set of 7*) (281)			2·00	12·00	☐	☐

(b) Ordinary gum
MS2588 115 × 102 mm. As Nos.
2582/2587 5·75 5·75 ☐ ☐
First Day Cover 6·00 ☐
The seven PHQ cards depict the six individual stamps and the miniature sheet.

Year Pack

2005 (1 Nov.) Comprises Nos. 2502/2523, 2525/2529, **MS**2531/2545, 2548/2553, 2555/2566, 2574/2579 and 2582/2587
CP2587*a* Year Pack 65·00 ☐

Post Office Yearbook

2005 (1 Nov.) Comprises Nos. 2502/2523, 2525/2529, **MS**2531/2545, 2548/2553, 2555/2566, 2574/2579 and 2582/2587
YB2587*a* Yearbook 60·00 ☐

Miniature Sheet Collection

2005 (21 Nov.) Comprises Nos. **MS**2524, **MS**2530/**MS**2531, **MS**2546/**MS**2547, **MS**2554, **MS**2573, **MS**2580 and **MS**2588
MS2588*a* Miniature Sheet Collection 45·00 ☐

1856 *The Tale of Mr. Jeremy Fisher* (Beatrix Potter)

1857 *Kipper* (Mick Inkpen)

1858 *The Enormous Crocodile* (Roald Dahl)

1859 *More About Paddington* (Michael Bond)

1860 *Comic Adventures of Boots* (Satoshi Kitamura)

1861 *Alice's Adventures in Wonderland* (Lewis Carroll)

1862 *The Very Hungry Caterpillar* (Eric Carle)

1863 *Maisy's ABC* (Lucy Cousins)

Animal Tales

2006 (10 Jan.) One side phosphor band (2nd) or two phosphor bands (others). Perf 14½

2589	**1856**	(2nd) multicoloured	90	90	☐	☐
		a. Horiz pair.				
		Nos. 2589/2590	1·75	1·75	☐	☐
2590	**1857**	(2nd) multicoloured	90	90	☐	☐
2591	**1858**	(1st) multicoloured	1·00	1·00	☐	☐
		a. Horiz pair.				
		Nos. 2591/2592	2·00	2·00	☐	☐
2592	**1859**	(1st) multicoloured	1·00	1·00	☐	☐
2593	**1860**	42p. multicoloured	80	80	☐	☐
		a. Horiz pair.				
		Nos. 2593/2594	1·60	1·60	☐	☐
2594	**1861**	42p. multicoloured	80	80	☐	☐

2595	**1862**	68p. multicoloured	1·00	1·00	☐ ☐
		a. Horiz pair.			
		Nos. 2595/2596	2·00	2·00	☐ ☐
2596	**1863**	68p. multicoloured	1·00	1·00	☐ ☐
Set of 8			6·75	6·75	☐ ☐
First Day Cover				7·75	☐
Presentation Pack (PO Pack No. 379)			8·75		☐
PHQ Cards (set of 8) (282)			2·50	7·75	☐ ☐
Set of 4 Gutter Blocks of 4			13·50		☐
Set of 4 Traffic Light Gutter Blocks of 8			50·00		☐

Nos. 2589/2590, 2591/2592, 2593/2594 and 2595/2596 were printed together, *se-tenant*, as horizontal pairs in sheets of 60 (2 panes 6×5).

No. 2595 contains two die-cut holes.

A design as No. 2592 but self-adhesive was also issued in sheets of 20 with each stamp accompanied by a *se-tenant* label.

1864 Carding Mill Valley, Shropshire   **1865** Beachy Head, Sussex

1866 St Paul's Cathedral, London   **1867** Brancaster, Norfolk

1868 Derwent Edge, Peak District   **1869** Robin Hood's Bay, Yorkshire

1870 Buttermere, Lake District   **1871** Chipping Campden, Cotswolds

1872 St Boniface Down, Isle of Wight   **1873** Chamberlain Square, Birmingham

A British Journey (5th series): England

2006 (7 Feb.) Two phosphor bands. Perf 14½

2597	**1864**	(1st) multicoloured	1·00	1·00	☐ ☐
		a. Block of 10.			
		Nos. 2597/2606	9·00	9·00	☐ ☐
2598	**1865**	(1st) multicoloured	1·00	1·00	☐ ☐
2599	**1866**	(1st) multicoloured	1·00	1·00	☐ ☐
2600	**1867**	(1st) multicoloured	1·00	1·00	☐ ☐
2601	**1868**	(1st) multicoloured	1·00	1·00	☐ ☐
2602	**1869**	(1st) multicoloured	1·00	1·00	☐ ☐
2603	**1870**	(1st) multicoloured	1·00	1·00	☐ ☐
2604	**1871**	(1st) multicoloured	1·00	1·00	☐ ☐
2605	**1872**	(1st) multicoloured	1·00	1·00	☐ ☐
2606	**1873**	(1st) multicoloured	1·00	1·00	☐ ☐
Set of 10			9·00	9·00	☐ ☐
First Day Cover				9·50	☐
Presentation Pack (PO Pack No. 380)			10·00		☐
PHQ Cards (set of 10) (283)			3·00	9·75	☐ ☐
Gutter Block of 20			18·00		☐

Nos. 2597/2606 were printed together, *se-tenant*, as blocks of ten (5×2) in sheets of 60 (2 panes of 30)

1874 Royal Albert Bridge

1875 Box Tunnel

1876 Paddington Station

1877 PSS *Great Eastern* (paddle-steamer)

1878 Clifton Suspension Bridge Design

1879 Maidenhead Bridge

Birth Bicentenary of Isambard Kingdom Brunel (engineer) (1st issue)

2006 (23 Feb.) Phosphor-coated paper (42p.) or two phosphor bands (others). Perf 14×13½

2607	**1874**	(1st) multicoloured	1·00	1·00	☐ ☐
2608	**1875**	40p. multicoloured	60	60	☐ ☐
2609	**1876**	42p. multicoloured	65	65	☐ ☐
2610	**1877**	47p. multicoloured	80	80	☐ ☐

2611	**1878**	60p. multicoloured	1·00	1·00	☐ ☐
2612	**1879**	68p. multicoloured	1·25	1·25	☐ ☐
Set of 6			4·75	4·75	☐ ☐
First Day Cover				5·25	☐
Presentation Pack (PO Pack No. 381)			5·75		☐
PHQ Cards (*set of 7*) (284)			2·00	11·00	☐ ☐
Set of 6 Gutter Pairs			9·50		☐
MS2613 190×65 mm. Nos. 2607/2612			5·00	5·00	☐ ☐
First Day Cover				5·50	☐

The phosphor bands on Nos. 2607/2608 and 2610/2612 are at just left of centre and at right of each stamp.

The complete miniature sheet is shown on one of the PHQ cards with the others depicting individual stamps.

Nos. 2607/2612 were also issued in the £7·40 Isambard Kingdom Brunel booklet, No. DX36.

Birth Bicentenary of Isambard Kingdom Brunel (engineer) (2nd issue). Booklet stamp

2006 (23 Feb.) Design as T **1739** (PS *Great Western* from 2004 Ocean Liners). Litho. Two phosphor bands. Perf 14½×14

2614	**1739**	68p. multicoloured	2·50	2·50	☐ ☐

No. 2614 was only issued in the £7·40 Isambard Kingdom Brunel stamp booklet, No. DX36.

For the miniature sheet celebrating the opening of the New Welsh Assembly, Cardiff, issued 1 March 2006, see the Regionals section.

1880 Sabre-tooth Cat

1881 Giant Deer

1882 Woolly Rhino

1883 Woolly Mammoth

1884 Cave Bear

Ice Age Animals

2006 (21 Mar.) Two phosphor bands. Perf 14½

2615	**1880**	(1st) black and silver	1·00	1·00	☐ ☐
2616	**1881**	42p. black and silver	90	90	☐ ☐
2617	**1882**	47p. black and silver	1·00	1·00	☐ ☐
2618	**1883**	68p. black and silver	1·10	1·10	☐ ☐
2619	**1884**	£1·12 black and silver	1·50	1·50	☐ ☐
Set of 5			5·00	5·00	☐ ☐
First Day Cover				5·50	☐
Presentation Pack (PO Pack No. 382)			5·50		☐
PHQ Cards (*set of 5*) (285)			1·50	5·75	☐ ☐
Set of 5 Gutter Pairs			10·00		☐

1885 On *Britannia*, 1972

1886 At Royal Windsor Horse Show, 1985

1887 At Heathrow Airport, 2001

1888 As Young Princess Elizabeth with Duchess of York, 1931

1889 At State Banquet, Ottawa, 1951

1890 Queen Elizabeth II in 1960

1891 As Princess Elizabeth, 1940

1892 With Duke of Edinburgh, 1951

80th Birthday of Queen Elizabeth II

2006 (18 Apr.) One side phosphor band (No. 2620), one centre phosphor band (No. 2621) or two phosphor bands (others). Perf 14½

2620	**1885**	(2nd) black, turquoise green and grey	90	90	☐ ☐
		a. Horiz pair. Nos. 2620/2621	1·75	1·75	☐ ☐
2621	**1886**	(2nd) black, turquoise-green and grey	90	90	☐ ☐
2622	**1887**	(1st) black, turquoise-green and grey	1·00	1·00	☐ ☐
		a. Horiz pair. Nos. 2622/2623	2·00	2·00	☐ ☐
2623	**1888**	(1st) black, turquoise-green and grey	1·00	1·00	☐ ☐
2624	**1889**	44p. black, turquoise-green and grey	75	75	☐ ☐
		a. Horiz pair. Nos. 2624/2625	1·50	1·50	☐ ☐
2625	**1890**	44p. black, turquoise-green and grey	75	75	☐ ☐
2626	**1891**	72p. black, turquoise-green and grey	1·00	1·00	☐ ☐
		a. Horiz pair. Nos. 2626/2627	2·00	2·00	☐ ☐
2627	**1892**	72p. black, turquoise-green and grey	1·00	1·00	☐ ☐
Set of 8			6·50	6·50	☐ ☐
First Day Cover				6·75	☐
Presentation Pack (PO Pack No. 383)			7·00		☐
PHQ Cards (*set of 8*) (286)			2·50	7·50	☐ ☐

Set of 4 Gutter Strips of 4   13·00   ☐
Nos. 2620/2621, 2622/2623, 2624/2625 and 2626/2627 were each printed together, *se-tenant*, as horizontal pairs in sheets of 60 (2 panes 6×5)

1893 England (1966)

1894 Italy (1934, 1938, 1982)

1895 Argentina (1978, 1986)

1896 Germany (1954, 1974, 1990)

1897 France (1998)

1898 Brazil (1958, 1962, 1970, 1994, 2002)

World Cup Football Championship, Germany.
World Cup Winners

2006 (6 June) Two phosphor bands. Perf 14½

2628	**1893**	(1st) multicoloured	1·00	1·00	☐ ☐
2629	**1894**	42p. multicoloured	80	80	☐ ☐
2630	**1895**	44p. multicoloured	85	85	☐ ☐
2631	**1896**	50p. multicoloured	1·00	1·00	☐ ☐
2632	**1897**	64p. multicoloured	1·25	1·25	☐ ☐
2633	**1898**	72p. multicoloured	1·40	1·40	☐ ☐
Set of 6			5·50	5·50	☐
First Day Cover				5·75	☐
Presentation Pack (PO Pack No. 384)			6·00		☐
PHQ Cards (*set of 6*) (287)			1·75	6·50	☐ ☐
Set of 6 Gutter Pairs			11·00		☐

The 1st class stamp was also issued in sheets of 20 with each stamp accompanied by a *se-tenant* label showing scenes from the 1966 World Cup final.

1899 30 St Mary Axe, London

1900 Maggie's Centre, Dundee

1901 Selfridges, Birmingham

1902 Downland Gridshell, Chichester

1903 An Turas, Isle of Tiree

1904 The Deep, Hull

Modern Architecture

2006 (20 June) Two phosphor bands. Perf 14½

2634	**1899**	(1st) multicoloured	1·00	1·00	☐ ☐
2635	**1900**	42p. multicoloured	65	65	☐ ☐
2636	**1901**	44p. multicoloured	70	70	☐ ☐
2637	**1902**	50p. multicoloured	85	85	☐ ☐
2638	**1903**	64p. multicoloured	1·00	1·00	☐ ☐
2639	**1904**	72p. multicoloured	1·25	1·25	☐ ☐
Set of 6			5·00	5·00	☐
First Day Cover				5·50	☐
Presentation Pack (PO Pack No. 385)			5·50		☐
PHQ Cards (*set of 6*) (288)			1·75	5·75	☐ ☐
Set of 6 Gutter Pairs			10·00		☐

1905 *Sir Winston Churchill* (Walter Sickert)

1906 *Sir Joshua Reynolds* (self-portrait)

1907 *T. S. Eliot* (Patrick Heron)

1908 *Emmeline Pankhurst* (Georgina Agnes Brackenbury)

1909 *Virginia Woolf* (photo by George Charles Beresford)

1910 *Bust of Sir Walter Scott* (Sir Francis Leggatt Chantry)

1911 *Mary Seacole* (Albert Charles Challen)

1912 *William Shakespeare* (attrib to John Taylor)

1913 *Dame Cicely Saunders* (Catherine Goodman)

1914 *Charles Darwin* (John Collier)

150th Anniversary of National Portrait Gallery, London

2006 (18 July) Two phosphor bands. Perf 14½

2640	**1905**	(1st) multicoloured	1·00	1·00	☐	☐
		a. Block of 10.				
		Nos. 2640/2649	9·00	9·00	☐	☐
2641	**1906**	(1st) multicoloured	1·00	1·00	☐	☐
2642	**1907**	(1st) multicoloured	1·00	1·00	☐	☐
2643	**1908**	(1st) multicoloured	1·00	1·00	☐	☐
2644	**1909**	(1st) multicoloured	1·00	1·00	☐	☐
2645	**1910**	(1st) multicoloured	1·00	1·00	☐	☐
2646	**1911**	(1st) multicoloured	1·00	1·00	☐	☐
2647	**1912**	(1st) multicoloured	1·00	1·00	☐	☐
2648	**1913**	(1st) multicoloured	1·00	1·00	☐	☐
2649	**1914**	(1st) multicoloured	1·00	1·00	☐	☐
Set of 10			9·00	9·00	☐	☐
First Day Cover				9·50		☐
Presentation Pack (PO Pack No. 386)			11·00		☐	
PHQ Cards (set of 10) (289)			3·00	10·00	☐	☐
Gutter Block of 20			18·00		☐	
Traffic Light Gutter Block of 20			40·00		☐	

Nos. 2640/2649 were printed together, *se-tenant*, as blocks of ten (5×2) in sheets of 60 (2 panes of 30)

> **For Nos. 2650/2657 and MS2658, Types 1915/1917, see Decimal Machin Definitives section.**

1918 Corporal Agansing Rai

1919 Boy Seaman Jack Cornwell

1920 Midshipman Charles Lucas

1921 Captain Noel Chavasse

1922 Captain Albert Ball

1923 Captain Charles Upham

150th Anniversary of the Victoria Cross (1st issue)

2006 (21 Sept.) One side phosphor band. Perf 14½×14

2659	**1918**	(1st) multicoloured	1·00	1·00	☐	☐
		a. Horiz pair.				
		Nos. 2659/2660	2·00	2·00	☐	☐
2660	**1919**	(1st) multicoloured	1·00	1·00	☐	☐
2661	**1920**	64p. multicoloured	90	90	☐	☐
		a. Horiz pair.				
		Nos. 2661/2662	1·75	1·75	☐	☐
2662	**1921**	64p. multicoloured	90	90	☐	☐
2663	**1922**	72p. multicoloured	1·25	1·25	☐	☐
		a. Horiz pair.				
		Nos. 2663/2664	2·50	2·50	☐	☐
2664	**1923**	72p. multicoloured	1·25	1·25	☐	☐
Set of 6			6·00	6·00	☐	☐
First Day Cover				6·25		☐
Presentation Pack (PO Pack No. 387)			6·25		☐	
PHQ Cards (set of 7) (290)			2·00	13·50	☐	
Set of 3 Gutter Strips of 4			12·00		☐	
MS2665 190×67 mm. No. 2666 and as						
Nos. 2659/2664 but 'all-over' phosphor			6·50	6·50	☐	
First Day Cover				6·75		☐

Nos. 2659/2660, 2661/2 and 2663/4 were each printed together, *se-tenant*, as horizontal pairs in sheets of 60 (2 panes 6×5) and were also issued in the £7·44 Victoria Cross booklet, No. DY37.

The seven PHQ cards depict the six individual stamps and the miniature sheet.

150th Anniversary of the Victoria Cross (2nd issue). Booklet stamp

2006 (21 Sept.) Design as No. 1517 (1990 Gallantry Awards). 'All-over' phosphor. Perf 14×14½

2666	**959**	20p multicoloured	1·50	1·50	☐	☐

No. 2666 was only issued in the £7·44 Victoria Cross booklet, No. DX37 and in No. **MS**2665.

1924 Sitar Player and Dancer

1925 Reggae Bass Guitarist and African Drummer

1926 Fiddler and Harpist

1927 Sax Player and Blues Guitarist

1928 Maraca Player and Salsa Dancers

Europa. Integration. Sounds of Britain

2006 (3 Oct.) 'All-over' phosphor. Perf 14½

2667	**1924**	(1st) multicoloured	1·00	1·00		
2668	**1925**	42p. multicoloured	1·00	1·00		
2669	**1926**	50p. multicoloured	1·10	1·10		
2670	**1927**	72p. multicoloured	1·25	1·25		
2671	**1928**	£1·19 multicoloured	1·75	1·75		
Set of 5			5·50	5·50		
First Day Cover				6·00		
Presentation Pack (PO Pack No. 388)			6·00			
PHQ Cards (set of 5) (291)			1·50	6·25		
Set of 5 Gutter Pairs			11·00			
Set of 5 Traffic Light Gutter Blocks of 4			26·00			

The 1st class and 50p. values include the EUROPA emblem.

1929 'New Baby' (Alison Carmichael)

1930 'Best Wishes' (Alan Kitching)

1931 'THANK YOU' (Alan Kitching)

1932 Balloons (Ivan Chermayeff)

1933 Firework (Kam Tang)

1934 Champagne, Flowers and Butterflies (Olaf Hajek)

Smilers (2nd series). Occasions. Booklet stamps

2006 (17 Oct.) Self-adhesive. Two phosphor bands. Die-cut perf 15×14

2672	**1929**	(1st) chrome-yellow	1·00	1·00		
		a. Booklet pane.				
		Nos. 2672/2677	6·00			
2673	**1930**	(1st) turquoise-blue	1·00	1·00		
2674	**1931**	(1st) scarlet-vermilion, rosine and yellow	1·00	1·00		
2675	**1932**	(1st) multicoloured	1·00	1·00		
2676	**1933**	(1st) multicoloured	1·00	1·00		
2677	**1934**	(1st) multicoloured	1·00	1·00		
Set of 6			6·00	6·00		
First Day Cover				6·25		
Presentation Pack (PO Pack No. M13)			10·00			
PHQ Cards (D29)			1·75	7·00		

Nos. 2672/2677 were printed together, se-tenant, in booklet panes of six in which the surplus self-adhesive paper around each stamp was removed.

They were also issued in sheets of 20, containing four of Nos. 2672 and 2677 and three of the other designs, and se-tenant labels. Separate sheets of each design were available with personal photographs on the labels.

Stamps as No. 2672 but perforated with one eliptical hole on each vertical side were issued on 28 October 2008 in sheets of ten or 20 with circular se-tenant Peter Rabbit labels.

Stamps as Nos. 2674 but perforated with one elliptical hole in each vertical side were issued, together with Nos. 2569, 2572, 2821/2823 and four designs from No. **MS**3024, on 8 May 2010 in sheets of 20 stamps with se-tenant greetings labels.

These generic sheets were all printed in lithography instead of gravure.

1935 Snowman

1936 Father Christmas

1937 Snowman

1938 Father Christmas

1939 Reindeer

1940 Christmas Tree

Christmas. Christmas scenes

2006 (7 Nov.) One centre phosphor band (2nd) or two phosphor bands (others). Perf 15×14

		(a) Self-adhesive				
2678	**1935**	(2nd) multicoloured	90	90		
2679	**1936**	(1st) multicoloured	1·00	1·00		
2680	**1937**	(2nd Large) multicoloured	1·10	1·00		
2681	**1938**	(1st Large) multicoloured	1·50	1·25		
2682	**1939**	72p. multicoloured	1·10	1·10		
2683	**1940**	£1·19 multicoloured	1·50	1·50		
Set of 6			6·50	6·00		
First Day Cover				7·00		
Presentation Pack (PO Pack No. 389)			7·25			
PHQ Cards (set of 7) (292)			2·00	13·50		
		(b) Ordinary gum				
MS2684 115×102 mm. As Nos. 2678/2683			6·50	6·75		
First Day Cover				7·00		

The seven PHQ cards depict the six individual stamps and the miniature sheet.

The 2nd and 1st class stamps were also issued in sheets of 20 printed in lithography instead of gravure containing ten 1st class and ten 2nd class stamps, each stamp accompanied by a se-tenant label. Separate sheets of 20 1st or 20 2nd class were available with personal photographs.

1941 Lest We Forget

Lest We Forget (1st series). 90th Anniversary of the Battle of the Somme. Miniature Sheet

2006 (9 Nov.) Sheet 124×71 mm. Containing new stamp as No. 2883 and designs as Nos. EN17, W109, S120 and NI102. Multicoloured. Two phosphor bands. Perf 14½ (1st) or 15×14 (with one elliptical hole in each vertical side) (72p.)

MS2685 **1941** (1st) Poppies on barbed wire stems; 72p.×4	5·50	5·50	☐	☐
First Day Cover		6·00	☐	
Presentation Pack (PO Pack No. 390)	7·25		☐	

No. **MS**2685 (including the Northern Ireland stamp) is printed in gravure.

The 1st class stamp was also issued in sheets of 20 with *se-tenant* labels showing war memorials, and on 6 Nov 2008, in a *se-tenant* strip of three, both issues printed in lithography instead of gravure. See No. 2883.

For the miniature sheet entitled Celebrating Scotland, issued 30 November 2006, see the Regionals section.

Year Pack

2006 (9 Nov.) Comprises Nos. 2589/2612, 2615/2649, 2659/2664, 2667/2671, 2678/2683 and **MS**2685

CP2685a Year Pack	65·00	☐

Post Office Yearbook

2006 (9 Nov.) Comprises Nos. 2589/2612, 2615/2649, 2659/2664, 2667/2671, 2678/2683 and **MS**2685

YB2685a Yearbook	75·00	☐

Miniature Sheet Collection

2006 (30 Nov.) Comprises Nos. **MS**2613, **MS**2658, **MS**2665, **MS**2684/**MS**2685, **MS**S153 and **MS**W143

MS2685a Miniature Sheet Collection	38·00	☐

1942 'with the beatles'

1943 'Sgt Pepper's Lonely Hearts Club Band'

1944 'Help!'

1945 'Abbey Road'

1946 'Revolver'

1947 'Let It Be'

1948 Beatles Memorabilia

The Beatles. Album Covers (1st issue)

2007 (9 Jan.) Two phosphor bands

(a) Gravure Walsall. Self-adhesive. Die-cut irregular perf 13½×14½

2686	**1942**	(1st) multicoloured	1·00	1·00	☐	☐
		a. Horiz pair. Nos. 2686/2687	2·00		☐	
2687	**1943**	(1st) multicoloured	1·00	1·00	☐	☐
2688	**1944**	64p. multicoloured	90	90	☐	☐
		a. Horiz pair. Nos. 2688/2689	1·75		☐	
2689	**1945**	64p. multicoloured	90	90	☐	☐
2690	**1946**	72p. multicoloured	1·25	1·25	☐	☐
		a. Horiz pair. Nos. 2690/2691	2·50		☐	
2691	**1947**	72p. multicoloured	1·25	1·25	☐	☐
Set of 6			6·00	6·00	☐	☐
First Day Cover				6·25		☐
Presentation Pack (Nos. 2686/**MS**2692) (PO Pack No. 392)			10·00		☐	
PHQ Cards (*set of* 11) (293)			3·25	15·50	☐	☐

(b) Litho Walsall. Ordinary gum. Two phosphor bands. Perf 14

MS2692 115×89 mm. **1948** (1st) Guitar; (1st) Yellow Submarine lunch-box and key-rings; (1st) Record 'Love Me Do'; (1st) Beatles badges			3·75	3·75	☐	☐
First Day Cover				6·25		☐

Nos. 2686/2691 are all die-cut in the shape of a pile of records.

Nos. 2686/2687, 2688/2689 and 2690/2691 were each printed together in sheets of 60 (2 panes of 30), with the two designs alternating horizontally and the surplus backing paper around each stamp removed.

Nos. 2686/2692 commemorate the 50th anniversary of the first meeting of Paul McCartney and John Lennon.

The complete miniature sheet is shown on one of the eleven PHQ cards, with the others depicting individual stamps, including those from No. **MS**2692.

Smilers (3rd series). Booklet stamp

2007 (16 Jan.)–**08** As No. 2569. Self-adhesive. Two phosphor bands. Die-cut Perf 15×14 (with one elliptical hole in each vertical side)

2693		(1st) multicoloured	5·50	5·50	☐ ☐

No. 2693 was issued in stamp booklets in which the surplus backing paper around each stamp was removed.

Nos. 2694/2698 are left vacant.

1949 Moon Jellyfish

1950 Common Starfish

1951 Beadlet Anemone

1952 Bass

1953 Thornback Ray

1954 Lesser Octopus

1955 Common Mussels

1956 Grey Seal

1957 Shore Crab

1958 Common Sun Star

Sea Life

2007 (1 Feb.) Two phosphor bands. Perf 14½

2699	**1949**	(1st) multicoloured	1·00	1·00	☐ ☐
		a. Block of 10.			
		Nos. 2699/2708	9·00	9·00	☐ ☐
2700	**1950**	(1st) multicoloured	1·00	1·00	☐ ☐
2701	**1951**	(1st) multicoloured	1·00	1·00	☐ ☐
2702	**1952**	(1st) multicoloured	1·00	1·00	☐ ☐
2703	**1953**	(1st) multicoloured	1·00	1·00	☐ ☐
2704	**1954**	(1st) multicoloured	1·00	1·00	☐ ☐
2705	**1955**	(1st) multicoloured	1·00	1·00	☐ ☐
2706	**1956**	(1st) multicoloured	1·00	1·00	☐ ☐
2707	**1957**	(1st) multicoloured	1·00	1·00	☐ ☐
2708	**1958**	(1st) multicoloured	1·00	1·00	☐ ☐
Set of 10			9·00	9·00	☐ ☐
First Day Cover				9·25	☐
Presentation Pack (PO Pack No. 393)			9·50		
PHQ Cards (*set of* 10) (294)			3·00	10·50	☐ ☐
Gutter Block of 20			18·00		☐

Nos. 2699/2708 were printed together, *se-tenant*, as blocks of ten (5×2) in sheets of 60 (2 panes of 30).

1959 Saturn Nebula C55

1960 Eskimo Nebula C39

1961 Cat's Eye Nebula C6

1962 Helix Nebula C63

1963 Flaming Star Nebula C31

1964 The Spindle C53

50th Anniversary of *The Sky at Night* (TV programme). Nebulae

2007 (13 Feb.) Self-adhesive. Two phosphor bands. Die-cut perf 14½×14

2709	**1959**	(1st) multicoloured	1·00	1·00	☐ ☐
		a. Horiz. pair. Nos.			
		2709/2710	2·00		☐
2710	**1960**	(1st) multicoloured	1·00	1·00	☐ ☐
2711	**1961**	50p. multicoloured	90	90	☐ ☐
		a. Horiz. pair. Nos.			
		2711/2712	1·75		☐
2712	**1962**	50p. multicoloured	90	90	☐ ☐
2713	**1963**	72p. multicoloured	1·25	1·25	☐ ☐
		a. Horiz. pair. Nos.			
		2713/2714	2·50		☐
2714	**1964**	72p. multicoloured	1·25	1·25	☐ ☐
Set of 6			5·75	5·75	☐ ☐
First Day Cover				6·25	☐
Presentation Pack (PO Pack No. 394)			7·00		☐
PHQ Cards (*set of* 6) (295)			1·75	7·00	☐ ☐

Nos. 2709/2710, 2711/2712 and 2713/2714 were each printed together in sheets of 60 (2 panes of 30), with the two designs alternating horizontally and the surplus backing paper around each stamp removed.

1965 Iron Bridge
(Thomas Telford)

1966 Steam Locomotive
and Railway Tracks

1967 Map of British Isles
and Australia (telephone)

1968 Camera and
Television (John Logie Baird)

1969 Globe as Web
(email and internet)

1970 Couple with
Suitcases on Moon
(space travel)

1971 William
Wilberforce and
Anti-Slavery
Poster

1972 Olaudah
Equiano and Map
of Slave Trade
Routes

1973 Granville
Sharp and Slave Ship

1974 Thomas Clarkson
and Diagram of Slave
Ship

1975 Hannah More
and Title Page of
*The Sorrows of
Yamba*

1976 Ignatius
Sancho and
Trade/Business Card

World of Invention (1st series)

2007 (1 Mar.) Self-adhesive. Two phosphor bands. Die-cut perf 14½×14

2715	**1965**	(1st) multicoloured	1·00	1·00		
		a. Horiz pair. Nos. 2715/2716	2·00			
2716	**1966**	(1st) multicoloured	1·00	1·00		
2717	**1967**	64p. multicoloured	90	90		
		a. Horiz pair. Nos. 2717/2718	1·75			
2718	**1968**	64p. multicoloured	90	90		
2719	**1969**	72p. multicoloured	1·25	1·25		
		a. Horiz pair. Nos. 2719/2720	2·50			
2720	**1970**	72p. multicoloured	1·25	1·25		
Set of 6			6·00	6·00		
First Day Cover				6·25		
Presentation Pack (PO Pack No. 395)			6·25			
PHQ Cards (*set of 7*) (296)			2·00	7·25		

The seven PHQ Cards depict the six individual stamps and No. **MS**2727.

Nos. 2715/2716, 2717/2718 and 2719/2720 were each printed together in sheets of 60 (2 panes of 30), with the two designs alternating horizontally and the surplus backing paper around each stamp removed.

World of Invention (2nd series). Booklet stamps

2007 (1 Mar.) Ordinary gum. Two phosphor bands. Perf 14½×14

2721	**1965**	(1st) multicoloured	1·00	1·00		
2722	**1966**	(1st) multicoloured	1·00	1·00		
2723	**1967**	64p. multicoloured	2·50	2·50		
2724	**1968**	64p. multicoloured	2·50	2·50		
2725	**1969**	72p. multicoloured	2·50	2·50		
2726	**1970**	72p. multicoloured	2·50	2·50		
Set of 6			11·00	11·00		
MS2727 115×104 mm. Nos. 2721/2726			12·00	12·00		
First Day Cover				12·50		

Nos. 2721/2726 were only issued in the £7·49 World of Invention booklet and in No. **MS**2727.

Bicentenary of the Abolition of the Slave Trade

2007 (22 Mar.) Two phosphor bands. Perf 14½

2728	**1971**	(1st) multicoloured	1·00	1·00		
		a. Horiz pair. Nos. 2728/2729	2·00	2·00		
2729	**1972**	(1st) multicoloured	1·00	1·00		
2730	**1973**	50p. multicoloured	80	80		
		a. Horiz pair. Nos. 2730/2731	1·60	1·60		
2731	**1974**	50p. multicoloured	80	80		
2732	**1975**	72p. multicoloured	1·25	1·25		
		a. Horiz pair. Nos. 2732/2733	2·50	2·50		
2733	**1976**	72p. multicoloured	1·25	1·25		
Set of 6			5·50	5·50		
First Day Cover				5·75		
Presentation Pack (PO Pack No. 396)			6·00			
PHQ Cards (*set of 6*) (297)			1·75	6·00		
Set of 3 Gutter Strips of 4			11·00			
Set of 3 Traffic Light Gutter Strips of 4			42·00			

Nos. 2728/2729, 2730/2731 and 2732/2733 were each printed together, *se-tenant*, in horizontal pairs throughout the sheets.

For the miniature sheet entitled Celebrating England, issued 23 April 2007, see Regionals section.

1977 Ice Cream Cone

1978 Sandcastle

149

1979 Carousel Horse

1980 Beach Huts

1981 Deckchairs

1982 Beach Donkeys

Beside the Seaside

2007 (15 May) Two phosphor bands. Perf 14½

2734	**1977**	(1st) multicoloured	1·00	1·00		
2735	**1978**	46p. multicoloured	80	80		
2736	**1979**	48p. multicoloured	90	90		
2737	**1980**	54p. multicoloured	1·00	1·00		
2738	**1981**	69p. multicoloured	1·10	1·10		
2739	**1982**	78p. multicoloured	1·25	1·25		
Set of 6			5·50	5·50		
First Day Cover				5·75		
Presentation Pack (PO Pack No. 397)			6·00			
PHQ Cards (set of 6) (298)			1·75	6·25		
Set of 6 Gutter Pairs			11·00			

For T **1977**, but self-adhesive, see No. 2848.

1983

New Wembley Stadium, London. Miniature Sheet

2007 (17 May) Sheet 113×103 mm. Containing design as T **1593** but with 'WORLD CUP 2002' inscription omitted, and Nos. EN6 and EN18, each×2. One centre band (2nd) or two phosphor bands (others). Perf 14½×14 (1st) or 15×14 (with one elliptical hole in each vertical side) (2nd, 78p.)

MS2740 **1983** (1st) As Type **1593**; (2nd) No. EN6×2; 78p. No. EN18×2 and one central stamp-size label	4·75	4·75	
First Day Cover		5·00	

The design as T **1593** was also issued in sheets of 20 with se-tenant labels showing scenes from Wembley Stadium.

1984 Arnold Machin

1985 1967 4d. Machin

1986

40th Anniversary of the First Machin Definitives. Booklet stamps and Miniature Sheet

2007 (5 June) 'All-over' phosphor (1st) or Two phosphor bands (others) Perf 14½ (1st) or 15×14 (with one elliptical hole in each vertical side) (£1)

2741	**1984**	(1st) multicoloured	1·75	1·75		
2742	**1985**	(1st) multicoloured	1·75	1·75		
MS2743 127×73 mm. **1986** Nos. 2741/2742, Y1743 and Y1744			4·75	4·75		
First Day Cover (No. **MS**2743)				5·00		
Presentation Pack (No. **MS**2743) (PO Pack No. 398)			5·50			
PHQ Cards (Set of 3) (Nos. 2741/ **MS**2743) (299)			1·00	7·50		

Nos. 2741/2742 were only issued in the £7·66 The Machin, the Making of a Masterpiece booklet, No. DX39, and in No. **MS**2743.

Stamps as T **1984** but with phosphor frames were issued in sheets of 20 with se-tenant labels showing the 1967–1969 Machin definitives.

1987 Stirling Moss in Vanwall 2.5L, 1957

1988 Graham Hill in BRM P57, 1962

1989 Jim Clark in Lotus 25 Climax, 1963

1990 Jackie Stewart in Tyrrell 006/2, 1973

1991 James Hunt in McLaren M23, 1976

1992 Nigel Mansell in Williams FW11, 1986

50th Anniversary of the British Grand Prix, Silverstone. Racing Cars

2007 (3 July) Two phosphor bands. Perf 14½

2744	**1987**	(1st) multicoloured	1·00	1·00	☐	☐
2745	**1988**	(1st) multicoloured	1·00	1·00	☐	☐
2746	**1989**	54p. multicoloured	90	90	☐	☐
2747	**1990**	54p. multicoloured	90	90	☐	☐
2748	**1991**	78p. multicoloured	1·25	1·25	☐	☐
2749	**1992**	78p. multicoloured	1·25	1·25	☐	☐
Set of 6			5·50	5·50	☐	
First Day Cover				6·00	☐	
Presentation Pack (PO Pack No. 399)			6·00		☐	
PHQ Cards (*set of 6*) (300)			1·75	6·25	☐	
Set of 6 Gutter Pairs			11·00		☐	

1993 *Harry Potter and the Philosopher's Stone*

1994 *Harry Potter and the Chamber of Secrets*

1995 *Harry Potter and the prisoner of Azkaban*

1996 *Harry Potter and the Goblet of Fire*

1997 *Harry Potter and the Order of the Phoenix*

1998 *Harry Potter and the Half-Blood Prince*

1999 *Harry Potter and the Deathly Hallows*

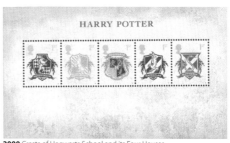

2000 Crests of Hogwarts School and its Four Houses

Publication of Final Book in the Harry Potter Series

2007 (17 July)

(a) Book Covers. 'All-over' phosphor. Perf 14½

2750	**1993**	(1st) multicoloured	1·00	1·00	☐	☐
		a. Horiz strip of 7.				
		Nos. 2750/2756	6·25	6·25	☐	☐
2751	**1994**	(1st) multicoloured	1·00	1·00	☐	☐
2752	**1995**	(1st) multicoloured	1·00	1·00	☐	☐
2753	**1996**	(1st) multicoloured	1·00	1·00	☐	☐
2754	**1997**	(1st) multicoloured	1·00	1·00	☐	☐
2755	**1998**	(1st) multicoloured	1·00	1·00	☐	☐
2756	**1999**	(1st) multicoloured	1·00	1·00	☐	☐
Set of 7			6·25	6·25	☐	☐
First Day Cover				6·50	☐	
Presentation Pack (Nos. 2750)						
(PO Pack No. M16)			12·00		☐	
PHQ Cards (*set of 13*) (HP)			4·00	19·50	☐	☐
Gutter Block of 14			12·50		☐	
Traffic Light Gutter Block of 14			32·00		☐	

(b) Crests of Hogwarts School and its Four Houses. Multicoloured. Two phosphor bands. Perf 15 × 14

MS2757	123×70 mm. **2000** (1st)					
	Gryffindor; (1st) Hufflepuff; (1st)					
	Hogwarts; (1st) Ravenclaw; (1st)					
	Slytherin		4·50	4·50	☐	☐
First Day Cover				5·75	☐	

Nos. 2750/2756 were printed together, *se-tenant*, as horizontal strips of seven stamps in sheets of 56 (2 panes 7×4)

The complete miniature sheet is shown on one of the 13 PHQ cards with the others depicting the individual stamps including those from No. **MS**2757.

Stamps as those within No. **MS**2757 but self-adhesive were issued in sheets of 20 containing the five designs *se-tenant* with labels depicting either magic spells or personal photographs. The magic spells labels are printed in thermochromic ink which fades temporarily when exposed to heat, revealing the meaning of the spells.

2001 Scout and Campfire

2002 Scouts Rock climbing

2003 Scout planting Tree

2004 Adult Volunteer teaching Scout Archery

2005 Scouts learning gliding   **2006** Scouts from Many Nations

2015 Corncrake   **2016** Peregrine Falcon

Centenary of Scouting and 21st World Scout Jamboree, Chelmsford, Essex

2007 (26 July) Two phosphor bands. Perf 14½ × 14

2758	**2001**	(1st) multicoloured	1·00	1·00	☐	☐
2759	**2002**	46p. multicoloured	80	80	☐	☐
2760	**2003**	48p. multicoloured	85	85	☐	☐
2761	**2004**	54p. multicoloured	95	95	☐	☐
2762	**2005**	69p. multicoloured	1·10	1·10	☐	☐
2763	**2006**	78p. multicoloured	1·25	1·25	☐	☐
Set of 6			5·50	5·50	☐	
First Day Cover				6·00	☐	
Presentation Pack (PO Pack No. 400)			6·00		☐	
PHQ Cards (set of 6) (301)			1·75	6·25	☐	☐
Set of 6 Gutter Pairs			11·00		☐	

The 1st class and 48p. values include the EUROPA emblem.

Action for Species (1st series). Birds

2007 (4 Sept.) Two phosphor bands. Perf 14½

2764	**2007**	(1st) multicoloured	1·00	1·00	☐	☐
		a. Block of 10.				
		Nos. 2764/2773	9·00	9·00	☐	☐
2765	**2008**	(1st) multicoloured	1·00	1·00	☐	☐
2766	**2009**	(1st) multicoloured	1·00	1·00	☐	☐
2767	**2010**	(1st) multicoloured	1·00	1·00	☐	☐
2768	**2011**	(1st) multicoloured	1·00	1·00	☐	☐
2769	**2012**	(1st) multicoloured	1·00	1·00	☐	☐
2770	**2013**	(1st) multicoloured	1·00	1·00	☐	☐
2771	**2014**	(1st) multicoloured	1·00	1·00	☐	☐
2772	**2015**	(1st) multicoloured	1·00	1·00	☐	☐
2773	**2016**	(1st) multicoloured	1·00	1·00	☐	☐
Set of 10			9·00	9·00	☐	☐
First Day Cover				9·50	☐	
Presentation Pack (PO Pack No. 401)			10·00		☐	
PHQ Cards (set of 10) (302)			3·00	9·75	☐	☐
Gutter Block of 20			18·00		☐	

Nos. 2764/2773 were printed together, se-tenant, in blocks of ten (5×2) in sheets of 60 (2 panes of 30)

2007 White-tailed Eagle   **2008** Bearded Tit

2009 Red Kite   **2010** Cirl Bunting

2011 Marsh Harrier   **2012** Avocet

2013 Bittern   **2014** Dartford Warbler

2017 NCO, Royal Military Police, 1999   **2018** Tank Commander, 5th Royal Tank Regiment, 1944   **2019** Observer, Royal Field Artillery, 1917

2020 Rifleman, 95th Rifles, 1813   **2021** Grenadier, Royal Regiment of Foot of Ireland, 1704   **2022** Trooper, Earl of Oxford's Horse, 1661

Military Uniforms (1st series). British Army Uniforms

2007 (20 Sept.) Two phosphor bands. Perf 14½

2774	**2017**	(1st) multicoloured	1·00	1·00	☐	☐
		a. Horiz strip of 3.				
		Nos. 2774/2776	3·00	3·00	☐	☐
2775	**2018**	(1st) multicoloured	1·00	1·00	☐	☐
2776	**2019**	(1st) multicoloured	1·00	1·00	☐	☐
2777	**2020**	78p. multicoloured	1·25	1·25	☐	☐
		a. Horiz strip of 3.				
		Nos. 2777/2779	3·75	3·75	☐	☐
2778	**2021**	78p. multicoloured	1·25	1·25	☐	☐

2779	**2022**	78p. multicoloured	1·25	1·25	☐	☐
Set of 6			6·50	6·50	☐	☐
First Day Cover				7·00	☐	
Presentation Pack (PO Pack No. 402)			7·00		☐	
PHQ Cards (*set of 6*) (303)			1·75	7·00	☐	☐
Set of 2 Gutter Strips of 6			13·00		☐	
Set of 2 Traffic Light Gutter Strips of 6			30·00		☐	

Nos. 2774/2776 and 2777/2779 were each printed together, *se-tenant*, in horizontal strips of three stamps in sheets of 60 (2 panes 6×5) and were also issued in the £7·66 British Army Uniforms booklet, No. DX40.

2023 Leaving St Paul's Cathedral after Thanksgiving Service, 2006

2024 Inspecting King's Troop Royal Horse Artillery, Regents Park, 1997

2025 At Garter Ceremony, Windsor, 1980

2026 At Royal Ascot, 1969

2027 At Premiere of *The Guns of Navarone*, 1961

2028 At Clydebank, 1947

2029 Photographs of the Royal Family

Royal Diamond Wedding Anniversary of Queen Elizabeth II and Duke of Edinburgh

2007 (16 Oct.)

(a) Ordinary gum. Litho Cartor. 'All-over' phosphor. Perf 14½×14

2780	**2023**	(1st) blackish-brown and black	1·00	1·00	☐	☐
		a. Horiz pair. Nos. 2780/2781	2·00	2·00	☐	☐
2781	**2024**	(1st) blackish-brown and black	1·00	1·00	☐	☐

2782	**2025**	54p. blackish-brown and black	85	85	☐	☐
		a. Horiz pair. Nos. 2782/2783	1·75	1·75	☐	☐
2783	**2026**	54p. blackish-brown and black	85	85	☐	☐
2784	**2027**	78p. blackish-brown and black	1·25	1·25	☐	☐
		a. Horiz pair. Nos. 2784/2785	2·50	2·50	☐	☐
2785	**2028**	78p. blackish-brown and black	1·25	1·25	☐	☐
Set of 6			5·50	5·50	☐	☐
First Day Cover				7·25	☐	
Presentation Pack (Nos. 2780/**MS**2786) (PO Pack No. 403)			11·00		☐	
PHQ Cards (*set of 11*) (304)			3·25	15·50	☐	☐
Set of 3 Gutter Blocks of 4			11·00		☐	

Nos. 2780/2781, 2782/2783 and 2784/2785 were each printed together, *se-tenant*, in horizontal pairs throughout the sheets.

(b) Self-adhesive. Gravure Walsall. Two phosphor bands. Perf 14½

MS2786	**2029**	115×89 mm. (1st) Royal family, Balmoral, 1972; (1st) Queen and Prince Philip, Buckingham Palace, 2007; 69p. Royal family, Windsor Castle, 1965; 78p. Princess Elizabeth, Prince Philip, Prince Charles and Princess Anne, Clarence House, 1951	4·00	4·25	☐	☐
First Day Cover				5·75	☐	

The complete miniature sheet is shown on one of the 11 PHQ cards with the others depicting individual stamps including those from No. **MS**2786.

2030 *Madonna and Child* (William Dyce), c 1827

2031 *The Madonna of Humility* (Lippo di Dalmasio), c 1390–1400

Christmas (1st issue).
Paintings of the Madonna and Child

2007 (6 Nov.) One centre band (2nd) or two phosphor bands (1st). Self-adhesive. Die-cut perf 15×14 (with one elliptical hole in each vertical side)

2787	**2030**	(2nd) multicoloured	90	90	☐	☐
2788	**2031**	(1st) multicoloured	1·10	1·10	☐	☐
First Day Cover				2·75	☐	

2032 Angel playing Trumpet ('PEACE')

2033 Angel playing Lute ('GOODWILL')

2034 Angel playing Trumpet ('PEACE')

2035 Angel playing Lute ('GOODWILL')

2036 Angel playing Flute ('JOY')

2037 Angel playing Tambourine ('GLORY')

Christmas (2nd issue). Angels

2007 (6 Nov.) One centre band (2nd) or two phosphor bands (others). Perf 15 × 14

(a) Self-adhesive

2789	**2032**	(2nd) multicoloured	90	90
2790	**2033**	(1st) multicoloured	1·00	1·00
2791	**2034**	(2nd Large) multicoloured	1·25	1·25
2792	**2035**	(1st Large) multicoloured	1·50	1·50
2793	**2036**	78p. multicoloured	1·50	1·50
2794	**2037**	£1·24 multicoloured	2·25	2·25
Set of 6			7·50	7·50
First Day Cover				7·75
Presentation Pack (Nos. 2787/2794) (PO Pack No. 404)			9.75	
PHQ Cards (set of 9) (305)			2·75	17·50

(b) Ordinary gum

MS2795 115 × 102 mm. As Nos. 2789/2794		7·50	7·50
First Day Cover			7·75

The phosphor bands on Nos. 2791/2792 are at the centre and right of each stamp.

The PHQ cards depict Nos. 2787/2794 and **MS**2795.

The 2nd class, 1st class and 78p. stamps were also issued in sheets of 20 printed in lithography instead of gravure containing eight 1st class, eight 2nd class and four 78p. stamps, each stamp accompanied by a *se-tenant* label. Separate sheets of 20 1st, 20 2nd or ten 78p. were available with personal photographs.

2038 Lest We Forget

Lest We Forget (2nd series). 90th Anniversary of the Battle of Passchendaele. Miniature Sheet

2007 (8 Nov.) Litho. Sheet 124 × 70 mm containing new stamp as No. 2884 and designs as Nos. EN18, W110, S121 and NI128. Two phosphor bands. Perf 14½ (1st) or 15 × 14 (with one elliptical hole in each vertical side) (78p.)

MS2796 **2038** (1st) Soldiers in poppy flower; 78p. × 4		6·00	6·00
First Day Cover			6·25
Presentation Pack (PO Pack No. 405)		6·50	

The 1st class stamp was also issued in sheets of 20 with *se-tenant* labels showing soldiers and their letters home and, on 6 Nov. 2008 in a *se-tenant* strip of three, see No. 2884.

Year Pack

2007 (8 Nov.) Comprises Nos. 2686/2692, 2699/2720, 2728/2739, **MS**2743/2794 and **MS**2796

CP2796*a* Year Pack	£120	

Post Office Yearbook

2007 (8 Nov.) Comprises Nos. 2686/2692, 2699/2720, 2728/2739, **MS**2743/2794 and **MS**2796

YB2796*a* Yearbook	80·00	

Miniature Sheet Collection

2007 (8 Nov.) Comprises Nos. **MS**2692, **MS**2727, **MS**2740, **MS**2743, **MS**2757, **MS**2786 and **MS**2795/**MS**2796

MS2796*a* Miniature Sheet Collection	48·00	

2039 *Casino Royale*

2040 *Dr. No*

2041 *Goldfinger*

2042 *Diamonds are Forever*

2043 *For Your Eyes Only*

2044 *From Russia with Love*

Birth Centenary of Ian Fleming (author of James Bond books) (1st issue). Book Covers

2008 (8 Jan.) Two phosphor bands. Perf 14½ × 14

2797	**2039**	(1st) multicoloured	1·00	1·00
2798	**2040**	(1st) multicoloured	1·00	1·00
2799	**2041**	54p. multicoloured	90	90
2800	**2042**	54p. multicoloured	90	90
2801	**2043**	78p. multicoloured	1·25	1·25
2802	**2044**	78p. multicoloured	1·25	1·25
Set of 6			5·50	5·50
First Day Cover				6·75
Presentation Pack (PO Pack No. 407)			6·50	
PHQ Cards (set of 7) (306)			2·00	15·00
Set of 6 Gutter Pairs			11·00	
MS2803 189 × 68 mm. Nos. 2797/2802			9·25	9·25
First Day Cover				9·50

No. 2797/2802 were also issued in the £7·40 Ian Fleming's James Bond booklet No DX41.

The seven PHQ cards depict the individual stamps and No. **MS**2803.

No. 2804 is vacant.

Birth Centenary of Ian Fleming (author of James Bond books) (2nd issue). Booklet stamps

2008 (8 Jan.) Design as T **1517** but printed in lithography. Two phosphor bands. Perf 14½

2805	**1517**	(1st) multicoloured	2·00	2·00	☐	☐

No. 2805 was only issued in the £7·40 Ian Fleming's James Bond booklet, No. DX41.

For White Ensign stamp from this booklet see No. 2581.

2045 Assistance Dog carrying Letter (Labrador Rowan)

2046 Mountain Rescue Dog (Cross-bred Merrick)

2047 Police Dog (German Shepherd Max)

2048 Customs Dog (Springer Spaniel Max)

2049 Sheepdog (Border Collie Bob)

2050 Guide Dog (Labrador Warwick)

Working Dogs

2008 (5 Feb.) Two phosphor bands. Perf 14½

2806	**2045**	(1st) multicoloured	1·00	1·00	☐	☐
2807	**2046**	46p. multicoloured	80	80	☐	☐
2808	**2047**	48p. multicoloured	80	80	☐	☐
2809	**2048**	54p. multicoloured	1·00	1·00	☐	☐
2810	**2049**	69p. multicoloured	1·10	1·10	☐	☐
2811	**2050**	78p. multicoloured	1·25	1·25	☐	☐
Set of 6			5·25	5·25	☐	☐
First Day Cover				6·75		☐
Presentation Pack (PO Pack No. 408)			6·50		☐	
PHQ Cards (set of 6) (307)			1·75	6·25	☐	☐
Set of 6 Gutter Pairs			10·50		☐	

The 1st value includes the EUROPA emblem.

2051 Henry IV (1399–1413)

2052 Henry V (1413–1422)

2053 Henry VI (1422–1461 & 1470–1471)

2054 Edward IV (1461–1470 & 1471–1473)

2055 Edward V (1483)

2056 Richard III (1483–1485)

2057 The Age of Lancaster and York

Kings and Queens (1st series). Houses of Lancaster and York

2008 (28 Feb.) Two phosphor bands. Perf 14½

2812	**2051**	(1st) multicoloured	1·00	1·00	☐	☐
2813	**2052**	(1st) multicoloured	1·00	1·00	☐	☐
2814	**2053**	54p. multicoloured	1·00	1·00	☐	☐
2815	**2054**	54p. multicoloured	1·00	1·00	☐	☐
2816	**2055**	69p. multicoloured	1·10	1·10	☐	☐
2817	**2056**	69p. multicoloured	1·10	1·10	☐	☐
Set of 6			5·25	5·25	☐	☐
First Day Cover				6·75		☐
Presentation Pack (Nos. 2812/**MS**2818)						
(PO Pack No. 409)			11·00		☐	
PHQ Cards (set of 11) (308)			3·25	15·00	☐	☐
Set of 6 Gutter Pairs			10·50		☐	
Set of 6 Traffic Light Gutter Blocks of 4			35·00		☐	

MS2818 123×70 mm. **2057** (1st) Owain Glyn Dwr ('Parliament'), 1404; (1st) Henry V's triumph at Battle of Agincourt, 1415; 78p. Yorkish victory at Battle of Tewkesbury, 1471; 78p. William Caxton, first English printer, 1477

		4·00	4·25	☐	☐
First Day Cover			5·00		☐

The complete miniature sheet is shown on one of the 11 PHQ cards with the others depicting individual stamps including those from No. **MS**2818.

Smilers (4th series). Booklet stamps

2008 (28 Feb.) Designs as Nos. 2567/2568, 2570 and 2675/2677. Self-adhesive. Two phosphor bands. Die-cut perf 15×14 (with one elliptical hole in each vertical side)

2819	**1569**	(1st) multicoloured	5·50	5·50	☐	☐

2820	**1842**	(1st) multicoloured	5·50	5·50	☐	☐
2821	**1517**	(1st) multicoloured	5·50	5·50	☐	☐
2822	**1932**	(1st) multicoloured	5·50	5·50	☐	☐
2823	**1933**	(1st) multicoloured	5·50	5·50	☐	☐
2824	**1934**	(1st) multicoloured	5·50	5·50	☐	☐
Set of 6			30·00	30·00	☐	☐

Nos. 2819/2824 were issued in £2·04 booklets in which the surplus backing paper around each stamp was removed.

Nos. 2820 and 2822 were reissued on 28 October 2008 in separate sheets of ten or 20 with circular *se-tenant* labels showing the Almond Blossom fairy (No. 2820), Mr. Men or Noddy (No. 2822).

Nos. 2819, 2820 and 2822 were issued again on 30 April 2009 in separate sheets of ten or 20 with circular *se-tenant* labels showing Jeremy Fisher (No. 2819), Wild Cherry fairy (No. 2820), Little Miss Sunshine or Big Ears (No. 2822).

No. 2819 was issued in sheets of 20 with *se-tenant* labels on 8 May 2010 for London 2010 Festival of Stamps, on 28 July 2011 for Philanippon '11 International Stamp Exhibition, Yokohama, on 18 June 2012 for Indonesia 2012 International Stamp Exhibition, Jakarta, on 10 May 2013 for Australia 2013 World Stamp Exhibition, on 2 August 2013 for Bangkok 2013 World Stamp Exhibition on 1 December 2014 for Kuala Lumpur 2014 FIP Exhibition on 13 May 2015 for London 2015 Europhilex International Stamp Exhibition, on 28 May 2016 for New York World Stamp Show, on 24 May 2017 for Finlandia 2017 FIP Exhibition, Tampere and on 29 May 2019 for Stockholmia 2019 International Stamp Exhibition.

Nos. 2821 (and Nos. 2822/2883) were issued, together with Nos. 2569, 2572, 2674 and four designs from No. **MS**3024, on 8 May 2010 in sheets of 20 with *se-tenant* greetings labels.

No. 2821 was issued on 12 February 2011 in sheets of 20 with *se-tenant* labels for Indipex International Stamp Exhibition.

No. 2821 was issued on 30 March 2011 in sheets of ten with *se-tenant* labels for the 50th Anniversary of the Jaguar E-type car.

No. 2823 was issued in sheets of 20 with *se-tenant* labels on 20 January 2012 (Lunar New Year – Year of the Dragon), 7 February 2013 (Lunar New Year – Year of the Snake), 10 December 2013 (Lunar New Year – Year of the Horse), 19 November 2014 (Lunar New Year – Year of the Sheep), 9 November 2015 (Lunar New Year – Year of the Monkey), 15 November 2016 (Lunar New Year – Year of the Rooster) 16 November 2017, (Lunar New Year – Year of the Dog), 15 November 2018 (Lunar New Year – Year of the Pig), 18 November 2019 (Lunar New Year – Year of the Rat) and on 8 December 2020 (Lunar New Year – Year of the Ox).

All these sheets were printed in lithography instead of gravure.

For the miniature sheet entitled Celebrating Northern Ireland, issued 11 March 2008, see the Regionals section).

2058 Lifeboat, Barra

2059 Lifeboat approaching Dinghy, Appledore

2060 Helicopter Winchman, Portland

2061 Inshore lifeboat, St Ives

2062 Rescue Helicopter, Lee-on-Solent

2063 Launch of Lifeboat, Dinbych-y-Pysgod, Tenby

Rescue at Sea

2008 (13 Mar.) 'All-over' phosphor. Perf 14½ × 14*

2825	**2058**	(1st) multicoloured	1·00	1·00	☐	☐
2826	**2059**	46p. multicoloured	80	80	☐	☐
2827	**2060**	48p. multicoloured	90	90	☐	☐
2828	**2061**	54p. multicoloured	1·00	1·00	☐	☐
2829	**2062**	69p. multicoloured	1·10	1·10	☐	☐
2830	**2063**	78p. multicoloured	1·25	1·25	☐	☐
Set of 6			5·25	5·25	☐	☐
First Day Cover				6·50		☐
Presentation Pack (PO Pack No. 411)			6·00		☐	
PHQ Cards (*set of 6*) (309)			1·50	6·25	☐	☐
Set of 6 Gutter Pairs			10·50		☐	

* Nos. 2825/2830 have interrupted perforations along the top and bottom edges of the stamps, the gaps in the perforations forming the three dots and three dashes that spell out 'SOS' in morse code.

2064 *Lysandra bellargus* (Adonis Blue)

2065 *Coenagrion mercuriale* (Southern Damselfly)

2066 *Formica rufibarbis* (Red-barbed Ant)

2067 *Pareulype berberata* (Barberry Carpet Moth)

2068 *Lucanus cervus* (Stag Beetle)

2069 *Cryptocephalus coryli* (Hazel Pot Beetle)

2070 *Gryllus campestris* (Field Cricket)

2071 *Hesperia comma* (Silver-Spotted Skipper)

2072 *Pseudepipona herrichii* (Purbeck Mason Wasp)

2073 *Gnorimus nobilis* (Noble Chafer)

Action for Species (2nd series). Insects

2008 (15 Apr.) Phosphor background. Perf 14½

2831	**2064**	(1st) multicoloured	1·00	1·00		
		a. Block of 10.				
		Nos. 2831/2840	9·00	9·00		
2832	**2065**	(1st) multicoloured	1·00	1·00		
2833	**2066**	(1st) multicoloured	1·00	1·00		
2834	**2067**	(1st) multicoloured	1·00	1·00		
2835	**2068**	(1st) multicoloured	1·00	1·00		
2836	**2069**	(1st) multicoloured	1·00	1·00		
2837	**2070**	(1st) multicoloured	1·00	1·00		
2838	**2071**	(1st) multicoloured	1·00	1·00		
2839	**2072**	(1st) multicoloured	1·00	1·00		
2840	**2073**	(1st) multicoloured	1·00	1·00		
Set of 10			9·00	9·00		
First Day Cover				9·25		
Presentation Pack (PO Pack No. 412)			10·00			
PHQ Cards (*set of 10*) (310)			3·00	9·75		
Gutter Block of 20			18·00			

Nos. 2831/2840 were printed together, *se-tenant*, in blocks of ten (5×2) in sheets of 60 (2 panes of 30).

2074 Lichfield Cathedral

2075 Belfast Cathedral

2076 Gloucester Cathedral

2077 St David's Cathedral

2078 Westminster Cathedral

2079 St Magnus Cathedral, Kirkwall, Orkney

2080 St Paul's Cathedral

Cathedrals

2008 (13 May) 'All-over' phosphor. Perf 14½

2841	**2074**	(1st) multicoloured	1·00	1·00		
2842	**2075**	48p. multicoloured	85	85		
2843	**2076**	50p. multicoloured	1·00	1·00		
2844	**2077**	56p. multicoloured	1·10	1·10		
2845	**2078**	72p. multicoloured	1·25	1·25		
2846	**2079**	81p. multicoloured	1·40	1·40		
Set of 6			6·00	6·00		
First Day Cover				6·75		
Presentation Pack (Nos. 2841/**MS**2847)						
(PO Pack No. 413)			11·00			
PHQ Cards (*set of 11*) (311)			3·25	16·00		
Set of 6 Gutter Pairs			12·00			
Set of 6 Traffic Light Gutter Pairs			32·00			

MS2847 115×89 mm. **2080** (1st) multi-coloured; (1st) multicoloured; 81p. multicoloured; 81p. multicoloured.

Perf 14½×14	4·00	4·00		
First Day Cover		4·50		

No. **MS**2847 commemorates the 300th anniversary of St Paul's Cathedral.

The complete miniature sheet is shown on one of the 11 PHQ cards with the others depicting individual stamps including those from No. **MS**2847.

Beside the Seaside (2nd series)

2008 (13 May) As T **1977** but self-adhesive. Two phosphor bands. Die-cut perf 14½

2848	**1977**	(1st) multicoloured	2·00	2·00		

No. 2848 was only issued in £2·16 booklets.

2081 *Carry on Sergeant*

2082 *Dracula*

2083 *Carry on Cleo*

2084 *The Curse of Frankenstein*

2085 *Carry on Screaming*   **2086** *The Mummy*

Posters for Carry On and Hammer Horror Films

2008 (10 June) Two phosphor bands. Perf 14

2849	**2081**	(1st) multicoloured	1·00	1·00	☐	☐
2850	**2082**	48p. multicoloured	80	80	☐	☐
2851	**2083**	50p. multicoloured	90	90	☐	☐
2852	**2084**	56p. multicoloured	1·00	1·00	☐	☐
2853	**2085**	72p. multicoloured	1·10	1·10	☐	☐
2854	**2086**	81p. multicoloured	1·25	1·25	☐	☐
Set of 6			5·50	5·50	☐	☐
First Day Cover				6·25	☐	
Presentation Pack (PO Pack No. 414)			6·25		☐	
PHQ Cards (*set of 6*) (312)			1·50	7·00	☐	☐
PHQ Cards ('brick wall' background) and Stamps Set			7·00		☐	
Set of 6 Gutter Pairs			11·00		☐	

Nos. 2849/2854 commemorate the 50th anniversary of *Dracula* and the first Carry On film (*Carry on Sergeant*).

2087 Red Arrows, Dartmouth Regatta Airshow, 2006   **2088** RAF Falcons Parachute Team, Biggin Hill, 2006

2089 Spectator watching Red Arrows, Farnborough   **2090** Prototype Avro Vulcan Bombers and Avro 707s, Farnborough, 1953

2091 Parachutist Robert Wyndham on Wing of Avro 504, 1933   **2092** Air Race rounding the Beacon, Hendon, c. 1912

Air Displays

2008 (17 July) Gravure. Two phosphor bands. Perf 14½ × 14

2855	**2087**	(1st) multicoloured	1·00	1·00	☐	☐
2856	**2088**	48p. multicoloured	80	80	☐	☐
2857	**2089**	50p. multicoloured	90	90	☐	☐
2858	**2090**	56p. multicoloured	1·00	1·00	☐	☐
2859	**2091**	72p. multicoloured	1·10	1·10	☐	☐
2860	**2092**	81p. multicoloured	1·25	1·25	☐	☐
Set of 6			5·50	5·50	☐	☐
First Day Cover				6·25	☐	
Presentation Pack (PO Pack No. 415)			6·25		☐	
PHQ Cards (*set of 6*) (313)			1·75	6·25	☐	☐
Set of 6 Gutter Pairs			11·00		☐	

The 1st class stamp was also issued in sheets of 20 with *se-tenant* labels and, on 18 September, in booklets, perf 14 both issues printed in lithography instead of gravure. For the booklet stamps, see also No. 2869.

2093 Landmarks of Beijing and London

Handover of Olympic Flag from Beijing to London. Miniature Sheet

2008 (22 Aug.) Sheet 115×76 mm. Multicoloured. Phosphorised paper. Perf 14½

MS2861	**2093**	(1st) National Stadium, Beijing; (1st) London Eye; (1st) Tower of London; (1st) Corner Tower of the Forbidden City, Beijing	5·00	5·00	☐	☐
First Day Cover				5·25	☐	
Presentation Pack (PO Pack No. M17)			30·00		☐	
PHQ Cards (*set of 5*) (OGH)			1·50	5·00	☐	☐

The Olympic rings overprinted on No. **MS**2861 are in silk-screen varnish.

The five PHQ cards show the four individual stamps and the complete miniature sheet.

2094 Drum Major, RAF Central Band, 2007   **2095** Helicopter Rescue Winchman, 1984   **2096** Hawker Hunter Pilot, 1951

2097 Lancaster Air Gunner, 1944   **2098** WAAF Plotter, 1940   **2099** Pilot, 1918

Military Uniforms (2nd series). RAF Uniforms

2008 (18 Sept.) Two phosphor bands. Perf 14

2862	**2094**	(1st) multicoloured	1·00	1·00	☐	☐
		a. Horiz strip of 3. Nos. 2862/2864	3·00	3·00	☐	☐
2863	**2095**	(1st) multicoloured	1·00	1·00	☐	☐
2864	**2096**	(1st) multicoloured	1·00	1·00	☐	☐
2865	**2097**	81p. multicoloured	1·40	1·40	☐	☐
		a. Horiz strip of 3. Nos. 2865/2867	4·25	4·25	☐	☐

2866 **2098**	81p. multicoloured	1·40	1·40	☐ ☐
2867 **2099**	81p. multicoloured	1·40	1·40	☐ ☐
Set of 6		6·75	6·75	☐ ☐
First Day Cover			7·00	☐
Presentation Pack (PO Pack No. 416)		7·00		☐
PHQ Cards (set of 6) (314)		1·75	7·75	☐ ☐
Set of 2 Gutter Strips of 6		13·50		☐
Set of 2 Traffic Light Gutter Blocks of 12		28·00		☐

Nos. 2862/2864 and 2865/2867 were each printed together, *se-tenant*, in horizontal strips of three stamps in sheets of 60 (2 panes 6×5) and were also issued in the £7·15 RAF Uniforms, Pilot to Plane booklet, No. DX42.

See also Nos. 2774/2779 and 2964/2969.

Pilot to Plane. RAF Uniforms. Booklet stamps

2008 (18 Sept.) Designs as T **1307** (Spitfire from 1997 British Aircraft Designers) and T **2087** (Red Arrows from 2008 Air Displays) but printed in lithography. Two phosphor bands. Perf 14

2868 **1307**	20p. multicoloured	1·25	1·25	☐ ☐
2869 **2087**	(1st) multicoloured	1·25	1·25	☐ ☐

Nos. 2868/2869 were only available from the £7·15 RAF Uniforms, Pilot to Plane booklet, No. DX42.

For the miniature sheet and booklet stamps issued 29 September 2008 to celebrate the 50th Anniversary of the Country Definitives, see the Regional section.

2100 Millicent Garrett Fawcett (suffragist)

2101 Elizabeth Garrett Anderson (physician–women's health)

2102 Marie Stopes (family planning pioneer)

2103 Eleanor Rathbone (family allowance campaigner)

2104 Claudia Jones (civil rights activist)

2105 Barbara Castle (politician–Equal Pay Act)

Women of Distinction

2008 (14 Oct.) 'All-over' phosphor. Perf 14×14½

2870 **2100**	(1st) multicoloured	1·00	1·00	☐ ☐
2871 **2101**	48p. multicoloured	80	80	☐ ☐
2872 **2102**	50p. multicoloured	90	90	☐ ☐
2873 **2103**	56p. multicoloured	1·00	1·00	☐ ☐
2874 **2104**	72p. multicoloured	1·10	1·10	☐ ☐
2875 **2105**	81p. multicoloured	1·25	1·25	☐ ☐
Set of 6		5·25	5·25	☐ ☐

First Day Cover			6·25	☐
Presentation Pack (PO Pack No. 417)		6·00		☐
PHQ Cards (set of 6) (315)		1·75	6·25	☐ ☐
Set of 6 Gutter Pairs		10·50		☐

2106 Ugly Sisters from *Cinderella*

2107 Genie from *Aladdin*

2108 Ugly Sisters from *Cinderella*

2109 Captain Hook from *Peter Pan*

2110 Genie from *Aladdin*

2111 Wicked Queen from *Snow White*

Christmas. Pantomimes

2008 (4 Nov.) One centre band (2nd) or two phosphor bands (others). Perf 15×14

		(a) Self-adhesive			
2876 **2106**	(2nd) multicoloured		90	90	☐ ☐
2877 **2107**	(1st) multicoloured		1·00	1·00	☐ ☐
2878 **2108**	(2nd Large) multicoloured		1·25	1·25	☐ ☐
2879 **2109**	50p. multicoloured		1·00	1·00	☐ ☐
2880 **2110**	(1st Large) multicoloured		1·50	1·50	☐ ☐
2881 **2111**	81p. multicoloured		1·75	1·75	☐ ☐
Set of 6			6·25	6·25	☐ ☐
First Day Cover				6·50	☐
Presentation Pack (PO Pack No. 418)			6·75		☐
PHQ Cards (set of 7) (316)			2·00	12·00	☐ ☐

	(b) Ordinary gum			
MS2882 114×102 mm. As Nos.				
2876/2881		6·50	6·50	☐ ☐
First Day Cover			6·75	☐

The phosphor bands on Nos. 2878 and 2880 are at the centre and right of each stamp.

The seven PHQ cards depict the six stamps and No. **MS**2882.

The 2nd class, 1st class and 81p. stamps were also issued in sheets of 20 printed in lithography instead of gravure containing eight 1st class, eight 2nd class and four 81p. stamps, each stamp accompanied by a *se-tenant* label. Separate sheets of 20 1st, 20 2nd, ten 1st or ten 81p. were available with personal photographs.

2112 Seven Poppies on Barbed Wire Stems

2113 Soldiers in Poppy Flower

2114 Soldier's Face in Poppy Flower

2115 'Lest We Forget'

Lest We Forget (3rd series).
90th Anniversary of the Armistice

2008 (6 Nov.) Phosphor background (No. 2885) or two phosphor bands (others). Perf 14½ (1st) or 15×14 (with one elliptical hole in each vertical side) (81p.)

2883	**2112**	(1st) multicoloured		1·00	1·00	☐ ☐
		a. Horiz strip of 3.				
		Nos. 2883/2885		2·75	2·75	☐ ☐
2884	**2113**	(1st) multicoloured		1·00	1·00	☐ ☐
2885	**2114**	(1st) multicoloured		1·00	1·00	☐ ☐
Set of 3				2·75	2·75	☐ ☐
Presentation Pack (Nos. 2883/**MS**2886)						
(PO Pack No. 419)				6·50		☐
PHQ Cards (*set of 6*) (317)				1·75	9·50	☐ ☐
Gutter Strip of 6				5·50		☐
Traffic Light Gutter Block of 12				16·00		☐
MS2886 124×70 mm. **2115** No. 2885 and						
as Nos. EN19, W111, S122 and NI129				5·75	5·75	☐ ☐
First Day Cover					6·75	☐

Nos. 2883/2885 were printed together, *se-tenant*, in horizontal strips of three stamps in sheets of 30.

No. **MS**2886 (including the Northern Ireland, Scotland and Wales stamps) is printed in lithography.

The six PHQ cards depict Nos. **MS**2685, **MS**2796 and 2883/**MS**2886.

The 1st class stamp was also issued in sheets of 20 with *se-tenant* labels.

Year Pack

2008 (6 Nov.) Comprises Nos. 2797/2802, 2806/**MS**2818, 2825/**MS**2847, 2849/2867, 2870/2881, **MS**2886 and **MS**NI152

CP2886*a*	Year Pack	85·00	☐

Post Office Yearbook

2008 (6 Nov.) Comprises Nos. 2797/2802, 2806/**MS**2818, 2825/**MS**2847, 2849/2867, 2870/2881, **MS**2886 and **MS**N152/**MS**N1523

YB2886*a*	Yearbook	85·00	☐

Miniature Sheet Collection

2008 (6 Nov.) Comprises Nos. **MS**2803, **MS**2818, **MS**2847, **MS**2861, **MS**2882, **MS**2886 and **MS**NI52/**MS**NI53

MS2886*a*	Miniature Sheet Collection	45·00	☐

2116 Supermarine Spitfire
(R. J. Mitchell)

2117 Mini Skirt
(Mary Quant)

2118 Mini
(Sir Alec Issigonis)

2119 Anglepoise Lamp
(George Carwardine)

2120 Concorde
(Aérospatiale-BAC)

2121 K2 Telephone Kiosk
(Sir Giles Gilbert Scott)

2122 Polypropylene Chair
(Robin Day)

2123 Penguin Books
(Edward Young)

2124 London
Underground Map

2125 Routemaster Bus
(design team led by
AAM Durrant)

British Design Classics (1st issue)

2009 (13 Jan.) Printed in lithography. Phosphor background.
Perf 14½

2887	**2116**	(1st) multicoloured	1·00	1·00	☐	☐
		a. Block of 10. Nos.				
		2887/2896	9·00	9·00	☐	☐
2888	**2117**	(1st) multicoloured	1·00	1·00	☐	☐
2889	**2118**	(1st) multicoloured	1·00	1·00	☐	☐
2890	**2119**	(1st) multicoloured	1·00	1·00	☐	☐
2891	**2120**	(1st) multicoloured	1·00	1·00	☐	☐
2892	**2121**	(1st) multicoloured	1·00	1·00	☐	☐
2893	**2122**	(1st) multicoloured	1·00	1·00	☐	☐
2894	**2123**	(1st) multicoloured	1·00	1·00	☐	☐
2895	**2124**	(1st) multicoloured	1·00	1·00	☐	☐
2896	**2125**	(1st) multicoloured	1·00	1·00	☐	☐
		Set of 10	9·00	9·00	☐	☐
		First Day Cover		9·50		☐
		Presentation Pack (PO Pack No. 421)	10·50			☐
		PHQ Cards (*set of* 10) (318)	3·00	9·75	☐	☐
		Gutter Block of 20	18·00			☐

Nos. 2887/2896 were printed together, *se-tenant*, in blocks of
ten (2×5) throughout the sheet and also in the £7·68 British
Design Classics booklet, No. DX44.

No. 2889 was also issued in sheets of 20 with *se-tenant* labels,
perforated 14×14½, on 13 January 2009.

No. 2891 was also issued in sheets of 20 with *se-tenant* labels,
perforated 14×14½, issued on 2 March 2009.

No. 2887 was also issued in sheets of 20 with *se-tenant* labels,
perforated 14×14½ issued on 15 September 2010.

British Design Classics (2nd issue). Booklet stamp

2009 (13 Jan.) Design as T **1589** (Concorde from 2002 Passenger
Jet Aviation) but printed in lithography. Two phosphor bands.
Perf 14½

2897	**1589**	(1st) multicoloured	4·50	4·50	☐	☐

No. 2897 was only issued in the £7·68 British Design Classics
booklet, No DX44.
See also Nos. 2911/2915*b*.

For the miniature sheet entitled Robert Burns 250th Anniversary,
issued on 22 January 2009, see the Regionals section.

2126 Charles Darwin

2127 Marine Iguana

2128 Finches

2129 Atoll

2130 Bee Orchid

2131 Orangutan

2132 Fauna and Map of the Galapagos Islands

Birth Bicentenary of Charles Darwin (naturalist and evolutionary theorist) (1st issue)

2009 (12 Feb.) (a) Self-adhesive. Printed in gravure. 'All-over' phosphor. Perf 14

2898	**2126**	(1st) multicoloured	1·00	1·00	☐ ☐
2899	**2127**	48p. multicoloured	1·10	1·10	☐ ☐
2900	**2128**	50p. multicoloured	1·25	1·25	☐ ☐
2901	**2129**	56p. multicoloured	1·40	1·40	☐ ☐
2902	**2130**	72p. multicoloured	1·75	1·75	☐ ☐
2903	**2131**	81p. multicoloured	2·00	2·00	☐ ☐
Set of 6			7·50	7·50	☐ ☐
First Day Cover				8·25	☐
Presentation Pack (Nos. 2898/**MS**2904)					
(PO Pack No. 423)			10·50		☐
PHQ Cards (*set of 11*) (320)			3·25	16·50	☐ ☐

(b) Ordinary gum. Printed in lithography.
Two phosphor bands. Perf 14

MS2904 115×89 mm. **2132** (1st) Flightless Cormorant; (1st) Giant Tortoise and Cactus Finch; 81p. Marine Iguana; 81p. Floreana Mockingbird	5.00	4.25	☐ ☐
First Day Cover		5.25	☐

Nos. 2898/2903 have 'jigsaw' perforations on the two vertical sides.

The complete miniature sheet is shown on one of the 11 PHQ cards with the others depicting individual stamps including those from No. **MS**2904.

Birth Bicentenary of Charles Darwin (naturalist) (2nd issue). Booklet stamps

2009 (12 Feb.) Printed in gravure. 'All-over' phosphor. Perf 14

2905	**2126**	(1st) multicoloured	6·00	6·00	☐ ☐
2906	**2127**	48p. multicoloured	6·00	6·00	☐ ☐
2907	**2128**	50p. multicoloured	6·00	6·00	☐ ☐
2908	**2129**	56p. multicoloured	6·00	6·00	☐ ☐
2909	**2130**	72p. multicoloured	6·00	6·00	☐ ☐
2910	**2131**	81p. multicoloured	6·00	6·00	☐ ☐
Set of 6			32·00	32·00	☐ ☐

Nos. 2905/2910 were only issued in the £7·75 Charles Darwin booklet, No. DX46. They have 'jigsaw' perforations on both vertical sides.

For Nos. U2911/U3109, Types **2132a/2132d**, see Decimal Machin Definitives section.

For the miniature sheet entitled Celebrating Wales, issued 26 Feb 2009, see the Regionals section.

British Design Classics (3rd series). Booklet stamps

2009 (10 Mar.)–**10** Designs as Nos. 2887/2889, 2891/2892 and 2896. Printed in gravure. Self-adhesive. Phosphor background. Die-cut perf 14½

2911	**2121**	(1st) multicoloured	1·50	1·50	☐ ☐
2912	**2125**	(1st) multicoloured	1·50	1·50	☐ ☐
2913	**2118**	(1st) multicoloured			
		(21.4.09)	1·50	1·50	☐ ☐
2914	**2120**	(1st) multicoloured			
		(18.8.09)	1·50	1·50	☐ ☐
2915	**2117**	(1st) multicoloured			
		(17.9.09)	1·50	1·50	☐ ☐
2915*b*	**2116**	(1st) multicoloured			
		(15.9.10)	1·50	1·50	☐ ☐
Set of 6			8·25	8·25	☐ ☐

Nos. 2911/2915*b* were only issued in booklets.

2133 Matthew Boulton and Factory (manufacturing)

2134 James Watt and Boulton & Watt Condensing Engine (steam engineering)

2135 Richard Arkwright and Spinning Machine (textiles)

2136 Josiah Wedgwood and Black Basalt Teapot and Vase (ceramics)

2137 George Stephenson and *Locomotion* (railways)

2138 Henry Maudslay and Table Engine (machine making)

2139 James Brindley and Bridgewater Canal Aqueduct (canal engineering)

2140 John McAdam (road building)

Pioneers of the Industrial Revolution

2009 (10 Mar.) 'All-over' phosphor. Perf 14×14½

2916	**2133**	(1st) multicoloured	1·00	1·00	☐ ☐
		a. Horiz pair.			
		Nos. 2916/2917	2·00	2·00	☐ ☐
2917	**2134**	(1st) multicoloured	1·00	1·00	☐ ☐
2918	**2135**	50p. multicoloured	70	70	☐ ☐
		a. Horiz pair.			
		Nos. 2918/2919	1·40	1·40	☐ ☐
2919	**2136**	50p. multicoloured	70	70	☐ ☐
2920	**2137**	56p. multicoloured	85	85	☐ ☐
		a. Horiz pair.			
		Nos. 2920/2921	1·75	1·75	☐ ☐
2921	**2138**	56p. multicoloured	85	85	☐ ☐
2922	**2139**	72p. multicoloured	1·00	1·00	☐ ☐
		a. Horiz pair.			
		Nos· 2922/2923	2·00	2·00	☐ ☐
2923	**2140**	72p. multicoloured	1·00	1·00	☐ ☐

Set of 8	6·50	6·50	☐ ☐
First Day Cover		7·50	☐
Presentation Pack (PO Pack No. 425)	7·25		☐
PHQ Cards (set of 8) (321)	2·40	8·00	☐ ☐
Set of 4 Gutter Strips of 4	13·00		☐

Nos. 2916/2917, 2918/2919, 2920/2921 and 2922/2923 were each printed together, *se-tenant*, in horizontal pairs throughout the sheets.

2141 Henry VII (1485–1509)   **2142** Henry VIII (1509–1547)   **2143** Edward VI (1547–1553)

2144 Lady Jane Grey (1553)   **2145** Mary I (1553–1558)   **2146** Elizabeth I (1558–1603)

2147 The Age of the Tudors

Kings and Queens (2nd series). House of Tudor

2009 (21 Apr.) Two phosphor bands. Perf 14

2924	**2141**	(1st) multicoloured	1·00	1·00	☐ ☐
2925	**2142**	(1st) multicoloured	1·00	1·00	☐ ☐
2926	**2143**	62p. multicoloured	90	90	☐ ☐
2927	**2144**	62p. multicoloured	90	90	☐ ☐
2928	**2145**	81p. multicoloured	1·25	1·25	☐ ☐
2929	**2146**	81p. multicoloured	1·25	1·25	☐ ☐
Set of 6			5·50	5·50	☐ ☐
First Day Cover				7·50	☐
Presentation Pack (Nos. 2924/**MS**2930)					
(PO Pack No. 426)			11·00		☐
PHQ Cards (set of 11) (322)			3·25	16·00	☐ ☐
Set of 6 Gutter Pairs			11·00		☐
Set of 6 Traffic Light Gutter Blocks of 4			30·00		☐

MS2930 123×70 mm. **2147** (1st) *Mary Rose* (galleon), 1510; (1st) Field of Cloth of Gold Royal Conference, 1520; 90p. Royal Exchange (centre of commerce), 1565; 90p. Francis Drake (circumnavigation), 1580 … 4·25 4·25 ☐ ☐

First Day Cover	5·00	☐

The complete miniature sheet is shown on one of the 11 PHQ cards with the others depicting individual stamps including those from No. **MS**2930.

2148 *Allium sphaerocephalon* (Round-headed Leek)

2149 *Luronium natans* (Floating Water-plantain)

2150 *Cypripedium calceolus* (Lady's Slipper Orchid)

2151 *Polygala amarella* (Dwarf Milkwort)

2152 *Saxifraga hirculus* (Marsh Saxifrage)

2153 *Stachys germanica* (Downy Woundwort)

2154 *Euphorbia serrulata* (Upright Spurge)

2155 *Pyrus cordata* (Plymouth Pear)

2156 *Polygonum maritimum* (Sea Knotgrass)

2157 *Dianthus armeria* (Deptford Pink)

2158 Royal Botanic Gardens, Kew

Action for Species (3rd series).
Plants and 250th Anniversary of Creation of
Royal Botanic Gardens, Kew (MS2941)

2009 (19 May)

(a) Phosphor background. Perf 14½

2931	**2148**	(1st) multicoloured	1·00	1·00	□	□
		a. Block of 10.				
		Nos. 2931/2940	9·00	9·00	□	□
2932	**2149**	(1st) multicoloured	1·00	1·00	□	□
2933	**2150**	(1st) multicoloured	1·00	1·00	□	□
2934	**2151**	(1st) multicoloured	1·00	1·00	□	□
2935	**2152**	(1st) multicoloured	1·00	1·00	□	□
2936	**2153**	(1st) multicoloured	1·00	1·00	□	□
2937	**2154**	(1st) multicoloured	1·00	1·00	□	□
2938	**2155**	(1st) multicoloured	1·00	1·00	□	□
2939	**2156**	(1st) multicoloured	1·00	1·00	□	□
2940	**2157**	(1st) multicoloured	1·00	1·00	□	□
Set of 10			9·00	9·00	□	□
First Day Cover				11·00	□	
Presentation Pack (Nos. 2931/**MS**2941)						
(PO Pack No. 427)			15·00		□	
PHQ Cards (*set of 15*) (323)			4·50	13·50	□	
Gutter Block of 10			18·00		□	

Nos. 2931/2940 were printed together, *se-tenant*, in blocks of ten (5×2) throughout the sheet.

(b) Two phosphor bands. Perf 14 × 14½

MS2941 115×89 mm. **2158** (1st)
Palm House, Kew Gardens; (1st)
Millennium Seed Bank, Wakehurst
Place; 90p. Pagoda, Kew Gardens;
90p. Sackler Crossing, Kew Gardens 4·25 4·25 □ □

First Day Cover 5·00 □

The complete miniature sheet is shown on one of the 15 PHQ cards with the others depicting individual stamps including those from No. **MS**2941.

50th Anniversary of National Association of Flower
Arrangement Societies. Booklet stamps

2009 (21 May) Designs as Nos. 1958 and 1962 (1997 Greetings Stamps 19th-century Flower Paintings) but printed in gravure. Self-adhesive. Two phosphor bands. Die-cut perf 14 (with one elliptical hole in each vert side)

2942	**1287**	(1st) multicoloured	4·25	4·25	□	□
2943	**1283**	(1st) multicoloured	4·25	4·25	□	□

Nos. 2942/2943 were only issued in £2·34 stamp booklets.

2159 Dragon

2160 Unicorn

2161 Giant

2162 Pixie

2163 Mermaid

2164 Fairy

Mythical Creatures

2009 (16 June) 'All-over' phosphor. Perf 14½

2944	**2159**	(1st) multicoloured	1·00	1·00	□	□
2945	**2160**	(1st) multicoloured	1·00	1·00	□	□
2946	**2161**	62p. multicoloured	1·00	1·00	□	□
2947	**2162**	62p. multicoloured	1·00	1·00	□	□
2948	**2163**	90p. multicoloured	1·50	1·50	□	□
2949	**2164**	90p. multicoloured	1·50	1·50	□	□
Set of 6			6·25	6·25	□	
First Day Cover				8·00	□	
Presentation Pack (PO Pack No. 428)			7·00		□	
PHQ Cards (*set of 6*) (324)			1·75	8·00	□	□
Set of 6 Gutter Pairs			12·50		□	

2165 George V
Type B Wall Letter
Box, 1933–1936

2166 Edward VII
Ludlow Letter Box,
1901–1910

2167 Victorian
Lamp Letter Box, 1896

2168 Elizabeth II Type A
Wall Letter Box, 1962–1963

2169 Post Boxes

Post Boxes

2009 (18 Aug.) 'All-over' phosphor. Perf 14

2950	**2165**	(1st) multicoloured	1·00	1·00	□	□
2951	**2166**	56p. multicoloured	1·10	1·10	□	□
2952	**2167**	81p. multicoloured	1·25	1·25	□	□
2953	**2168**	90p. multicoloured	1·25	1·25	□	□
Set of 4			4·25	4·25	□	□
MS2954 **2169** 145 × 74 mm. Nos.						
2950/2953			4·25	4·25	□	□

First Day Cover		5·00	☐
Presentation Pack (PO Pack No. 430)	4·75		☐
PHQ Cards (*set of* 5) (326)	1·50	9·25	☐ ☐

Nos. 2950/2953 were only issued in the £8·18 Treasures of the Archive booklet, No. DX46, and in No. **MS**2954.

The five PHQ cards show the four individual stamps and the miniature sheet.

T **2165** was also issued in sheets of 20 with *se-tenant* labels showing post boxes.

Treasures of the Archive (1st series). Booklet stamps

2009 (18 Aug.) Designs as T **929** (1990 150th anniversary of the Penny Black) and T **1446** (with with redrawn 1st face value). Printed in lithography. Two phosphor bands. Perf 14½ × 14 (with one elliptical hole in each vertical side)

2955	**929**	20p. brownish-black and			
		grey-brown	80	80	☐ ☐
2956	**1446**	(1st) brownish-black and			
		grey-brown	1·25	1·25	☐ ☐

Nos. 2955/2956 were only issued in the £8·18 Treasures of the Archive stamp booklet No. DX46.

See also Nos. 1478 and 2133/2133a.

Treasures of the Archive (2nd series). Booklet stamps

2009 (18 Aug.) Design as T **919** (1989 Lord Mayor's Show) but printed in lithography. 'All-over' phosphor. Perf 14

2957	**919**	20p multicoloured	1·50	1·50	☐ ☐

No. 2957 was only issued in the £8·18 Treasures of the Archive stamp booklets, No. DX46.

2170 Firefighting

2171 Chemical Fire

2172 Emergency Rescue

2173 Flood Rescue

2174 Search and Rescue

2175 Fire Safety

Fire and Rescue Service

2009 (1 Sept.) 'All-over' phosphor. Perf 14 × 14½

2958	**2170**	(1st) multicoloured	1·00	1·00	☐ ☐
2959	**2171**	54p. multicoloured	90	90	☐ ☐
2960	**2172**	56p. multicoloured	1·10	1·10	☐ ☐
2961	**2173**	62p. multicoloured	1·25	1·25	☐ ☐
2962	**2174**	81p. multicoloured	1·25	1·25	☐ ☐
2963	**2175**	90p. multicoloured	1·40	1·40	☐ ☐
Set of 6			6·25	6·25	☐

First Day Cover		7·50	☐
Presentation Pack (PO Pack No. 429)	6·75		☐
PHQ Cards (*set of* 6) (325)	1·75	7·50	☐ ☐
Set of 6 *Gutter Pairs*	12·50		☐

2176 Flight Deck Officer, 2009

2177 Captain, 1941

2178 Second Officer WRNS, 1918

2179 Able Seaman, 1880

2180 Royal Marine, 1805

2181 Admiral, 1795

Military Uniforms (3rd series). Royal Navy Uniforms

2009 (17 Sept.) Phosphor background. Perf 14

2964	**2176**	(1st) multicoloured	1·00	1·00	☐ ☐
		a. Horiz strip of 3.			
		Nos. 2964/2966	3·00	3·00	☐ ☐
2965	**2177**	(1st) multicoloured	1·00	1·00	☐ ☐
2966	**2178**	(1st) multicoloured	1·00	1·00	☐ ☐
2967	**2179**	90p. multicoloured	1·40	1·40	☐ ☐
		a. Horiz strip of 3.			
		Nos. 2967/2969	4·00	4·00	☐ ☐
2968	**2180**	90p. multicoloured	1·40	1·40	☐ ☐
2969	**2181**	90p. multicoloured	1·40	1·40	☐ ☐
Set of 6			6·50	6·50	☐
First Day Cover				7·75	☐
Presentation Pack (PO Pack No. 431)			7·50		☐
PHQ Cards (*set of* 6) (327)			1·75	7·75	☐ ☐
Set of 2 *Gutter Strips of* 6			13·00		☐
Set of 2 *Traffic Light Gutter Blocks of* 12		30·00			☐

Nos. 2964/2966 and 2967/2969 were each printed together, *se-tenant*, in horizontal strips of three stamps in sheets of 60 (2 panes 6×5) and in the £7·93 Royal Navy Uniforms booklet, No. DX47.

See also Nos. 2774/2779 and 2862/2867.

Royal Navy Uniforms. Booklet stamp

2009 (17 Sept.) Design as T **1518** (Jolly Roger flag from 2001 Submarine Centenary) but printed in lithography. Two phosphor bands. Perf 14½

2970	**1518**	(1st) multicoloured	4·75	6·00	☐ ☐

No. 2970 was only issued in the £7·93 Royal Navy Uniforms stamp booklet, No DX47.

2182 Fred Perry 1909–1995 (lawn tennis champion)

2183 Henry Purcell 1659–1695 (composer and musician)

2184 Sir Matt Busby 1909–1994 (footballer and football manager)

2185 William Gladstone 1809–1898 (statesman and Prime Minister)

2186 Mary Wollstonecraft 1759–1797 (pioneering feminist)

2187 Sir Arthur Conan Doyle 1859–1930 (writer and creator of Sherlock Holmes)

2188 Donald Campbell 1921–1967 (water speed record broken 1959)

2189 Judy Fryd 1909–2000 (campaigner and founder of MENCAP)

2190 Samuel Johnson 1709–1784 (lexicographer, critic and poet)

2191 Sir Martin Ryle 1918–1984 (radio survey of the Universe 1959)

Eminent Britons

2009 (8 Oct.) Phosphor background. Perf 14½

2971	**2182**	(1st) multicoloured	1·00	1·00
		a. Horiz strip of 5. Nos. 2971/2975	4·50	4·50
2972	**2183**	(1st) multicoloured	1·00	1·00
2973	**2184**	(1st) multicoloured	1·00	1·00
2974	**2185**	(1st) multicoloured	1·00	1·00
2975	**2186**	(1st) multicoloured	1·00	1·00
2976	**2187**	(1st) multicoloured	1·00	1·00
		a. Horiz strip of 5. Nos. 2976/2980	4·50	4·50
2977	**2188**	(1st) multicoloured	1·00	1·00
2978	**2189**	(1st) multicoloured	1·00	1·00
2979	**2190**	(1st) multicoloured	1·00	1·00
2980	**2191**	(1st) multicoloured	1·00	1·00
Set of 10			9·00	9·00
First Day Cover				9·25
Presentation Pack (PO Pack No. 432)			10·50	
PHQ Cards (set of 10) (328)			3·00	9·75
Set of 2 Gutter Strips of 10			18·00	

Nos. 2971/2975 and 2976/2980 were each printed together, *se-tenant*, in horizontal strips of five stamps throughout the sheets. No. 2980 includes the EUROPA emblem.

2192 Canoe Slalom

2193 Paralympic Games Archery

2194 Athletics: Track

2195 Diving

2196 Paralympic Games Boccia

2197 Judo

2198 Paralympic Games Dressage

2199 Badminton

2200 Weightlifting

2201 Basketball

Olympic and Paralympic Games, London (2012) (1st series)

2009 (22 Oct.) 'All-over' phosphor. Perf 14½

2981	**2192**	(1st) multicoloured	1·00	1·00
		a. Horiz strip of 5. Nos. 2981/2985	4·50	4·50
2982	**2193**	(1st) multicoloured	1·00	1·00
2983	**2194**	(1st) multicoloured	1·00	1·00
2984	**2195**	(1st) multicoloured	1·00	1·00
2985	**2196**	(1st) multicoloured	1·00	1·00
2986	**2197**	(1st) multicoloured	1·00	1·00
		a. Horiz strip of 5. Nos. 2986/2990	4·50	4·50
2987	**2198**	(1st) multicoloured	1·00	1·00

2988	**2199**	(1st) multicoloured	1·00	1·00	☐ ☐
2989	**2200**	(1st) multicoloured	1·00	1·00	☐ ☐
2990	**2201**	(1st) multicoloured	1·00	1·00	☐ ☐
Set of 10			9·00	9·00	☐ ☐
First Day Cover				9·25	☐
Presentation Pack (PO Pack No. M18)			10·50		☐
PHQ Cards (set of 10) (OXPG1)			3·00	10·00	☐ ☐
Set of 2 Gutter Strips of 10			18·00		☐

Nos. 2981/2985 and 2986/2990 were each printed together, *se-tenant*, in horizontal strips of five stamps throughout the sheets and were also issued on 27 July 2011, in a sheetlet containing all 30 stamps in the series. See **MS**3204*a*.

See also Nos. 3020/3023.

2202 Angel playing Lute (William Morris), Church of St James, Staveley, Kendal, Cumbria

2203 Madonna and Child (Henry Holiday), Church of Ormesby St Michael, Great Yarmouth, Norfolk

2204 Angel playing Lute (William Morris), Church of St James, Staveley, Kendal, Cumbria

2205 Joseph (Henry Holiday), Parish Church of St Michael, Minehead, Somerset

2206 Madonna and Child (Henry Holiday), Church of Ormesby St Michael, Ormesby, Great Yarmouth, Norfolk

2207 Wise Man (Sir Edward Burne-Jones), Church of St Mary the Virgin, Rye, East Sussex

2208 Shepherd (Henry Holiday), St Mary's Church, Upavon, Wiltshire

Christmas. Stained Glass windows

2009 (3 Nov.) Gravure. One centre band (2nd) or two phosphor bands (others). Perf 14½ × 14 (with one elliptical hole in each vert side)

		(a) Self-adhesive			
2991	**2202**	(2nd) multicoloured	90	90	☐ ☐
2992	**2203**	(1st) multicoloured	1·00	1·00	☐ ☐
2993	**2204**	(2nd Large) multicoloured	1·10	1·10	☐ ☐
2994	**2205**	56p. multicoloured	1·10	1·10	☐ ☐
2995	**2206**	(1st Large) multicoloured	1·50	1·40	☐ ☐
2996	**2207**	90p. multicoloured	1·75	1·75	☐ ☐
2997	**2208**	£1·35 multicoloured	2·40	2·40	☐ ☐
Set of 7			8·75	8·75	☐ ☐
First Day Cover				9·00	☐
Presentation Pack (PO Pack No. 433)			9·25		☐
PHQ Cards (set of 8) (328)			2·40	17·50	☐ ☐
		(b) Ordinary gum			
MS2998 115 × 102 mm. As Nos.					
2991/2997			8·25	8·25	☐ ☐
First Day Cover				9·00	☐

The eight PHQ cards show the seven individual stamps and the miniature sheet.

The 2nd class, 1st class, 56p. and 90p. stamps were also issued in sheets of 20 containing eight 2nd class, eight 1st class, two 56p. and two 90p. stamps, each stamp accompanied by a *se-tenant* label. Separate sheets of 20 2nd, 20 1st, ten 1st, ten 56p. and ten 90p. were available with personal photographs.

All these sheets were printed in lithography instead of gravure.

For the 2nd class stamp printed in lithography with ordinary gum see No. 3186*a*.

For Nos. U3045/52 see Decimal Machin Definitives section.

Year Pack

2009 (3 Nov.) Comprises Nos. 2887/2896, 2898/**MS**2904, 2916/**MS**2941, 2944/2949, **MS**2954, 2958/2969, 2971/2997, **MS**S157 and **MS**W147

CP2998*a*	Year Pack	95·00	☐

Post Office Yearbook

2009 (3 Nov.) Comprises Nos. 2887/2896, 2898/**MS**2904, 2916/**MS**2941, 2944/2949, **MS**2954, 2958/2969, 2971/2997, **MS**S157 and **MS**W147

YB2998*a*	Yearbook	95·00	☐

Miniature Sheet Collection

2009 (3 Nov.) Comprises Nos. **MS**2904, **MS**2930, **MS**2941, **MS**2954, **MS**2998, **MS**S157 and **MS**W147

MS2998*a*	Miniature Sheet Collection	32·00	☐

2209 *The Division Bell* (Pink Floyd)

2210 *A Rush of Blood to the Head* (Coldplay)

2211 *Parklife* (Blur)

2212 *Power Corruption and Lies* (New Order)

2213 *Let It Bleed* (Rolling Stones)

2214 *London Calling* (The Clash)

2215 *Tubular Bells* (Mike Oldfield)

2216 *IV* (Led Zeppelin)

2217 *Screamadelica*
(Primal Scream)

2218 *The Rise and Fall of
Ziggy Stardust and the Spiders
from Mars* (David Bowie)

Classic Album Covers (1st issue)

2010 (7 Jan.) 'All-over' phosphor. Self-adhesive. Gravure De La Rue. Die-cut perf 14½ (interrupted)

2999	**2209**	(1st) multicoloured	1·00	1·00	☐	☐
		a. Horiz strip of 5. Nos. 2999/3003	4·50		☐	
3000	**2210**	(1st) multicoloured	1·00	1·00	☐	☐
3001	**2211**	(1st) multicoloured	1·00	1·00	☐	☐
3002	**2212**	(1st) multicoloured	1·00	1·00	☐	☐
3003	**2213**	(1st) multicoloured	1·00	1·00	☐	☐
3004	**2214**	(1st) multicoloured	1·00	1·00	☐	☐
		a. Horiz strip of 5. Nos. 3004/3008	4·50		☐	
3005	**2215**	(1st) multicoloured	1·00	1·00	☐	☐
3006	**2216**	(1st) multicoloured	1·00	1·00	☐	☐
3007	**2217**	(1st) multicoloured	1·00	1·00	☐	☐
3008	**2218**	(1st) multicoloured	1·00	1·00	☐	☐
Set of 10			9·00	9·00	☐	
First Day Cover				9·25	☐	
Presentation Pack (PO Pack No. 435)			11·00		☐	
PHQ Cards (set of 10) (330)			4·00	12·00	☐	☐

Nos. 2999/3003 and 3004/3008 were each printed together as horizontal strips of five stamps in sheets of 50 (2 panes of 25)

Classic Album Covers (2nd issue)

2010 (7 Jan.) 'All-over' phosphor. Litho Cartor. Perf 14½ (interrupted)

3009	**2213**	(1st) multicoloured	1·25	1·25	☐	☐
3010	**2216**	(1st) multicoloured	1·25	1·25	☐	☐
3011	**2218**	(1st) multicoloured	1·25	1·25	☐	☐
3012	**2212**	(1st) multicoloured	1·25	1·25	☐	☐
3013	**2217**	(1st) multicoloured	1·25	1·25	☐	☐
3014	**2209**	(1st) multicoloured	1·25	1·25	☐	☐
3015	**2215**	(1st) multicoloured	1·25	1·25	☐	☐
3016	**2214**	(1st) multicoloured	1·25	1·25	☐	☐
3017	**2211**	(1st) multicoloured	1·25	1·25	☐	☐
3018	**2210**	(1st) multicoloured	1·25	1·25	☐	☐
Set of 10			13·00	13·00	☐	☐
MS3019 223 × 189 mm. As Nos. 3009/3018			25·00	25·00	☐	☐
First Day Cover				26·00	☐	

Nos. 3009/3018 were only issued in the £8·06 Classic Album Covers, Nos. DX48, and **MS**3019.

The right-hand edges of Nos. 2999/3018 and the miniature sheet No. **MS**3019 are all cut around in an imperforate section to show the vinyl disc protruding from the open edge of the album cover. Stamps from the miniature sheet have a white background, while those from the booklet have a brown background containing descriptive texts.

A miniature sheet containing No. 3014×10 *The Division Bell* (Pink Floyd) was issued on 6 March 2010 and sold for £4·75 per sheet.

Olympic and Paralympic Games, London (2012) (2nd series). Booklet stamps

2010 (7 Jan.–25 Feb.) Designs as Nos. 2982/2983, 2986 and 2990 but printed in photogravure. Self-adhesive. 'All-over' phosphor. Die-cut perf 14½

3020	**2197**	(1st) multicoloured	1·50	1·50	☐	☐
3021	**2193**	(1st) multicoloured	1·50	1·50	☐	☐
3022	**2194**	(1st) multicoloured				
		(25.2.10)	1·50	1·50	☐	☐
3023	**2201**	(1st) multicoloured				
		(25.2.10)	1·50	1·50	☐	☐
Set of 4			5·50	5·50	☐	☐

Nos. 3020/3021 and 3022/3023 were only issued in separate booklets, each originally sold for £2·34.

2219

Business and Consumer Smilers Miniature Sheet

2010 (26 Jan.) Sheet 124×71 mm. Multicoloured. Two phosphor bands. Perf 14½×14 (with one elliptical hole in each vertical side)

MS3024	**2219**	(1st) Propeller driven aircraft; (1st) Vintage sports roadster; (1st) Recreation of crown seal; (1st) Birthday cake; (1st) Steam locomotive; (1st) Ocean liner; (1st) Six Poppies on barbed wire stems; (1st) Birthday present; (Europe up to 20 grams) Bird carrying envelope; (Worldwide up to 20 grams) 'Hello' in aeroplane vapour trail		9·50	9·50	☐	☐
First Day Cover				9·75	☐	
Presentation Pack (PO Pack No. M19)			10·50		☐	
PHQ Cards (set of 11) (D31)			4·25	20·00	☐	☐

No. **MS**3024 was sold for £4·58.

The 11 PHQ cards show the ten individual stamps and the complete miniature sheet.

Stamps in designs as within No. **MS**3024 but self-adhesive were available printed together, *se-tenant*, in sheets of 20 containing two of each design with greetings labels.

The (1st) birthday cake, (1st) birthday present, Europe and Worldwide designs were also available in separate sheets with personal photographs.

A stamp as the crown seal design in No. **MS**3024 but self-adhesive was issued on 15 September 2011 in sheets of 20 with postmark labels for the 350th Anniversary of the Postmark.

The other 1st class designs were for the business customised service.

Stamps as the 1st Birthday cake (×4), 1st Birthday present (×4), Europe Bird carrying envelope (×2) and Worldwide 'Hello' in aeroplane vapour trail (×2) designs but self-adhesive were issued, together with Nos. 2569, 2572, 2674 and 2821/2823 on 8 May 2010 in sheets of 20 stamps with *se-tenant* greetings labels.

For the self-adhesive (1st) six poppies stamp, see No. 3414.

2220 Girlguiding UK

Centenary of Girlguiding. Miniature Sheet

2010 (2 Feb.) Sheet 190×67 mm. Multicoloured. Phosphor background. Perf 14×14½
MS3025 **2220** (1st) Rainbows; 56p. Brownies; 81p. Guides; 90p. Senior
Section members   4·25   4·50 ☐ ☐
First Day Cover   5·25 ☐
Presentation Pack (PO Pack No. 436)   5·50 ☐
PHQ Cards (*set of* 5) (331)   2·00   9·00 ☐ ☐
The five PHQ cards show the four individual stamps and the complete miniature sheet.

2221 Sir Robert Boyle (chemistry)   **2222** Sir Isaac Newton (optics)

2223 Benjamin Franklin (electricity)   **2224** Edward Jenner (pioneer of smallpox vaccination)

2225 Charles Babbage (computing)   **2226** Alfred Russel Wallace (theory of evolution)

2227 Joseph Lister (antiseptic surgery)   **2228** Ernest Rutherford (atomic structure)

2229 Dorothy Hodgkin (crystallography)   **2230** Sir Nicholas Shackleton (earth sciences)

350th Anniversary of the Royal Society

2010 (25 Feb.) 'All-over' phosphor. Perf 14½
3026 **2221**   (1st) multicoloured   1·00   1·00 ☐ ☐

			a. Block of 10.		
			Nos. 3026/3035	9·00	9·00 ☐ ☐
3027	**2222**	(1st) multicoloured		1·00	1·00 ☐ ☐
3028	**2223**	(1st) multicoloured		1·00	1·00 ☐ ☐
3029	**2224**	(1st) multicoloured		1·00	1·00 ☐ ☐
3030	**2225**	(1st) multicoloured		1·00	1·00 ☐ ☐
3031	**2226**	(1st) multicoloured		1·00	1·00 ☐ ☐
3032	**2227**	(1st) multicoloured		1·00	1·00 ☐ ☐
3033	**2228**	(1st) multicoloured		1·00	1·00 ☐ ☐
3034	**2229**	(1st) multicoloured		1·00	1·00 ☐ ☐
3035	**2230**	(1st) multicoloured		1·00	1·00 ☐ ☐
Set of 10				9·00	9·00 ☐ ☐
First Day Cover					10·00 ☐
Presentation Pack (PO Pack No. 437)				11·00	☐
PHQ Cards (*set of* 10) (332)				4·00	11·50 ☐ ☐
Gutter Block of 20				18·00	☐

Nos. 3026/3035 were printed together, *se-tenant*, as blocks of ten (5×2) in sheets of 60 (2 panes of 30) and were also issued in the £7·72 350th Anniversary of the Royal Society booklet, No. DX49.

2231 Pixie (Mastiff cross)   **2232** Button

2233 Herbie (mongrel)   **2234** Mr. Tumnus

2235 Tafka (Border Collie)   **2236** Boris (Bulldog cross)

2237 Casey (Lurcher)   **2238** Tigger

2239 Leonard (Jack Russell cross)   **2240** Tia (Terrier cross)

150th Anniversary of Battersea Dogs and Cats Home

2010 (11 Mar.) Phosphor background. Perf 14½

3036	**2231**	(1st) multicoloured	1·00	1·00	☐ ☐
		a. Block of 10.			
		Nos. 3036/3045	9·00	9·00	☐ ☐
3037	**2232**	(1st) multicoloured	1·00	1·00	☐ ☐
3038	**2233**	(1st) multicoloured	1·00	1·00	☐ ☐
3039	**2234**	(1st) multicoloured	1·00	1·00	☐ ☐
3040	**2235**	(1st) multicoloured	1·00	1·00	☐ ☐
3041	**2236**	(1st) multicoloured	1·00	1·00	☐ ☐
3042	**2237**	(1st) multicoloured	1·00	1·00	☐ ☐
3043	**2238**	(1st) multicoloured	1·00	1·00	☐ ☐
3044	**2239**	(1st) multicoloured	1·00	1·00	☐ ☐
3045	**2240**	(1st) multicoloured	1·00	1·00	☐ ☐
Set of 10			9·00	9·00	
First Day Cover				9·50	☐
Presentation Pack (PO Pack No. 438)			11·00		☐
PHQ Cards (*set of 10*) (333)			4·00	11·50	☐ ☐
Gutter Block of 20			18·00		☐

Nos. 3036/3045 were printed together, *se-tenant*, as blocks of ten (5×2) in sheets of 60 (2 panes of 30).

2241 James I
(1406–1437)

2242 James II
(1437–1460)

2243 James III
(1460–1488)

2244 James IV
(1488–1513)

2245 James V
(1513–1542)

2246 Mary
(1542–1567)

2247 James VI
(1567–1625)

2248 The Age of the Stewarts

Kings and Queens (3rd series). House of Stewart

2010 (23 Mar.) Two phosphor bands. Perf 14

3046	**2241**	(1st) multicoloured	1·00	1·00	☐ ☐
3047	**2242**	(1st) multicoloured	1·00	1·00	☐ ☐
3048	**2243**	(1st) multicoloured	1·00	1·00	☐ ☐
3049	**2244**	62p. multicoloured	1·00	1·00	☐ ☐
3050	**2245**	62p. multicoloured	1·00	1·00	☐ ☐
3051	**2246**	81p. multicoloured	1·25	1·25	☐ ☐
3052	**2247**	81p. multicoloured	1·25	1·25	☐ ☐
Set of 7			6·75	6·75	☐ ☐
First Day Cover				8·00	☐
Presentation Pack (Nos. 3046/**MS**3053					
(PO Pack No. 439)			11·00		☐
PHQ Cards (*set of 12*) (334)			4·75	10·50	☐ ☐
Set of 7 Gutter Pairs			13·50		☐
Set of 7 Traffic Light Gutter Blocks of 4			30·00		☐

MS3053   123×70   mm.   **2248**   (1st)
Foundation of the University of St Andrews, 1413; (1st) Foundation of the College of Surgeons, Edinburgh, 1505; 81p. Foundation of Court of Session, 1532; 81p. John Knox (Reformation, 1559)

		4·25	4·25 ☐ ☐
First Day Cover			4·75 ☐

The complete miniature sheet is shown on one of the 12 PHQ cards with the others depicting individual stamps including those from No. **MS**3053.

2249 Humpback Whale
(*Megaptera novaeangliae*)

2250 Wildcat
(*Felis silvestris*)

2251 Brown Long-eared
Bat (*Plecotus auritus*)

2252 Polecat
(*Mustela putorius*)

2253 Sperm Whale
(*Physeter macrocephalus*)

2254 Water Vole
(*Arvicola terrestris*)

2255 Greater Horseshoe
Bat (*Rhinolophus
ferrumequinum*)

2256 Otter (*Lutra lutra*)

2257 Dormouse
(*Muscardinus avellanarius*)

2258 Hedgehog
(*Erinaceus europaeus*)

Action for Species (4th series). Mammals.

2010 (13 Apr.) 'All-over' phosphor. Perf 14½

3054	**2249**	(1st) multicoloured	1·00	1·00	☐	☐
		a. Block of 10.				
		Nos. 3054/3063	9·00	9·00	☐	☐
3055	**2250**	(1st) multicoloured	1·00	1·00	☐	☐
3056	**2251**	(1st) multicoloured	1·00	1·00	☐	☐
3057	**2252**	(1st) multicoloured	1·00	1·00	☐	☐
3058	**2253**	(1st) multicoloured	1·00	1·00	☐	☐
3059	**2254**	(1st) multicoloured	1·00	1·00	☐	☐
3060	**2255**	(1st) multicoloured	1·00	1·00	☐	☐
3061	**2256**	(1st) multicoloured	1·00	1·00	☐	☐
3062	**2257**	(1st) multicoloured	1·00	1·00	☐	☐
3063	**2258**	(1st) multicoloured	1·00	1·00	☐	☐
Set of 10			9·00	9·00	☐	☐
First Day Cover				9·50	☐	
Presentation Pack (PO Pack No. 440)			11·00		☐	
PHQ Cards (*set of 10*) (335)			4·00	11·00	☐	☐
Gutter Block of 20			18·00		☐	

Nos. 3054/3063 were printed together, *se-tenant*, as blocks of ten (5×2) in sheets of 60 (2 panes of 30).

See also Nos. 3095/3096.

No. 3064, and T **2259** are vacant.

2260 King George V and Queen Elizabeth II (1st); Two portraits of King George V (£1)

London 2010 Festival of Stamps (1st issue) and Centenary of Accession of King George V

2010 (6 May) 'All-over' phosphor. Perf 14½ × 14. Sheet 141 × 74 mm

MS3065	**2260**	(1st) rosine; £1 blackish brown, grey-brown and silver	3·75	4·00	☐	☐
First Day Cover				12·00	☐	

A miniature sheet as No. **MS**3065 but inscr 'BUSINESS DESIGN CENTRE, LONDON 8–15 MAY 2010' along the top right margin was only available at London 2010 Festival of Stamps. (Price £9·75)

For presentation pack and PHQ cards for No. **MS**3065 see below No. **MS**3072.

2261 King George V and Queen Elizabeth II

2262 1924 British Empire Exhibition 1½d. Brown Stamp

2263 1924 British Empire Exhibition 1d. Scarlet Stamp

2264 Two Portraits of King George V

2265 1913 £1 Green 'Sea Horses' Design Stamp

2266 1913 10s. Blue 'Sea Horses' Design Stamp

2267

London 2010 Festival of Stamps (2nd issue) and Centenary of Accession of King George V

2010 (6-8 May) Litho (Nos. 3066 and 3069) or recess and litho. 'All-over' phosphor. Perf 14½ × 14

3066	**2261**	(1st) rosine *(6.5.10)*	1·25	1·25	☐	☐
3067	**2262**	(1st) multicoloured *(8.5.10)*	1·50	1·50	☐	☐
3068	**2263**	(1st) multicoloured *(8.5.10)*	1·50	1·50	☐	☐
3069	**2264**	£1 blackish brown, grey-brown and silver *(8.5.10)*	2·50	2·50	☐	☐
3070	**2265**	£1 multicoloured *(8.5.10)*	2·25	2·25	☐	☐
3071	**2266**	£1 multicoloured *(8.5.10)*	2·25	2·25	☐	☐
Set of 6			11·00	11·00	☐	☐
Gutter Pair (No. 3066)			2·50		☐	
MS3072 115 × 90 mm. **2267**						
Nos. 3067/3068 and 3070/3071 *(8.5.10)*			4·50	4·75	☐	☐
First Day Cover (No. **MS**3072)				12·00	☐	
Presentation Pack (Nos. **MS**3065 and **MS**3072) (PO Pack No. 441)			8·50		☐	
PHQ Cards (*set of 8*) (336)			3·25	13·00	☐	☐

No. 3066 was issued as a sheet stamp on 6 May 2010.

Nos. 3066/3071 all come from the £11·15 1910–1936, King George V stamp booklet, No. DX50 issued on 8 May 2010.

Nos. 3066 and 3069 also come from miniature sheet No. **MS**3065, issued on 6 May 2010.

Nos. 3067/3068 and 3070/3071 also come from No. **MS**3072, issued on 8 May 2010.

The eight PHQ cards depict the individual stamps from Nos. **MS**3065 and **MS**3072 and the complete miniature sheets.

For No. **MS**3073, Type **2268**, see Decimal Machin Definitives section.

2269 Winston Churchill

2270 Land Girl

2271 Home Guard

2272 Evacuees

2273 Air Raid Wardens

2274 Woman working in Factory

2275 Royal Broadcast by Princess Elizabeth and Princess Margaret

2276 Fire Service

Britain Alone (1st issue)

2010 (13 May) 'All-over' phosphor. Perf 14½

3074	**2269**	(1st) pale stone, pale bistre and black	1·00	1·00	☐	☐
3075	**2270**	(1st) pale stone, pale bistre and black	1·00	1·00	☐	☐
3076	**2271**	60p. pale stone, pale bistre and black	90	90	☐	☐
3077	**2272**	60p. pale stone, pale bistre and black	90	90	☐	☐
3078	**2273**	67p. pale stone, pale bistre and black	1·00	1·00	☐	☐
3079	**2274**	67p. pale stone, pale bistre and black	1·00	1·00	☐	☐
3080	**2275**	97p. pale stone, pale bistre and black	1·40	1·40	☐	☐

3081	**2276**	97p. pale stone, pale bistre and black	1·40	1·40	☐	☐
Set of 8			7·50	7·50	☐	☐
First Day Cover				8·50		☐
Presentation Pack (Nos. 3074/3081 and **MS**3086) (PO Pack No. 442)			13·00		☐	
PHQ Cards (set of 13) (337)			5·25	11·00	☐	☐
Set of 8 Gutter Pairs			15·00		☐	

Nos. 3074/3081 were also issued in the £9·76 Britain Alone booklet, No. DX51.

The 13 PHQ cards depict Nos. 3074/3085 and the complete miniature sheet No. **MS**3086.

2277 Evacuation of British Soldiers from Dunkirk

2278 Vessels from Upper Thames Patrol in 'Operation Little Ships'

2279 Rescued Soldiers on Board Royal Navy Destroyer, Dover

2280 Steamship and Other Boat loaded with Troops

2281 Evacuation of British Troops from Dunkirk, 1940

Britain Alone (2nd issue)

2010 (13 May) 'All-over' phosphor. Perf 14½

3082	**2277**	(1st) pale stone, pale bistre and black	1·40	1·40	☐	☐
3083	**2278**	60p. pale stone, pale bistre and black	1·40	1·40	☐	☐
3084	**2279**	88p. pale stone, pale bistre and black	1·40	1·40	☐	☐
3085	**2280**	97p. pale stone, pale bistre and black	1·40	1·40	☐	☐
Set of 4			5·00	5·00	☐	☐
MS3086 115×89 mm. **2281** Nos. 3082/3085			5·00	5·00	☐	☐
First Day Cover (No. **MS**3086)				5·50		☐

Nos. 3082/3085 were only issued in the £9·76 Britain Alone booklet, No. DX51 and in No. **MS**3086.

2282 James I
(1603–1625)

2283 Charles I
(1625–1649)

2284 Charles II
(1660–1685)

2285 James II
(1685–1688)

2286 William III
(1689–1702)

2287 Mary II
(1689–1694)

2288 Anne
(1702–1714)

2289 The Age of the Stuarts

Kings and Queens (4th series). House of Stuart

2010 (15 June) Two phosphor bands. Perf 14

3087	**2282**	(1st) multicoloured	1·00	1·00	☐	☐
3088	**2283**	(1st) multicoloured	1·00	1·00	☐	☐
3089	**2284**	60p. multicoloured	90	90	☐	☐
3090	**2285**	60p. multicoloured	90	90	☐	☐
3091	**2286**	67p. multicoloured	1·10	1·10	☐	☐
3092	**2287**	67p. multicoloured	1·10	1·00	☐	☐
3093	**2288**	88p. multicoloured	1·40	1·40	☐	☐
Set of 7			6·50	6·50	☐	☐
First Day Cover				8·50		☐
Presentation Pack (Nos. 3087/**MS**3094)						
(PO Pack No. 443)			10·00		☐	
PHQ Cards (*set of 12*) (338)			4·75	16·00	☐	☐
Set of 7 Gutter Pairs			13·00		☐	
Set of 7 Traffic Light Gutter Blocks of 4			30·00		☐	

MS3094 123×70 mm. **2289** (1st) William
Harvey (discovery of blood circu-
lation, 1628); 60p. Civil War Battle
of Naseby, 1645; 88p. John Milton
(*Paradise Lost*, 1667); 97p. Castle
Howard (John Vanbrugh, 1712) .... 4·75   4·75 ☐ ☐
First Day Cover .... 5·00   ☐

The complete miniature sheet is shown on one of the 12 PHQ
cards with the others depicting individual stamps including
those from No. **MS**3094.

Mammals. Booklet stamps

2010 (15 June) Designs as Nos. 3061 and 3063 but printed in
gravure. Self-adhesive. 'All-over' phosphor. Die-cut perf 14½

3095	**2256**	(1st) multicoloured	2·75	2·75	☐	☐
3096	**2258**	(1st) multicoloured	2·75	2·75	☐	☐

Nos. 3095/3096 were only issued in stamp booklets, originally
sold for £2·46.

2290 Paralympic Games:
Rowing

2291 Shooting

2292 Modern Pentathlon

2293 Taekwondo

2294 Cycling

2295 Paralympic Games:
Table Tennis

2296 Hockey

2297 Football

2298 Paralympic Games: Goalball

2299 Boxing

Olympic and Paralympic Games, London (2012) (3rd series)

2010 (27 July) 'All-over' phosphor. Perf 14½

3097	**2290**	(1st) multicoloured	1·00	1·00	☐	☐
		a. Horiz strip of 5.				
		Nos. 3097/3101	4·50	4·50	☐	☐

3098	**2291**	(1st) multicoloured	1·00	1·00	☐ ☐
3099	**2292**	(1st) multicoloured	1·00	1·00	☐ ☐
3100	**2293**	(1st) multicoloured	1·00	1·00	☐ ☐
3101	**2294**	(1st) multicoloured	1·00	1·00	☐ ☐
3102	**2295**	(1st) multicoloured	1·00	1·00	☐ ☐
		a. Horiz strip of 5. Nos. 3102/3106	4·50	4·50	☐ ☐
3103	**2296**	(1st) multicoloured	1·00	1·00	☐ ☐
3104	**2297**	(1st) multicoloured	1·00	1·00	☐ ☐
3105	**2298**	(1st) multicoloured	1·00	1·00	☐ ☐
3106	**2299**	(1st) multicoloured	1·00	1·00	☐ ☐
Set of 10			9·00	9·00	☐ ☐
First Day Cover				9·25	☐
Presentation Pack (PO Pack No. 444)			11·00		☐
PHQ Cards (*set of 10*) (339)			4·00	11·00	☐ ☐
Set of 2 Gutter Strips of 10			18·00		☐

Nos. 3097/3101 and 3102/3106 were each printed together, *se-tenant*, in horizontal strips of five stamps in sheets of 50 (2 panes 5×5) and were also issued on 27 July 2011 in a miniature sheet containing all 30 stamps in the series.

See also No. **MS**3204*a*.

Olympic and Paralympic Games, London (2012) (4th series). Booklet stamps

2010 (27 July–12 Oct.) Designs as Nos. 3097, 3101/3102 and 3104 but printed in gravure. Self-adhesive. 'All-over' phosphor. Die-cut perf 14½

3107	**2290**	(1st) multicoloured	1·50	1·50	☐ ☐
3108	**2295**	(1st) multicoloured	1·50	1·50	☐ ☐
3108*a*	**2297**	(1st) multicoloured (12.10.10)	1·50	1·50	☐ ☐
3108*b*	**2294**	(1st) multicoloured (12.10.2010)	1·50	1·50	☐ ☐
Set of 4			5·50	5·50	☐ ☐

Nos. 3107/3108 and 3108*a*/3108*b* were only issued in two separate stamp booklets each originally sold for £2·46.

2300 LMS Coronation Class Locomotive, Euston Station, 1938

2301 BR Class 9F Locomotive *Evening Star*, Midsomer Norton, 1962

2302 GWR King Class Locomotive *King William IV*, near Teignmouth, 1935

2303 LNER Class A1 Locomotive *Royal Lancer*, 1929

2304 SR King Arthur Class Locomotive *Sir Mador de la Porte*, Bournemouth Central Station, 1935–1939

2305 LMS NCC Class WT No. 2, Larne Harbour, c. 1947

Great British Railways

2010 (19 Aug.) 'All-over' phosphor. Perf 14

3109	**2300**	(1st) gold, bluish grey and black	1·00	1·00	☐ ☐
3110	**2301**	(1st) gold, bluish grey and black	1·00	1·00	☐ ☐
3111	**2302**	67p. gold, bluish grey and black	90	90	☐ ☐
3112	**2303**	67p. gold, bluish grey and black	90	90	☐ ☐
3113	**2304**	97p. gold, bluish grey and black	1·25	1·25	☐ ☐
3114	**2305**	97p. gold, bluish grey and black	1·25	1·25	☐ ☐
Set of 6			5·75	5·75	☐ ☐
First Day Cover				7·00	☐
Presentation Pack (PO Pack No. 445)			7·00		☐
PHQ Cards (*set of 6*) (340)			2·50	7·50	☐ ☐
Set of 6 Gutter Pairs			12·00		☐

2306 Heart-regulating Beta Blockers (Sir James Black, 1962)

2307 Antibiotic Properties of Penicillin (Sir Alexander Fleming, 1928)

2308 Total Hip Replacement Operation (Sir John Charnley, 1962)

2309 Artificial Lens Implant Surgery (Sir Harold Ridley, 1949)

2310 Malaria Parasite transmitted by Mosquitoes (proved by Sir Ronald Ross, 1897)

2311 Computed Tomography Scanner (Sir Godfrey Hounsfield, 1971)

Medical Breakthroughs

2010 (16 Sept.) 'All-over' phosphor. Perf 14×14½

3115	**2306**	(1st) multicoloured	1·00	1·00	☐ ☐
3116	**2307**	58p. multicoloured	90	90	☐ ☐
3117	**2308**	60p. multicoloured	1·00	1·00	☐ ☐
3118	**2309**	67p. multicoloured	1·10	1·10	☐ ☐
3119	**2310**	88p. multicoloured	1·25	1·25	☐ ☐
3120	**2311**	97p. multicoloured	1·40	1·40	☐ ☐
Set of 6			6·00	6·00	☐ ☐
First Day Cover				8·00	☐
Presentation Pack (PO Pack No. 446)			7·25		☐
PHQ Cards (*set of 6*) (341)			2·50	7·50	☐ ☐
Set of 6 Gutter Pairs			12·00		☐

See also No. 3153.

2312 Winnie the Pooh and Christopher Robin (*Now we are Six*)

2313 Winnie the Pooh and Piglet (*The House at Pooh Corner*)

2314 Winnie the Pooh and Rabbit (*Winnie the Pooh*)

2315 Winnie the Pooh and Eeyore (*Winnie the Pooh*)

2316 Winnie the Pooh and Friends (*Winnie the Pooh*)

2317 Winnie the Pooh and Tigger (*The House at Pooh Corner*)

2318 Winnie the Pooh

Europa. Children's Books. Winnie the Pooh by A. A. Milne. Book Illustrations by E. H. Shepard

2010 (12 Oct.) 'All-over' phosphor. Perf 14 × 14½

3121	**2312**	(1st) yellow-brown, pale stone and black	1·00	1·00	
3122	**2313**	58p. yellow-brown, pale stone and black	90	90	
3123	**2314**	60p. yellow-brown, pale stone and black	1·00	1·00	
3124	**2315**	67p. yellow-brown, pale stone and black	1·10	1·10	
3125	**2316**	88p. yellow-brown, pale stone and black	1·25	1·25	
3126	**2317**	97p. yellow-brown, pale stone and black	1·40	1·40	
Set of 6			6·00	6·00	
First Day Cover				8·00	
Presentation Pack (Nos. 3121/**MS**3127) (PO Pack No. 447)			11·50		

PHQ Cards (set of 11) (342)	4·25	15·00	
Set of 6 Gutter Pairs	12·00		

MS3127 115 × 89 mm. **2318** (1st) Winnie the Pooh and Christopher Robin (from *Now we are Six*); 60p. Christopher Robin reads to Winnie the Pooh (from *Winnie the Pooh*); 88p. Winnie the Pooh and Christopher Robin sailing in umbrella (from *Winnie the Pooh*); 97p. Christopher Robin (putting on wellingtons) and Pooh (from *Winnie the Pooh*). Perf 14½ .... 4·75 4·75

First Day Cover .... 6·25

The 1st class value includes the 'EUROPA' emblem.

Stamps from No. **MS**3127 show lines from poem *We Too* by A. A. Milne: 'Wherever I am, there's always Pooh' (1st); 'There's always Pooh and Me. Whatever I do, he wants to do' (60p.); 'Where are you going to-day?' says Pooh: 'Well that's very odd 'cos I was too' (88p.); 'Let's go together,' says Pooh, says he. 'Let's go together,' says Pooh (97p.).

The 11 PHQ cards show the six stamps, the four individual stamps within No. **MS**3127 and the complete miniature sheet.

2319 Wallace and Gromit carol singing

2320 Gromit posting Christmas Cards

2321 Wallace and Gromit carol singing

2322 Wallace and Gromit decorating Christmas Tree

2323 Gromit posting Christmas Cards

2324 Gromit carrying Christmas Pudding

2325 Gromit putting on Bone-themed Pullover

Christmas with Wallace and Gromit

2010 (2 Nov.) One centre band (No. 3128) or two phosphor bands (others). Perf 14½ × 14 (with one elliptical hole in each vert side)

		(a) Self-adhesive			
3128	**2319**	(2nd) multicoloured	90	90	
3129	**2320**	(1st) multicoloured	1·00	1·00	
3130	**2321**	(2nd Large) multicoloured	1·10	1·10	
3131	**2322**	60p. multicoloured	1·10	1·10	
3132	**2323**	(1st Large) multicoloured	1·50	1·40	
3133	**2324**	97p. multicoloured	1·40	1·40	
3134	**2325**	£1·46 multicoloured	2·00	2·00	
Set of 7			8·00	8·00	
First Day Cover				9·50	
Presentation Pack (PO Pack No. 448)			10·00		
PHQ Cards (set of 8) (343)			3·25	16·00	
		(b) Ordinary gum			

MS3135 115 × 102 mm. As Nos.

3128/3134		8·00	8·00	
First Day Cover			9·50	

The eight PHQ cards show the seven individual stamps and the miniature sheet.

The 2nd class, 1st class, 60p. and 97p. stamps were also issued together in sheets of 20 containing eight 2nd class, eight 1st class, two 60p. and two 97p. stamps, each stamps accompanied by a *se-tenant* label. Separate sheets of 20 2nd, 20 1st, ten 1st, ten 60p. and ten 97p. were available with personal photographs on the labels. All these sheets were printed in lithography instead of gravure.

Year Pack

2010 (2 Nov.) Comprises Nos. 2999/3008, **MS**3025/3063, **MS**3065, **MS**3072, 3074/3081, **MS**3086/**MS**3094, 3097/3106 and 3109/3134

CP3135*a* Year Pack	£125	☐

Post Office Yearbook

2010 (2 Nov.) Comprises Nos. 2999/3008, **MS**3025/3063, **MS**3065, **MS**3072, 3074/3081, **MS**3086/**MS**3094, 3097/3106 and 3109/3134

YB3135*a* Yearbook	£110	☐

Miniature Sheet Collection

2010 (2 Nov.) Comprises Nos. **MS**3024, **MS**3025, **MS**3053, **MS**3065, **MS**3072, **MS**3086, **MS**3094, **MS**3127 and **MS**3135

MS3135*a* Miniature Sheet Collection	50·00	☐

2326 *Joe 90*

2327 *Captain Scarlet*

2328 Thunderbird 2 (*Thunderbirds*)

2329 *Stingray*

2330 *Fireball XL5*

2331 *Supercar*

2332 Thunderbird 4; Thunderbird 3;Thunderbird 2; Thunderbird 1

F.A.B. The Genius of Gerry Anderson (producer of TV programmes)

2011 (11 Jan.) 'All-over' phosphor

(a) Litho. Ordinary gum. Perf 14

3136	**2326**	(1st) multicoloured	1·00	1·00	☐	☐
		a. Horiz strip of 3.				
		Nos. 3136/3138	3·00	3·00	☐	☐
3137	**2327**	(1st) multicoloured	1·00	1·00	☐	☐
3138	**2328**	(1st) multicoloured	1·00	1·00	☐	☐
3139	**2329**	97p. multicoloured	1·50	1·50	☐	☐
		a. Horiz strip of 3.				
		Nos. 3139/3141	4·50	4·50	☐	☐
3140	**2330**	97p. multicoloured	1·50	1·50	☐	☐
3141	**2331**	97p. multicoloured	1·50	1·50	☐	☐
		Set of 6	6·75	6·75	☐	☐
		First Day Cover		7·75	☐	
		Presentation Pack (PO Pack No. 450)	12·50		☐	
		PHQ Cards (*set of 11*) (344)	4·25	17·00	☐	☐
		Set of 2 Gutter Strips of 6	13·50		☐	

(b) Microlenticular. 'All-over' phosphor Perf 14

MS3142 116×89 mm. **2332** 41p. Thunderbird 4, 60p. Thunderbird 3, 88p. Thunderbird 2, 97p. Thunderbird 1 multicoloured

	5·25	5·50	☐	☐
First Day Cover		6·00	☐	

(c) Self-adhesive. As No. 3138 but printed in gravure. Die-cut perf 14

3143	**2328**	(1st) multicoloured	1·50	1·50	☐	☐

Nos. 3136/3138 and 3139/3141 were each printed together, *se-tenant*, as horizontal strips of three stamps in sheets of 60 (2 panes 6×5).

The stamps within No. **MS**3142 use microlenticular technology to show each vehicle's launch sequences when the miniature sheet is tilted.

No. 3143 was only issued in booklets originally sold for £1·46.

2333 Classic Locomotives of England

Classic Locomotives (1st series). England Miniature Sheet

2011 (1 Feb.) Sheet 180×74 mm. Multicoloured. 'All-over' phosphor. Perf 14

MS3144 **2333** (1st) BR Dean Goods No. 2532; 60p. Peckett R2 *Thor*; 88p. Lancashire and Yorkshire Railway 1093 No. 1100; 97p. BR WD No. 90662

	4·25	4·50	☐	☐
First Day Cover		5·00	☐	
Presentation Pack (PO Pack No. 451)	5·25		☐	
PHQ Cards (*set of 5*) (345)	2·00	9·00	☐	☐

The five PHQ cards show the four individual stamps and the complete miniature sheet.

See also No. 3215.

2334 *Oliver* **2335** *Blood Brothers* **2336** *We Will Rock You*

2337 *Spamalot*   **2338** *Rocky Horror Show*   **2339** *Me and My Girl*

2340 *Return to the Forbidden Planet*   **2341** *Billy Elliot*

Musicals

2011 (24 Feb.) 'All-over' phosphor. Perf 14

3145	**2334**	(1st) multicoloured	1·00	1·00	
3146	**2335**	(1st) multicoloured	1·00	1·00	
3147	**2336**	(1st) multicoloured	1·00	1·00	
3148	**2337**	(1st) multicoloured	1·00	1·00	
3149	**2338**	97p. multicoloured	1·25	1·25	
3150	**2339**	97p. multicoloured	1·25	1·25	
3151	**2340**	97p. multicoloured	1·25	1·25	
3152	**2341**	97p. multicoloured	1·25	1·25	
Set of 8			8·25	8·25	
First Day Cover				9·25	
Presentation Pack (PO Pack No. 452)			9·75		
PHQ Cards (*set of 8*) (346)			3·25	11·00	
Set of 8 Gutter Pairs			16·50		
Set of 8 Traffic Light Gutter Pairs			25·00		

50th Anniversary of the British Heart Foundation. Booklet stamp

2011 (24 Feb.) Design as No. 3115 but printed in gravure. Self-adhesive. 'All-over' phosphor. Die-cut perf 14 × 14½

3153	**2306**	(1st) multicoloured	1·50	1·50	

No. 3153 was only issued in booklets originally sold for £2·46.

2342 Rincewind (Terry Pratchett's *Discworld*)   **2343** Nanny Ogg (Terry Pratchett's *Discworld*)

2344 Michael Gambon as Dumbledore (J. K. Rowling's *Harry Potter*)   **2345** Ralph Fiennes as Lord Voldemort (J. K. Rowling's *Harry Potter*)

2346 Merlin (Arthurian Legend)   **2347** Morgan Le Fay (Arthurian Legend)

2348 Aslan (C. S. Lewis's *Narnia*)   **2349** Tilda Swinton as The White Witch (C. S. Lewis's *Narnia*)

Magical Realms

2011 (8 Mar.–2 Dec.) 'All-over' phosphor. Perf 14½

3154	**2342**	(1st) multicoloured	1·00	1·00	
		a. Vert pair. Nos. 3154/3155	2·00	2·00	
3155	**2343**	(1st) multicoloured	1·00	1·00	
3156	**2344**	(1st) multicoloured	1·00	1·00	
		a. Vert pair. Nos. 3156/3157	2·00	2·00	
3157	**2345**	(1st) multicoloured	1·00	1·00	
3158	**2346**	60p. multicoloured	1·10	1·10	
		a. Vert pair. Nos. 3158/3159	2·25	2·25	
3159	**2347**	60p. multicoloured	1·10	1·10	
3160	**2348**	97p. multicoloured	1·25	1·25	
		a. Vert pair. Nos. 3160/3161	2·50	2·50	
3161	**2349**	97p. multicoloured	1·25	1·25	
Set of 8			7·50	7·50	
First Day Cover				7·75	
Presentation Pack (PO Pack No. 453)			8·50		
Presentation Pack (Heroes and Villains containing Nos. 3156/3157, each × 5) (2.12.11)			12·00		
PHQ Cards (*set of 8*) (347)			3·25	9·25	
Set of 4 Gutter Strips of 4			15·00		

Nos. 3154/3155, 3156/3157, 3158/3159 and 3160/3161 were each printed together, *se-tenant*, as vertical pairs in sheets of 60 (2 panes 5 × 6).

For Nos. U3055/U3059 see Decimal Machin Definitives section.

2350 African Elephant   **2351** Mountain Gorilla

2352 Siberian Tiger

2353 Polar Bear

2354 Amur Leopard

2355 Iberian Lynx

2356 Red Panda

2357 Black Rhinoceros

2358 African Wild Dog

2359 Golden Lion Tamarin

2360 Wildlife of the Amazon Rainforest

50th Anniversary of the WWF

2011 (22 Mar.) 'All-over' phosphor. Perf 14 (No. **MS**3172) or 14½ (others)

3162	**2350**	(1st) multicoloured	1·00	1·00
		a. Horiz strip of 5.		
		Nos. 3162/3166	4·50	4·50

3163	**2351**	(1st) multicoloured	1·00	1·00
3164	**2352**	(1st) multicoloured	1·00	1·00
3165	**2353**	(1st) multicoloured	1·00	1·00
3166	**2354**	(1st) multicoloured	1·00	1·00
3167	**2355**	(1st) multicoloured	1·00	1·00
		a. Horiz strip of 5.		
		Nos. 3167/3171	4·50	4·50
3168	**2356**	(1st) multicoloured	1·00	1·00
3169	**2357**	(1st) multicoloured	1·00	1·00
3170	**2358**	(1st) multicoloured	1·00	1·00
3171	**2359**	(1st) multicoloured	1·00	1·00
Set of 10			9·00	9·00
First Day Cover				9·50
Presentation Pack (Nos. 3162/**MS**3172)				
(PO Pack No. 454)			15·00	
PHQ Cards (*set of* 15) (348)			6·00	21·00
Set of 2 Gutter Strips of 10			18·00	

MS3172 115×89 mm. **2360** (1st) Spider Monkey; 60p. Hyacinth Macaw; 88p. Poison Dart Frog; 97p. Jaguar ..... 4·25 4·50

First Day Cover ..... 5·25

Nos. 3162/3166 and 3167/3171 were each printed together, *se-tenant*, as horizontal strips of five stamps in sheets of 50 (2 panes 5×5) and were also issued in the £9·05 50th Anniversary of the WWF booklet, No. DX52.

The 1st class value from No. **MS**3172 includes the EUROPA emblem.

2361 David Tennant as Hamlet, 2008

2362 Antony Sher as Prospero, *The Tempest*, 2009

2363 Chuk Iwuji as Henry VI, 2006

2364 Paul Schofield as King Lear, 1962

2365 Sara Kestelman as Titania, *A Midsummer Night's Dream*, 1970

2366 Ian McKellen and Francesca Annis as Romeo and Juliet, 1976

2367 The Four Theatres of the Royal Shakespeare Company, Stratford-upon-Avon

50th Anniversary of the Royal Shakespeare Company

2011 (12 Apr.) 'All-over' phosphor

(a) Gravure Walsall. Perf 14½

3173	**2361**	(1st) black, brownish black and bright scarlet	1·00	1·00 ☐ ☐
3174	**2362**	66p. black, brownish black and bright scarlet	1·00	1·00 ☐ ☐
3175	**2363**	68p. black, brownish black and bright scarlet	1·10	1·10 ☐ ☐
3176	**2364**	76p. black, brownish black and bright scarlet	1·25	1·25 ☐ ☐
3177	**2365**	£1 black, brownish black and bright scarlet	1·50	1·50 ☐ ☐
3178	**2366**	£1·10 black, brownish black and bright scarlet	1·75	1·75 ☐ ☐

Set of 6	6·75	6·75 ☐ ☐
First Day Cover		8·00 ☐
Presentation Pack (Nos. 3173/**MS**3179) (PO Pack No. 455)	13·00	☐
PHQ Cards (set of 11) (349)	4·50	18·00 ☐ ☐
Set of 6 Gutter Pairs	13·50	☐

(b) Litho Cartor. Multicoloured. Perf 14

MS3179 115×89 mm. **2367** (1st) Janet Suzman as Ophelia, *Hamlet*, 1965, Royal Shakespeare Theatre; 68p. Patrick Stewart in *Antony and Cleopatra*, 2006, Swan Theatre; 76p. Geoffrey Streatfeild in *Henry V*, 2007, The Courtyard Theatre; £1 Judy Dench as Lady Macbeth, 1976, The Other Place ..... 4·25 ..... 4·25 ☐ ☐

First Day Cover	5·00 ☐

The 11 PHQ cards show the six stamps, the four individual stamps within No. **MS**3179 and the complete miniature sheet.

2368 Prince William and Miss Catherine Middleton

Royal Wedding. Official Engagement Portraits by Mario Testino. Miniature Sheet

2011 (21 Apr.) Sheet 115×89 mm. Multicoloured. 'All-over' phosphor. Perf 14½×14

MS3180 **2368** (1st)×2 Prince William and Miss Catherine Middleton embracing; £1·10×2 Formal portrait of Prince William and Miss Catherine Middleton in Council Chamber, St James's Palace ..... 5·50 ..... 5·50 ☐ ☐

First Day Cover		7·00 ☐
Presentation Pack (PO Pack No. M20)	13·00	☐
Commemorative Document	15·00	☐

2369 Cray (fabric print by William Morris), 1884

2370 Cherries (detail from panel by Philip Webb), 1867

2371 Seaweed (wallpaper pattern by John Henry Dearle), 1901

2372 Peony (ceramic tile design by Kate Faulkner), 1877

2373 Acanthus (tile by William Morris and William de Morgan), 1876

2374 The Merchant's Daughter (detail of stained glass window by Edward Burne-Jones), 1864

150th Anniversary of Morris and Company (designers and manufacturers of textiles, wallpaper and furniture) (1st issue)

2011 (5 May) 'All-over' phosphor. Perf 14×14½

3181	**2369**	(1st) multicoloured	1·00	1·00 ☐ ☐
3182	**2370**	(1st) multicoloured	1·00	1·00 ☐ ☐
3183	**2371**	76p. multicoloured	1·25	1·25 ☐ ☐
3184	**2372**	76p. multicoloured	1·25	1·25 ☐ ☐
3185	**2373**	£1·10 multicoloured	1·75	1·75 ☐ ☐
3186	**2374**	£1·10 multicoloured	1·75	1·75 ☐ ☐

Set of 6	7·00	7·00 ☐ ☐
First Day Cover		8·00 ☐
Presentation Pack (PO Pack No. 456)	7·75	☐
PHQ Cards (set of 6) (350)	2·50	8·25 ☐ ☐
Set of 6 Gutter Pairs	14·00	☐

Nos. 3181/3186 were also issued in the £9·99 Morris & Co booklet, No. DY1.

150th Anniversary of Morris and Company (2nd issue)

2011 (5 May) Design as T **2202** (2009 Christmas stained-glass windows). One centre band. Perf 14½×14 (with one elliptical hole in each vert side)

3186a**2202**　(2nd) multicoloured　　　1·50　　1·50 ☐ ☐

No. 3186a was only issued in the £9·99 'Morris & Co' stamp booklet, No. DY1.

2375 Thomas the Tank Engine

2376 James the Red Engine

2377 Percy the Small Engine

2378 Daisy (diesel railcar)

2379 Toby the Tram Engine

2380 Gordon the Big Engine

2381 Book Illustrations by John T. Kenny (76p.) or C. Reginald Dalby (others)

2382 "Goodbye, Bertie," called Thomas (from *Tank Engine Thomas Again*)

Thomas the Tank Engine

2011 (14 June) 'All-over' phosphor

(a) Ordinary gum. Perf 14 (No. **MS**3193) or 14½×14 (others)

3187	**2375**	(1st) multicoloured	1·00	1·00	☐	☐
3188	**2376**	66p. multicoloured	1·00	1·00	☐	☐
3189	**2377**	68p. multicoloured	1·10	1·10	☐	☐
3190	**2378**	76p. multicoloured	1·25	1·25	☐	☐
3191	**2379**	£1 multicoloured	1·50	1·50	☐	☐
3192	**2380**	£1·10 multicoloured	1·75	1·75	☐	☐
Set of 6			6·75	6·75		
First Day Cover				8·00	☐	

Presentation Pack (Nos. 3187/**MS**3193)

(PO Pack No. 457)　　　　　　　13·00　　　　　☐

PHQ Cards (*set of 11*) (351)　4·50　18·00 ☐ ☐

Set of 6 Gutter Pairs　　　　13·50　　　　　☐

MS3193　115×89 mm. **2381** "Goodbye, Bertie," called Thomas (from *Tank Engine Thomas Again*) (1st); James was more dirty than hurt (from *Toby the Tram Engine*) (68p.); "Yes Sir," Percy shivered miserably (from *The Eight Famous Engines*) (76p.); They told Henry, "We shall leave you there for always" (from *The Three Railway Engines*) (£1)　　　　4·25　4·25 ☐ ☐

First Day Cover　　　　　　　　　5·00　　☐

(b) Self-adhesive. Die-cut perf 14

3194　**2382**　(1st) multicoloured　　1·50　1·50 ☐ ☐

The 11 PHQ Cards show the six stamps, the four individual stamps within No. **MS**3193 and the complete miniature sheet.

Nos. 3187/3192 show scenes from TV series *Thomas and Friends*, and Nos. No. **MS**3193/3194 book illustrations from The Railway Series.

No. 3194 was only issued in stamp booklets originally sold for £2·76.

2383 Paralympic Games: Sailing

2384 Athletics: Field

2385 Volleyball

2386 Wheelchair Rugby

2387 Wrestling

2388 Wheelchair Tennis

2389 Fencing

2390 Gymnastics

2391 Triathlon

2392 Handball

2393 The Sovereign's Sceptre with Cross

2394 St Edward's Crown

2395 Rod and Sceptre with Doves

2396 Queen Mary's Crown

2397 The Sovereign's Orb

2398 Jewelled Sword of Offering

2399 Imperial State Crown

2400 Coronation Spoon

Olympic and Paralympic Games, London (2012) (5th series)

2011 (27 July) 'All-over' phosphor. Perf 14½

3195	**2383**	(1st) multicoloured	1·00	1·00	☐	☐
		a. Horiz strip of 5.				
		Nos. 3195/3199	5·00	5·00	☐	☐
3196	**2384**	(1st) multicoloured	1·00	1·00	☐	☐
3197	**2385**	(1st) multicoloured	1·00	1·00	☐	☐
3198	**2386**	(1st) multicoloured	1·00	1·00	☐	☐
3199	**2387**	(1st) multicoloured	1·00	1·00	☐	☐
3200	**2388**	(1st) multicoloured	1·00	1·00	☐	☐
		a. Horiz strip of 5.				
		Nos. 3200/3204	5·00	5·00	☐	☐
3201	**2389**	(1st) multicoloured	1·00	1·00	☐	☐
3202	**2390**	(1st) multicoloured	1·00	1·00	☐	☐
3203	**2391**	(1st) multicoloured	1·00	1·00	☐	☐
3204	**2392**	(1st) multicoloured	1·00	1·00	☐	☐
Set of 10			9·00	9·00	☐	☐
First Day Cover				9·50	☐	
Presentation Pack (PO Pack No. 458)			10·00		☐	
PHQ Cards (*set of 10*) (352)			4·00	12·00	☐	☐
Set of 2 Gutter Strips of 10			18·00		☐	
MS3204*a* 210×300 mm. Nos. 2981/2990,						
3097/3106 and 3195/3204			35·00	35·00	☐	☐

Nos. 3195/3199 and 3200/3204 were each printed together, *se-tenant*, in horizontal strips of five stamps in sheets of 50 (2 panes 5×5) and in No. **MS**3204*a*.

Olympic and Paralympic Games (2012) (6th series)

2011 (27 July) Booklet stamps. Designs as Nos. 3195, 3198 and 3201/3202. Self-adhesive. 'All-over' phosphor. Die-cut perf 14½×14

3205	**2386**	(1st) multicoloured	1·50	1·50	☐	☐
3206	**2383**	(1st) multicoloured	1·50	1·50	☐	☐
3206*a*	**2390**	(1st) multicoloured	1·50	1·50	☐	☐
3206*b*	**2389**	(1st) multicoloured	1·50	1·50	☐	☐
Set of 4			5·50	5·50	☐	☐

Nos. 3205/3206 and 3206*a*/3206*b* were only issued in two separate stamp booklets originally sold for £2·76.

Crown Jewels

2011 (23 Aug.) Phosphor background. Perf 14×14½

3207	**2393**	(1st) multicoloured	1·00	1·00	☐	☐
3208	**2394**	(1st) multicoloured	1·00	1·00	☐	☐
3209	**2395**	68p. multicoloured	1·10	1·10	☐	☐
3210	**2396**	68p. multicoloured	1·10	1·10	☐	☐
3211	**2397**	76p. multicoloured	1·25	1·25	☐	☐
3212	**2398**	76p. multicoloured	1·25	1·25	☐	☐
3213	**2399**	£1·10 multicoloured	1·60	1·60	☐	☐
3214	**2400**	£1·10 multicoloured	1·60	1·60	☐	☐
Set of 8			8·75	8·75	☐	☐
First Day Cover				10·00	☐	
Presentation Pack (PO Pack No. 459)			10·00		☐	
PHQ Cards (*set of 8*) (353)			3·25	11·00	☐	☐
Set of 8 Gutter Pairs			17·50		☐	

2401 BR Dean Goods Locomotive No. 2532, 1951

Classic Locomotives. Booklet stamps

2011 (23 Aug.) Design as 1st class stamp within No. **MS**3144 but printed in gravure. Self-adhesive. 'All-over' phosphor. Die-cut perf 14

3215 **2401**   (1st) black and gold   1·50   1·50 ☐ ☐
No. 3215 was only issued in stamp booklets originally sold for £2·76.

2402 Pilot Gustav Hamel receiving   **2403** Gustav Hamel in cockpit
mailbag

2404 Pilot Clement Greswell and   **2405** Delivery of first airmail to
Blériot monoplane   Postmaster General at Windsor

2406 First United Kingdom Aerial Post, 9 September 1911

Centenary of First United Kingdom Aerial Post (1st issue)

2011 (9 Sept.) 'All-over' phosphor. Perf 14

3216 **2402**   (1st) purple-black and
                  pale grey-lilac   1·75   1·75 ☐ ☐
3217 **2403**   68p. brownish black
                  and stone   1·75   1·75 ☐ ☐
3218 **2404**   £1 deep sepia and
                  pale grey-brown   5·00   5·00 ☐ ☐
3219 **2405**   £1·10 black and pale grey 5·00   5·00 ☐ ☐
Set of 4   13·50   13·50 ☐ ☐
MS3220 **2406** 146×74 mm. Nos.
      3216/3219   8·50   8·50 ☐ ☐
First Day Cover   9·50   ☐
Presentation Pack (PO Pack No. 460)   9·50   ☐
PHQ Cards (*set of 5*) (354)   2·00   21·00 ☐ ☐
Nos. 3216/3219 were only issued in the £9·97 First United Kingdom Aerial Post stamp booklet, No. DY2.

  The five PHQ cards show the four individual stamps and the complete miniature sheet.

2407 Windsor Castle

Centenary of First United Kingdom Aerial Post (2nd issue)

2011 (9 Sept.) Recess and Litho. Perf 11×11½
3221 **2407**   50p. black on cream   2·00   2·00 ☐ ☐
No. 3221 was only issued in the £9·99 First United Kingdom Aerial Post stamp booklet, No. DY2.

> For No. **MS**3222, Type **2048**, see Decimal Machin Definitives section.

2409 George I   **2410** George II   **2411** George III
(1714–1727)   (1727–1760)   (1760–1820)

2412 George IV   **2413** William IV   **2414** Victoria
(1820–1830)   (1830–1837)   (1837–1901)

2415 The Age of the Hanoverians

Kings and Queens (5th series). House of Hanover

2011 (15 Sept.) Two phosphor bands. Perf 14
3223 **2409**   (1st) multicoloured   1·00   1·00 ☐ ☐
3224 **2410**   (1st) multicoloured   1·00   1·00 ☐ ☐
3225 **2411**   76p. multicoloured   1·25   1·25 ☐ ☐
3226 **2412**   76p. multicoloured   1·25   1·25 ☐ ☐
3227 **2413**   £1·10 multicoloured   1·75   1·75 ☐ ☐
3228 **2414**   £1·10 multicoloured   1·75   1·75 ☐ ☐
Set of 6   7·00   7·00 ☐ ☐
First Day Cover   8·00   ☐
Presentation Pack (Nos. 3223/**MS**3229)
(PO Pack No. 461)   13·00   ☐
PHQ Cards (*set of 11*) (355)   4·50   18·00 ☐ ☐
Set of 6 Gutter Pairs   14·00   ☐
Set of 6 Traffic Light Gutter Blocks of 4 50·00   ☐
MS3229 123×70 mm. **2415** (1st) Robert
      Walpole (first Prime Minister), 1721;
      68p. Ceiling by Robert Adam, Kedles-
      ton Hall, 1763; 76p. Penny Black (uni-
      form postage), 1840; £1 Queen Victo-
      ria (Diamond Jubilee), 1897   4·25   4·25 ☐ ☐
First Day Cover   5·00   ☐
The complete miniature sheet is shown on one of the 11 PHQ cards with the others depicting individual stamps, including those from No. **MS**3229.

2416 *Angel of the North*

2417 Blackpool Tower

2418 Carrick-a-Rede,
Co. Antrim

2419 Downing Street

2420 Edinburgh Castle

2421 Forth Railway Bridge

2422 Glastonbury Tor

2423 Harlech Castle

2424 Ironbridge

2425 Jodrell Bank

2426 Kursaal, Southend,
Essex

2427 Lindisfarne Priory

UK A-Z (1st series). Famous Landmarks A-L

2011 (13 Oct.) 'All-over' phosphor. Perf 14½

3230	**2416**	(1st) multicoloured	1·00	1·00	☐	☐
		a. Horiz strip of 6.				
		Nos. 3230/3235	4·50	4·50	☐	☐
3231	**2417**	(1st) multicoloured	1·00	1·00	☐	☐
3232	**2418**	(1st) multicoloured	1·00	1·00	☐	☐
3233	**2419**	(1st) multicoloured	1·00	1·00	☐	☐
3234	**2420**	(1st) multicoloured	1·00	1·00	☐	☐

3235	**2421**	(1st) multicoloured	1·00	1·00	☐	☐
3236	**2422**	(1st) multicoloured	1·00	1·00	☐	☐
		a. Horiz strip of 6.				
		Nos. 3236/3241	4·50	4·50	☐	☐
3237	**2423**	(1st) multicoloured	1·00	1·00	☐	☐
3238	**2424**	(1st) multicoloured	1·00	1·00	☐	☐
3239	**2425**	(1st) multicoloured	1·00	1·00	☐	☐
3240	**2426**	(1st) multicoloured	1·00	1·00	☐	☐
3241	**2427**	(1st) multicoloured	1·00	1·00	☐	☐
		Set of 12	9·00	9·00	☐	☐
		First Day Covers (2)		11·00		☐
		Presentation Pack (PO Pack No. 462)	12·00			☐
		PHQ Cards (*set of 12*) (356)	4·75	13·00	☐	☐
		Set of 2 Gutter Strips of 12	18·00			☐
		Set of 2 Traffic Light Gutter Strips of 24	48·00			☐

Nos. 3230/3235 and 3236/3241 were each printed together, *se-tenant*, as horizontal strips of six stamps in sheets of 60 (2 panes of 30) and were also issued on 10 April 2012 in a sheet containing all 26 stamps.

See also No. **MS**3308.

2428 Joseph
visited by
the Angel
(Matthew 1:21)

2429 Madonna
and Child
(Matthew 1:23)

2430 Joseph visited
by the Angel
(Matthew 1:21)

2431 Madonna and
Child (Matthew 1:23)

2432 Baby
Jesus in the
Manger (Luke 2:7)

2433 Shepherds
visited by the
Angel (Luke 2:10)

2434 Wise Men
and Star
(Matthew 2:10)

Christmas. 400th Anniversary of the King James Bible

2011 (8 Nov.) One centre band (No. 3242) or two phosphor bands (others). Perf 14½ × 14 (with one elliptical hole in each vert side)

(a) Self-adhesive

3242	**2428**	(2nd) multicoloured	90	90	☐	☐
3243	**2429**	(1st) multicoloured	1·00	1·00	☐	☐
3244	**2430**	(2nd Large)				
		multicoloured	1·10	1·10	☐	☐
3245	**2431**	(1st Large)				
		multicoloured	1·50	1·40	☐	☐
3246	**2432**	68p. multicoloured	1·25	1·25	☐	☐
3247	**2433**	£1·10 multicoloured	1·90	1·90	☐	☐
3248	**2434**	£1·65 multicoloured	2·50	2·50	☐	☐
		Set of 7	9·00	9·00	☐	☐
		First Day Cover		11·00		☐
		Presentation Pack (PO Pack No. 463)	10·00			☐
		PHQ Cards (*set of 8*) (357)	3·25	19·00	☐	☐

(b) Ordinary gum

MS3249 116 × 102 mm.

As Nos. 3242/3248	9·00	9·00	☐	☐
First Day Cover		10·00		☐

The eight PHQ cards show the seven individual stamps and the miniature sheet.

The 2nd class, 1st class, 68p., £1·10 and £1·65 stamps were also issued in sheets of 20 containing eight 2nd class, eight 1st class, two 68p. and two £1·10 stamps, each stamp accompanied by a *se-tenant* label with a verse from the King James Bible.

Separate sheets of 20 2nd, ten 1st, ten 68p. and ten £1·10 were available with personal photographs.

Year Pack

2011 (8 Nov.) Comprises Nos. 3136/3142, **MS**3144/3152, 3154/3193, 3195/3204, 3207/3214, **MS**3220 and 3223/3248
CP3244*a*   Year Pack   £130   ☐

Post Office Yearbook

2011 (8 Nov.) Comprises Nos. 3136/3142, **MS**3144/3152, 3154/3193, 3195/3204, 3207/3214, **MS**3220 and 3223/3248
YB3244*a*   Yearbook   £130   ☐

Miniature Sheet Collection

2011 (8 Nov.) Comprises Nos. **MS**3142, **MS**3144, **MS**3172, **MS**3179/ **MS**3180, **MS**3193, **MS**3220, **MS**3229 and **MS**3249
MS3244*a* Miniature Sheet Collection   45·00   ☐

2435 Paralympic Games Emblem

2436 Olympic Games Emblem

Olympic and Paralympic Games (7th issue)

2012 (5 Jan.) Self-adhesive. Two phosphor bands. Die-cut perf 14½ × 14 (with one elliptical hole in each vert side)

3250	**2435**	(1st) black and orange-red	1·25	1·25	☐	☐
3251	**2436**	(1st) black and orange-red	1·25	1·25	☐	☐
3252	**2435**	(World wide up to 20 g) black, bright scarlet and greenish blue	2·25	2·25	☐	☐
3253	**2436**	(World wide up to 20 g) black, bright scarlet and greenish blue	2·25	2·25	☐	☐
Set of 4			7·00	7·00	☐	☐
First Day Cover				8·00	☐	
Presentation Pack (PO Pack No. 93)			9·00		☐	
PHQ Cards (*set of 4*) (D32)			1·50	8·00	☐	☐

Nos. 3250/3251 were printed together in sheets of 50 (2 panes 5×5), with the two designs alternating horizontally and vertically. The upper pane had No. 3250 at top left and contained 13 of No. 3250 and 12 of No. 3251. The lower pane had No. 3251 at top left and contained 13 of No. 3251 and 12 of No. 3250.

Nos. 3250/3251 were also issued in booklets of six originally sold for £2·76. The panes from this booklet exist in two versions which differ in the order of the stamps within the block of six.

Nos. 3252/3253 were printed together in sheets of 25 (5×5) with the two designs alternating horizontally and vertically. There were two versions of the sheets of 25, one having No. 3252 at top left and containing 13 of No. 3252 and 12 of No. 3253, and the other having No. 3253 at top left and containing 13 of No. 3253 and 12 of No. 3252.

Nos. 3250/3253 were also issued on 27 June 2012 in sheets of 20 with *se-tenant* labels showing Games venues, printed in lithography instead of gravure, each sheet containing eight each of Nos. 3250/3251 and two each of Nos. 3252/3253.

2437 *Charlie and the Chocolate Factory*

2438 *Fantastic Mr. Fox*

2439 *James and the Giant Peach*

2440 *Matilda*

2441 *The Twits*

2442 *The Witches*

Roald Dahl's Children's Stories (1st issue). Book Illustrations by Quentin Blake

2012 (10 Jan.) 'All-over' phosphor. Perf 14

3254	**2437**	(1st) multicoloured	1·00	1·00	☐	☐
3255	**2438**	66p. multicoloured	1·00	1·00	☐	☐
3256	**2439**	68p. multicoloured	1·10	1·10	☐	☐
3257	**2440**	76p. multicoloured	1·25	1·25	☐	☐
3258	**2441**	£1 multicoloured	1·50	1·50	☐	☐
3259	**2442**	£1·10 multicoloured	1·75	1·75	☐	☐
Set of 6			6·75	6·75	☐	☐
First Day Cover				9·00	☐	
Presentation Pack (Nos. 3254/3259 and **MS**3264) (PO Pack No. 465)			16·00		☐	
PHQ Cards (*set of 11*) (358)			4·25	25·00	☐	☐
Set of 6 Gutter Pairs			13·50		☐	
Traffic light *Gutter Blocks of* 4			30·00		☐	

The complete miniature sheet is shown on one of the 11 PHQ cards with the others showing individual stamps including those from No. **MS**3264.

2443 The BFG carrying Sophie in his Hand

2444 The BFG wakes up the Giants

2445 Sophie sat on Buckingham Palace Window-sill

2446 The BFG and Sophie at Writing Desk

2452 Elizabeth II (1952–)

2447 Roald Dahl's *The BFG*

Roald Dahl's Children's Stories (2nd issue). Book Illustrations by Quentin Blake

2012 (10 Jan.) 'All-over' phosphor. Perf 14 × 14½

3260	**2443**	(1st) multicoloured	2·40	2·40	
3261	**2444**	68p. multicoloured	2·40	2·40	
3262	**2445**	76p. multicoloured	2·40	2·40	
3263	**2446**	£1 multicoloured	2·40	2·40	
Set of 4			9·00	9·00	
MS3264 115 × 89 mm. **2447** Nos. 3260/3263			9·00	9·00	
First Day Cover				9·50	

Nos. 3260/3263 were only issued in the £11·47 Roald Dahl, Master Storyteller premium booklet, No. DY73 and in No. **MS**3264.

No. **MS**3264 commemorates the 30th Anniversary of the publication of *The BFG*.

2448 Edward VII (1901–1910)

2449 George V (1910–1936)

2450 Edward VIII (1936)

2451 George VI (1936–1952)

2453 The Age of the Windsors

Kings and Queens (6th series). House of Windsor

2012 (2 Feb-6 Feb.) Two phosphor bands. Perf 14

3265	**2448**	(1st) multicoloured	1·00	1·00	
3266	**2449**	68p. multicoloured	1·00	1·00	
3267	**2450**	76p. multicoloured	1·40	1·40	
3268	**2451**	£1 multicoloured	1·90	1·90	
3269	**2452**	£1·10 multicoloured	2·25	2·25	
Set of 5			6·75	6·75	
First Day Cover				7·50	
Presentation Pack (PO Pack No. 466)			11·50		
PHQ Cards (set of 10) (359)			4·00	16·50	
Set of 5 Gutter Pairs			13·50		
Set of 5 Traffic Light Gutter Blocks of 4			25·00		

MS3270 123 × 70 mm. **2453** (1st) Scott Expedition to South Pole, 1912; 68p. Queen Elizabeth the Queen Mother and King George VI in bomb damaged street, *c.* 1940; 76p. England's World Cup winning football team, 1966; £1 Channel Tunnel, 1996 .... 4·25 4·25

First Day Cover .... 5·50

The complete miniature sheet is shown on one of the ten PHQ cards with the others depicting individual stamps including those from No. **MS**3270.

For Nos. U3271 and U3276 see Decimal Machin Definitives section.

2454 Diamond Jubilee

Diamond Jubilee. Miniature Sheet

2012 (6 Feb.) Two phosphor bands. Perf 14½×14 (with one elliptical hole in each vertical side)

MS3272 146×74 mm. **2454** (1st)×6 Portrait from photograph by Dorothy Wilding; 1960 £1 Banknote portrait by Robert Austin; 1971 £5 Banknote portrait by Harry Eccleston; 1953 Coinage portrait by Mary Gillick; 1971 decimal coin portrait by Arnold Machin; As No. U3279 | 5·50 | 5·50 | ☐ ☐

First Day Cover		6·00	☐
Presentation Pack (PO Pack No. 93)	6·75		☐
PHQ Cards (set of 7) (D33)	2·75	11·00	☐ ☐
Commemorative Document	10·00		☐

The 1st class slate-blue machin stamp from No. **MS**3272 has an iridescent overprint reading 'DIAMOND JUBILEE'.

The seven PHQ cards show the six individual stamps and the complete miniature sheet.

2455 Coventry Cathedral, 1962 (Sir Basil Spence, architect)

2456 Frederick Delius (1862–1934, composer)

2457 Orange Tree Embroidery (Mary 'May' Morris 1862–1938, designer and textile artist)

2458 Odette Hallowes (1912–1995, SOE agent in occupied France)

2459 Steam Engine, 1712 (Thomas Newcomen, inventor of atmospheric steam engine)

2460 Kathleen Ferrier (1912–1953, contralto)

2461 Interior of Palace of Westminster (Augustus Pugin 1812–1852, Gothic revival architect and designer)

2462 Montagu Rhodes James (1862–1936 scholar and author)

2463 Bombe Code Breaking Machine (Alan Turing 1912–1954, mathematician and World War II code breaker)

2464 Joan Mary Fry (1862–1955) relief worker and social reformer)

Britons of Distinction

2012 (23 Feb.) 'All-over' phosphor. Perf 14½

3273	**2455**	(1st) multicoloured	1·00	1·00	☐ ☐
		a. Horiz strip of 5. Nos. 3273/3277	4·50	4·50	☐ ☐
3274	**2456**	(1st) multicoloured	1·00	1·00	☐ ☐
3275	**2457**	(1st) multicoloured	1·00	1·00	☐ ☐
3276	**2458**	(1st) multicoloured	1·00	1·00	☐ ☐
3277	**2459**	(1st) multicoloured	1·00	1·00	☐ ☐
3278	**2460**	(1st) multicoloured	1·00	1·00	☐ ☐
		a. Horiz strip of 5. Nos. 3278/3282	4·50	4·50	☐ ☐
3279	**2461**	(1st) multicoloured	1·00	1·00	☐ ☐
3280	**2462**	(1st) multicoloured	1·00	1·00	☐ ☐
3281	**2463**	(1st) multicoloured	1·00	1·00	☐ ☐
3282	**2464**	(1st) multicoloured	1·00	1·00	☐ ☐
Set of 10			9·00	9·00	☐ ☐
First Day Cover				9·25	☐
Presentation Pack (PO Pack No. 467)			9·50		☐
PHQ Cards (set of 10) (360)			4·00	11·50	☐ ☐
Set of 2 Gutter Strips of 10			18·00		☐

Nos. 3273/3277 and 3278/2782 were each printed together, se-tenant, as horizontal strips of five stamps in sheets of 50 (2 panes 5×5).

2465 Classic Locomotives of Scotland

Classic Locomotives (2nd series). Scotland

2012 (8 Mar.) Sheet 180×74 mm. 'All-over' phosphor. Perf 14

MS3283 **2465** (1st) BR Class D34 Nos. 62471 *Glen Falloch* and 62496 *Glen Loy* at Ardlui, 9 May 1959; 68p. BR Class D40 No. 62276 Andrew Bain at Macduff, July 1950; £1 Andrew Barclay No. 807 *Bon Accord* propelling wagons along Miller Street, Aberdeen, June 1962; £1·10 BR Class 4P No. 54767 *Clan Mackinnon* pulling fish train, Kyle of Lochalsh, October 1948 | 4·75 | 4·75 | ☐ ☐

First Day Cover		6·00	☐
Presentation Pack (PO Pack No. 468)	5·50		☐
PHQ Cards (set of 5) (361)	2·00	9·00	☐ ☐

The five PHQ cards show the four individual stamps and the complete miniature sheet

2466 *The Dandy* and Desperate Dan

2467 *The Beano* and Dennis the Menace

2468 *Eagle* and Dan Dare

2469 *The Topper* and Beryl the Peril

2470 *Tiger* and Roy of the Rovers

2471 *Bunty* and the Four Marys

2472 *Buster* and Cartoon Character Buster

2473 *Valiant* and the Steel Claw

2474 *Twinkle* and Nurse Nancy

2475 *2000 AD* and Judge Dredd

Comics

2012 (20 Mar.) 'All-over' phosphor. Perf 14½

3284	**2466**	(1st) multicoloured	1·00	1·00	☐	☐
		a. Horiz strip of 5.				
		Nos. 3284/3288	4·50	4·50	☐	☐
3285	**2467**	(1st) multicoloured	1·00	1·00	☐	☐
3286	**2468**	(1st) multicoloured	1·00	1·00	☐	☐
3287	**2469**	(1st) multicoloured	1·00	1·00	☐	☐
3288	**2470**	(1st) multicoloured	1·00	1·00	☐	☐

3289	**2471**	(1st) multicoloured	1·00	1·00	☐	☐
		a. Horiz strip of 5.				
		Nos. 3289/3293	4·50	4·50	☐	☐
3290	**2472**	(1st) multicoloured	1·00	1·00	☐	☐
3291	**2473**	(1st) multicoloured	1·00	1·00	☐	☐
3292	**2474**	(1st) multicoloured	1·00	1·00	☐	☐
3293	**2475**	(1st) multicoloured	1·00	1·00	☐	☐
Set of 10			9·00	9·00	☐	☐
First Day Cover				15·00		
Presentation Pack (PO Pack No. 469)			10·00		☐	
PHQ Cards (*set of 10*) (362)			4·00	11·50	☐	☐
Set of 2 Gutter Strips of 5			18·00		☐	

2476 Manchester Town Hall

2477 Narrow Water Castle, Co. Down

2478 Old Bailey, London

2479 Portmeirion, Wales

2480 The Queen's College, Oxford

2481 Roman Baths, Bath

2482 Stirling Castle, Scotland

2483 Tyne Bridge, Newcastle

2484 Urquhart Castle, Scotland

2485 Victoria and Albert Museum, London

2486 White Cliffs of Dover

2487 Station X, Bletchley Park, Buckinghamshire

2488 York Minster

2489 London Zoo

2490 Skirt Suit by Hardy Amies, late 1940s

2491 Outfit by Norman Hartnell, 1950s

2492 Jacket designed by John Pearce for Granny Takes a Trip Boutique, 1960s

2493 Print by Celia Birtwell for Outfit by Ossie Clark, late 1960s

2494 Suit designed for Ringo Starr by Tommy Nutter

2495 Outfit by Jean Muir, late 1970s/early 1980s

2496 'Royal' Dress by Zandra Rhodes, 1981

2497 Harlequin dress by Vivienne Westwood, 1993

2498 Suit by Paul Smith, 2003

2499 'Black Raven' by Alexander McQueen, 2009

UK A–Z (2nd series)

2012 (10 Apr.) 'All-over' phosphor. Perf 14½

3294	**2476**	(1st) multicoloured	1·00	1·00	☐	☐
		a. Horiz strip of 6.				
		Nos. 3294/3299	5·50	5·50	☐	☐
3295	**2477**	(1st) multicoloured	1·00	1·00	☐	☐
3296	**2478**	(1st) multicoloured	1·00	1·00	☐	☐
3297	**2479**	(1st) multicoloured	1·00	1·00	☐	☐
3298	**2480**	(1st) multicoloured	1·00	1·00	☐	☐
3299	**2481**	(1st) multicoloured	1·00	1·00	☐	☐
3300	**2482**	(1st) multicoloured	1·00	1·00	☐	☐
		a. Horiz strip of 6.				
		Nos. 3300/3305	5·50	5·50	☐	☐
3301	**2483**	(1st) multicoloured	1·00	1·00	☐	☐
3302	**2484**	(1st) multicoloured	1·00	1·00	☐	☐
3303	**2485**	(1st) multicoloured	1·00	1·00	☐	☐
3304	**2486**	(1st) multicoloured	1·00	1·00	☐	☐
3305	**2487**	(1st) multicoloured	1·00	1·00	☐	☐
3306	**2488**	(1st) multicoloured	1·00	1·00	☐	☐
		a. Horiz pair.				
		Nos. 3306/3307	1·75	1·75	☐	☐
3307	**2489**	(1st) multicoloured	1·00	1·00	☐	☐
Set of 14			12·50	12·50	☐	☐
First Day Covers (2)				13·00		☐
Presentation Pack (PO Pack No. 470)			13·00			☐
PHQ Cards (set of 14) (363)			5·50	13·00	☐	☐
Set of 2 Gutter Strips of 12 and						
1 Gutter Strip of 4			25·00			☐
Set of 2 Traffic Light Gutter Strips of 24						
and 1 Gutter Block of 8			50·00			☐
MS3308 297×210 mm. Nos. 3230/3241						
and 3294/3307			£100	£120	☐	☐

Nos. 3294/3299 and 3300/3305 were each printed together, *se-tenant*, as horizontal strips of six stamps in sheets of 60 (2 panes 6×5).

Nos. 3306/3307 were printed together, *se-tenant*, as horizontal pairs in sheets of 60 (2 panes 6×5).

No. 3303 includes the EUROPA emblem.

Great British Fashion

2012 (15 May) Phosphor background. Perf 14½ × 14

3309	**2490**	(1st) multicoloured	1·00	1·00	☐	☐
		a. Horiz strip of 5. Nos. 3309/3313	4·50	4·50	☐	☐
3310	**2491**	(1st) multicoloured	1·00	1·00	☐	☐
3311	**2492**	(1st) multicoloured	1·00	1·00	☐	☐
3312	**2493**	(1st) multicoloured	1·00	1·00	☐	☐
3313	**2494**	(1st) multicoloured	1·00	1·00	☐	☐
3314	**2495**	(1st) multicoloured	1·00	1·00	☐	☐
		a. Horiz strip of 5. Nos. 3314/3318	4·50	4·50	☐	☐
3315	**2496**	(1st) multicoloured	1·00	1·00	☐	☐
3316	**2497**	(1st) multicoloured	1·00	1·00	☐	☐
3317	**2498**	(1st) multicoloured	1·00	1·00	☐	☐
3318	**2499**	(1st) multicoloured	1·00	1·00	☐	☐
Set of 10			9·00	9·00	☐	☐
First Day Cover				11·00		☐
Presentation Pack (PO Pack No. 471)			10·00		☐	
PHQ Cards (*set of 10*) (364)			4·00	12·00	☐	☐
Set of 2 Gutter Strips of 10			18·00		☐	
Set of 2 Traffic Light Gutter Strips of 20			40·00		☐	

Nos. 3309/3313 and 3314/3318 were each printed together, *se-tenant*, as horizontal strips of five stamps in sheets of 50 (2 panes 5 × 5).

2500 Queen Elizabeth II at Golden Jubilee Thanksgiving Service, St Paul's Cathedral, London, 2002

2501 Queen Elizabeth II Trooping the Colour, 1967

2502 Queen Elizabeth II inspecting 2nd Battalion Royal Welsh, Tidworth, 1 March 2007

2503 First Christmas Television Broadcast, 1957

2504 Silver Jubilee Walkabout, 1977

2505 Queen Elizabeth II in Garter Ceremony Procession, 1997

2506 Queen Elizabeth II addressing the UN General Assembly, 1957

2507 Queen Elizabeth II at Commonwealth Games, Brisbane, Australia, 1982

Diamond Jubilee (3rd issue)

2012 (31 May) 'All-over' phosphor.

(a) Sheet stamps. Ordinary gum. Gravure. Perf 14 × 14½.

3319A	**2500**	(1st) multicoloured	1·00	1·00	☐	☐
		a. Horiz pair. Nos. 3319/3320	2·00	2·00	☐	☐
3320A	**2501**	(1st) black and brownish grey	1·00	1·00	☐	☐
3321A	**2502**	77p. multicoloured	1·00	1·00	☐	☐
		a. Horiz pair. Nos. 3321/3322	2·00	2·00	☐	☐
3322A	**2503**	77p. black and brownish grey	1·00	1·00	☐	☐
3323A	**2504**	87p. black and brownish grey	1·25	1·25	☐	☐
		a. Horiz pair. Nos. 3323/3324	2·50	2·50	☐	☐
3324A	**2505**	87p. multicoloured	1·25	1·25	☐	☐
3325A	**2506**	£1·28 black and brownish grey	1·75	1·75	☐	☐
		a. Horiz pair. Nos. 3325/3326	3·50	3·50	☐	☐
3326A	**2507**	£1·28 multicoloured	1·75	1·75	☐	☐
Set of 8			9·00	9·00	☐	☐
First Day Cover				11·00		☐
Presentation Pack (PO Pack No. 472)			17·00		☐	
PHQ Cards (*set of 8*) (365)			3·25	12·00	☐	☐
Set of 4 Gutter Strips of 4			18·00		☐	

(b) Booklet stamps. Ordinary gum. Litho. Perf 14 × 14½.

3319B	**2500**	(1st) multicoloured	1·40	1·40	☐	☐
3320B	**2501**	(1st) black and brownish grey	1·40	1·40	☐	☐
3321B	**2502**	77p. multicoloured	1·40	1·40	☐	☐
3322B	**2503**	77p. black and brownish grey	1·40	1·40	☐	☐
3323B	**2504**	87p. black and brownish grey	1·40	1·40	☐	☐
3324B	**2505**	87p. multicoloured	1·40	1·40	☐	☐
3325B	**2506**	£1·28 black and brownish grey	1·75	1·75	☐	☐
3326B	**2507**	£1·28 multicoloured	1·75	1·75	☐	☐
Set of 8			11·00	11·00	☐	☐

(c) Self-adhesive booklet stamp. Die-cut perf 14.

3327	**2500**	(1st) multicoloured	1·50	1·50	☐	☐

Nos. 3319A/3320A, 3321A/3322A, 3323A/3324A and 3325A/3326A were printed together, *se-tenant*, as horizontal pairs in sheets of 60 (2 panes 6 × 5).

Nos. 3319B/3326B come from the £12·77 Diamond Jubilee Prestige booklet, No. DY4.

No. 3327 was only issued in Diamond Jubilee stamp booklets, containing Nos. 3327 × 2 and U3274 × 4, originally sold for £3·60.

No. 3328 is vacant.

Diamond Jubilee (4th issue)

2012 (31 May) As T **159** but redrawn with 1st value indicator (No. 3329). Two phosphor bands. Perf 14½ × 14 (with one elliptical hole in each vert side)

3329		(1st) light brown	1·25	1·25	☐	☐

Nos. U3279/3329 were issued in £12·27 Diamond Jubilee booklet, No. DY4.

Similar stamps were issued in No. **MS**3272.

2508 Mr. Bumble
(*Oliver Twist*)

2509 Mr. Pickwick
(*The Pickwick Papers*)

2510 The Marchioness
(*The Old Curiosity Shop*)

2511 Mrs. Gamp
(*Martin Chuzzlewit*)

2512 Captain Cuttle
(*Dombey and Son*)

2513 Mr. Micawber
(*David Copperfield*)

2514 Scenes from *Nicholas Nickleby*, *Bleak House*, *Little Dorrit* and *A Tale of Two Cities*

Birth Bicentenary of Charles Dickens

2012 (19 June) Illustrations from Character Sketches from Charles Dickens, *c.* 1890 by Joseph Clayton Clarke ('Kyd') (Nos. 3330/3335) or Book Illustrations by Hablot Knight Browne ('Phiz') (No. **MS**3336). One centre band (2nd) or 'all-over' phosphor (others). Perf 14 (Nos. 3330/3335) or 14 × 14½ (No. **MS**3336).

3330	**2508**	(2nd) multicoloured	90	90	☐ ☐
3331	**2509**	(1st) multicoloured	1·00	1·00	☐ ☐
3332	**2510**	77p. multicoloured	1·00	1·00	☐ ☐
3333	**2511**	87p. multicoloured	1·40	1·40	☐ ☐
3334	**2512**	£1·28 multicoloured	2·00	2·00	☐ ☐
3335	**2513**	£1·90 multicoloured	3·00	3·00	☐ ☐
Set of 6			8·50	8·50	☐
First Day Cover				11·00	☐
Presentation Pack (PO Pack No. 473)			14·00		☐
PHQ Cards (*set of 11*) (366)			4·50	17·00	☐ ☐
Set of 6 Gutter Pairs			17·00		☐
Set of 6 Traffic Light Gutter Blocks of 4			38·00		☐

MS3336 190×67 mm. **2514** (1st)×4 Nicholas Nickleby caning headmaster Wackford Squeers (*Nicholas Nickleby*); Mrs. Bagnet is charmed with Mr. Bucket (*Bleak House*); Amy Dorrit introduces Maggy to Arthur Clennam (*Little Dorrit*); Charles Darnay arrested by French revolutionaries (*A Tale of Two Cities*)   3·75   3·75 ☐ ☐
First Day Cover   4·50 ☐
The complete miniature sheet is shown on one of the 11 PHQ cards with the others depicting individual stamps including those from No. **MS**3336.

Olympic and Paralympic Games (8th series)

2012 (27 July) Designs as Nos. 3250/3253. Two phosphor bands. Perf 14½ × 14 (with one elliptical hole in each vert side)

3337	**2436**	(1st) black and orange-red	4·00	4·00	☐ ☐
3338	**2435**	(1st) black and orange-red	4·00	4·00	☐ ☐
3339	**2436**	(World wide up to 20 g) black, bright scarlet and greenish blue	6·00	6·00	☐ ☐
3340	**2435**	(World wide up to 20 g) black, bright scarlet and greenish blue	6·00	6·00	☐ ☐
Set of 4			18·00	18·00	☐ ☐
First Day Cover				20·00	☐

Nos. 3339/3340 were for use on Worldwide Mail up to 20g.
　　Nos. 3337/3340 were only issued in the £10·71 Olympic and the Paralympic Games stamp booklet, No. DY5.
　　See also Nos. 3250/3253.

2515 Sports and London Landmarks

Welcome to London, Olympic Games

2012 (27 July) Sheet 192×75 mm. 'All-over' phosphor. Perf 14½

MS3341 **2515** (1st) Fencer and Tower Bridge; (1st) Athletes in race and Olympic Stadium; £1·28 Diver and Tate Modern; £1·28 Cyclist and London Eye   5·50   5·50 ☐ ☐
First Day Cover   10·00 ☐
Presentation Pack (PO Pack No. 474)   20·00 ☐
PHQ Cards (*set of 5*) (367)   2·00   9·00 ☐ ☐
The five PHQ cards show the four individual stamps and the complete miniature sheet.

2516 Helen Glover and Heather Stanning (rowing, women's pairs)

2517 Bradley Wiggins (cycling: road, men's time trial)

2518 Tim Baillie and Etienne Stott (canoe slalom: men's canoe double (C2))

2519 Peter Wilson (shooting: shotgun men's double trap)

2520 Philip Hindes, Chris Hoy and Jason Kenny (cycling: track men's team sprint)

2521 Katherine Grainger and Anna Watkins (rowing: women's double sculls)

2522 Steven Burke, Ed Clancy, Peter Kennaugh and Geraint Thomas (cycling: track men's team pursuit)

2523 Victoria Pendleton (cycling: track women's keirin)

2524 Alex Gregory, Tom James, Pete Reed and Andrew Triggs Hodge (rowing: men's fours)

2525 Katherine Copeland and Sophie Hosking (rowing: lightweight women's double sculls)

2526 Dani King, Joanna Rowsell and Laura Trott (cycling: track women's team pursuit)

2527 Jessica Ennis (athletics: combined women's heptathlon)

2528 Greg Rutherford (athletics: field men's long jump)

2529 Mo Farah (athletics: track men's 10,000 m)

2530 Ben Ainslie (sailing: Finn men's heavyweight dinghy)

2531 Andy Murray (tennis: men's singles)

2532 Scott Brash, Peter Charles, Ben Maher and Nick Skelton (equestrian: jumping team)

2533 Jason Kenny (cycling: track men's sprint)

2534 Alistair Brownlee (men's triathlon)

2535 Laura Bechtolsheimer, Charlotte Dujardin and Carl Hester (equestrian: dressage team)

2536 Laura Trott (cycling: track women's omnium)

2537 Chris Hoy (cycling: track men's keirin)

2538 Charlotte Dujardin (equestrian: dressage individual)

2539 Nicola Adams (boxing: women's fly weight)

2540 Jade Jones (taekwondo women's under 57 kg)

2541 Ed McKeever (canoe sprint: men's kayak single (K1) 200 m)

2542 Mo Farah (athletics: track men's 5000 m)

2543 Luke Campbell (boxing: men's bantam weight)

2544 Anthony Joshua (boxing: men's super heavy weight)

British Gold Medal Winners at London Olympic Games

2012 (2–13 Aug.) Self-adhesive. Two phosphor panels. Die-cut perf 15 × 14½

3342	**2516**	(1st) multicoloured	1·25	1·25		
		a. Sheetlet. No. 3342 × 6	6·75	6·75		
3343	**2517**	(1st) multicoloured	1·25	1·25		
		a. Sheetlet. No. 3343 × 6	6·76	6·75		
3344	**2518**	(1st) multicoloured *(3.8.12)*	1·25	1·25		
		a. Sheetlet. No. 3344 × 6	6·75	6·75		
3345	**2519**	(1st) multicoloured *(3.8.12)*	1·25	1·25		
		a. Sheetlet. No. 3345 × 6	6·75	6·75		
3346	**2520**	(1st) multicoloured *(3.8.12)*	1·25	1·25		
		a. Sheetlet. No. 3346 × 6	6·75	6·75		
3347	**2521**	(1st) multicoloured *(4.8.12)*	1·25	1·25		
		a. Sheetlet. No. 3347 × 6	6·75	6·75		
3348	**2522**	(1st) multicoloured *(4.8.12)*	1·25	1·25		
		a. Sheetlet. No. 3348 × 6	6·75	6·75		
3349	**2523**	(1st) multicoloured *(4.8.12)*	1·25	1·25		
		a. Sheetlet. No. 3349 × 6	6·75	6·75		
3350	**2524**	(1st) multicoloured *(5.8.12)*	1·25	1·25		
		a. Sheetlet. No. 3350 × 6	6·75	6·75		
3351	**2525**	(1st) multicoloured *(5.8.12)*	1·25	1·25		
		a. Sheetlet. No. 3351 × 6	6·75	6·75		
3352	**2526**	(1st) multicoloured *(5.8.12)*	1·25	1·25		
		a. Sheetlet. No. 3352 × 6	6·75	6·75		
3353	**2527**	(1st) multicoloured *(5.8.12)*	1·25	1·25		
		a. Sheetlet. No. 3353 × 6	6·75	6·75		
3354	**2528**	(1st) multicoloured *(5.8.12)*	1·25	1·25		
		a. Sheetlet. No. 3354 × 6	6·75	6·75		
3355	**2529**	(1st) multicoloured *(5.8.12)*	1·25	1·25		
		a. Sheetlet. No. 3355 × 6	6·75	6·75		
3356	**2530**	(1st) multicoloured *(6.8.12)*	1·25	1·25		
		a. Sheetlet. No. 3356 × 6	6·75	6·75		
3357	**2531**	(1st) multicoloured *(6.8.12)*	1·25	1·25		
		a. Sheetlet. No. 3357 × 6	6·75	6·75		
3358	**2532**	(1st) multicoloured *(7.8.12)*	1·25	1·25		
		a. Sheetlet. No. 3358 × 6	6·75	6·75		
3359	**2533**	(1st) multicoloured *(7.8.12)*	1·25	1·25		
		a. Sheetlet. No. 3359 × 6	6·75	6·75		
3360	**2534**	(1st) multicoloured *(8.8.12)*	1·25	1·25		
		a. Sheetlet. No. 3360 × 6	6·75	6·75		
3361	**2535**	(1st) multicoloured *(8.8.12)*	1·25	1·25		
		a. Sheetlet. No. 3361 × 6	6·75	6·75		
3362	**2536**	(1st) multicoloured *(8.8.12)*	1·25	1·25		
		a. Sheetlet. No. 3362 × 6	6·75	6·75		
3363	**2537**	(1st) multicoloured *(8.8.12)*	1·25	1·25		
		a. Sheetlet. No. 3363 × 6	6·75	6·75		
3364	**2538**	(1st) multicoloured *(10.8.12)*	1·25	1·25		
		a. Sheetlet. No. 3364 × 6	6·75	6·75		
3365	**2539**	(1st) multicoloured *(10.8.12)*	1·25	1·25		
		a. Sheetlet. No. 3365 × 6	6·75	6·75		
3366	**2540**	(1st) multicoloured *(10.8.12)*	1·25	1·25		
		a. Sheetlet. No. 3366 × 6	6·75	6·75		
3367	**2541**	(1st) multicoloured *(12.8.12)*	1·25	1·25		
		a. Sheetlet. No. 3367 × 6	6·75	6·75		
3368	**2542**	(1st) multicoloured *(12.8.12)*	1·25	1·25		
		a. Sheetlet. No. 3368 × 6	6·75	6·75		
3369	**2543**	(1st) multicoloured *(12.8.12)*	1·25	1·25		
		a. Sheetlet. No. 3369 × 6	6·75	6·75		
3370	**2544**	(1st) multicoloured *(13.8.12)*	1·25	1·25		
		a. Sheetlet. No. 3370 × 6	6·75	6·75		
Set of 29				35·00	35·00	

First Day Covers (Sheetlets, Nos. 3342a/3370a) (29)   £250

First Day Cover (any single gold medal stamp)   4·25

The self-adhesive base sheetlets for Nos. 3342/3370 were produced by Walsall with the image, name and event of the winning athletes digitally printed by regional printers in six different locations: Attleborough, Edinburgh, London, Preston, Solihull and Swindon. Nos. 3368/3370 were not produced by the Preston printer due to machinery breakdown. These sheetlets of 24 stamps were divided by roulettes into four portions of six stamps (3×2) each with either of the following inscriptions on the left margin: emblem 'TEAM GB' and Olympic rings; 'The XXX Olympiad'; barcode; Sheet number, Issue date and Printer location.

2545 Paralympic Sports and London Landmarks

Welcome to London, Paralympic Games

2012 (29 Aug.) Sheet 193×75 mm. 'All-over' phosphor. Perf 14½

MS3371 **2545** (1st) Athlete wearing running blades and Olympic Stadium; (1st) Wheelchair basketball player and Palace of Westminster; £1·28 Powerlifter, Millennium Bridge and St Paul's Cathedral; £1·28 Cyclist and London Eye

	5·50	5·50	☐ ☐
First Day Cover		10·00	☐
Presentation Pack (PO Pack No. 475)	9·00		☐
PHQ Cards (*set of 5*) (368)	2·00	9·00	☐ ☐

The five PHQ cards show the four individual stamps and the complete miniature sheet.

2546 Sarah Storey (cycling: track women's C5 pursuit)

2547 Jonathan Fox (swimming: men's 100 m backstroke, S7)

2548 Mark Colbourne (cycling: track men's C1 pursuit)

2549 Hannah Cockroft (athletics: track women's 100 m, T34)

2550 Neil Fachie and Barney Storey (cycling: men's B 1 km time trial)

2551 Richard Whitehead (athletics: track men's 200 m, T42)

2552 Natasha Baker (equestrian: individual championship test, grade II)

2553 Sarah Storey (cycling: track – women's C4-5 500 m time trial)

2554 Ellie Simmonds (swimming: women's 400 m freestyle, S6)

2555 Pamela Relph, Naomi Riches, James Roe, David Smith and Lily van den Broecke (rowing: mixed coxed four, LTAmix4+)

2556 Aled Davies (athletics: field men's discus, F42)

2557 Anthony Kappes and Craig MacLean (cycling: track men's B sprint)

2558 Jessica-Jane Applegate (swimming: women's 200 m freestyle, S14)

2559 Sophie Christiansen (equestrian: individual championship test, grade 1a)

2560 David Weir (athletics: track men's 5000 m, T54)

2561 Natasha Baker (equestrian: individual freestyle test, grade II)

2562 Ellie Simmonds (swimming: women's 200 m individual medley, SM6)

2563 Mickey Bushell (athletics: track men's 100 m, T53)

2564 Danielle Brown (archery: women's individual compound, open)

2565 Heather Frederiksen (swimming: women's 100 m backstroke, S8)

2566 Sophie Christiansen (equestrian: individual freestyle test, grade 1a)

2567 David Weir (athletics: track men's 1500 m, T54)

2568 Sarah Storey (cycling: road women's C5 time trial)

2569 Ollie Hynd (swimming: men's 200 m individual medley, SM8)

2570 Sophie Christiansen, Deb Criddle, Lee Pearson and Sophie Wells (equestrian team, open)

2571 Helena Lucas (sailing: single-person keelboat, 2.4mR)

2572 Sarah Storey (cycling: road women's C4-5 road race)

2573 Josef Craig (swimming: men's 400 m freestyle, S7)

2574 Hannah Cockroft (athletics: track women's 200 m, T34)

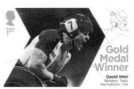

2575 David Weir (athletics: track men's 800 m, T54)

2576 Jonnie Peacock (athletics: track men's 100 m, T44)

2577 Josie Pearson (athletics: field women's discus, F51/52/53)

2578 David Stone (cycling: road mixed T1-2 road race)

2579 David Weir (athletics: road men's marathon, T54)

British Gold Medal Winners at London Paralympic Games

2012 (31 Aug.–10 Sept.) Self-adhesive. Two phosphor panels. Die-cut perf 15×14½

3372 **2546**	(1st) multicoloured	1·25	1·25	
	a. Sheetlet. No. 3372×2	2·50	2·50	
3373 **2547**	(1st) multicoloured (1.9.12)	1·25	1·25	
	a. Sheetlet. No. 3373×2	2·50	2·50	
3374 **2548**	(1st) multicoloured (3.9.12)	1·25	1·25	
	a. Sheetlet. No. 3374×2	2·50	2·50	
3375 **2549**	(1st) multicoloured (3.9.12)	1·25	1·25	
	a. Sheetlet. No. 3375×2	2·50	2·50	
3376 **2550**	(1st) multicoloured (3.9.12)	1·25	1·25	
	a. Sheetlet. No. 3376×2	2·50	2·50	
3377 **2551**	(1st) multicoloured (3.9.12)	1·25	1·25	
	a. Sheetlet. No. 3377×2	2·50	2·50	
3378 **2552**	(1st) multicoloured (3.9.12)	1·25	1·25	
	a. Sheetlet. No. 3378×2	2·50	2·50	
3379 **2553**	(1st) multicoloured (3.9.12)	1·25	1·25	
	a. Sheetlet. No. 3379×2	2·50	2·50	
3380 **2554**	(1st) multicoloured (3.9.12)	1·25	1·25	
	a. Sheetlet. No. 3380×2	2·50	2·50	
3381 **2555**	(1st) multicoloured (4.9.12)	1·25	1·25	
	a. Sheetlet. No. 3381×2	2·50	2·50	
3382 **2556**	(1st) multicoloured (4.9.12)	1·25	1·25	
	a. Sheetlet. No. 3382×2	2·50	2·50	
3383 **2557**	(1st) multicoloured (4.9.12)	1·25	1·25	
	a. Sheetlet. No. 3383×2	2·50	2·50	
3384 **2558**	(1st) multicoloured (4.9.12)	1·25	1·25	
	a. Sheetlet. No. 3384×2	2·50	2·50	
3385 **2559**	(1st) multicoloured (4.9.12)	1·25	1·25	
	a. Sheetlet. No. 3385×2	2·50	2·50	
3386 **2560**	(1st) multicoloured (4.9.12)	1·25	1·25	
	a. Sheetlet. No. 3386×2	2·50	2·50	
3387 **2561**	(1st) multicoloured (4.9.12)	1·25	1·25	
	a. Sheetlet. No. 3387×2	2·50	2·50	
3388 **2562**	(1st) multicoloured (4.9.12)	1·25	1·25	
	a. Sheetlet. No. 3388×2	2·50	2·50	
3389 **2563**	(1st) multicoloured (5.9.12)	1·25	1·25	
	a. Sheetlet. No. 3389×2	2·50	2·50	
3390 **2564**	(1st) multicoloured (5.9.12)	1·25	1·25	
	a. Sheetlet. No. 3390×2	2·50	2·50	
3391 **2565**	(1st) multicoloured (5.9.12)	1·25	1·25	
	a. Sheetlet. No. 3391×2	2·50	2·50	
3392 **2566**	(1st) multicoloured (5.9.12)	1·25	1·25	
	a. Sheetlet. No. 3392×2	2·50	2·50	
3393 **2567**	(1st) multicoloured (7.9.12)	1·25	1·25	
	a. Sheetlet. No. 3393×2	2·50	2·50	
3394 **2568**	(1st) multicoloured (7.9.12)	1·25	1·25	
	a. Sheetlet. No. 3394×2	2·50	2·50	
3395 **2569**	(1st) multicoloured (7.9.12)	1·25	1·25	
	a. Sheetlet. No. 3395×2	2·50	2·50	
3396 **2570**	(1st) multicoloured (7.9.12)	1·25	1·25	
	a. Sheetlet. No. 3396×2	2·50	2·50	
3397 **2571**	(1st) multicoloured (8.9.12)	1·25	1·25	
	a. Sheetlet No. 3397×2	2·50	2·50	
3398 **2572**	(1st) multicoloured (8.9.12)	1·25	1·25	
	a. Sheetlet. No. 3398×2	2·50	2·50	
3399 **2573**	(1st) multicoloured (8.9.12)	1·25	1·25	
	a. Sheetlet. No. 3399×2	2·50	2·50	
3400 **2574**	(1st) multicoloured (8.9.12)	1·25	1·25	
	a. Sheetlet. No. 3400×2	2·50	2·50	
3401 **2575**	(1st) multicoloured (10.9.12)	1·25	1·25	
	a. Sheetlet. No. 3401×2	2·50	2·50	
3402 **2576**	(1st) multicoloured (10.9.12)	1·25	1·25	
	a. Sheetlet. No. 3402×2	2·50	2·50	
3403 **2577**	(1st) multicoloured (10.9.12)	1·25	1·25	
	a. Sheetlet. No. 3403×2	2·50	2·50	
3404 **2578**	(1st) multicoloured (10.9.12)	1·25	1·25	
	a. Sheetlet. No. 3404×2	2·50	2·50	
3405 **2579**	(1st) multicoloured (10.9.12)	1·25	1·25	
	a. Sheetlet. No. 3405×2	2·50	2·50	
Set of 34		40·00	40·00	

First Day Covers (Sheetlets, Nos. 3372a/3405a) (34) £125

First Day Cover (any single gold medal stamp) 4·25

The self-adhesive base sheetlets for Nos. 3372/3405 were produced by Walsall with the image, name and event of the winning athletes digitally printed by regional printers in six different locations: Attleborough, Edinburgh, London, Preston, Solihull and Swindon. These sheetlets of 16 stamps were divided by roulettes into eight panes of two stamps (1×2). The left margins were inscribed as follows (reading downwards): emblem and 'ParalympicsGB'; 'London 2012 Paralympic Games'; barcode; Sheet number, Issue date and Printer location.

Nos. 3372, 3373 and 3405 were each printed in separate sheetlets of 16 stamps. Nos. 3374/3377, 3381/3384, 3385/3388, 3389/3392, 3393/3396, 3397/3400 and 3401/3404 were printed in sheetlets of 16 containing four stamps of each design. The sheetlets of 16 containing Nos. 3378/3380 contained four each of Nos. 3378/3379 and eight of No. 3380.

2580 Scenes from Olympic and Paralympic Games

Memories of London 2012 Olympic and Paralympic Games

2012 (27 Sept.) Sheet 192×75 mm. 'All-over' phosphor. Perf 14½

MS3406 **2580** (1st) Procession of athletes, Paralympic Games; (1st) Games makers and Olympic Stadium; £1·28 Opening ceremony of Paralympic Games; £1·28 Olympic Games closing ceremony and handover to Rio 9·00 9·00

First Day Cover 13·00

Presentation Pack (PO Pack No. 476) 17·50

PHQ Cards (*set of* 5) (369) 2·00 16·50

The five PHQ cards show the four individual stamps and the complete miniature sheet.

2581 BR Class D34 Nos. 62471 *Glen Falloch* and 62496 *Glen Loy* at Ardlui, 9 May 1959

Classic Locomotives of Scotland. Booklet stamp

2012 (27 Sept.) Design as 1st class stamp within No. **MS**3283 but printed in gravure. Self-adhesive. 'All-over' phosphor. Die-cut perf 14

3407 **2581** (1st) multicoloured 1·25 1·25 ☐ ☐

No. 3407 was only issued in booklets containing No. 3407×2 and U3274×4, originally sold for £3·60.

2582 Sun and Particles ejected from Solar Surface seen from SOHO Observatory

2583 Venus with Clouds in Southern Hemisphere seen from *Venus Express*

2584 Ice in Martian Impact Crater seen from *Mars Express*

2585 Surface of Asteroid Lutetia seen from *Rosetta Probe*

2586 Saturn and its Rings seen from *Cassini Satellite*

2587 Titan (Saturn's largest moon) seen from *Huygens Probe*

Space Science

2012 (16 Oct.) 'All-over' phosphor. Perf 14

3408	**2582**	(1st) multicoloured	1·00	1·00	☐ ☐
3409	**2583**	(1st) multicoloured	1·00	1·00	☐ ☐
3410	**2584**	77p. multicoloured	1·25	1·25	☐ ☐
3411	**2585**	77p. black	1·25	1·25	☐ ☐
3412	**2586**	£1·28 multicoloured	2·00	2·00	☐ ☐
3413	**2587**	£1·28 multicoloured	2·00	2·00	☐ ☐
Set of 6			7·50	7·50	☐
First Day Cover				9·75	☐
Presentation Pack (PO Pack No. 477)			8·75		☐
PHQ Cards (*set of 6*) (370)			2·40	9·00	☐ ☐
Set of 6 Gutter Pairs			15·00		☐

2588 Six Poppies on Barbed Wire Stems

Lest We Forget (4th series)

2012 (23 Oct.) Self-adhesive. Two phosphor bands. Perf 14½×14 (with one elliptical hole in each vert side)

3414 **2588** (1st) multicoloured 1·25 1·25 ☐ ☐

For T **2588** with ordinary gum, see No. 3717

2589 Reindeer with Decorated Antlers

2590 Santa with Robin

2591 Reindeer with Decorated Antlers

2592 Snowman and Penguin

2593 Santa with Robin

2594 Robin with Star Decoration in Beak

2595 Cat and Mouse decorating Christmas Tree

Christmas. Illustrations by Axel Scheffler

2012 (6 Nov.) One centre band (No. 3415) or two phosphor bands (others). Perf 14½×14 (with one elliptical hole in each vert side)

(a) Self-adhesive

3415	**2589**	(2nd) multicoloured	90	90	☐ ☐
3416	**2590**	(1st) multicoloured	1·00	1·00	☐ ☐
3417	**2591**	(2nd Large) multicoloured	1·10	1·10	☐ ☐
3418	**2592**	87p. multicoloured	1·40	1·40	☐ ☐
3419	**2593**	(1st Large) multicoloured	1·50	1·40	☐ ☐
3420	**2594**	£1·28 multicoloured	2·00	2·00	☐ ☐
3421	**2595**	£1·90 multicoloured	3·00	3·00	☐ ☐
Set of 7			9·75	9·75	☐
First Day Cover				12·50	☐
Presentation Pack (PO Pack No. 478)			11·50		☐
PHQ Cards (*set of 8*) (371)			3·25	21·00	☐ ☐

(b) Ordinary gum.

MS3422 115×102 mm. As Nos.

3415/3421		9·75	9·75 ☐ ☐
First Day Cover			10·00 ☐

Year Pack

2012 (6 Nov.) Comprises Nos. 3254/3259, **MS**3264/**MS**3270, 3273/**MS**3307, 3309/3318, 3319A/3326A, 3330/3336, **MS**3341, **MS**3371, **MS**3406, 3408/3413 and 3415/3421

CP3422*a* Year Pack £175 ☐

Post Office Yearbook

2012 (6 Nov.) Comprises Nos. 3254/3259, **MS**3264/**MS**3270, 3273/**MS**3307, 3309/3318, 3319A/3326A, 3330/3336, **MS**3341, **MS**3371, **MS**3406, 3408/3413 and 3415/3421

YB3422*a* Yearbook £300 ☐

Miniature Sheet Collection

2012 (6 Nov.) Comprises Nos. **MS**3264, **MS**3270, **MS**3272, **MS**3283, **MS**3336, **MS**3341, **MS**3371, **MS**3406 and **MS**3422

MS3422*a* Miniature Sheet Collection 55·00 ☐

2596 Steam Locomotive on Metropolitan Railway, 1863

2597 Navvies excavating 'Deep Cut' Tube Tunnel, 1898

2598 Commuters in Carriage, 1911

2599 Boston Manor Art Deco Station, 1934

2600 Train on Deep Cut Line, 1938

2601 Canary Wharf Station, 1999

2602 Classic London Underground Posters

150th Anniversary of the London Underground

2013 (9 Jan.) One centre band (2nd) or 'all-over' phosphor (others)

(a) Ordinary gum. Perf 14½

3423	**2596**	(2nd) multicoloured	90	90		
3424	**2597**	(2nd) multicoloured	90	90		
3425	**2598**	(1st) multicoloured	1·00	1·00		
3426	**2599**	(1st) multicoloured	1·00	1·00		
3427	**2600**	£1·28 multicoloured	2·00	2·00		
3428	**2601**	£1·28 multicoloured	2·00	2·00		
Set of 6			7·00	7·00		
First Day Cover				8·75		
Presentation Pack (Nos. 3423/**MS**3429)						
(PO Pack No. 480)			15·00			
PHQ Cards (*set of* 11) (372)			4·50	18·00		
Set of 6 Gutter Pairs			14·00			

MS3429 184×74 mm. **2602** (1st) Golders Green, 1908, By Underground to fresh air (Maxwell Armfield), 1915 and Summer Sales (Mary Koop), 1925; 77p. For the Zoo (Charles Paine), 1921, Power (Edward McKnight-Kauffer), 1931 and The Seen (James Fitton), 1948; 87p. A train every 90 seconds (Abram Games), 1937, Thanks to the Underground (Zero (Hans Schleger), 1935 and Cut travelling time, Victoria Line (Tom Eckersley), 1969; £1·28 The London Transport Collection (Tom Eckersley), 1975, London Zoo (Abram Games), 1976 and The Tate Gallery by Tube (David Booth), 1987 ... 5·00 ... 5·25

First Day Cover ... 6·50

(b) Self-adhesive. Die-cut perf 14½

3430 **2599** (1st) multicoloured ... 1·40 ... 1·40

No. 3430 was issued in stamp booklets containing No. 3430×2 and 4×1st vermilion, each booklet originally sold for £3·60.

The complete miniature sheet is shown on one of the 11 PHQ cards with the others depicting individual stamps, including those from No. **MS**3429.

2603 Elinor and Marianne Dashwood (*Sense and Sensibility*)

2604 Elizabeth Bennet and Portrait of Mr. Darcy (*Pride and Prejudice*)

2605 Fanny Price (*Mansfield Park*)

2606 Emma Woodhouse and Mr. Knightley (*Emma*)

2607 Catherine Morland (*Northanger Abbey*)

2608 Anne Elliot and Captain Wentworth (*Persuasion*)

Bicentenary of the Publication of Jane Austen's *Pride and Prejudice*

2013 (21 Feb.) 'All-over' phosphor. Perf 14

3431	**2603**	(1st) multicoloured	1·00	1·00		
3432	**2604**	(1st) multicoloured	1·00	1·00		
3433	**2605**	77p. multicoloured	1·25	1·25		
3434	**2606**	77p. multicoloured	1·25	1·25		
3435	**2607**	£1·28 multicoloured	2·00	2·00		
3436	**2608**	£1·28 multicoloured	2·00	2·00		
Set of 6			7·50	7·50		

First Day Cover	10·00	☐
Presentation Pack (PO Pack No. 481)	9·00	☐
PHQ Cards (set of 6) (373)	2·50 9·25	☐ ☐
Set of 6 Gutter Pairs	15·00	☐
Set of 6 Traffic Light Gutter Pairs	32·00	☐

2609 The Eleventh Doctor (Matt Smith, 2010–2014)

2610 The Tenth Doctor (David Tennant, 2005–2010

2611 The Ninth Doctor (Christopher Eccleston, 2005)

2612 The Eighth Doctor (Paul McGann, 1996)

2613 The Seventh Doctor (Sylvester McCoy, 1987–1989)

2614 The Sixth Doctor (Colin Baker, 1984–1986)

2615 The Fifth Doctor (Peter Davison, 1982–1984)

2616 The Fourth Doctor (Tom Baker, 1974–1981)

2617 The Third Doctor (Jon Pertwee, 1970–1974)

2618 The Second Doctor (Patrick Troughton, 1966–1969)

2619 The First Doctor (William Hartnell, 1963–1966)

2620 TARDIS

2621 *Dr. Who* 1963–2013

**50th Anniversary of *Doctor Who*
(TV programme) (1st issue)**

2013 (26 Mar.) 'All-over' phosphor

(a) Ordinary gum. 'All-over' phosphor. Perf 14

3437	**2609**	(1st) multicoloured	1·00	1·00	☐	☐
		a. Horiz strip of 3.				
		Nos. 3437/3439	3·00	3·00	☐	☐
3438	**2610**	(1st) multicoloured	1·00	1·00	☐	☐
3439	**2611**	(1st) multicoloured	1·00	1·00	☐	☐
3440	**2612**	(1st) multicoloured	1·00	1·00	☐	☐
		a. Horiz strip of 4.				
		Nos. 3440/3443	4·00	4·00	☐	☐
3441	**2613**	(1st) multicoloured	1·00	1·00	☐	☐
3442	**2614**	(1st) multicoloured	1·00	1·00	☐	☐
3443	**2615**	(1st) multicoloured	1·00	1·00	☐	☐
3444	**2616**	(1st) multicoloured	1·00	1·00	☐	☐
		a. Horiz strip of 4.				
		Nos. 3444/3447	4·00	4·00	☐	☐
3445	**2617**	(1st) multicoloured	1·00	1·00	☐	☐
3446	**2618**	(1st) multicoloured	1·00	1·00	☐	☐
3447	**2619**	(1st) multicoloured	1·00	1·00	☐	☐
Set of 11			10·00	10·00	☐	☐
First Day Covers (2)				12·00	☐	
Presentation Pack (PO Pack No. 482)			15·00		☐	
PHQ Cards (set of 17) (374)			6·75	18·50	☐	☐
Set of 1 *Gutter Strip of* 6 *and*						
2 *Gutter Strips of* 8			20·00		☐	

(b) Self-adhesive. One centre band (2nd) or two bands (others). Die-cut perf 14½ × 14 (with one elliptical hole in each vert side) (No. 3449) or 14½ (others)

3448	**2609**	(1st) multicoloured	4·50	4·50	☐	☐
3449	**2620**	(1st) multicoloured	1·25	1·25	☐	☐
3450	**2619**	(1st) multicoloured	4·50	4·50	☐	☐
MS3451	115 × 89	mm· **2621**	(2nd)			
	Dalek; (2nd) The Ood; (2nd)					
	Weeping Angel; (2nd) Cyberman;					
	(1st) TARDIS		4·00	4·25	☐	☐
First Day Cover				5·00	☐	

Nos. 3437/3439 were printed together, *se-tenant*, as horizontal strips of three stamps in sheets of 48 (2 panes 6 × 4)

Nos. 3440/3443 and 3444/3447 were each printed together, *se-tenant*, as horizontal strips of four stamps in sheets of 60 (2 panes 4 × 6)

Nos. 3448/3450 were issued in stamp booklets, each booklet containing Nos. 3448, 3449 × 4 and 3450 and originally sold for £3·60.

A 1st class TARDIS stamp perforated 15 all round comes from the £13·37 *Dr. Who* premium booklet, No. DY6.

The design area of No. 3449 measures 17½ × 21 mm, slightly smaller than the same TARDIS design (T **2620**) from the miniature sheet and premium booklet pane which measures 18 × 22 mm (all are 20 × 24 mm measured perf to perf edge).

The complete miniature sheet is shown on one of the 17 PHQ cards with the others depicting individual stamps including those from the miniature sheet.

No. 3449 was also issued in sheets of 20 with *se-tenant* labels, printed in lithography instead of gravure.

**50th Anniversary of *Doctor Who*
(TV programme) (2nd issue)**

2013 (26 Mar.) As No. 3449 but ordinary gum
3452 **2620** (1st) multicoloured   1·25   1·25 ☐ ☐
No. 3452 only comes from the £13·37 *Dr. Who* premium booklet, No. DY6.

2622 Norman Parkinson (1913–1990, portrait and fashion photographer)

2623 Vivien Leigh (1913–1967, actress)

2624 Peter Cushing (1913–1994, actor)

2625 David Lloyd George (1863–1945, Prime Minister 1916–1922)

2626 Elizabeth David (1913–1992, cookery writer)

2627 John Archer (1863–1932, politician and civil rights campaigner)

2628 Benjamin Britten (1913–1976, composer and pianist)

2629 Mary Leakey (1913–1996, archaeologist and anthropologist)

2630 Bill Shankly (1913–1981, football player and manager)

2631 Richard Dimbleby (1913–1965, journalist and broadcaster)

Great Britons

2013 (16 Apr.) 'All-over' phosphor. Perf 14½

3453	**2622**	(1st) multicoloured	1·00	1·00	☐	☐
		a. Horiz strip of 5. Nos. 3453/3457	4·50	4·50	☐	☐
3454	**2623**	(1st) multicoloured	1·00	1·00	☐	☐
3455	**2624**	(1st) multicoloured	1·00	1·00	☐	☐
3456	**2625**	(1st) multicoloured	1·00	1·00	☐	☐
3457	**2626**	(1st) multicoloured	1·00	1·00	☐	☐
3458	**2627**	(1st) multicoloured	1·00	1·00	☐	☐
		a. Horiz strip of 5. Nos. 3458/3462	4·50	4·50	☐	☐
3459	**2628**	(1st) multicoloured	1·00	1·00	☐	☐
3460	**2629**	(1st) multicoloured	1·00	1·00	☐	☐
3461	**2630**	(1st) multicoloured	1·00	1·00	☐	☐
3462	**2631**	(1st) multicoloured	1·00	1·00	☐	☐
Set of 10			9·00	9·00	☐	
First Day Cover				11·00	☐	
Presentation Pack (PO Pack No. 483)			10·00		☐	
PHQ Cards (*set of 10*) (375)			4·00	12·00	☐	☐
Set of 2 Gutter Strips of 10			18·00		☐	

Nos. 3453/3457 and 3458/3462 were each printed together, *se-tenant*, as horizontal strips of five stamps in sheets of 50 (2 panes 5×5).

2632 Jimmy Greaves (England)

2633 John Charles (Wales)

2634 Gordon Banks (England)

2635 George Best (Northern Ireland)

2636 John Barnes (England)

2637 Kevin Keegan (England)

2638 Denis Law (Scotland)

2639 Bobby Moore (England)

2640 Bryan Robson (England)

2641 Dave Mackay (Scotland)

2642 Bobby Charlton (England)

Football Heroes (1st issue)

2013 (9 May)–**14** 'All-over' phosphor

(a) Ordinary paper. Perf 14½

3463	**2632**	(1st) multicoloured	1·00	1·00		
		a. Horiz strip of 5.				
		Nos. 3463/3467	4·50	4·50		
3464	**2633**	(1st) multicoloured	1·00	1·00		
3465	**2634**	(1st) multicoloured	1·00	1·00		
3466	**2635**	(1st) multicoloured	1·00	1·00		
3467	**2636**	(1st) multicoloured	1·00	1·00		
3468	**2637**	(1st) multicoloured	1·00	1·00		
		a. Horiz strip of 6.				
		Nos. 3468/3473	5·50	5·50		
3469	**2638**	(1st) multicoloured	1·00	1·00		
3470	**2639**	(1st) multicoloured	1·00	1·00		
3471	**2640**	(1st) multicoloured	1·00	1·00		
3472	**2641**	(1st) multicoloured	1·00	1·00		
3473	**2642**	(1st) multicoloured	1·00	1·00		
Set of 11			10·00	10·00		
First Day Cover				11·00		
Presentation Pack (PO Pack No. 484)			11·00			
PHQ Cards (set of 12) (376)			4·75	11·00		
Set of 1 Gutter Strip of 12 and						
1 Gutter Strip of 10			20·00			
MS3474 192×74 mm. Nos. 3463/3473			10·00	10·00		
First Day Cover				12·00		

(b) Self-adhesive. Gravure Walsall. Die-cut perf 14½

3475	**2635**	(1st) multicoloured	4·50	4·50		
3476	**2639**	(1st) multicoloured	4·50	4·50		
3477	**2633**	(1st) multicoloured (20.2.14)	4·50	4·50		
3478	**2641**	(1st) multicoloured (20.2.14)	4·50	4·50		
Set of 4			16·00	16·00		

Nos. 3463/3467 were printed together, *se-tenant*, as horizontal strips of five stamps in sheets of 30 (5×6).

Nos. 3468/3473 were printed together, *se-tenant*, as horizontal strips of six stamps in sheets of 30 (6×5).

Nos. 3475/3476 were issued in booklets, each containing Nos. 3475/3476 and 4×1st vermilion and originally sold for £3·60.

Nos. 3463/3487 commemorate the 150th anniversary of the Football Association and the 140th Anniversary of the Scottish Football Association.

The 12 PHQ cards depict the 11 individual stamps and the complete miniature sheet.

Football Heroes (2nd issue)

2013 (9 May) Self-adhesive. Litho. 'All-over' phosphor. Die-cut perf 14½×14

3479	**2632**	(1st) multicoloured	1·60	1·60		
3480	**2633**	(1st) multicoloured	1·60	1·60		

3481	**2634**	(1st) multicoloured	1·60	1·60		
3482	**2635**	(1st) multicoloured	1·60	1·60		
3483	**2636**	(1st) multicoloured	1·60	1·60		
3484	**2637**	(1st) multicoloured	1·60	1·60		
3485	**2638**	(1st) multicoloured	1·60	1·60		
3486	**2639**	(1st) multicoloured	1·60	1·60		
3487	**2640**	(1st) multicoloured	1·60	1·60		
3488	**2641**	(1st) multicoloured	1·60	1·60		
3489	**2642**	(1st) multicoloured	1·60	1·60		
Set of 11			16·00	16·00		

Nos. 3479/3489 were only issued in the £11·11 Football Heroes premium booklet No. DY7.

No.3490 is vacant

2646 Preliminary Oil Sketch for The Coronation of Queen Elizabeth II (Terence Cuneo), 1953

2647 Queen Elizabeth II in Garter Robes (Nicky Philipps), 2012

2648 Portrait by Andrew Festing, 1999

2649 Portrait by Pietro Annigoni, 1955

2650 Portrait by Sergei Pavlenko, 2000

2651 Her Majesty Queen Elizabeth II (Richard Stone), 1992

60th Anniversary of the Coronation. Six Decades of Royal Portraits

2013 (30 May–2 June) Phosphor band at left (2nd) or 'all-over' phosphor (others). Perf 14

3491	**2646**	(2nd) multicoloured	90	90		
3492	**2647**	(1st) multicoloured	1·00	1·00		
3493	**2648**	78p. multicoloured	1·10	1·10		
3494	**2649**	88p. multicoloured	1·50	1·50		
3495	**2650**	£1·28 multicoloured	2·10	2·10		
3496	**2651**	£1·88 multicoloured	3·00	3·00		
Set of 6			8·50	8·50		
First Day Cover				11·00		
Presentation Pack (PO Pack No. 485)			10·00			
PHQ Cards (set of 6) (377)			2·40	10·50		
Commemorative Document						
(Nos. 3491/3492) (2.6.13)			12·50			
Set of 6 Gutter Pairs			17·00			
Set of 6 Traffic Light Gutter Blocks of 4			36·00			

2652 UTA W No. 103

2653 Classic Locomotives of Northern Ireland

Classic Locomotives (3rd series). Northern Ireland

2013 (18 June) 'All-over' phosphor

(a) Self-adhesive. Die-cut perf 14

3497	**2652**	(1st) black, grey and gold	1·25	1·25 ☐ ☐

b) Ordinary gum. Sheet 180×74 mm. Perf 14

MS3498 **2653** (1st) As Type **2652**; 78p.
UTA SG3 No. 35; 88p. Peckett No. 2;
£1·28 CDRJC Class 5 No. 4   5·00   5·25 ☐ ☐

First Day Cover		6·50 ☐
Presentation Pack (PO Pack No. 486)	6·25	
PHQ Cards (*set of* 5) (378)	2·00	6·50 ☐ ☐

No. 3497 was issued in booklets, each containing No. 3497×2 and 4×1st vermilion and sold for £3·60.

The five PHQ cards show the four individual stamps and the complete miniature sheet.

2654 Comma
(*Polygonia c-album*)

2655 Orange-tip (*Anthocharis cardamines*)

2656 Small Copper
(*Lycaena phlaeas*)

2657 Chalkhill Blue
(*Polyommatus coridon*)

2658 Swallowtail
(*Papilio machaon*)

2659 Purple Emperor
(*Apatura iris*)

2660 Marsh Fritillary
(*Euphydrygus awinea*)

2661 Brimstone
(*Gonepteryx rhamni*)

2662 Red Admiral
(*Vanessa atalanta*)

2663 Marbled White
(*Melanargia galathea*)

Butterflies

2013 (11 July) 'All-over' phosphor

(a) Ordinary paper. Perf 14×14½

3499	**2654**	(1st) multicoloured	1·00	1·00 ☐ ☐
		a. Horiz strip of 5.		
		Nos. 3499/3503	4·50	4·50 ☐ ☐
3500	**2655**	(1st) multicoloured	1·00	1·00 ☐ ☐
3501	**2656**	(1st) multicoloured	1·00	1·00 ☐ ☐
3502	**2657**	(1st) multicoloured	1·00	1·00 ☐ ☐
3503	**2658**	(1st) multicoloured	1·00	1·00 ☐ ☐
3504	**2659**	(1st) multicoloured	1·00	1·00 ☐ ☐
		a. Horiz strip of 5.		
		Nos. 3504/3508	4·50	4·50 ☐ ☐
3505	**2660**	(1st) multicoloured	1·00	1·00 ☐ ☐
3506	**2661**	(1st) multicoloured	1·00	1·00 ☐ ☐
3507	**2662**	(1st) multicoloured	1·00	1·00 ☐ ☐
3508	**2663**	(1st) multicoloured	1·00	1·00 ☐ ☐

Set of 10	9·00	9·00 ☐
First Day Cover		12·00 ☐
Presentation Pack (PO Pack No. 487)	11·00	
PHQ Cards (*set of* 10) (379)	4·00	11·00 ☐ ☐
Set of 2 *Gutter Strips of* 10	18·00	☐

(b) Self-adhesive. Die-cut perf 14×14½

3509	**2657**	(1st) multicoloured	1·50	1·50 ☐ ☐
3510	**2654**	(1st) multicoloured	1·50	1·50 ☐ ☐

Nos. 3499/3503 and 3504/3508 were each printed together, *se-tenant*, as horizontal strips of five stamps in sheets of 50 (2 panes 5×5).

Nos. 3509/3510 were issued in stamp booklets, each containing Nos. 3509/3510 and 4×1st vermilion and sold for £3·60.

2664 Andy Murray's Wimbledon Victory

Andy Murray, Men's Singles Champion, Wimbledon

2013 (8 Aug.) Sheet 192×75 mm. Multicoloured. 'All-over' phosphor. Perf 14½

MS3511 **2664** (1st) Andy Murray kissing
Wimbledon Trophy; (1st) Andy
Murray serving; £1·28 In action;
£1·28 Holding Trophy   5·25   5·50 ☐ ☐

First Day Cover	7·00	☐
Presentation Pack (PO Pack No. M21)	6·50	☐

2665 Jaguar E-Type, 1961

2666 Rolls-Royce Silver Shadow, 1965

2667 Aston Martin DB5, 1963

2668 MG MGB, 1962

2669 Morgan Plus 8, 1968

2670 Lotus Esprit, 1976

2671 The Workhorses

British Auto Legends

2013 (13 Aug.) 'All-over' phosphor. Perf 13½ (Nos. 3512/3517) or 14 (No. **MS**3518).

3512	**2665**	(1st) multicoloured	1·00	1·00	☐ ☐
		a. Horiz strip of 3.			
		Nos. 3512/3514	2·75	2·75	☐ ☐
3513	**2666**	(1st) multicoloured	1·00	1·00	☐ ☐
3514	**2667**	(1st) multicoloured	1·00	1·00	☐ ☐
3515	**2668**	£1·28 multicoloured	1·60	1·60	☐ ☐
		a. Horiz strip of 3.			
		Nos. 3515/3517	4·25	4·25	☐ ☐
3516	**2669**	£1·28 multicoloured	1·60	1·60	☐ ☐
3517	**2670**	£1·28 multicoloured	1·60	1·60	☐ ☐
Set of 6			7·00	7·00	☐
First Day Cover				9·00	☐
Presentation Pack (Nos. 3512/**MS**3518)					
(PO Pack No. 488)			13·50		☐
PHQ Cards (*set of* 11) (380)			4·50	17·00	☐ ☐
Set of 2 Gutter Strips of 6			14·00		☐

MS3518 180×74 mm. **2671** (1st)×4 Morris Minor Royal Mail van (1953–1971); Austin FX4 (1958–1997) London taxi; Ford Anglia 105E (1959–1967) police car; Coastguard Land Rover Defender 110 (from 1990)

	4·00	4·00	☐ ☐
First Day Cover		4·50	☐

The complete miniature sheet is shown on one of the 11 PHQ cards with the others depicting individual stamps including those from the miniature sheet.

The 1st value from No. **MS**3518 is inscribed EUROPA.

2672 East Indiaman *Atlas*, 1813

2673 Royal Mail Ship *Britannia*, 1840

2674 Tea Clipper *Cutty Sark*, 1870

2675 Cargo Liner *Clan Matheson*, 1919

2676 Royal Mail Ship *Queen Elizabeth*, 1940

2677 Bulk Carrier *Lord Hinton*, 1986

Merchant Navy (1st issue)

2013 (19 Sept.) 'All-over' phosphor. Perf 14

3519	**2672**	(1st) multicoloured	1·00	1·00	☐ ☐
3520	**2673**	(1st) multicoloured	1·00	1·00	☐ ☐
3521	**2674**	(1st) multicoloured	1·00	1·00	☐ ☐
3522	**2675**	£1·28 multicoloured	1·60	1·60	☐ ☐
3523	**2676**	£1·28 multicoloured	1·60	1·60	☐ ☐
3524	**2677**	£1·28 multicoloured	1·60	1·60	☐ ☐
Set of 6			7·00	7·00	☐
First Day Cover				9·00	☐
Presentation Pack (PO Pack No. 489)			13·50		☐
PHQ Cards (*set of* 11) (381)			4·50	17·00	☐ ☐
Set of 6 Gutter Pairs			14·00		☐

The complete miniature sheet is shown on one of the 11 PHQ cards with the others depicting individual stamps including those from No. **MS**3529.

2678 Destroyer HMS *Vanoc* escorting Atlantic Convoy

2679 Merchant Ship passing the Naval Control Base in the Thames Estuary

2680 Sailors clearing Ice from the Decks of HMS *King George V* in Arctic Waters

2681 Naval Convoy of 24 Merchant Ships in the North Sea

2682 Second World War Atlantic and Arctic Convoys

Merchant Navy (2nd issue)

2013 (19 Sept.) 'All-over' phosphor. Perf 14

3525	**2678**	(1st) multicoloured	2·25	2·25
3526	**2679**	(1st) multicoloured	2·25	2·25
3527	**2680**	(1st) multicoloured	2·25	2·25
3528	**2681**	(1st) multicoloured	2·25	2·25
Set of 4			8·00	8·00
MS3529 115×89 mm **2682**				
Nos. 3525/3528			6·00	6·00
First Day Cover				6·75

Nos. 3525/3528 were only issued in the £11·19 Merchant Navy premium booklet, No. DY8 and in No. **MS**3529.

2683 Royal Mail Van

Royal Mail Transport: By Land and Sea

2013 (19 Sept.) Self-adhesive booklet stamps. Die-cut perf 14

3530	**2683**	(1st) multicoloured	5·50	5·50
3531	**2673**	(1st) multicoloured	5·50	5·50

The design of No. 3530 is as the Royal Mail van stamp within No. **MS**3518.

Nos. 3530/3531 were only issued in booklets, each containing Nos. 3530/3531 and 4×1st vermilion and sold for £3·60.

No. 3530 includes the EUROPA emblem.

2684 Polacanthus

2685 Ichthyosaurus

2686 Iguanodon

2687 Ornithocheirus

2688 Baryonyx

2689 Dimorphodon

2690 Hypsilophodon

2691 Cetiosaurus

2692 Megalosaurus

2693 Plesiosaurus

Dinosaurs

2013 (10 Oct.) Self-adhesive. 'All-over' phosphor. Die-cut perf 13½×14 (with no teeth around protruding parts at top or foot of the designs)

3532	**2684**	(1st) multicoloured	1·00	1·00
		a. Horiz strip of 5.		
		Nos. 3532/3536	4·50	
3533	**2685**	(1st) multicoloured	1·00	1·00
3534	**2686**	(1st) multicoloured	1·00	1·00
3535	**2687**	(1st) multicoloured	1·00	1·00
3536	**2688**	(1st) multicoloured	1·00	1·00
3537	**2689**	(1st) multicoloured	1·00	1·00
		a. Horiz strip of 5.		
		Nos. 3537/3541	4·50	
3538	**2690**	(1st) multicoloured	1·00	1·00
3539	**2691**	(1st) multicoloured	1·00	1·00
3540	**2692**	(1st) multicoloured	1·00	1·00
3541	**2693**	(1st) multicoloured	1·00	1·00
Set of 10			9·00	9·00
First Day Cover				11·00
Presentation Pack (PO Pack No. 490)			10·00	
PHQ Cards (*set of* 10) (382)			4·00	11·00

Nos. 3532/3536 and 3537/3541 were each printed together as horizontal strips of five stamps in sheets of 50 (2 panes 5×5).

2694 *Madonna and Child* (Francesco Granacci)

2695 *Virgin and Child with the Young St John the Baptist* (detail) (Antoniazzo Romano)

2696 *Madonna and Child* (Francesco Granacci)

2697 *St Roch Praying to the Virgin for an End to the Plague* (detail) (Jacques-Louis David)

2698 *Virgin and Child with the Young St John the Baptist* (detail) (Antoniazzo Romano)

2699 *La Vierge au Lys* (William-Adolphe Bouguereau)

2700 *Theotokos, Mother of God* (Fadi Mikhail)

Christmas. Madonna and Child Paintings

2013 (5 Nov.) One centre band (No. 3542) or two bands (others). Perf 14½ × 15

(a) Self-adhesive						
3542	**2694**	(2nd) multicoloured	90	90		
3543	**2695**	(1st) multicoloured	1·00	1·00		
3544	**2696**	(2nd Large) multicoloured	1·10	1·10		
3545	**2697**	88p. multicoloured	1·40	1·40		
3546	**2698**	(1st Large) multicoloured	1·50	1·40		
3547	**2699**	£1·28 multicoloured	2·00	2·00		
3548	**2700**	£1·88 multicoloured	3·00	3·00		
Set of 7			9·50	9·50		
First Day Cover				12·50		
Presentation Pack (PO Pack No. 491)			11·50			
PHQ Cards (set of 8) (383)			3·25	19·00		
(b) Ordinary gum						
MS3549 146 × 74 mm. As Nos. 3542/3548			9·50	9·50		
First Day Cover				12·50		

The eight PHQ cards show the seven individual stamps and the complete miniature sheet.

The 2nd class, 1st class, 88p., £1·28 and £1·88 stamps were also issued in sheets of 20 containing eight 2nd class, eight 1st class, two 88p., one £1·28 and one £1·88 stamps, each stamp accompanied by a *se-tenant* label.

Separate sheets of 20 2nd, ten 1st, ten 88p. and ten £1·28 were available with personal photographs.

2701 Angels (Rosie Hargreaves)

2702 Santa (Molly Robson)

Children's Christmas

2013 (5 Nov.) One phosphor band at right (2nd) or two phosphor bands (1st). Self-adhesive. Die-cut perf 14½

3550	**2701**	(2nd) multicoloured	1·00	1·00		
3551	**2702**	(1st) multicoloured	1·25	1·25		
First Day Cover				4·25		
Presentation Pack (PO Pack No. M22)			4·25			

Year Pack

2013 (5 Nov.) Comprises Nos. 3423/3429, 3431/3447, **MS**3451, 3453/3473, 3491/3496, **MS**3498/3508, **MS**3511/3524, **MS**3529 and 3532/3548

CP3551*a* Year Pack	£140	

Post Office Yearbook

2013 (5 Nov.) Comprises Nos. 3423/3429, 3431/3447, **MS**3451, 3453/3473, 3491/3496, **MS**3498/3508, **MS**3511/3524, **MS**3529, 3532/3548 and 3550/3551

YB3551*a* Yearbook	£150	

Miniature Sheet Collection

2013 (5 Nov.) Comprises Nos. **MS**3429, **MS**3451, **MS**3474, **MS**3498, **MS**3511, **MS**3518, **MS**3529 and **MS**3549

MS3551*a* Miniature Sheet Collection	45·00	

2703 Andy Pandy

2704 Ivor the Engine

2705 Dougal (*The Magic Roundabout*)

2706 Windy Miller (*Camberwick Green*)

2707 Mr. Benn

2708 Great Uncle Bulgaria (*The Wombles*)

2709 Bagpuss

2710 Paddington Bear

2711 Postman Pat

2712 Bob the Builder

2713 Peppa Pig

2714 Shaun the Sheep

Classic Children's TV

2014 (7 Jan.) 'All-over' phosphor. Self-adhesive. Die-cut perf 15

3552	**2703**	(1st) multicoloured	1·00	1·00
		a. Horiz strip of 6. Nos. 3552/3557	5·50	5·50
3553	**2704**	(1st) multicoloured	1·00	1·00
3554	**2705**	(1st) multicoloured	1·00	1·00
3555	**2706**	(1st) multicoloured	1·00	1·00
3556	**2707**	(1st) multicoloured	1·00	1·00
3557	**2708**	(1st) multicoloured	1·00	1·00
3558	**2709**	(1st) multicoloured	1·00	1·00
		a. Horiz strip of 6. Nos. 3558/3563	5·50	5·50
3559	**2710**	(1st) multicoloured	1·00	1·00
3560	**2711**	(1st) multicoloured	1·00	1·00
3561	**2712**	(1st) multicoloured	1·00	1·00
3562	**2713**	(1st) multicoloured	1·00	1·00
3563	**2714**	(1st) multicoloured	1·00	1·00
Set of 12			11·00	11·00
First Day Cover				13·50
Presentation Pack (PO Pack No. 493)			12·50	
PHQ Cards (set of 12) (384)			4·75	12·50
Set of 2 Gutter Strips of 12			22·00	

Nos. 3552/3557 and 3558/3563 were each printed together se-tenant in horizontal strips of six stamps in sheets of 60 (6×10).

2715 Riding for the Disabled Association

2716 The King's Troop Ceremonial Horses

2717 Dray Horses

2718 Royal Mews Carriage Horses

2719 Police Horses

2720 Forestry Horse

Working Horses

2014 (4 Feb.) 'All-over' phosphor. Perf 14

3564	**2715**	(1st) multicoloured	1·00	1·00
3565	**2716**	(1st) multicoloured	1·00	1·00
3566	**2717**	88p. multicoloured	1·40	1·40
3567	**2718**	88p. multicoloured	1·40	1·40
3568	**2719**	£1·28 multicoloured	2·10	2·10
3569	**2720**	£1·28 multicoloured	2·10	2·10
Set of 6			8·00	8·00
First Day Cover				10·00
Presentation Pack (PO Pack No. 494)			9·50	
PHQ Cards (set of 6) (385)			2·50	9·50
Set of 6 Gutter Pairs			16·00	

2721 BR Dean Goods No. 2532

2722 BR D34 Nos. 62471 & 62496

2723 UTA Class W No. 103 Thomas Somerset with Belfast Express, Downhill, near Castlerock, c.1950

2724 LMS No. 7720

2725 Peckett R2 Thor

2726 BR D40 No. 62276

2727 UTA SG3 No. 35

2728 Hunslet No. 589 Blanche

2729 Classic Locomotives of Wales

Classic Locomotives (4th and 5th series). Wales (No. MS3578) and United Kingdom (booklet)

2014 (20 Feb.) 'All-over' phosphor. Perf 14

3570	**2721**	(1st) multicoloured	2.75	2.75
3571	**2722**	(1st) multicoloured	2.75	2.75
3572	**2723**	(1st) multicoloured	2.75	2.75
3573	**2724**	(1st) multicoloured	2.75	2.75
3574	**2725**	60p. multicoloured	2.75	2.75
3575	**2726**	68p. multicoloured	2.75	2.75
3576	**2727**	78p. multicoloured	2.75	2.75
3577	**2728**	78p. multicoloured	2.75	2.75
Set of 8			15.00	15.00

MS3578 180×74 mm. **2729** No. 3573; No. 3577; 88p. W&LLR No. 822 *The Earl*; £1·28 BR 5600 No. 5652   5.00   5.25

First Day Cover		6.50
Presentation Pack (PO Pack No. 495)	6.00	
PHQ Cards (set of 5) (386)	2·00	10·00

Nos. 3570/3577 were issued only in the £13·97 Classic Locomotives booklet, No. DY9 or also in No. **MS**3578 (Nos. 3573 and 3577).

The five PHQ cards show the four individual stamps in the miniature sheet and the complete miniature sheet.

For the self-adhesive version of No. 3573, see No. 3634.

2730 Roy Plomley (1914–1985, broadcaster and writer)

2731 Barbara Ward (1914–1981, economist and broadcaster)

2732 Joe Mercer (1914–1990, football player and manager)

2733 Kenneth More (1914–1982, stage and screen actor)

2734 Dylan Thomas (1914–1953, poet and writer)

2735 Sir Alec Guinness (1914–2000, stage and screen actor)

2736 Noorunissa Inayat Khan (1914–1944, SOE agent in occupied France)

2737 Max Perutz (1914–2002, molecular biologist and Nobel laureate)

2738 Joan Littlewood (1914–2002, theatre director and writer)

2739 Abram Games (1914–1996, graphic designer)

Remarkable Lives

2014 (25 Mar.) 'All-over' phosphor. Perf 14½

3579	**2730**	(1st) multicoloured	1·00	1·00
		a. Horiz strip of 5. Nos. 3579/3583	4·50	4·50
3580	**2731**	(1st) multicoloured	1·00	1·00
3581	**2732**	(1st) multicoloured	1·00	1·00
3582	**2733**	(1st) multicoloured	1·00	1·00
3583	**2734**	(1st) multicoloured	1·00	1·00
3584	**2735**	(1st) multicoloured	1·00	1·00
		a. Horiz strip of 5. Nos. 3584/3588	4·50	4·50
3585	**2736**	(1st) multicoloured	1·00	1·00
3586	**2737**	(1st) multicoloured	1·00	1·00
3587	**2738**	(1st) multicoloured	1·00	1·00
3588	**2739**	(1st) multicoloured	1·00	1·00
Set of 10			9·00	9·00
First Day Cover				11·00
Presentation Pack (PO Pack No. 496)			10·00	
PHQ Cards (set of 10) (387)			4·00	11·00
Set of 2 Gutter Strips of 10			18·00	

Nos. 3579/3583 and 3584/3588 were each printed together, *se-tenant*, as horizontal strips of five stamps in sheets of 50 (2 panes 5×5).

2740 Buckingham Palace, 2014

2741 Buckingham Palace, c. 1862

2742 Buckingham Palace, 1846

2743 Buckingham House, 1819

2744 Buckingham House, 1714

2745 Buckingham House, c. 1700

2746 The Grand Staircase

2747 The Throne Room

Buckingham Palace, London (1st issue)

2014 (15 Apr.) 'All-over' phosphor.

(a) Ordinary gum. Perf 14½

3589	**2740**	(1st) multicoloured	1·00	1·00	☐☐
		a. Horiz strip of 3.			
		Nos. 3589/3591	2·75	2·75	☐☐
		b. Perf 14×13½.	1·25	1·25	☐☐
3590	**2741**	(1st) multicoloured	1·00	1·00	☐☐
		b. Perf 14×13½.	1·25	1·25	☐☐
3591	**2742**	(1st) multicoloured	1·00	1·00	☐☐
		b. Perf 14×13½.	1·25	1·25	☐☐
3592	**2743**	(1st) multicoloured	1·00	1·00	☐☐
		a. Horiz strip of 3.			
		Nos. 3592/3594	2·75	2·75	☐☐
		b. Perf 14×13½.	1·25	1·25	☐☐
3593	**2744**	(1st) multicoloured	1·00	1·00	☐☐
		b. Perf 14×13½.	1·25	1·25	☐☐
3594	**2745**	(1st) multicoloured	1·00	1·00	☐☐
		b. Perf 14×13½.	1·25	1·25	☐☐
Set of 6			5·50	5·50	☐
First Day Cover				6·75	☐

Presentation Pack (Nos. 3589/3544 and
MS3601) (PO Pack No. 497) 10·00 ☐
PHQ Cards (*set of 11*) 4·50 13·00 ☐☐
Set of 2 Gutter Strips of 6 11·00 ☐

(b) Self-adhesive. Die-cut perf 14

3595	**2746**	(1st) multicoloured	2·25	2·25	☐☐
3596	**2747**	(1st) multicoloured	2·25	2·25	☐☐

Nos. 3589/3591 and 3592/3594 were each printed together, *se-tenant*, as horizontal strips of three stamps in sheets of 36 (2 panes 3×6).

Nos 3589b/3594b come from £11·39 premium booklets, No. DY10.

Nos. 3595/3596 were only issued in stamp booklets, each containing Nos. 3595/3596 and 4×1st vermilion and originally sold for £3·72.

The complete miniature sheet is shown on one of the 11 PHQ cards with the others depicting individual stamps including those from No. **MS**3601.

2748 The Blue Drawing Room

2749 The Green Drawing Room

2750 Buckingham Palace

Buckingham Palace, London (2nd issue)

2014 (15 Apr.) 'All-over' phosphor. Perf 14

3597	**2747**	(1st) multicoloured	1·00	1·00	☐☐
3598	**2746**	(1st) multicoloured	1·00	1·00	☐☐
3599	**2748**	(1st) multicoloured	1·00	1·00	☐☐
3600	**2749**	(1st) multicoloured	1·00	1·00	☐☐
Set of 4			3·50	3·50	☐
MS3601 146×74 mm. **2750**					
Nos. 3597/3600			3·50	3·50	☐☐
First Day Cover				4·50	☐

Nos. 3597/3600 were only issued in the £11·39 Buckingham Palace premium booklet No. DY10, and in No. **MS**3601.

2751 *A Matter of Life and Death* (1946)

2752 *Lawrence of Arabia* (1962)

2753 *2001 A Space Odyssey* (1968)

2754 *Chariots of Fire* (1981)

2755 *Secrets and Lies* (1996)

2756 *Bend It Like Beckham* (2002)

2757 Films by GPO Film Unit

Great British Films

2014 (13 May) 'All-over' phosphor. Perf 14½ (Nos. 3602/3607) or 14 (No. **MS**3608)

3602	**2751**	(1st) multicoloured	1·00	1·00	☐	☐
		a. Horiz strip of 3.				
		Nos· 3602/3604	2·75	2·75	☐	☐
3603	**2752**	(1st) multicoloured	1·00	1·00	☐	☐
3604	**2753**	(1st) multicoloured	1·00	1·00	☐	☐
3605	**2754**	£1·28 multicoloured	1·60	1·60	☐	☐
		a. Horiz strip of 3.				
		Nos. 3605/3607	4·25	4·25	☐	☐
3606	**2755**	£1·28 multicoloured	1·60	1·60	☐	☐
3607	**2756**	£1·28 multicoloured	1·60	1·60	☐	☐
Set of 6			7·00	7·00	☐	☐
First Day Cover				10·00	☐	
Presentation Pack (Nos. 3602/3607 and						
MS3608) (PO Pack No. 498)			14·00		☐	
PHQ Cards (*set of 11*) (389)			4·50	18·00	☐	☐
Set of 2 Gutter Strips of 6			14·00		☐	

MS3608 115×89 mm. **2757** (1st)×4
  Night Mail (1936) directed by
  Harry Watt and Basil Wright;
  Love on the Wing (1938) directed
  by Norman McLaren; *A Colour
  Box* (1935) directed by Len Lye;
  Spare Time (1939) directed by
  Humphrey Jennings   4·50   4·75 ☐ ☐
First Day Cover   5·00 ☐

Nos. 3602/3604 and 3605/3607 were each printed together, *se-tenant*, as horizontal strips of three stamps in sheets of 36 (2 panes 3×6).

The complete miniature sheet is shown on one of the 11 PHQ cards with the others depicting individual stamps including those from No. **MS**3608.

2758 Herring

2759 Red Gurnard

2760 Dab

2761 Pouting

2762 Cornish Sardine

2763 Common Skate

2764 Spiny Dogfish

2765 Wolffish

2766 Sturgeon

2767 Conger Eel

Sustainable Fish (Nos. 3609/3613) and Threatened Fish (Nos. 3614/3618)

2014 (5 June) 'All-over' phosphor. Perf 14×14½

3609	**2758**	(1st) multicoloured	1·00	1·00	☐	☐
		a. Horiz strip of 5.				
		Nos. 3609/3613	4·50	4·50	☐	☐
3610	**2759**	(1st) multicoloured	1·00	1·00	☐	☐
3611	**2760**	(1st) multicoloured	1·00	1·00	☐	☐
3612	**2761**	(1st) multicoloured	1·00	1·00	☐	☐
3613	**2762**	(1st) multicoloured	1·00	1·00	☐	☐
3614	**2763**	(1st) multicoloured	1·00	1·00	☐	☐
		a. Horiz strip of 5.				
		Nos. 3614/3618	4·50	4·50	☐	☐

3615	**2764**	(1st) multicoloured	1·00	1·00	☐ ☐
3616	**2765**	(1st) multicoloured	1·00	1·00	☐ ☐
3617	**2766**	(1st) multicoloured	1·00	1·00	☐ ☐
3618	**2767**	(1st) multicoloured	1·00	1·00	☐ ☐
Set of 10			9·00	9·00	☐ ☐
First Day Cover				11·50	☐
Presentation Pack (PO Pack No. 499)			10·50		☐
PHQ Cards (set of 10)			4·00	11·00	☐
Set of 2 Gutter Strips of 10			18·00		☐

Nos. 3609/3613 and 3614/3618 were each printed together, *se-tenant*, as horizontal strips of five in sheets of 50 (2 panes 5×5).

2768 Judo

2769 Swimming

2770 Marathon

2771 Squash

2772 Netball

2773 Para-athlete Cycling

Commonwealth Games, Glasgow

2014 (17 July) One phosphor band (No. 3619) or two bands (others)

(a) Ordinary gum. Perf 14 × 14½

3619	**2768**	(2nd) multicoloured	90	90	☐ ☐
3620	**2769**	(1st) multicoloured	1·00	1·00	☐ ☐
3621	**2770**	97p. multicoloured	1·40	1·40	☐ ☐
3622	**2771**	£1·28 multicoloured	1·75	1·75	☐ ☐
3623	**2772**	£1·47 multicoloured	2·50	2·50	☐ ☐
3624	**2773**	£2·15 multicoloured	3·50	3·50	☐ ☐
Set of 6			10·00	10·00	☐ ☐
First Day Cover				11·50	☐
Presentation Pack (PO Pack No. 500)			10·50		☐
PHQ Cards (set of 6) (391)			2·50	11·50	☐ ☐
Set of 6 Gutter Pairs			20·00		☐

(b) Self-adhesive. Die-cut perf 14 × 14½.

3625	**2769**	(1st) multicoloured	1·50	1·50	☐ ☐

The phosphor band on No. 3619 is at centre right of the stamps.

No. 3625 was only issued in stamp booklets, each containing No. 3625×2 and 4×1st vermilion and originally sold for £3·72.

2774 *Poppy* (Fiona Strickland)

2775 Lines from *For the Fallen* (Laurence Binyon)

2776 Private William Cecil Tickle

2777 *A Star Shell* (C. R. W. Nevinson)

2778 *The Response* (sculpture by William Goscombe John)

2779 Princess Mary's Gift Box Fund

Centenary of the First World War (1st issue)

2014 (28 July) 'All-over' phosphor (Nos. 3627, 3629) or two bands (others). Perf 14½.

3626	**2774**	(1st) multicoloured	1·00	1·00	☐ ☐
		a. 'All-over' phosphor	1·25	1·50	☐ ☐
3627	**2775**	(1st) multicoloured	1·00	1·00	☐ ☐
3628	**2776**	(1st) multicoloured	1·00	1·00	☐ ☐
		a. 'All-over' phosphor	1·25	1·50	☐ ☐
3629	**2777**	£1·47 multicoloured	2·50	2·50	☐ ☐
3630	**2778**	£1·47 multicoloured	2·50	2·50	☐ ☐
		a. 'All-over' phosphor	3·25	3·50	☐ ☐
3631	**2779**	£1·47 multicoloured	2·50	2·50	☐ ☐
		a. 'All-over' phosphor	3·25	3·50	☐ ☐
Set of 6			9·25	9·25	☐ ☐
First Day Cover				11·50	☐
Presentation Pack (PO Pack No. 501)			10·50		☐
PHQ Cards (set of 6) (392)			2·50	10·50	☐ ☐
Set of 6 Gutter Pairs			18·50		☐

Nos. 3626a, 3628a, 2630a and 3631a only come from the £11·30 Centenary of the First World War booklet, No. DY11. No. 3627 also comes from DY26.

Sustainable Fish and Threatened Fish (2nd issue)

2014 (18 Aug.) Designs as Nos. 3613/3614. Self-adhesive. Die-cut perf 14 × 14½

3632	**2763**	(1st) multicoloured	1·50	1·60	☐ ☐
3633	**2762**	(1st) multicoloured	1·50	1·60	☐ ☐

Nos. 3632/3633 were only issued in stamp booklets, each containing Nos. 3632/3633 and 4×1st vermilion and originally sold for £3·72.

Classic Locomotives of Wales

2014 (18 Sept.) Booklet stamp as T **2724**. 'All-over' phosphor. Self-adhesive. Die-cut perf 14

3634	**2724**	(1st) multicoloured	1·50	1·50	☐	☐

No. 3634 was only issued in stamp booklets, containing No. 3634×2 and 4×1st vermilion and originally sold for £3·72.

2780 Eastbourne Bandstand   **2781** Tinside Lido, Plymouth

2782 Bangor Pier   **2783** Southwold Lighthouse

2784 Blackpool Pleasure Beach   **2785** Bexhill-on-Sea Shelter

2786 British Piers

Seaside Architecture

2014 (18 Sept.) Two bands (Nos. 3635/3640) or 'All-over' phosphor (No. **MS**3641). Perf 14

3635	**2780**	(1st) multicoloured	1·00	1·00	☐	☐
3636	**2781**	(1st) multicoloured	1·00	1·00	☐	☐
3637	**2782**	97p. multicoloured	1·40	1·40	☐	☐
3638	**2783**	97p. multicoloured	1·40	1·40	☐	☐
3639	**2784**	£1·28 multicoloured	2·10	2·10	☐	☐
3640	**2785**	£1·28 multicoloured	2·10	2·10	☐	☐
Set of 6			8·00	8·00	☐	
First Day Cover				10·00		☐
Presentation Pack (Nos. 3635/3640 and						
MS3641) (PO Pack No. 502)			16·00			☐
PHQ Cards (*set of 11*) (393)			4·50	19·00	☐	☐
Set of 6 Gutter Pairs			16·00			☐

MS3641 125×89 mm. **2786** (1st) Llandudno Pier; (1st) Worthing Pier; £1·28 Dunoon Pier; £1·28 Brighton Pier

	5·25	5·50	☐	☐
First Day Cover		7·00		☐

No. 3635 includes the EUROPA emblem.

The complete miniature sheet is shown on one of the 11 PHQ cards with the others depicting individual stamps including those from the miniature sheet.

2787 Margaret Thatcher   **2788** Harold Wilson

2789 Clement Attlee   **2790** Winston Churchill

2791 William Gladstone   **2792** Robert Peel

2793 Charles Grey   **2794** William Pitt the Younger

Prime Ministers

2014 (14 Oct.) 'All-over' phosphor. Perf 14½

3642	**2787**	(1st) multicoloured	1·00	1·00	☐	☐
		a. Horiz strip of 4.				
		Nos. 3642/3645	3·75	3·75	☐	
3643	**2788**	(1st) multicoloured	1·00	1·00	☐	
3644	**2789**	(1st) multicoloured	1·00	1·00	☐	
3645	**2790**	(1st) multicoloured	1·00	1·00	☐	
3646	**2791**	97p. multicoloured	1·60	1·60	☐	
		a. Horiz strip of 4.				
		Nos. 3646/3649	5·75	5·75	☐	
3647	**2792**	97p. multicoloured	1·60	1·60	☐	
3648	**2793**	97p. multicoloured	1·60	1·60	☐	
3649	**2794**	97p. multicoloured	1·60	1·60	☐	
Set of 8			9·50	9·50	☐	
First Day Cover				11·00		☐
Presentation Pack (PO Pack No. 503)			11·00			☐
PHQ Cards (*set of 8*) (394)			3·25	11·50	☐	☐
Set of 2 Gutter strips of 8			19·00			☐

Nos. 3642/3645 and 3646/3649 were each printed together, *se-tenant*, as horizontal strips of four stamps in sheets of 48 (2 panes 4×6).

2795 Collecting the Christmas Tree

2796 Posting Christmas Cards

2797 Collecting the Christmas Tree

2798 Posting Christmas Cards

2799 Building a Snowman

2800 Carol Singing

2801 Ice Skating

Christmas. Illustrations by Andrew Bannecker

2014 (4 Nov.) One centre band (No. 3650) or two bands (others). Perf 14½×15

		(a) Self-adhesive				
3650	**2795**	(2nd) multicoloured	90	90		
3651	**2796**	(1st) multicoloured	1·00	1·00		
3652	**2797**	(2nd Large) multicoloured	1·10	1·10		
3653	**2798**	(1st Large) multicoloured	1·40	1·40		
3654	**2799**	£1·28 multicoloured	2·00	2·00		
3655	**2800**	£1·47 multicoloured	2·50	2·50		
3656	**2801**	£2·15 multicoloured	3·25	3·25		
Set of 7			11·00	11·00		
First Day Cover				14·00		
Presentation Pack (PO Pack No. 504)			13·00			
PHQ Cards (set of 8) (395)			3·25	20·00		

	(b) Ordinary gum				
MS3657 146×74 mm. As Nos. 3650/3656		11·00	11·00		
First Day Cover			14·00		

The eight PHQ cards show the seven individual stamps and the complete miniature sheet.

The 2nd class, 1st class, £1·28 and £1·47 stamps were also issued in sheets of 20 containing eight 2nd class, eight 1st class, two £1·28 and two £1·47 stamps, each stamp accompanied by a *se-tenant* label.

Separate sheets of 20 2nd, 20 1st, 10 1st, 10 £1·28 and ten £1·47 were available with personal photographs.

Year Pack

2014 (4 Nov.) Comprises Nos. 3552/3569, **MS**3578/3594, **MS**3601/3624, 3626/3631, 3635/3656

CP3657a	Year Pack	£140	

Post Office Yearbook

2014 (4 Nov.) Comprises Nos. 3552/3569, **MS**3578/3594, **MS**3601/3624, 3626/3631, 3635/3656

YB3657a	Yearbook	£160	

Miniature Sheet Collection

2014 (4 Nov.) Comprises Nos. **MS**3578, **MS**3601, **MS**3608, **MS**3641 and **MS**3657

MS3657a Miniature Sheet Collection	30·00	

2802 The White Rabbit

2803 Down the Rabbit Hole

2804 Drink Me

2805 The White Rabbit's House

2806 The Cheshire Cat

2807 A Mad Tea-Party

2808 The Queen of Hearts

2809 The Game of Croquet

2810 Alice's Evidence

2811 A Pack of Cards

Alice in Wonderland

2015 (6 Jan.) One phosphor band at right (2nd) or two bands (others)

		(a) Ordinary gum. Litho. Perf 14½				
3658	**2802**	(2nd) multicoloured	90	90		
		a. Vert pair.				
		Nos. 3658/3659	1·75	1·75		
3659	**2803**	(2nd) multicoloured	90	90		
3660	**2804**	(1st) multicoloured	1·00	1·00		
		a. Vert pair.				
		Nos. 3660/3661	2·00	2·00		
3661	**2805**	(1st) multicoloured	1·00	1·00		
3662	**2806**	81p. multicoloured	1·50	1·50		

	a. Vert pair.			
	Nos. 3662/3663	3·00	3·00	☐ ☐
3663 **2807**	81p. multicoloured	1·50	1·50	☐ ☐
3664 **2808**	£1·28 multicoloured	2·50	2·50	☐ ☐
	a. Vert pair.			
	Nos. 3664/3665	5·00	5·00	☐ ☐
3665 **2809**	£1·28 multicoloured	2·50	2·50	☐ ☐
3666 **2810**	£1·47 multicoloured	3·25	3·25	☐ ☐
	a. Vert pair.			
	Nos. 3666/3667	6·50	6·50	☐ ☐
3667 **2811**	£1·47 multicoloured	3·25	3·25	☐ ☐
Set of 10		16·50	16·50	☐ ☐
First Day Cover			17·50	☐
Presentation Pack (PO Pack No. 506)		25·00		☐
PHQ Cards *(set of 10)* (396)		5·00	18·00	☐ ☐
Set of 5 Gutter Strips of 4		35·00		☐

(b) Self-adhesive. Gravure. Die-cut perf 14½

3668 **2804**	(1st) multicoloured	5·00	5·00	☐ ☐
3669 **2805**	(1st) multicoloured	5·00	5·00	☐ ☐

Nos. 3658/3659, 3660/3661, 3662/3663, 3664/3665 and 3666/3667 were each printed together, *se-tenant*, as vertical pairs in sheets of 60 (2 panes 5×6).

Nos. 3658/3667 commemorate the 150th anniversary of the Publication of *Alice's Adventures in Wonderland* by Lewis Carroll.

Nos. 3668/3669 were issued in stamp booklets, each containing Nos. 3668/3669 and 4×1st vermilion and originally sold for £3·72.

2812 Happy Birthday   **2813** Well Done   **2814** Wedding

2815 Love   **2816** Mum   **2817** New Baby

2818 Grandparent   **2819** Dad

Smilers (5th series). Booklet stamps

2015 (20 Jan.) Two phosphor bands.

(a) Self-adhesive. Gravure. Die-cut perf 14½ × 14 (with one elliptical hole in each vert side).

3670 **2812**	(1st) multicoloured	1·90	1·90	☐ ☐
3671 **2813**	(1st) multicoloured	2·75	2·75	☐ ☐
3672 **2814**	(1st) multicoloured	1·90	1·90	☐ ☐
3673 **2815**	(1st) multicoloured	1·90	1·90	☐ ☐
3674 **2816**	(1st) multicoloured	2·75	2·75	☐ ☐
3675 **2817**	(1st) multicoloured	1·90	1·90	☐ ☐
3676 **2818**	(1st) multicoloured	2·75	2·75	☐ ☐
3677 **2819**	(1st) multicoloured	2·75	2·75	☐ ☐
Set of 8		15·00	15·00	☐ ☐

(b) Ordinary gum. Litho. Perf 14½ × 14 (with one elliptical hole in each vert side).

MS3678 134×70 mm. As Nos. 3670/3677		7·00	7·00	☐ ☐
First Day Cover			9·25	☐
Presentation Pack (Pack No. M23)		8·25		☐

PHQ Cards *(set of 9)* (D34)   6·75   17·00   ☐ ☐

Nos. 3670/3677 were issued in booklets of 12 originally sold for £7·44.

Nos. 3670/3677 were also issued in sheets of 20 with *se-tenant* greetings labels printed in lithography.

The complete miniature sheet is shown on one of the nine PHQ cards with the others depicting individual stamps.

2820 Colossus – world's first electronic digital computer

2821 World Wide Web – revolutionary global communications system

2822 Catseyes – light-reflecting road safety innovation

2823 Fibre Optics – pioneering rapid-data-transfer technology

2824 Stainless Steel – non-corrosive, versatile, 100% recyclable alloy

2825 Carbon Fibre – high-strength, lightweight, composite material

2826 DNA Sequencing – revolution in understanding the genome

2827 i-LIMB – bionic hand with individually powered digits

Inventive Britain

2015 (19 Feb.) Two phosphor bands. Perf 14½

3679 **2820**	(1st) multicoloured	1·00	1·00	☐ ☐
	a. Horiz pair.			
	Nos. 3679/3680	2·00	2·00	☐ ☐
3680 **2821**	(1st) multicoloured	1·00	1·00	☐ ☐
3681 **2822**	81p. multicoloured	1·10	1·10	☐ ☐
	a. Horiz pair.			
	Nos. 3681/3682	2·25	2·25	☐ ☐
3682 **2823**	81p. multicoloured	1·10	1·10	☐ ☐
3683 **2824**	£1·28 multicoloured	1·75	1·75	☐ ☐
	a. Horiz pair.			
	Nos. 3683/3684	3·50	3·50	☐ ☐
3684 **2825**	£1·28 multicoloured	1·75	1·75	☐ ☐
3685 **2826**	£1·47 multicoloured	2·25	2·25	☐ ☐
	a. Horiz pair.			
	Nos. 3685/3686	4·50	4·50	☐ ☐
3686 **2827**	£1·47 multicoloured	2·25	2·25	☐ ☐

Set of 8		11·00	11·00 ☐ ☐
First Day Cover			15·50 ☐
Presentation Pack (PO Pack No. 507)		13·50	☐
PHQ Cards (set of 8) (397)		4·00	17·00 ☐ ☐
Set of 4 Gutter Blocks of 4		22·00	

Nos. 3679/3680, 3681/3682, 3683/3684 and 3685/3686 were each printed together, *se-tenant*, as horizontal pairs in sheets of 60 (2 panes 6×5).

2828 Tarr Steps, River Barle

2829 Row Bridge, Mosedale Beck

2830 Pulteney Bridge, River Avon

2831 Craigellachie Bridge, River Spey

2832 Menai Suspension Bridge, Menai Strait

2833 High Level Bridge, River Tyne

2834 Royal Border Bridge, River Tweed

2835 Tees Transporter Bridge, River Tees

2836 Humber Bridge, River Humber

2837 Peace Bridge, River Foyle

Bridges

2015 (5 Mar.) Two phosphor bands. Perf 14½×14.

3687	**2828**	(1st) multicoloured	1·00	1·00 ☐ ☐
		a. Horiz strip of 5.		
		Nos. 3687/3691	4·50	4·50 ☐ ☐
3688	**2829**	(1st) multicoloured	1·00	1·00 ☐ ☐

3689	**2830**	(1st) multicoloured	1·00	1·00 ☐ ☐
3690	**2831**	(1st) multicoloured	1·00	1·00 ☐ ☐
3691	**2832**	(1st) multicoloured	1·00	1·00 ☐ ☐
3692	**2833**	(1st) multicoloured	1·00	1·00 ☐ ☐
		a. Horiz strip of 5.		
		Nos. 3692/3696	4·50	4·50 ☐ ☐
3693	**2834**	(1st) multicoloured	1·00	1·00 ☐ ☐
3694	**2835**	(1st) multicoloured	1·00	1·00 ☐ ☐
3695	**2836**	(1st) multicoloured	1·00	1·00 ☐ ☐
3696	**2837**	(1st) multicoloured	1·00	1·00 ☐ ☐
Set of 10			9·00	9·00 ☐ ☐
First Day Cover				11·50 ☐
Presentation Pack (PO Pack No. 508)			10·50	☐
PHQ Cards (set of 10) (398)			5·00	12·50 ☐ ☐
Set of 2 Gutter Strips of 10			18·00	☐
Set of 2 Traffic Light Gutter Strips of 10			25·00	☐

Nos. 3687/3691 and 3692/3696 were each printed together, *se-tenant*, as horizontal strips of five stamps in sheets of 50 (2 panes 5×5).

2838 Spike Milligan

2839 The Two Ronnies

2840 Billy Connolly

2841 Morecambe and Wise

2842 Norman Wisdom

2843 Lenny Henry

2844 Peter Cook and Dudley Moore

2845 Monty Python

2846 French and Saunders

2847 Victoria Wood

Comedy Greats

2015 (1 Apr.) Two phosphor bands

(a) Ordinary gum. Litho. Perf 14

3697	**2838**	(1st) multicoloured	1·00	1·00 ☐ ☐
		a. Horiz strip of 5.		
		Nos. 3697/3701	4·50	4·50 ☐ ☐
3698	**2839**	(1st) multicoloured	1·00	1·00 ☐ ☐

3699	**2840**	(1st) multicoloured	1·00	1·00	□ □
3700	**2841**	(1st) multicoloured	1·00	1·00	□ □
3701	**2842**	(1st) multicoloured	1·00	1·00	□ □
3702	**2843**	(1st) multicoloured	1·00	1·00	□ □
		a. Horiz strip of 5.			
		Nos. 3702/3706	4·50	4·50	□ □
3703	**2844**	(1st) multicoloured	1·00	1·00	□ □
3704	**2845**	(1st) multicoloured	1·00	1·00	□ □
3705	**2846**	(1st) multicoloured	1·00	1·00	□ □
3706	**2847**	(1st) multicoloured	1·00	1·00	□ □
Set of 10			9·00	9·00	□ □
First Day Cover				11·50	□
Presentation Pack (PO Pack No. 509)			10·50		□
PHQ Cards (*set of* 10) (399)			5·00	12·50	□ □
Set of 2 Gutter Strips of 10			18·00		□

(b) Self-adhesive. Gravure. Die-cut perf 14

| 3707 | **2842** | (1st) multicoloured | 3·50 | 3·50 | □ □ |
| 3708 | **2841** | (1st) multicoloured | 3·50 | 3·50 | □ □ |

Nos. 3697/3701 and 3702/3706 were each printed together, *se-tenant*, as horizontal strips of five stamps in sheets of 50 (2 panes 5×5).

Nos. 3707/3708 were issued in stamp booklets, each containing Nos. 3707/3708 and 4×1st vermilion and originally sold for £3·72.

2848 Penny Black

2849 Penny Black and 1840 2d. blue

175th Anniversary of the Penny Black

2015 (6 May) Two phosphor bands.

(a) Self-adhesive booklet stamps. Gravure. Die-cut perf 14½×14 (with one elliptical hole in each vert side)

| 3709 | **2848** | (1st) black and gold | 2·00 | 2·00 | □ □ |

(b) Ordinary gum. Litho. Perf 14½×14 (with one elliptical hole in each vert side)

MS3710 156×74 mm. **2849** (1st) Penny				
Black×2; (1st) 1840 2d. blue×2	3·50	3·75	□ □
First Day Cover		4·75	□
Presentation Pack (PO Pack No. 510)	4·25		□
PHQ Cards (*set of* 3) (400)	1·50	4·00	□ □

No. 3709 was issued in booklets of six.

The three PHQ cards show the two individual stamps and the complete miniature sheet.

Designs as No. 3709 and (1st) Twopenny Blue as within No. **MS**3710 but self-adhesive were also issued in sheets of 20, printed in lithography, containing ten 1st class Penny Black and ten 1st class Twopenny Blue, each stamp accompanied by a *se-tenant* label.

Sheets of ten or 20 1st Penny Black were available with personal photographs.

See also No. **MS**4355.

2850 *Poppies* (Howard Hodgkin)

2851 *All the Hills and Vales Along* (Charles Hamilton Sorley)

2852 *Rifleman Kulbir Thapa*

2853 *The Kensingtons at Laventie* (Eric Kennington)

2854 *'A British Soldier visits his Comrade's Grave on the Cliffs near Cape Helles', Gallipoli (posed photo by Ernest Brooks)*

2855 *London Irish Rifles' Football from Loos*

Centenary of the First World War (2nd issue)

2015 (14 May) Two phosphor bands. Perf 14½

3711	**2850**	(1st) multicoloured	1·00	1·00	□ □
3712	**2851**	(1st) multicoloured	1·00	1·00	□ □
3713	**2852**	(1st) multicoloured	1·00	1·00	□ □
3714	**2853**	£1·52 multicoloured	2·40	2·40	□ □
3715	**2854**	£1·52 multicoloured	2·40	2·40	□ □
3716	**2855**	£1·52 multicoloured	2·40	2·40	□ □
Set of 6			9·00	9·00	□ □
First Day Cover				12·00	□
Presentation Pack (PO Pack No. 511)			10·75		□
PHQ Cards (*set of* 6) (401)			3·00	11·50	□ □
Set of 6 Gutter Pairs			18·00		□

2015 (14 May)–**17** Premium Booklet stamp. As No. 3414 but ordinary gum. Two phosphor bands. Perf 14½×14 (with one elliptical hole in each vertical side)

| 3717 | **2588** | (1st) multicoloured | 1·50 | 1·50 | □ □ |

No. 3717 comes from the Centenary of the First World War premium booklets (2nd, 3rd, 4th and 5th issues), Nos. DY13, DY18, DY22 and DY26.

2856 *Magna Carta, 1215*

2857 Simon de Montfort's Parliament, 1265

2858 Bill of Rights, 1689

2859 American Bill of Rights, 1791

2860 Universal Declaration of Human Rights, 1948

2861 Charter of the Commonwealth, 2013

800th Anniversary of Magna Carta

2015 (2 June) Two phosphor bands. Perf 14½

3718	**2856**	(1st) multicoloured	1·00	1·00		
3719	**2857**	(1st) multicoloured	1·00	1·00		
3720	**2858**	£1·33 multicoloured	1·60	1·60		
3721	**2859**	£1·33 multicoloured	1·60	1·60		
3722	**2860**	£1·52 multicoloured	3·00	3·00		
3723	**2861**	£1·52 multicoloured	3·00	3·00		
Set of 6			10·00	10·00		
First Day Cover				11·50		
Presentation Pack (PO Pack No. 512)			13·00			
PHQ Cards (set of 6) (402)			3·00	12·50		
Set of 6 Gutter Pairs			20·00			

2862 The Defence of Hougoumont

2863 The Scots Greys during the Charge of the Union Brigade

2864 The French Cavalry's Assault on Allied Defensive Squares

2865 The Defence of La Haye Sainte by the King's German Legion

2866 The Capture of Plancenoit by the Prussians

2867 The French Imperial Guard's Final Assault

Bicentenary of the Battle of Waterloo (1st issue)

2015 (18 June) Two phosphor bands. Perf 14½

3724	**2862**	(1st) multicoloured	1·00	1·00		
3725	**2863**	(1st) multicoloured	1·00	1·00		
3726	**2864**	£1 multicoloured	1·40	1·40		
3727	**2865**	£1 multicoloured	1·40	1·40		
3728	**2866**	£1·52 multicoloured	2·50	2·50		
3729	**2867**	£1·52 multicoloured	2·50	2·50		
Set of 6			8·75	8·75		
First Day Cover				11·50		
Presentation Pack (Nos. 3724/3729 and MS3734) (PO Pack No. 513)			17·00			
PHQ Cards (set of 11) (403)			5·50	22·00		
Set of 6 Gutter Pairs			17·00			

The 11 PHQ cards depict the individual stamps, including those from No. **MS**3734, and the complete miniature sheet.

2868 15th Infantry Regiment, IV Corps, Prussian Army

2869 Light Infantry, King's German Legion, Anglo-Allied Army

2870 92nd Gordon Highlanders, Anglo-Allied Army

2871 Grenadiers, Imperial Guard, French Army

2872 Soldiers and Battle of Waterloo Map

Bicentenary of the Battle of Waterloo (2nd issue)

2015 (18 June) Two phosphor bands. Perf 14

3730	**2868**	(1st) multicoloured	1·50	1·50	☐	☐
3731	**2869**	(1st) multicoloured	1·50	1·50	☐	☐
3732	**2870**	£1·33 multicoloured	1·75	1·75	☐	☐
3733	**2871**	£1·33 multicoloured	1·75	1·75	☐	☐
Set of 4			5·50	5·50	☐	☐
MS3734	156×74	mm. **2872** Nos.				
3730/3733			5·75	5·75	☐	☐
First Day Cover				7·50	☐	

Nos. 3730/3733 come from £14·47 Bicentenary of the Battle of Waterloo premium booklet, No. DY14, and No. **MS**3734.

2873 Battle of Britain

75th Anniversary of the Battle of Britain.

2015 (16 July) 'All-over' phosphor. Perf 14

MS3735 **2873** 190×74 mm. (1st) Pilots scramble to their Hurricanes; (1st) Supermarine Spitfires of 610 Squadron, Biggin Hill, on patrol; (1st) Armourer Fred Roberts replaces ammunition boxes on Supermarine Spitfire; £1·33 Spotters of the Auxiliary Territorial Service looking for enemy aircraft; £1·33 Operations Room at Bentley Priory; £1·33 Pilots of 32 Squadron await orders, RAF Hawkinge, Kent   8·25   8·25 ☐ ☐

First Day Cover		11·00 ☐
Presentation Pack (PO Pack No. 514)	10·00	☐
PHQ Cards (*set of 7*) (404)	3·50	13·50 ☐ ☐

The seven PHQ cards show the six individual stamps and the complete miniature sheet.
See also Nos. 4071/4073.

2874 Scabious Bee (*Andrena hattorfiana*) on Field Scabious (*Knautia arvensis*)

2875 Great Yellow Bumblebee (*Bombus distinguendus*) on Bird's-foot Trefoil (*Lotus corniculatus*)

2876 Northern Colletes Bee (*Colletes floralis*) on Wild Carrot (*Daucus carota*)

2877 Bilberry Bumblebee (*Bombus monticola*) on Bilberry (*Vaccinium myrtillus*)

2878 Large Mason Bee (*Osmia xanthomelana*) on Horseshoe Vetch (*Hippocrepis comosa*)

2879 Potter Flower Bee (*Anthophora retusa*) on Ground Ivy (*Glechoma hederacea*)

2880 The Honey Bee

Bees

2015 (18 Aug.) Bees.

(a) Ordinary gum. Litho. One centre band (No. 3736), two phosphor bands (Nos. 3737/3741) or phosphor background (No. **MS**3742). Perf 14×14½

3736	**2874**	(2nd) multicoloured	90	90	☐	☐
3737	**2875**	(1st) multicoloured	1·00	1·00	☐	☐
3738	**2876**	£1 multicoloured	1·50	1·50	☐	☐
3739	**2877**	£1·33 multicoloured	1·75	1·75	☐	☐
3740	**2878**	£1·52 multicoloured	2·25	2·25	☐	☐
3741	**2879**	£2·25 multicoloured	3·75	3·75	☐	☐
Set of 6			10·00	10·00	☐	☐
First Day Cover				13·50	☐	
Presentation Pack (Nos. 3736/3741 and						
MS3743) (PO Pack No. 515)			19·00		☐	
PHQ Cards (*set of 7*) (405)			3·50	18·00	☐ ☐	
Set of 6 Gutter Pairs			20·00		☐	

MS3742 191×74 mm. **2880** (1st) Waggle
dance; (1st) Pollination; £1·33 Making
honey; £1·33 Tending young   5·50   5·75 ☐ ☐
First Day Cover   6·00   ☐
   (b) Self-adhesive. Gravure. Two phosphor bands.
     Die-cut perf 14×14½
3743 **2875**   (1st) multicoloured   1·50   1·50 ☐ ☐
No. 3743 was issued in stamp booklets, each containing No.
3743×2 and 4×1st vermilion and originally sold for £3·78.
   The seven PHQ cards depict the six individual stamps and
the complete miniature sheet.

Nos. 3744/3746 are vacant.

2881 'Long to Reign Over Us'

Long to Reign Over Us

2015 (9 Sept.) Two phosphor bands. Perf 14½×14 (with one
elliptical hole in each vertical side) (Machin) or 14 (others)
MS3747 194×75 mm. **2881** (1st) William
Wyon's City Medal depicting Queen
Victoria; (1st) Portrait of Queen
Elizabeth II from photo by Dorothy
Wilding; As No. U3744; £1·52 Badge
of the House of Windsor depicting
Round Tower of Windsor Castle;
£1·52 Device from The Queen's Per-
sonal Flag   8·00   8·00 ☐ ☐
First Day Cover   10·00   ☐
Presentation Pack (PO Pack No. 516)   10·00   ☐
PHQ Cards (*set of 6*) (406)   3·00   12·00 ☐ ☐
Stamps from No. **MS**3747 all have an iridescent overprint
reading 'LONG TO REIGN OVER US'.
   The PHQ cards depict the five individual stamps and the
complete miniature sheet.

2882 Tackle

2883 Scrum

2884 Try

2885 Conversion

2886 Pass

2887 Drop Goal

2888 Ruck

2889 Line-Out

Rugby World Cup

2015 (18 Sept.) Two phosphor bands
     (a) Ordinary gum. Litho. Perf 14
3748 **2882**   (2nd) multicoloured   90   90 ☐ ☐
    a. Horiz pair.
     Nos. 3748/3749   1·75   1·75 ☐ ☐
3749 **2883**   (2nd) multicoloured   90   90 ☐ ☐
3750 **2884**   (1st) multicoloured   1·00   1·00 ☐ ☐
    a. Horiz pair.
     Nos. 3750/3751   2·00   2·00 ☐ ☐
3751 **2885**   (1st) multicoloured   1·00   1·00 ☐ ☐
3752 **2886**   £1 multicoloured   1·50   1·50 ☐ ☐
    a. Horiz pair.
     Nos. 3752/3753   3·00   3·00 ☐ ☐
3753 **2887**   £1 multicoloured   1·50   1·50 ☐ ☐
3754 **2888**   £1·52 multicoloured   2·00   2·00 ☐ ☐
    a. Horiz pair.
     Nos. 3754/3755   4·00   4·00 ☐ ☐
3755 **2889**   £1·52 multicoloured   2·00   2·00 ☐ ☐
Set of 8   9·75   9·75 ☐ ☐
First Day Cover   12·50   ☐
Presentation Pack (PO Pack No. 517)   12·50   ☐
PHQ Cards (*set of 8*) (407)   4·00   13·00 ☐ ☐
Set of 4 Gutter Blocks of 4   19·00   ☐
   (b) Self-adhesive. Gravure. Die-cut perf 14
3756 **2884**   (1st) multicoloured   2·00   2·00 ☐ ☐
3757 **2885**   (1st) multicoloured   2·00   2·00 ☐ ☐
Nos. 3748/3749, 3750/3751, 3752/3753 and 3754/3755 were each
printed together, *se-tenant*, as horizontal pairs in sheets of 60
(2 panes 6×5).
   Nos. 3756/3757 were issued in stamp booklets, each
containing Nos. 3756/3757 and 4×1st vermilion and originally
sold for £3·78.

2890 Darth Vader

2891 Yoda

2892 Obi-Wan Kenobi

2893 Stormtrooper

2894 Han Solo

2895 Rey

2896 Princess Leia

2897 The Emperor

2898 Luke Skywalker

2899 Boba Fett

2900 Finn

2901 Kylo Ren

2902 Star Wars

Star Wars

2015 (20 Oct.) Two phosphor bands (Nos. 3758/3769) or 'All-over' phosphor (No. **MS**3770)

		(a) Ordinary gum. Perf 14½				
3758	**2890**	(1st) multicoloured	1·00	1·00		
		a. Horiz strip of 6.				
		Nos. 3758/3763	5·50	5·50		
3759	**2891**	(1st) multicoloured	1·00	1·00		
3760	**2892**	(1st) multicoloured	1·00	1·00		
3761	**2893**	(1st) multicoloured	1·00	1·00		
3762	**2894**	(1st) multicoloured	1·00	1·00		
3763	**2895**	(1st) multicoloured	1·00	1·00		
3764	**2896**	(1st) multicoloured	1·00	1·00		
		a. Horiz strip of 6.				
		Nos. 3764/3769	5·50	5·50		
3765	**2897**	(1st) multicoloured	1·00	1·00		
3766	**2898**	(1st) multicoloured	1·00	1·00		
3767	**2899**	(1st) multicoloured	1·00	1·00		
3768	**2900**	(1st) multicoloured	1·00	1·00		
3769	**2901**	(1st) multicoloured	1·00	1·00		

Set of 12		11·00	11·00
First Day Cover			14·00
Presentation Pack (Nos. 3758/3769 and			
MS3770) (PO Pack No. 518)		19·00	
PHQ Cards (set of 19) (408)		9·50	28·00
Set of 2 Gutter Strips of 12		22·00	

(b) Self-adhesive

MS3770 204×75 mm. **2902** (1st) X-wing Starfighter (60×21 mm, Perf 14½×14); (1st) TIE fighters (35×36 mm, Perf 14); (1st) X-wing Starfighters (60×21 mm, Perf 14½×14); (1st) AT-AT Walkers (41×30 mm, Perf 14); (1st) TIE fighters (27×37 mm, Perf 14); (1st) Millennium Falcon (60×30 mm, P 14½)   6·50   6·50

First Day Cover   7·00

Nos. 3758/3763 and 3764/3769 were each printed together, se-tenant, as horizontal strips of six stamps in sheets of 60 (2 panes 6×5).

The 19 PHQ cards depict the individual stamps including those from No. **MS**3770 and the complete miniature sheet.

Nos. 3758/3769 were reissued on 12 October 2017 with Nos. 4007/4014 in a sheet entitled 'Star Wars. The Ultimate Collectors Sheet' (No. **MS**4014a).

Designs as Nos. 3758/3759 and 3761/3762 but self-adhesive were issued in sheets of ten with se-tenant labels, each sheet containing Nos. 3758/3759, each ×3, and Nos. 3761/3762, each ×2.

The four designs were available in separate sheets of ten with personal photographs.

2903 The Journey to Bethlehem

2904 The Nativity

2905 The Journey to Bethlehem

2906 The Nativity

2907 The Animals of the Nativity

2908 The Shepherds

2909 The Three Wise Men

2910 The Annunciation

Christmas

2015 (3 Nov.) One centre band (No. 3771) or two bands (others). Perf 14½×15

		(a) Self-adhesive				
3771	**2903**	(2nd) multicoloured	90	90		
3772	**2904**	(1st) multicoloured	1·00	1·00		

3773	**2905**	(2nd Large)				
		multicoloured	1·10	1·10	☐	☐
3774	**2906**	(1st Large)				
		multicoloured	1·40	1·40	☐	☐
3775	**2907**	£1·00 multicoloured	1·75	1·75	☐	☐
3776	**2908**	£1·33 multicoloured	2·10	2·10	☐	☐
3777	**2909**	£1·52 multicoloured	2·50	2·50	☐	☐
3778	**2910**	£2·25 multicoloured	3·50	3·50	☐	☐
Set of 8			12·50	12·50	☐	☐
First Day Cover				16·50		☐
Presentation Pack (PO Pack No. 519)			15·00			☐
PHQ Cards (*set of 9*) (409)			4·50	26·00	☐	☐

(b) Ordinary gum

| **MS**3779 190 × 74 mm. As Nos. 3771/3778 | 12·50 | 12·50 | ☐ | ☐ |
| *First Day Cover* | | 16·50 | | ☐ |

The nine PHQ cards show the eight individual stamps and the complete miniature sheet.

The 2nd class, 1st class, £1, £1·33, £1·52 and £2·25 stamps were also issued in sheets of 20, printed in lithography instead of gravure and containing eight 2nd class, eight 1st class and one each of £1, £1·33, £1·52 and £2·25 stamps, each stamp accompanied by a *se-tenant* label with a verse from the *King James Bible*.

Year Pack

2015 (3 Nov.) Comprises Nos. 3658/3667, **MS**3678/3706, **MS**3710/3716, 3718/3729, **MS**3734, **MS**3735/**MS**3742, **MS**3747/**MS**3755 and 3758/3778

| CP3779*a* | Year Pack | £150 | ☐ |

Post Office Yearbook

2015 (3 Nov.) Comprises Nos. 3658/3667, **MS**3678/3706, **MS**3710/3729, **MS**3734, **MS**3735/**MS**3742, **MS**3747/3755 and 3758/3778

| YB3779*a* | Yearbook | £180 | ☐ |

Miniature Sheet Collection

2015 (3 Nov.) Comprises Nos. **MS**3678, **MS**3710, **MS**3734, **MS**3735, **MS**3742, **MS**3747, **MS**3770 and **MS**3779

| **MS**3779*a* Miniature Sheet Collection | 55·00 | ☐ |

2911 X-wing Starfighter

2912 AT-AT Walkers

2913 TIE fighters   2914 TIE fighters

2915 X-wing Starfighters

2916 *Millennium Falcon*

Star Wars (2nd issue)

2015 (17 Dec.) Self-adhesive. 'All-over' phosphor. Die-cut perf 14½ × 14 (Nos. 3780, 3784), 14 (Nos. 3781/3783) or 14½ (No. 3785)

3780	**2911**	(1st) multicoloured	1·25	1·25	☐	☐
3781	**2912**	(1st) multicoloured	1·25	1·25	☐	☐
3782	**2913**	(1st) multicoloured	1·25	1·25	☐	☐
3783	**2914**	(1st) multicoloured	1·25	1·25	☐	☐
3784	**2915**	(1st) multicoloured	1·25	1·25	☐	☐
3785	**2916**	(1st) multicoloured	1·25	1·25	☐	☐
Set of 6			6·75	6·75	☐	☐

Nos. 3780/3785 were only issued in £16·99 *Star Wars* premium booklets or No. **MS**3770.

2917 Union Flag

Star Wars (3rd issue)

2015 (17 Dec.) As No. 2570 but ordinary gum. Two phosphor bands. Perf 14½ × 14 (with one elliptical hole in each vert side)

| 3786 | **2917** | (1st) multicoloured | 1·50 | 1·50 | ☐ | ☐ |

No. 3786 comes from booklet pane No. U3014ab from the £16·99 *Star Wars* premium booklet.

2918 Entering the Antarctic Ice, December 1914

2919 *Endurance* Frozen in Pack Ice, January 1915

2920 Striving to Free *Endurance*, February 1915

2921 Trapped in a Pressure Crack, October 1915

2922 Patience Camp, December 1915 – April 1916

2923 Safe Arrival at Elephant Island, April 1916

2924 Setting out for South Georgia, April 1916

2925 Rescue of *Endurance* Crew, August 1916

2930 Mail Coach

2931 Medway Mail Centre

Shackleton and the *Endurance* Expedition

2016 (7 Jan.) Two phosphor bands. Perf 14 × 14½.

3787	**2918**	(1st) bluish grey, grey and black	1·00	1·00	☐ ☐
		a. Horiz pair. Nos. 3787/3788	2·00	2·00	☐ ☐
3788	**2919**	(1st) bluish grey, grey and black	1·00	1·00	☐ ☐
3789	**2920**	£1 bluish grey, grey and black	1·50	1·50	☐ ☐
		a. Horiz pair. Nos. 3789/3790	3·00	3·00	☐ ☐
3790	**2921**	£1 bluish grey, grey and black	1·50	1·50	☐ ☐
3791	**2922**	£1·33 bluish grey, grey and black	1·75	1·75	☐ ☐
		a. Horiz pair. Nos. 3791/3792	3·50	3·50	☐ ☐
3792	**2923**	£1·33 bluish grey, grey and black	1·75	1·75	☐ ☐
3793	**2924**	£1·52 bluish grey, grey and black	2·25	2·25	☐ ☐
		a. Horiz pair. Nos. 3793/3794	4·50	4·50	☐ ☐
3794	**2925**	£1·52 bluish grey, grey and black	2·25	2·25	☐ ☐
Set of 8			12·00	12·00	☐ ☐
First Day Cover				16·00	☐
Presentation Pack (PO Pack 521)			15·00		☐
PHQ Cards (*set of 8*) (410)			4·00	15·00	☐ ☐
Set of 4 Gutter Blocks of 4			24·00		☐

Nos. 3787/3788, 3789/3790, 3791/3792 and 3793/3794 were each printed together, *se-tenant*, as horizontal pairs in sheets of 60 (2 panes 6 × 5).

2926 Sir Brian Tuke, Master of the Posts

2927 Mail Packet off Eastbourne (Captain Victor Howes)

2928 Penfold Pillar Box

2929 River Post

2932 Classic GPO Posters

Royal Mail 500 (1st issue)

2016 (17 Feb.) Two phosphor bands. Perf 14½ × 14 (Nos. 3795/3800) or 14 (**MS**3801)

3795	**2926**	(1st) multicoloured	1·00	1·00	☐ ☐
3796	**2927**	(1st) multicoloured	1·00	1·00	☐ ☐
3797	**2928**	(1st) multicoloured	1·00	1·00	☐ ☐
3798	**2929**	£1·52 multicoloured	2·50	2·50	☐ ☐
3799	**2930**	£1·52 multicoloured	2·50	2·50	☐ ☐
3800	**2931**	£1·52 multicoloured	2·50	2·50	☐ ☐
Set of 6			9·50	9·50	☐ ☐
First Day Cover				12·00	☐
Presentation Pack (Nos. 3795/3800 and **MS**3801) (PO Pack No. 522)			17·00		☐
PHQ Cards (*set of 11*) (411)			5·50	24·00	☐ ☐
Set of 6 Gutter Pairs			19·00		☐
Set of 6 Traffic Light Gutter Pairs (2 stamps only in each pair)			20·00		☐
MS3801 125 × 89 mm. **2932** (1st) 'QUICKEST WAY BY AIR MAIL' (Edward McKnight Kauffer, 1935); (1st) 'ADDRESS your letters PLAINLY' (Hans Schleger, 1942); £1·33 'pack your parcels carefully' (Hans Unger, 1950); £1·33 'STAMPS IN BOOKS SAVE TIME' (Harry Stevens, 1960)			7·00	7·25	☐ ☐
First Day Cover				7·50	☐

Nos. 3795/**MS**3801 commemorate 500 years of a regular, organised postal service.

The complete miniature sheet is shown on one of the 11 PHQ cards with the others depicting individual stamps including those from the miniature sheet.

2933 'Quickest way by Air Mail' (Edward McKnight Kauffer, 1935)

2934 'address your letters plainly' (Hans Schleger, 1942)

2935 'stamps in books save time' (Harry Stevens, 1960)

2936 'pack your parcels carefully' (Hans Unger, 1950)

Royal Mail 500 (2nd issue)

2016 (17 Feb.) Two phosphor bands. Perf 14

3802	**2933**	(1st) multicoloured	1·75	1·75	☐	☐
3803	**2934**	(1st) multicoloured	1·75	1·75	☐	☐
3804	**2935**	£1·33 multicoloured	1·75	1·75	☐	☐
3805	**2936**	£1·33 multicoloured	1·75	1·75	☐	☐
Set of 4			6·25	6·25	☐	☐

Nos. 3802/3805 come from No. **MS**3801 and £16·36 500 Years of Royal Mail premium booklets which were issued on 18 February 2016.

2937 Penny Red

175th Anniversary of the Penny Red

2016 (18 Feb.) Two phosphor bands. Self-adhesive. Gravure. Die-cut perf 14½ × 14 (with one elliptical hole in each vert side)

3806	**2937**	(1st) Penny Red	1·50	1·50	☐	☐

No. 3806 was issued in booklets of six stamps.

No. 3806 was also issued printed in lithography in sheets of 20 with attached labels showing the 'Rainbow Trials' from which the Penny Red evolved.

Sheets of ten or 20 of these Penny Red stamps were available from Royal Mail with personal photographs on the labels.

2938 Two Pence Blue

Royal Mail 500 (3rd issue)

2016 (18 Feb.) Two phosphor bands. Litho. Perf 14½ × 14 (with one elliptical hole in each vert side)

3807	**2848**	(1st) Penny Black	1·75	1·75	☐	☐
3808	**2937**	(1st) Penny Red	1·50	1·50	☐	☐
3809	**2938**	(1st) Two Pence Blue	1·50	1·50	☐	☐

Nos. 3807/3809 come from £16·36 500 Years of Royal Mail premium booklets.

See also No. 4331.

2939 Nicholas Winton (1909–2015)

2940 Sue Ryder (1924–2000)

2941 John Boyd Orr (1880–1971)

2942 Eglantyne Jebb (1876–1928)

2943 Joseph Rowntree (1836–1925)

2944 Josephine Butler (1828–1906)

British Humanitarians

2016 (15 Mar.) Two phosphor bands. Perf 14½.

3810	**2939**	(1st) black	1·00	1·00	☐	☐
		a. Horiz strip of 3.				
		Nos. 3810/3812	3·00	3·00	☐	☐
3811	**2940**	(1st) black	1·00	1·00	☐	☐
3812	**2941**	(1st) black	1·00	1·00	☐	☐
3813	**2942**	£1·33 black	2·00	2·00	☐	☐
		a. Horiz strip of 3.				
		Nos. 3813/3815	6·00	6·00	☐	☐
3814	**2943**	£1·33 black	2·00	2·00	☐	☐
3815	**2944**	£1·33 black	2·00	2·00	☐	☐
Set of 6			8·25	8·25	☐	☐
First Day Cover				11·00	☐	
Presentation Pack (PO Pack No. 523)			10·00		☐	
PHQ Cards (set of 6) (412)			3·00	11·00	☐	☐
Set of 2 Gutter Strips of 6			17·00		☐	

Nos. 3810/3812 and 3813/3815 were each printed together, se-tenant, as horizontal strips of three stamps in sheets of 60 (2 panes 6 × 5).

2945 'to thine own self be true' (Hamlet)

2946 'cowards die many times before their deaths. the valiant never taste of death but once.' (Julius Caesar)

2947 'Love is a smoke made with the fume of sighs' (Romeo and Juliet)

2948 'the fool doth think he is wise, but the wise man knows himself to be a fool.' (As You Like It)

2949 'there was a star danced, and under that was I born. (*Much Ado About Nothing*)

2950 'but if the while I think on thee, dear friend, all losses are restored and sorrows end.' (*Sonnet 30*)

2951 'Love comforteth like sunshine after rain' (*Venus and Adonis*)

2952 'we are such stuff as dreams are made on; and our little life is rounded with a sleep.' (*The Tempest*)

2953 'Life's but a walking shadow, a poor player That struts and frets his hour upon the stage' (*Macbeth*)

2954 'I wasted time, and now doth time waste me' (*Richard II*)

400th Death Anniversary of William Shakespeare (playwright)

2016 (5 Apr.) Two phosphor bands. Perf 14½.

3816	**2945**	(1st) carmine, pale grey-brown and black	1·00	1·00	☐	☐
		a. Horiz strip of 5. Nos. 3816/3820	4·50	4·50	☐	☐
3817	**2946**	(1st) carmine, pale grey-brown and black	1·00	1·00	☐	☐
3818	**2947**	(1st) carmine, pale grey-brown and black	1·00	1·00	☐	☐
3819	**2948**	(1st) carmine, pale grey-brown and black	1·00	1·00	☐	☐
3820	**2949**	(1st) carmine, pale grey-brown and black	1·00	1·00	☐	☐
3821	**2950**	(1st) carmine, pale grey-brown and black	1·00	1·00	☐	☐
		a. Horiz strip of 5. Nos. 3821/3825	4·50	4·50	☐	☐
3822	**2951**	(1st) carmine, pale grey-brown and black	1·00	1·00	☐	☐
3823	**2952**	(1st) carmine, pale grey-brown and black	1·00	1·00	☐	☐
3824	**2953**	(1st) carmine, pale grey-brown and black	1·00	1·00	☐	☐
3825	**2954**	(1st) carmine, pale grey-brown and black	1·00	1·00	☐	☐
		Set of 10	9·00	9·00	☐	☐
		First Day Cover		12·00		☐
		Presentation Pack (PO Pack No. 524)	11·00		☐	
		PHQ Cards (*set of 10*) (413)	5·00	12·00	☐	☐
		Set of 2 Gutter Strips of 10	18·00			☐

Nos. 3816/3820 and 3821/3825 were each printed together, *se-tenant*, as horizontal strips of five stamps in sheets of 50 (2 panes 5×5).

2955 Princess Elizabeth and her Father, the Duke of York (later King George VI), *c.* 1930

2956 Queen Elizabeth II at State Opening of Parliament, 2012

2957 Queen Elizabeth II with Prince Charles and Princess Anne, 1952

2958 Queen Elizabeth II on Visit to New Zealand, 1977

2959 Queen Elizabeth II and Duke of Edinburgh, 1957

2960 Queen Elizabeth II with Nelson Mandela, 1996

2961 Prince Charles, Queen Elizabeth II, Prince George and Prince William

2962 Prince Charles

2963 Queen Elizabeth II

2964 Prince George

2965 Prince William

90th Birthday of Queen Elizabeth II

2016 (21 Apr.–9 June) Two phosphor bands (Nos. 3826/3831) or 'all-over' phosphor (Nos. **MS**3832, 3833/3836)

(a) Ordinary gum. Litho.
Perf 14 × 14½ (Nos. 3826/3831) or 14 (No. **MS**3832)

3826	**2955**	(1st) multicoloured	1·00	1·00
		a. Horiz strip of 3.		
		Nos. 3826/3828	3·00	3·00
3827	**2956**	(1st) multicoloured	1·00	1·00
3828	**2957**	(1st) multicoloured	1·00	1·00
3829	**2958**	£1·52 multicoloured	2·25	2·25
		a. Horiz strip of 3.		
		Nos. 3829/3831	6·75	6·75
3830	**2959**	£1·52 multicoloured	2·25	2·25
3831	**2960**	£1·52 multicoloured	2·25	2·25
Set of 6			8·75	8·75
First Day Cover				11·50

Presentation Pack (Nos. 3826/3831) and
MS3832) (PO Pack No. 525) 14·00
PHQ Cards (set of 11) (414) 5·50 19·00
Set of 2 Gutter Strips of 6 18·00

MS3832 189×75 mm. **2961** (1st) multi-coloured; (1st) multicoloured; (1st) multicoloured; (1st) multicoloured			3·75	3·75
First Day Cover				4·75

(b) Self-adhesive. Gravure. Die-cut perf 14.

3833	**2962**	(1st) multicoloured	1·60	1·60
3834	**2963**	(1st) multicoloured	1·60	1·60
3835	**2964**	(1st) multicoloured		
		(9.6.16)	1·60	1·60
3836	**2965**	(1st) multicoloured		
		(9.6.16)	1·60	1·60
Set of 4			6·00	6·00

Nos. 3833/3836 were issued in stamp booklets containing either Nos. 3833/3834 or 3835/3836 and 4 × 1st bright lilac, each booklet originally sold for £3·84.

2966 Animail

Animail

2016 (17 May) 'All-over' phosphor. Die-cut and die-cut perf 14
Multicoloured

MS3837 **2966** 203×74 mm. (1st) Woodpecker; (1st) Snake; £1·05 Chimpanzee; £1·05 Bat; £1·33 Orangutan; £1·33 Koala			8·50	8·75
First Day Cover				11·00

Presentation Pack (PO Pack No. 526) 10·00
PHQ Cards (set of 7) (415) 3·50 15·00
The seven PHQ cards show the six individual stamps and the complete miniature sheet.

2967 Battlefield Poppy (Giles Revell)

2968 Your battle wounds are scars upon my heart (poem To My Brother, Vera Brittain)

2969 Munitions Worker Lottie Meade

2970 Travoys arriving with wounded at a Dressing-Station at Smol, Macedonia, September 1916 (Stanley Spencer)

2971 Thiepval Memorial, Somme, France

2972 Captain A. C. Green's Battle of Jutland Commemorative Medal

Centenary of the First World War (3rd issue)

2016 (21 June) Two phosphor bands. Perf 14½.

3838	**2967**	(1st) multicoloured	1·00	1·00
3839	**2968**	(1st) multicoloured	1·00	1·00
3840	**2969**	(1st) multicoloured	1·00	1·00
3841	**2970**	£1·52 multicoloured	2·50	2·50
3842	**2971**	£1·52 multicoloured	2·50	2·50
3843	**2972**	£1·52 multicoloured	2·50	2·50
Set of 6			9·50	9·50
First Day Cover				12·00

Presentation Pack (Nos. 3838/3843) and
MS3848) (PO Pack No. 527) 17·50
PHQ Cards (set of 11) (416) 5·50 26·00
Set of 6 Gutter Pairs 19·00

No. **MS**3848 is shown on one of the 11 PHQ cards with the others depicting individual stamps including those from No. **MS**3848.

The Post Office Rifles
2973 The Post Office Rifles

Writing a letter from the Western Front
2974 Writing a Letter from the Western Front

Delivering the mail on the Home Front
2975 Delivering the Mail on the Home Front

Home Depot at Regent's Park, London
2976 Home Depot at Regent's Park, London

2977 The Post Office at War, 1914–1918

Centenary of the First World War (3rd issue)

2016 (21 June) Two phosphor bands. Perf 14.

3844	**2973**	(1st) multicoloured	1·60	1·60	☐	☐
3845	**2974**	(1st) multicoloured	1·60	1·60	☐	☐
3846	**2975**	£1·33 multicoloured	2·50	2·50	☐	☐
3847	**2976**	£1·33 multicoloured	2·50	2·50	☐	☐
Set of 4			7·25	7·25	☐	☐
MS3848 156×74 mm. **2977** Nos. 3844/3847			7·25	7·25	☐	☐
First Day Cover				8·25	☐	

Nos. 3844/3847 were issued in £16·49 Centenary of the First World War (3rd issue, No. DY18) premium booklets and in No. **MS**3848.

2978 The Piper at the Gates of Dawn (1967)

2979 Atom Heart Mother (1970)

2980 The Dark Side of the Moon (1973)

2981 Animals (1977)

2982 Wish You Were Here (1975)

2983 The Endless River (2014)

2984 Pink Floyd on Stage

Pink Floyd

2016 (7 July)

(a) Album Covers. Self-adhesive. Gravure. Two phosphor bands. Die-cut perf 14½.

3849	**2978**	(1st) multicoloured	1·00	1·00	☐	☐
3850	**2979**	(1st) multicoloured	1·00	1·00	☐	☐
3851	**2980**	(1st) multicoloured	1·00	1·00	☐	☐
3852	**2981**	£1·52 multicoloured	2·50	2·50	☐	☐
3853	**2982**	£1·52 multicoloured	2·50	2·50	☐	☐
3854	**2983**	£1·52 multicoloured	2·50	2·50	☐	☐
Set of 6			9·50	9·50	☐	☐
First Day Cover				12·00		
Presentation Pack (PO Pack No. 528)			18·00		☐	
PHQ Cards (set of 11) (417)			5·50	24·00	☐	☐

(b) Pink Floyd on Stage. Ordinary gum. Litho. Phosphor frame. Perf 14½.

MS3855	202×74 mm. **2984** (1st) UFO Club, 1966; (1st) The Dark Side of the Moon Tour, 1973; £1·52 The Wall Tour, 1981; £1·52 The Division Bell Tour, 1994		6·25	6·25	☐	☐
First Day Cover				8·00	☐	

The right-hand edges of Nos. 3849/3854 are all cut around to show the vinyl disc protruding from the open edge of the album cover.

A *Dark Side of the Moon* maxi sheet containing No. 3851×10 was sold at £12·95, a premium of £6·55 over face value.

The 11 PHQ cards depict the individual stamps including those from No. **MS**3855 and the complete miniature sheet.

2985 Peter Rabbit

2986 Mrs. Tiggywinkle

2987 Squirrel Nutkin

2988 Jemima Puddle-Duck

2989 Tom Kitten

2990 Benjamin Bunny

150th Birth Anniversary of Beatrix Potter (writer, illustrator and conservationist) (1st issue)

2016 (28 July) Two phosphor bands.

(a) Ordinary gum. Litho. Perf 14½×14.

3856	**2985**	(1st) multicoloured	1·00	1·00	☐	☐
		a. Horiz pair. Nos. 3856/3857	2·00	2·00	☐	☐
3857	**2986**	(1st) multicoloured	1·00	1·00	☐	☐
3858	**2987**	£1·33 multicoloured	2·00	2·00	☐	☐
		a. Horiz pair. Nos. 3858/3859	4·00	4·00	☐	☐
3859	**2988**	£1·33 multicoloured	2·00	2·00	☐	☐
3860	**2989**	£1·52 multicoloured	2·25	2·25	☐	☐
		a. Horiz pair. Nos. 3860/3861	4·50	4·50	☐	☐
3861	**2990**	£1·52 multicoloured	2·25	2·25	☐	☐
Set of 6			9·50	9·50	☐	☐
First Day Cover				12·00	☐	
Presentation Pack (Nos. 3856/3861 and **MS**3868) (PO Pack No. 529)			18·50		☐	

PHQ Cards (*set of* 11) (418)			5·50	24·00	☐	☐
Set of 3 Gutter Pairs (2 stamps only in each pair)			19·00		☐	
Set of 3 Traffic Light Gutter Pairs (2 stamps only in each pair)			20·00		☐	

(b) Self-adhesive. Gravure. Die-cut perf 14½×14.

3862	**2985**	(1st) multicoloured	1·50	1·50	☐	☐
3863	**2986**	(1st) multicoloured	1·50	1·50	☐	☐

Nos. 3856/3857, 3858/3859 and 3860/3861 were printed together, *se-tenant*, as horizontal pairs in sheets of 60 (2 panes 6×5).

Nos. 3862/3863 were issued in stamp booklets, each containing Nos. 3862/3863 and 4×1st bright lilac and originally sold for £3·84.

The 11 PHQ cards depict the ten individual stamps including those from No. **MS**3868 and the complete miniature sheet.

2991 Now run along, and don't get into mischief.

2992 And then, feeling rather sick, he went to look for some parsley.

2993 But Peter, who was very naughty, ran straight away to Mr. McGregor's garden, and squeezed under the gate!

2994 He slipped underneath the gate, and was safe at last….

2995 Illustrations from *The Tale of Peter Rabbit*

150th Birth Anniversary of Beatrix Potter (writer, illustrator and conservationist) (2nd issue)

2016 (28 July) Two phosphor bands. Perf 14½.

3864	**2991**	(1st) multicoloured	2·25	2·25	☐	☐
3865	**2992**	(1st) multicoloured	2·25	2·25	☐	☐
3866	**2993**	£1·33 multicoloured	2·25	2·25	☐	☐

3867	**2994**	£1·33 multicoloured	2·25	2·25	☐	☐
Set of 4			8·25	8·25	☐	☐
MS3868 125×89 mm. **2995** (1st) multi-coloured; (1st) multicoloured; £1·33 multicoloured; £1·33 multicoloured			5·50	5·75	☐	☐
First Day Cover				7·50		☐

Nos. 3864/3867 were issued in £15·37 The Tale of Beatrix Potter premium booklets and in No. **MS**3868.

2996 Blenheim Palace

2997 Longleat

2998 Compton Verney

2999 Highclere Castle

3000 Alnwick Castle

3001 Berrington Hall

3002 Stowe

3003 Croome Park

Landscape Gardens

2016 (16 Aug.) One centre band (2nd) or two phosphor bands (others)

(a) Ordinary gum. Perf 14.

3869	**2996**	(2nd) multicoloured	90	90	☐	☐
		a. Horiz pair. Nos. 3869/3870	1·75	1·75	☐	☐
3870	**2997**	(2nd) multicoloured	90	90	☐	☐
3871	**2998**	(1st) multicoloured	1·00	1·00	☐	☐
		a. Horiz pair. Nos. 3871/3872	2·00	2·00	☐	☐
3872	**2999**	(1st) multicoloured	1·00	1·00	☐	☐
3873	**3000**	£1·05 multicoloured	1·50	1·50	☐	☐
		a. Horiz pair. Nos. 3873/3874	3·00	3·00	☐	☐
3874	**3001**	£1·05 multicoloured	1·50	1·50	☐	☐

3875	**3002**	£1·33 multicoloured	2·00	2·00	☐	☐
		a. Horiz pair.				
		Nos. 3875/3876	4·00	4·00	☐	☐
3876	**3003**	£1·33 multicoloured	2·00	2·00	☐	☐
Set of 8			10·00	10·00	☐	☐
First Day Cover				13·00		☐
Presentation Pack (PO Pack No. 530)			13·00			☐
PHQ Cards (set of 8) (419)			4·00	12·00	☐	☐
Set of 4 Gutter Blocks of 4			20·00			☐

(b) Self-adhesive. Die-cut perf 14.

3877	**2998**	(1st) multicoloured	1·50	1·50	☐	☐
3878	**2999**	(1st) multicoloured	1·50	1·50	☐	☐

Nos. 3869/3878 commemorate the 300th birth anniversary of Capability Brown and show his landscape gardens.

Nos. 3869/3870, 3871/3872, 3873/3874 and 3875/3876 were each printed together, *se-tenant*, as horizontal pairs in sheets of 60 (2 panes 6×5).

Nos. 3877/3878 were issued in stamp booklets containing Nos. 3877/3878 and 4×1st bright lilac, originally sold for £3·84.

3004 Fire Breaks Out in Bakery on Pudding Lane, and Thomas Farriner and his Daughter escape through a Window, Sunday 2nd September 1666

3005 The Fire Spreads Rapidly, and Many People Flee to the River with Their Possessions, Sunday 2nd September 1666

3006 Houses are Pulled Down to Create Breaks and Prevent the Fire from Spreading, Monday 3rd September 1666

3007 As the Fire reaches St Paul's Citizens witness the Cathedral's Destruction as Belongings stored inside Fuel the Flames, Tuesday 4th September 1666

3008 The Fire Dies Out, Many Gather at Moorfields and Temporary Food Markets are set up across London, Wednesday 5th September 1666

3009 Christopher Wren develops Plans for the Regeneration of the City and presents them to the King, Tuesday 11th September 1666

350th Anniversary of the Great Fire of London

2016 (2 Sept.) Two phosphor bands. Perf 14½.

3879	**3004**	(1st) multicoloured	1·00	1·00	☐	☐
		a. Horiz pair.				
		Nos. 3879/3880	2·00	2·00	☐	☐
3880	**3005**	(1st) multicoloured	1·00	1·00	☐	☐

3881	**3006**	£1·05 multicoloured	1·60	1·60	☐	☐
		a. Horiz pair.				
		Nos. 3881/3882	3·25	3·25	☐	☐
3882	**3007**	£1·05 multicoloured	1·60	1·60	☐	☐
3883	**3008**	£1·52 multicoloured	2·25	2·25	☐	☐
		a. Horiz pair.				
		Nos. 3883/3884	4·50	4·50	☐	☐
3884	**3009**	£1·52 multicoloured	2·25	2·25	☐	☐
Set of 6			9·00	9·00	☐	☐
First Day Cover				12·00		☐
Presentation Pack (PO Pack No. 531)			11·00			☐
PHQ Cards (set of 6) (420)			3·00	11·00	☐	☐
Set of 3 Gutter Blocks of 4			18·00			☐

Nos. 3879/3880, 3881/3882 and 3883/3884 were each printed together, *se-tenant*, as horizontal pairs in sheets of 60 (2 panes 6×5).

3010 *Murder on the Orient Express*

3011 *And Then There Were None*

3012 *The Mysterious Affair at Styles*

3013 *The Murder of Roger Ackroyd*

3014 *The Body in the Library*

3015 *A Murder is Announced*

40th Death Anniversary of Agatha Christie (writer)

2016 (15 Sept.) Two phosphor bands. Perf 14½

3885	**3010**	(1st) multicoloured	1·00	1·00	☐ ☐
		a. Vert pair. Nos. 3885/3886	2·00	2·00	☐ ☐
3886	**3011**	(1st) multicoloured	1·00	1·00	☐ ☐
3887	**3012**	£1·33 vermilion, turquoise-green and black	2·00	2·00	☐ ☐
		a. Vert pair. Nos. 3887/3888	4·00	4·00	☐ ☐
3888	**3013**	£1·33 vermilion, turquoise-green and black	2·00	2·00	☐ ☐
3889	**3014**	£1·52 bright magenta, new blue and black	2·25	2·25	☐ ☐
		a. Vert pair. Nos. 3889/3890	4·50	4·50	☐ ☐
3890	**3015**	£1·52 bright magenta, new blue and black	2·25	2·25	☐ ☐
Set of 6			9·50	9·50	☐
First Day Cover				13·00	☐
Presentation Pack (PO Pack No. 532)			12·00		☐
PHQ Cards (*set of 6*) (421)			3·00	11·00	☐ ☐
Set of 3 Gutter Pairs (only 2 stamps in each gutter pair)			10·00		☐

Nos. 3885/3886, 3887/3888 and 3889/3890 were each printed together, *se-tenant*, as vertical pairs in sheets of 48 (2 panes 4 × 6).

3016 *Mr. Happy*

3017 *Little Miss Naughty*

3018 *Mr. Bump*

3019 *Little Miss Sunshine*

3020 *Mr. Tickle*

3021 *Mr. Grumpy*

3022 *Little Miss Princess*

3023 *Mr. Strong*

3024 *Little Miss Christmas*

3025 *Mr. Messy*

Mr. Men and Little Miss
(children's books by Roger Hargreaves)

2016 (20 Oct.) Two phosphor bands

(a) Ordinary gum. Litho. Perf 14½

3891	**3016**	(1st) multicoloured	1·00	1·00	☐ ☐
		a. Horiz strip of 5. Nos. 3891/3895	4·50	4·50	☐ ☐
3892	**3017**	(1st) multicoloured	1·00	1·00	☐ ☐
3893	**3018**	(1st) multicoloured	1·00	1·00	☐ ☐
3894	**3019**	(1st) multicoloured	1·00	1·00	☐ ☐
3895	**3020**	(1st) multicoloured	1·00	1·00	☐ ☐
3896	**3021**	(1st) multicoloured	1·00	1·00	☐ ☐
		a. Horiz strip of 5. Nos. 3896/3900	4·50	4·50	☐ ☐
3897	**3022**	(1st) multicoloured	1·00	1·00	☐ ☐
3898	**3023**	(1st) multicoloured	1·00	1·00	☐ ☐
3899	**3024**	(1st) multicoloured	1·00	1·00	☐ ☐
3900	**3025**	(1st) multicoloured	1·00	1·00	☐ ☐
Set of 10			9·00	9·00	☐
First Day Cover				11·50	☐
Presentation Pack (PO Pack No. 533)			11·00		☐
PHQ Cards (*set of 10*) (422)			5·00	12·50	☐ ☐
Set of 2 Gutter Strips of 5			18·00		☐

(b) Self-adhesive. Gravure. Die-cut perf 14½

3901	**3016**	(1st) multicoloured	1·50	1·50	☐ ☐
3902	**3020**	(1st) multicoloured	1·50	1·50	☐ ☐

Nos. 3901/3902 were issued in stamp booklets containing Nos. 3901/3902 and 4 × 1st vermilion, originally sold for £3·84.

Designs as Nos. 3891/3900 but self-adhesive were issued in sheets of ten with *se-tenant* labels.

Designs as Nos. 3891, 3893/3894, 3896/3897 and 3900 were also available in sheets of ten with personal photographs on the labels.

3026 *Snowman*

3027 *Robin*

3028 *Snowman*

3029 *Robin*

3030 Christmas Tree

3031 Lantern

3032 Stocking

3033 Christmas Pudding

Christmas

2016 (8 Nov.) One centre band (No. 3903) or two bands (others).
Perf 14½×15

(a) Self-adhesive

3903	**3026**	(2nd) multicoloured	90	90 ☐ ☐
3904	**3027**	(1st) multicoloured	1·00	1·00 ☐ ☐
3905	**3028**	(2nd Large) multicoloured	1·10	1·10 ☐ ☐
3906	**3029**	(1st Large) multicoloured	1·40	1·40 ☐ ☐
3907	**3030**	£1·05 multicoloured	1·75	1·75 ☐ ☐
3908	**3031**	£1·33 multicoloured	2·00	2·00 ☐ ☐
3909	**3032**	£1·52 multicoloured	2·50	2·50 ☐ ☐
3910	**3033**	£2·25 multicoloured	3·50	3·50 ☐ ☐

Set of 8		13·00	13·00 ☐ ☐
First Day Cover			16·50 ☐
Presentation Pack (PO Pack No. 534)		16·50	☐
PHQ Cards (set of 9) (423)		4·50	28·00 ☐ ☐

(b) Ordinary gum

MS3911 189×74 mm. As Nos. 3903/3910		13·00	13·00 ☐ ☐
First Day Cover			16·50 ☐

The nine PHQ cards show the eight individual stamps and the complete miniature sheet.

The 2nd class and 1st class values were also issued in sheets of 20 with *se-tenant* labels 'Celebrating 50 Years of Christmas Stamps'.

The 2nd class, 1st class, £1·05, £1·33, £1·52 and £2·25 values were also issued in sheets of 20 containing eight 2nd class, eight 1st class and one each of the £1·05, £1·33, £1·52 and £2·25 stamps, each stamp accompanied by a *se-tenant* label.

Separate sheets of 20 2nd, 20 1st, ten 1st, ten £1·05, ten £1·33 and ten £1·52 were available with personal photographs on the labels.

Year Pack

2016 (8 Nov.) Comprises Nos. 3787/**MS**3801, 3810/**MS**3832, **MS**3837/3843, **MS**3848/3861, **MS**3868/3876, 3879/3900, 3903/3910

CP3911*a* Year Pack	£160	☐

Post Office Yearbook

2016 (8 Nov.) Comprises Nos. 3787/**MS**3801, 3810/**MS**3832, **MS**3837/3843, **MS**3848/3861, **MS**3868/3876, 3879/3900, 3903/3910

YB3911*a* Yearbook	£180	☐

Miniature Sheet Collection

2016 (8 Nov.) Comprises Nos. **MS**3801, **MS**3832, **MS**3837, **MS**3848, **MS**3855, **MS**3868 and **MS**3911

MS3911*a* Miniature Sheet Collection	50.00	☐

3034 Battersea Shield, London, 350–50 BC

3035 Skara Brae Village, Orkney Islands, 3100–2500 BC

3036 Star Carr Headdress, Yorkshire, 9000 BC

3037 Maiden Castle Hill Fort, Dorset, 400 BC

3038 Avebury Stone Circles, Wiltshire, 2500 BC

3039 Drumbest Horns, County Antrim, 800 BC

3040 Grime's Graves Flint Mines, Norfolk, 2500 BC

3041 Mold Cape, Flintshire, 1900–1600 BC

Ancient Britain

2017 (17 Jan.) Two phosphor bands. Perf 14

3912	**3034**	(1st) multicoloured	1·00	1·00	☐	☐
		a. Horiz pair. Nos. 3912/3913	2·00	2·00	☐	☐
3913	**3035**	(1st) multicoloured	1·00	1·00	☐	☐
3914	**3036**	£1·05 multicoloured	1·75	1·75	☐	☐
		a. Horiz pair. Nos. 3914/3915	3·50	3·50	☐	☐
3915	**3037**	£1·05 multicoloured	1·75	1·75	☐	☐
3916	**3038**	£1·33 multicoloured	2·00	2·00	☐	☐
		a. Horiz pair. Nos. 3916/3917	4·00	4·00	☐	☐
3917	**3039**	£1·33 multicoloured	2·00	2·00	☐	☐
3918	**3040**	£1·52 multicoloured	2·25	2·25	☐	☐
		a. Horiz pair. Nos. 3918/3919	4·50	4·50	☐	☐
3919	**3041**	£1·52 multicoloured	2·25	2·25	☐	☐
Set of 8			12·50	12·50	☐	
First Day Cover				17·00		☐
Presentation Pack (PO Pack No. 536)			15·50		☐	
PHQ Cards (set of 8) (424)			4·00	15·00	☐	☐
Set of 4 Gutter Blocks of 4			25·00		☐	

Nos. 3912/3913, 3914/3915, 3916/3917 and 3918/3919 were each printed together, *se-tenant*, as horizontal pairs in sheets of 60 (2 panes 6×5).

For No. U3920, Type **3041a**, See Decimal Machin section

3042 The Long Walk

3043 The Round Tower

3044 The Norman Gate

3045 St George's Hall

3046 The Queen's Ballroom

3047 The Waterloo Chamber

3048 St George's Chapel Nave: Sir Reginald Bray Roof Boss

3049 St. George's Chapel Nave: Fan-vaulted Roof

Windsor Castle (1st issue)

2017 (15 Feb.) Two phosphor bands.

(a) Ordinary gum. Litho. Perf 14½

3920	**3042**	(1st) multicoloured	1·00	1·00	☐	☐
		a. Horiz strip of 3. Nos. 3920/3922	3·00	3·00	☐	☐

3921	**3043**	(1st) multicoloured	1·00	1·00	☐ ☐
3922	**3044**	(1st) multicoloured	1·00	1·00	☐ ☐
3923	**3045**	£1·52 multicoloured	2·00	2·00	☐ ☐
		a. Horiz strip of 3.			
		Nos. 3923/3925	6·00	6·00	☐ ☐
3924	**3046**	£1·52 multicoloured	2·00	2·00	☐ ☐
3925	**3047**	£1·52 multicoloured	2·00	2·00	☐ ☐
Set of 6			8·25	8·25	☐ ☐
First Day Cover				12·00	☐

Presentation Pack (Nos. 3920/3925 and
MS3932) (PO Pack No. 537)   18·00   ☐
PHQ Cards (set of 11) (425)   5·00   23·00 ☐ ☐
Set of 2 Gutter Strips of 3   16·50   ☐

		(b) Self-adhesive. Gravure. Die-cut perf 14½			
3926	**3048**	(1st) multicoloured	1·50	1·50	☐ ☐
3927	**3049**	(1st) multicoloured	1·50	1·50	☐ ☐

Nos. 3920/3922 and 3923/3925 were each printed together, se-tenant, as horizontal strips of three stamps in sheets of 60 (2 panes 6×5).

Nos. 3926/3927 were issued in stamp booklets containing Nos. 3926/3927 and 4×1st bright scarlet, originally sold for £3·84.

3050 St George's Chapel Quire: Garter Banners

3051 St George's Chapel Quire: St George's Cross Roof Boss

3052 St George's Chapel

Windsor Castle (2nd issue)

2017 (15 Feb.) Two phosphor bands. Litho. Perf 14½

3928		(1st) As No. 3926	1·60	1·60	☐ ☐
3929		(1st) As No. 3927	1·60	1·60	☐ ☐
3930	**3050**	£1·33 multicoloured	2·50	2·50	☐ ☐
3931	**3051**	£1·33 multicoloured	2·50	2·50	☐ ☐
Set of 4			7·25	7·25	☐ ☐
MS3932 125×89 mm. **3052** Nos. 3928/3931			7·25	7·25	☐ ☐
First Day Cover				8·00	☐

Nos. 3928/3931 come from No. **MS**3932 and £14·58 Windsor Castle premium booklets.

3053 Hunky Dory

3054 Aladdin Sane

3055 Heroes

3056 Let's Dance

3057 Earthling

3058 Blackstar

3059 David Bowie Live

David Bowie (1947–2016, singer, songwriter and actor) Commemoration

2017 (14 Mar.) Two phosphor bands

		(a) Self-adhesive. Gravure. Die-cut perf 14½			
3933	**3053**	(1st) multicoloured	1·00	1·00	☐ ☐
3934	**3054**	(1st) multicoloured	1·00	1·00	☐ ☐
3935	**3055**	(1st) multicoloured	1·00	1·00	☐ ☐
3936	**3056**	£1·52 multicoloured	2·25	2·25	☐ ☐
3937	**3057**	£1·52 multicoloured	2·25	2·25	☐ ☐
3938	**3058**	£1·52 multicoloured	2·25	2·25	☐ ☐
Set of 6			8·75	8·75	☐ ☐
First Day Cover				11·50	☐

Presentation Pack (Nos. 3933/3938 and
MS3939) (PO Pack No. 538)   17·00   ☐
PHQ Cards (set of 11) (426)   5·50   24·00 ☐ ☐

(b) Ordinary gum. Litho. Perf 14½
MS3939 126×89 mm. **3059** (1st) The Ziggy Stardust Tour, 1973; (1st) The Serious Moonlight Tour, 1983; £1·52 Isolar II Tour, 1978; £1·52 A Reality Tour, 2004   6·25   6·25 ☐ ☐
First Day Cover   8·25   ☐

Nos. 3933/3938 were printed in separate sheets of 50 (2 panes 5×5).

Nos. 3934/3935 were also issued in booklets containing Nos. 3934/3935 and 4×1st bright scarlet, originally sold for £3·84.

The right-hand edges of Nos. 3933/3938 are all cut around to show the vinyl disc protruding from the open edge of the album cover.

The 11 PHQ cards show the individual stamps, including those from No. **MS**3959, and the complete miniature sheet.

Four 'fan' sheets, comprising the complete set, Types **3053/3058**, T **3053**×5 and T **3055**×5, all printed on ordinary gummed paper, were available from Royal Mail at premium prices.

3060 Frankel

3061 Red Rum

3062 Shergar

3063 Kauto Star

3064 Desert Orchid

3065 Brigadier Gerard

3066 Arkle

3067 Estimate

Racehorse Legends

2017 (6 Apr.) Two phosphor bands. Perf 14

3940	**3060**	(1st) multicoloured	1·00	1·00	
3941	**3061**	(1st) multicoloured	1·00	1·00	
3942	**3062**	£1·17 multicoloured	1·75	1·75	
3943	**3063**	£1·17 multicoloured	1·75	1·75	
3944	**3064**	£1·40 multicoloured	2·25	2·25	
3945	**3065**	£1·40 multicoloured	2·25	2·25	
3946	**3066**	£1·57 multicoloured	2·50	2·50	
3947	**3067**	£1·57 multicoloured	2·50	2·50	
Set of 8			13·50	13·50	
First Day Cover				17·00	
Presentation Pack (PO Pack No. 539)			16·00		
PHQ Cards (set of 8) (427)			4·00	17·00	
Set of 8 Gutter Pairs			27·00		

3068 Great Tit (*Parus major*)

3069 Wren (*Troglodytes troglodytes*)

3070 Willow Warbler (*Phylloscopus trochilus*)

3071 Goldcrest (*Regulus regulus*)

3072 Skylark (*Alauda arvensis*)

3073 Blackcap (*Sylvia atricapilla*)

3074 Song Thrush (*Turdus philomelos*)

3075 Nightingale (*Luscinia megarhynchos*)

3076 Cuckoo (*Cuculus canorus*)

3077 Yellowhammer (*Emberiza citrinella*)

Songbirds

2017 (4 May) Two phosphor bands. Perf 14½

3948	**3068**	(1st) multicoloured	1·00	1·00	
		a. Horiz strip of 5. Nos. 3948/3952	4·50	4·50	
3949	**3069**	(1st) multicoloured	1·00	1·00	
3950	**3070**	(1st) multicoloured	1·00	1·00	
3951	**3071**	(1st) multicoloured	1·00	1·00	
3952	**3072**	(1st) multicoloured	1·00	1·00	
3953	**3073**	(1st) multicoloured	1·00	1·00	
		a. Horiz strip of 5. Nos. 3953/3957	4·50	4·50	
3954	**3074**	(1st) multicoloured	1·00	1·00	
3955	**3075**	(1st) multicoloured	1·00	1·00	
3956	**3076**	(1st) multicoloured	1·00	1·00	
3957	**3077**	(1st) multicoloured	1·00	1·00	
Set of 10			9·00	9·00	
First Day Cover				12·00	
Presentation Pack (PO Pack No. 540)			14·00		
PHQ Cards (set of 10) (428)			5·00	12·50	
Set of 2 Gutter Strips of 5			18·00		

Nos. 3948/3952 and 3953/3957 were each printed together, se-tenant, as horizontal strips of five in sheets of 50 (2 panes 5×5).

3078 Preliminary Sketch by Arnold Machin based on the Penny Black, January 1966

3079 Preparatory Work by Arnold Machin using Photograph of his Coin Mould, February 1966

3080 Essay with Coinage Head surrounded by Country Symbols, April/May 1966

3081 Essay of Coinage Head cropped and simplified, with Only the Denomination, October 1966

3082 Photo by John Hedgecoe with Queen Elizabeth II wearing the Diadem, August 1966

3083 Essay of the First Plaster Cast of the Diadem Head, without Corsage, October 1966

3084 The Machin Definitive 50 Years of a Design Icon

3085 The Machin Definitive Golden Anniversary Celebration

50th Anniversary of the Machin Definitive (1st issue)

2017 (5 June) Two phosphor bands. Gravure and embossed. Perf 14×15

3958	**3078**	(1st) multicoloured	1·25	1·25		
3959	**3079**	(1st) multicoloured	1·25	1·25		
3960	**3080**	(1st) multicoloured	1·25	1·25		
3961	**3081**	(1st) multicoloured	1·25	1·25		
3962	**3082**	(1st) multicoloured	1·25	1·25		
3963	**3083**	(1st) multicoloured	1·25	1·25		
Set of 6			6·75	6·75		

MS3964 202×74 mm. **3084** (1st) One of many preliminary sketches by Arnold Machin based on the Penny Black, January 1966; (1st) Preparatory work by Arnold Machin using a photograph of his coin mould, February 1966; (1st) One of many essays with the 'Coinage' head surrounded by Country Symbols, April/May 1966; (1st) Essay of the 'Coinage' head cropped and simplified, with only the denomination, October 1966; (1st) Photograph by John Hedgecoe with Queen Elizabeth II wearing the diadem, August 1966; (1st) Essay of the first plaster cast of the 'Diadem' head, without corsage, October 1966 ... 10·00 ... 10·00

MS3965 202×74 mm. **3085** No. X866; No. 1470; As Type **1116**; No. 2124; No. 2651; As No. U3067 (but 'MMIL' code); Type **3086** ... 10·00 ... 10·00

First Day Cover (No. **MS**3964)		11·00
First Day Cover (No. **MS**3965)		11·00
Presentation Pack (Nos. **MS**3964/**MS**3965) (PO Pack No. 541)	18·00	
PHQ Cards (*set of* 11) (429)	5·50	21·00

Nos. 3958/3963 were issued in £15·14 50th Anniversary of the Machin Definitive premium booklets and in No. **MS**3964. The 5p., 20p. and £1 stamps from No. **MS**3965 do not have an elliptical perforation hole in each vertical side.

On No. **MS**3965 only the £1 gold foil stamp is embossed.

For No. U3966, Type **3086**, See Decimal Machin section.

3087 Nutley Windmill, East Sussex

3088 New Abbey Corn Mill, Dumfries and Galloway

3089 Ballycopeland Windmill, County Down

3090 Cheddleton Flint Mill, Staffordshire

3091 Woodchurch Windmill, Kent

3092 Felin Cochwillan Mill, Gwynedd

Windmills and Watermills

2017 (20 June) Two phosphor bands. Perf 14½×14

3967	**3087**	(1st) multicoloured	1·00	1·00		

	a. Vert pair.			
	Nos. 3967/3968	2·00	2·00	☐ ☐
3968 **3088**	(1st) multicoloured	1·00	1·00	☐ ☐
3969 **3089**	£1·40 multicoloured	2·25	2·25	☐ ☐
	a. Vert pair.			
	Nos. 3969/3970	4·50	4·50	☐ ☐
3970 **3090**	£1·40 multicoloured	2·25	2·25	☐ ☐
3971 **3091**	£1·57 multicoloured	2·50	2·50	☐ ☐
	a. Vert pair.			
	Nos. 3971/3972	5·00	5·00	☐ ☐
3972 **3092**	£1·57 multicoloured	2·50	2·50	☐ ☐
Set of 6		10·50	10·50	☐
First Day Cover			13·50	☐
Presentation Pack (PO Pack No. 542)		12·00		☐
PHQ Cards (*set of 6*) (430)		3·00	12·00	☐ ☐
Set of 3 Gutter Blocks of 4		21·00		☐

Nos. 3967/3968, 3969/3970 and 3971/3972 were each printed together, *se-tenant*, as vertical pairs in sheets of 60 (2 panes 5×6).

3093 Aquatics Centre, Queen Elizabeth Olympic Park, London

3094 Library of Birmingham

3095 SEC Armadillo (formerly Clyde Auditorium), Glasgow

3096 Scottish Parliament, Edinburgh

3097 Giant's Causeway Visitor Centre, Co. Antrim

3098 National Assembly for Wales, Cardiff

3099 Eden Project, St Austell

3100 Everyman Theatre, Liverpool

3101 IWM (Imperial War Museum) North, Manchester

3102 Switch House, Tate Modern, London

Landmark Buildings

2017 (13 July) Two phosphor bands. Perf 14½

3973 **3093**	(1st) multicoloured	1·00	1·00	☐ ☐
	a. Horiz strip of 5.			
	Nos. 3973/3977	4·50	4·50	☐
3974 **3094**	(1st) multicoloured	1·00	1·00	☐ ☐
3975 **3095**	(1st) multicoloured	1·00	1·00	☐ ☐
3976 **3096**	(1st) multicoloured	1·00	1·00	☐ ☐
3977 **3097**	(1st) multicoloured	1·00	1·00	☐ ☐
3978 **3098**	(1st) multicoloured	1·00	1·00	☐ ☐
	a. Horiz strip of 5.			
	Nos. 3978/3982	4·50	4·50	☐
3979 **3099**	(1st) multicoloured	1·00	1·00	☐ ☐
3980 **3100**	(1st) multicoloured	1·00	1·00	☐ ☐
3981 **3101**	(1st) multicoloured	1·00	1·00	☐ ☐
3982 **3102**	(1st) multicoloured	1·00	1·00	☐ ☐
Set of 10		9·00	9·00	☐
First Day Cover			12·00	☐
Presentation Pack (PO Pack No. 543)		11·00		☐
PHQ Cards (*set of 10*) (430)		5·00	10·00	☐ ☐
Set of 2 Gutter Strips of 5		18·00		☐

Nos. 3973/3977 and 3978/3982 were each printed together, *se-tenant*, as horizontal strips of five stamps in sheets of 50 (2 panes 5×5).

3103 *Shattered Poppy* (John Ross)

3104 *Dead Man's Dump* (Isaac Rosenberg)

3105 Nurses Elsie Knocker and Mairi Chisholm

3106 *Dry Docked for Sealing and Painting* (Edward Wadsworth)

3107 Tyne Cot Cemetery, Zonnebeke, Ypres Salient Battlefields, Belgium

3108 Private Lemuel Thomas Rees's Life-saving Bible

Centenary of the First World War (4th issue)

2017 (31 July) Two phosphor bands. Perf 14½

3983	3103	(1st) multicoloured	1·00	1·00	☐	☐
3984	3104	(1st) multicoloured	1·00	1·00	☐	☐
3985	3105	(1st) multicoloured	1·00	1·00	☐	☐
3986	3106	£1·57 multicoloured	2·50	2·50	☐	☐
3987	3107	£1·57 multicoloured	2·50	2·50	☐	☐
3988	3108	£1·57 multicoloured	2·50	2·50	☐	☐
Set of 6			9·50	9·50	☐	☐
First Day Cover				12·50		☐
Presentation Pack (PO Pack No. 544)			11·50		☐	
PHQ Cards (set of 6) (431)			3·00	12·00	☐	☐
Set of 6 Gutter Pairs			19·00		☐	

3109 The Merrythought Bear

3110 Cindy Weekender Doll

3111 Spirograph

3112 Stickle Bricks Super Set House

3113 Herald Trojan Warriors

3114 Spacehopper

3115 Fuzzy-Felt Farm Set

3116 Meccano Ferris Wheel

3117 Action Man Red Devil Parachutist

3118 Hornby Dublo Electric Train and TPO Mail Van

Classic Toys

2017 (22 Aug.) Two phosphor bands. Perf 14½

3989	3109	(1st) multicoloured	1·00	1·00	☐	☐

		a. Horiz strip of 5.				
		Nos. 3989/3993	4·50	4·50	☐	☐
3990	3110	(1st) multicoloured	1·00	1·00	☐	☐
3991	3111	(1st) multicoloured	1·00	1·00	☐	☐
3992	3112	(1st) multicoloured	1·00	1·00	☐	☐
3993	3113	(1st) multicoloured	1·00	1·00	☐	☐
3994	3114	(1st) multicoloured	1·00	1·00	☐	☐
		a. Horiz strip of 5.				
		Nos. 3994/3998	4·50	4·50	☐	☐
3995	3115	(1st) multicoloured	1·00	1·00	☐	☐
3996	3116	(1st) multicoloured	1·00	1·00	☐	☐
3997	3117	(1st) multicoloured	1·00	1·00	☐	☐
3998	3118	(1st) multicoloured	1·00	1·00	☐	☐
Set of 10			9·00	9·00	☐	☐
First Day Cover				12·00		☐
Presentation Pack (PO Pack No. 545)			11·00		☐	
PHQ Cards (set of 10) (432)			5·00	10·00	☐	☐
Set of 2 Gutter Strips of 5			18·00		☐	

Nos. 3989/3993 and 3994/3998 were each printed together, se-tenant, as horizontal strips of five stamps in sheets of 50 (2 panes 5×5).

3119 The Story of Nelson, The Story of the First Queen Elizabeth and Florence Nightingale (Adventures from History)

3120 The Gingerbread Boy, Cinderella and The Elves and the Shoemaker (Well-loved Tales)

3121 We have fun, Look at this and Things we do (Key Words Reading Scheme)

3122 Piggly Plays Truant, Tootles the Taxi and Other Rhymes and Smoke and Fluff (Early Tales and Rhymes)

3123 The Ladybird Book of Things to Make, How it works: The Telephone and Tricks and Magic (Hobbies and How it Works)

3124 The Nurse, The Postman and The Fireman (People at Work)

3125 The Ladybird Book of British Wild Flowers, Wild Life in Britain and Garden Flowers (Nature and Conservation)

3126 The Story of Ships, The Story of the Motor Car and The Story of Metals (Achievements)

Ladybird Books

2017 (14 Sept.) One centre band (Nos. 3999/4000) or two bands (others). Perf 14

3999	3119	(2nd) multicoloured	90	90	☐	☐

	a. Horiz pair.			
	Nos. 3999/4000	1·75	1·75	
4000 **3120**	(2nd) multicoloured	90	90	
4001 **3121**	(1st) multicoloured	1·00	1·00	
	a. Horiz pair.			
	Nos. 4001/4002	2·00	2·00	
4002 **3122**	(1st) multicoloured	1·00	1·00	
4003 **3123**	£1·40 multicoloured	2·25	2·25	
	a. Horiz pair. Nos.			
	4003/4004	4·50	4·50	
4004 **3124**	£1·40 multicoloured	2·25	2·25	
4005 **3125**	£1·57 multicoloured	2·50	2·50	
	a. Horiz pair.			
	Nos. 4005/4006	5·00	5·00	
4006 **3126**	£1·57 multicoloured	2·50	2·50	
Set of 8		12·00	12·00	
First Day Cover			16·00	
Presentation Pack (PO Pack No. 546)		14·00		
PHQ Cards (set of 8) (433)		4·00	12·50	
Set of 4 Gutter Blocks of 4		24·00		

Nos. 3999/4000, 4001/4002, 4003/4004 and 4005/4006 were each printed together, se-tenant, as horizontal pairs in sheets of 60 (2 panes 6×5).

3127 Maz Kanata

3128 Chewbacca

3129 Supreme Leader Snoke

3130 Porg

3131 BB-8

3132 R2-D2

3133 C-3PO

3134 K-2SO

Star Wars (4th issue). Aliens and Droids.

2017 (12 Oct.) Two phosphor bands

	(a) Ordinary gum. Litho. Perf 14½			
4007 **3127**	(1st) multicoloured	1·00	1·00	
	a. Horiz strip of 4.			
	Nos. 4007/4010	4·00	4·00	

4008 **3128**	(1st) multicoloured	1·00	1·00	
4009 **3129**	(1st) multicoloured	1·00	1·00	
4010 **3130**	(1st) multicoloured	1·00	1·00	
4011 **3131**	(1st) multicoloured	1·00	1·00	
	a. Horiz strip of 4.			
	Nos. 4011/4014	4·00	4·00	
4012 **3132**	(1st) multicoloured	1·00	1·00	
4013 **3133**	(1st) multicoloured	1·00	1·00	
4014 **3134**	(1st) multicoloured	1·00	1·00	
Set of 8		7·25	7·25	
First Day Cover			9·00	
Presentation Pack (PO Pack No. 547)		9·25		
PHQ Cards (set of 8) (434)		4·00	9·00	
Set of 2 Gutter Strips of 4		14·50		
MS4014a 210×297 mm. Nos. 3758/3769				
and 4007/4014		30·00	30·00	

(b) Self-adhesive. Gravure. Die-cut perf 14½			
4015 **3127**	(1st) multicoloured	1·50	1·50
4016 **3128**	(1st) multicoloured	1·50	1·50
4017 **3131**	(1st) multicoloured	1·50	1·50
4018 **3132**	(1st) multicoloured	1·50	1·50

Nos. 4007/4010 and 4011/4014 were each printed together, se-tenant, as horizontal strips of four stamps in sheets of 48 (2 panes 4×6).

No. **MS**4014a was inscribed 'THE ULTIMATE COLLECTOR'S SHEET' but was sold at face value (£13).

A 'DROID'S ALIENS AND CREATURES COLLECTOR'S SHEET' containing Nos. 4007/4010, 4011×2, 4012/4013 and 4014×2 and ten labels was sold at £7·20, a 70p. premium over face value.

Nos. 4015/4016 and 4017/4018 were each issued in stamp booklets with 4×1st bright scarlet stamps, originally sold for £3·90 each.

3135 Virgin and Child (attr. Gerard David)

3136 The Madonna and Child (William Dyce)

3137 Virgin and Child (attr. Gerard David)

3138 The Madonna and Child (William Dyce)

3139 Virgin Mary with Child (attr. Quinten Massys)

3140 The Small Cowper Madonna (Raphael)

3141 The Sleep of the Infant Jesus (Giovanni Battista Sassoferrato

3142 St Luke painting the Virgin (detail) (Eduard Jakob von Steinle)

Christmas. Madonna and Child

2017 (7 Nov.) One phosphor band (No. 4019) or two bands
(a) Self-adhesive. Gravure. Die-cut perf 14½ × 15

4019	**3135**	(2nd) multicoloured	90	90	☐	☐
4020	**3136**	(1st) multicoloured	1·00	1·00	☐	☐
4021	**3137**	(2nd Large) multicoloured	1·10	1·10	☐	☐
4022	**3138**	(1st Large) multicoloured	1·40	1·40	☐	☐
4023	**3139**	£1·17 multicoloured	1·75	1·75	☐	☐
4024	**3140**	£1·40 multicoloured	2·25	2·25	☐	☐
4025	**3141**	£1·57 multicoloured	2·50	2·50	☐	☐
4026	**3142**	£2·27 multicoloured	3·50	3·50	☐	☐
Set of 8			13·00	13·00	☐	

First Day Cover (Nos. 4019/4026 and 4028/4031)   23·00 ☐

Presentation Pack (Nos. 4019/4026 and 4028/4031) (PO Pack No. 548)   21·00 ☐

PHQ Cards (*set of 13*) (435)   6·50   30·00 ☐ ☐

(b) Ordinary gum. Litho. Perf 14½ × 15

MS4027 189 × 74 mm As Nos. 4019/4026   13·00   13·00 ☐ ☐

First Day Cover   18·00 ☐

The 13 PHQ cards show the 12 individual stamps and No. **MS**4027.
The 2nd class (No. 4019), 1st class (No. 4020), £1·17, £1·40, £1·57 and £2·27 values were also issued in sheets of 20 containing eight 2nd class, eight 1st class and one each of the £1·17, £1·40, £1·57 and £2·27 values, each stamp accompanied by a *se-tenant* label.

3143 *Snow Family*
(Arwen Wilson)

3144 *Santa Claus on his sleigh on a starry night* (Ted Lewis-Clark)

3145 *Snow Family*
(Arwen Wilson)

3146 *Santa Claus on his sleigh on a starry night*
(Ted Lewis-Clark)

Children's Christmas

2017 (7 Nov.) One phosphor band (No. 4028) or two bands. Self-adhesive. Die-cut perf 14½ × 15

4028	**3143**	(2nd) multicoloured	90	90	☐	☐
4029	**3144**	(1st) multicoloured	1·00	1·00	☐	☐
4030	**3145**	(2nd Large) multicoloured	1·10	1·10	☐	☐
4031	**3146**	(1st Large) multicoloured	1·40	1·40	☐	☐
Set of 4			4·00	4·00	☐	☐

3147 Platinum Anniversary

Royal Platinum Wedding Anniversary of Queen Elizabeth II and Duke of Edinburgh

2017 (20 Nov.) Two Phosphor Bands Litho. Perf 14½

MS4032   190 × 67 mm   **3147**   (1st) Engagement of Princess Elizabeth and Lieutenant Philip Mountbatten; (1st) Princess Elizabeth and Duke of Edinburgh after their wedding at Westminster Abbey; (1st) Princess Elizabeth and Duke of Edinburgh looking at wedding photographs during their honeymoon; £1·57 Engagement photograph; £1·57 Princess Elizabeth and Duke of Edinburgh on their wedding day; £1·57 Princess Elizabeth and Duke of Edinburgh on honeymoon at Broadlands   10·00   10·00 ☐ ☐

First Day Cover   12·50 ☐

Presentation Pack (PO Pack No. 549)   14·00 ☐

PHQ Cards (*set of 7*) (436)   3·50   18·00 ☐ ☐

Souvenir Pack   15·00 ☐

Collectors Pack

2017 (20 Nov.) Comprises Nos. 3912/3925, **MS**3932/3957, **MS**3964/**MS**3965, 3967/4014, 4019/4029 and **MS**4032

CP4031*a*   Collectors Pack   £250 ☐

Post Office Yearbook

2017 (20 Nov.) Comprises Nos. 3912/3925, **MS**3932/3957, **MS**3964/**MS**3965, 3967/4014, 4019/4031 and **MS**4032

YB4031*a*   Yearbook   £325 ☐

Miniature Sheet Collection

2017 (20 Nov.) Comprises Nos. **MS**3932, **MS**3939, **MS**3964/**MS**3965, **MS**4027 and **MS**4032

MS4031*a* Miniature Sheet Collection   85·00 ☐

3148 Sansa Stark (Sophie Tucker)   **3149** Jon Snow (Kit Harington)

3150 Eddard Stark (Sean Bean)   **3151** Olenna Tyrell (Diana Rigg)

3152 Tywin Lannister (Charles Dance)   **3153** Tyrion Lannister (Peter Dinklage)

3154 Cersei Lannister (Lena Headey)

3155 Arya Stark (Maisie Williams)

3156 Jaime Lannister
(Nikolaj Coster-Waldau)

3157 Daenerys Targaryen
(Emilia Clarke)

3158 *Game of Thrones* (non-human characters)

3159 The Iron Throne

Game of Thrones (1st issue)

2018 (23 Jan.) Two phosphor bands.

(a) Ordinary gum. Litho. Perf 14

4033	**3148**	(1st) multicoloured	1·00	1·00
		a. Horiz strip of 5. Nos.		
		4033/4037	4·50	4·50
4034	**3149**	(1st) multicoloured	1·00	1·00
4035	**3150**	(1st) multicoloured	1·00	1·00
4036	**3151**	(1st) multicoloured	1·00	1·00
4037	**3152**	(1st) multicoloured	1·00	1·00
4038	**3153**	(1st) multicoloured	1·00	1·00
		a. Horiz strip of 5. Nos.		
		4038/4042	4·50	4·50
4039	**3154**	(1st) multicoloured	1·00	1·00
4040	**3155**	(1st) multicoloured	1·00	1·00
4041	**3156**	(1st) multicoloured	1·00	1·00
4042	**3157**	(1st) multicoloured	1·00	1·00
Set of 10			9·00	9·00
First Day Cover				12·00
Presentation Pack (PO Pack 551)			17·00	
PHQ Cards (set of 16) (438)			8·00	23·00
Set of 2 Gutter Strips of 10			18·00	

(b) Self-adhesive. Litho. Die-cut perf 14½×14 (with one elliptical hole in each vert side) (iron throne) or 14½ (others)

MS4043	202×75 mm. **3158** (1st) The			
	Night King and White Walkers; (1st)			
	Giants; (1st) The Iron Throne (18×22			
	mm); (1st) Direwolves; (1st) Dragons	7·50	7·50
First Day Cover				8·50

(c) Self-adhesive booklet stamps. Gravure. Die-cut perf 14½×14 (with one elliptical hole in each vert side)

4044	**3159**	(1st) multicoloured	1·50	1·50

Nos. 4033/4037 and 4038/4042 were each printed together, *se-tenant*, as horizontal strips of five stamps in sheets of 60 (2 panes 5×6).

No. 4044 was issued in stamp booklets of six originally sold for £3·90.

The 16 PHQ cards show the 15 individual stamps including those within No. **MS**4043 and the complete miniature sheet.

Designs as Nos. 4033/4042 but self-adhesive were issued in sheets of ten with *se-tenant* labels, originally sold for £7·50.

3160 The Night King and White Walkers

3161 Giants

3162 Direwolves

3163 Dragons

Game of Thrones (2nd issue).

2018 (23 Jan.) Two phosphor bands. Litho. Perf 14½

4045	**3160**	(1st) multicoloured	1·50	1·50
4046	**3161**	(1st) multicoloured	1·50	1·50
4047	**3162**	(1st) multicoloured	1·50	1·50
4048	**3163**	(1st) multicoloured	1·50	1·50
Set of 4			5·50	5·50

Nos. 4045/4048 were issued in the £13·95 *Game of Thrones* premium booklet, No. DY24.

Game of Thrones (3rd issue)

2018 (23 Jan.) Two phosphor bands. Litho. Die-cut perf 14½×14 (with one elliptical hole in each vert side)

4049		(1st) As Type **3159**	1·50	1·50

No. 4049 was issued in the Machin booklet pane from the £13·95 *Game of Thrones* premium booklet, No. DY24.

3164 The Lone Suffragette in Whitehall, c. 1908

3165 The Great Pilgrimage of Suffragists, 1913

3166 Suffragette Leaders at Earls Court, 1908

3167 Women's Freedom League Poster Parade, c. 1907

3168 Welsh Suffragettes, Coronation Procession, 1911

3169 Mary Leigh and Edith New released from Prison, 1908

3170 Sophia Duleep Singh sells The Suffragette, 1913

3171 Suffragette Prisoners' Pageant, 1911

3172 Lightning F6

3173 Hawker Hurricane Mk. I

3174 Vulcan B2

3175 Typhoon FGR4

3176 Sopwith Camel F.1

3177 Nimrod MR2

3178 RAF Red Arrows

Votes for Women

2018 (15 Feb.) One centre band (Nos. 4050/4051) or two phosphor bands (others). Perf 14½×14.

4050	**3164**	(2nd) multicoloured	90	90	☐ ☐
		a. Horiz pair. Nos. 4050/4051	1·75	1·75	☐ ☐
4051	**3165**	(2nd) multicoloured	90	90	☐ ☐
4052	**3166**	(1st) multicoloured	1·00	1·00	☐ ☐
		a. Horiz pair. Nos. 4052/4053	2·00	2·00	☐ ☐
4053	**3167**	(1st) multicoloured	1·00	1·00	☐ ☐
4054	**3168**	£1·40 multicoloured	2·25	2·25	☐ ☐
		a. Horiz pair. Nos. 4054/4055	4·50	4·50	☐ ☐
4055	**3169**	£1·40 multicoloured	2·25	2·25	☐ ☐
4056	**3170**	£1·57 multicoloured	2·50	2·50	☐ ☐
		a. Horiz pair. Nos. 4056/4057	5·00	5·00	☐ ☐
4057	**3171**	£1·57 multicoloured	2·50	2·50	☐ ☐
Set of 8			12·00	12·00	☐ ☐
First Day Cover				16·00	☐
Presentation Pack (PO Pack No. 552)			15·00		☐
PHQ Cards (set of 8) (439)			4·00	13·00	☐ ☐
Set of 4 Gutter Blocks of 4			24·00		☐

Nos. 4050/4051, 4052/4053, 4054/4055 and 4056/4057 were each printed together, *se-tenant*, as horizontal pairs in sheets of 60 (2 panes 6×5).

Centenary of the RAF (Royal Air Force) (1st issue)

2018 (20 Mar.) Two phosphor bands.

(a) Ordinary gum. Litho. Perf 14½×14.

4058	**3172**	(1st) multicoloured	1·50	1·50	☐ ☐
		a. Horiz pair. Nos. 4058/4059	3·00	3·00	☐ ☐
4059	**3173**	(1st) multicoloured	1·50	1·50	☐ ☐
4060	**3174**	£1·40 multicoloured	3·25	3·25	☐ ☐
		a. Horiz pair. Nos. 4060/4061	6·50	6·50	☐ ☐
4061	**3175**	£1·40 multicoloured	3·25	3·25	☐ ☐
4062	**3176**	£1·57 multicoloured	3·75	3·75	☐ ☐
		a. Horiz pair. Nos. 4062/4063	7·50	7·50	☐ ☐
4063	**3177**	£1·57 multicoloured	3·75	3·75	☐ ☐
Set of 6			15·00	15·00	☐ ☐
First Day Cover				13·50	☐
Presentation Pack (Nos. 4058/4063 and **MS**4064) (PO Pack No. 553)			20·00		☐
PHQ Cards (set of 11) (440)			10·00	32·00	☐ ☐

MS4064 202×74 mm. **3178** (1st) Flypast; (1st) Swan formation; £1·40 Synchro; £1·40 Python

		9·50	9·50 ☐ ☐
First Day Cover			8·00 ☐

(b) Self-adhesive. Gravure. Die-cut perf 14½.

4065	**3172**	(1st) multicoloured	1·75	1·75	☐ ☐
4066	**3173**	(1st) multicoloured	1·75	1·75	☐ ☐

Nos. 4058/4059, 4060/4061 and 4062/4063 were each printed together, *se-tenant*, as horizontal pairs in sheets of 60 (2 panes 6×5).

Nos. 4065/4066 were issued in stamp booklets with 4×1st bright scarlet stamps originally sold for £3·90.

The 11 PHQ cards show the individual stamps, including those from No. **MS**4070, and the complete miniature sheet.

3179 Red Arrows, Flypast

3180 Red Arrows, Swan

3181 Red Arrows, Syncro pair

3182 Red Arrows, Python

Centenary of the RAF (Royal Air Force) (2nd issue).
Red Arrows

2018 (20 Mar.) Two phosphor bands. Litho. Perf 14½×14.

4067	**3179**	(1st) multicoloured	1·50	1·50
4068	**3180**	(1st) multicoloured	1·50	1·50
4069	**3181**	£1·40 multicoloured	3·25	3·25
4070	**3182**	£1·40 multicoloured	3·25	3·25
Set of 4			8·50	8·50

Nos. 4067/4070 come from No. **MS**4064 and £18·69 RAF Centenary premium booklets, No. DY25.

3183 Pilots scramble to their Hurricanes

3184 Supermarine Spitfires of 610 Squadron, Biggin Hill, on Patrol

3185 Armourer Fred Roberts replaces Ammunition Boxes on Supermarine Spitfire

Centenary of the RAF (Royal Air Force) (3rd issue).
Battle of Britain

2018 (20 Mar.) Stamps as No. **MS**3735. Two phosphor bands. Litho. Perf 14.

4071	**3183**	(1st) multicoloured	1·50	1·50
4072	**3184**	(1st) multicoloured	1·50	1·50
4073	**3185**	(1st) multicoloured	1·50	1·50
Set of 3			4·00	4·00

Nos. 4071/4073 come from £18·69 premium booklets, No. DY25. The images on these three stamps were previously used in No. **MS**3735 issued on 17 July 2015 to commemorate the 75th Anniversary of the Battle of Britain; those stamps were 'all-over' phosphor.

3186 Osprey (*Pandion haliaetus*)

3187 Large Blue Butterfly (*Maculinea arion*)

3188 Eurasian Beaver (*Castor fiber*)

3189 Pool Frog (*Pelophylax lessonae*)

3190 Stinking Hawk's-beard (*Crepis foetida*)

3191 Sand Lizard (*Lacerta agilis*)

Reintroduced Species

2018 (17 Apr.) Two phosphor bands. Perf 14½.

4074	**3186**	(1st) multicoloured	1·00	1·00
		a. Horiz. pair. Nos. 4074/4075	2·00	2·00
4075	**3187**	(1st) multicoloured	1·00	1·00
4076	**3188**	£1·45 multicoloured	2·25	2·25
		a. Horiz. pair. Nos. 4076/4077	4·50	4·50
4077	**3189**	£1·45 multicoloured	2·25	2·25
4078	**3190**	£1·55 multicoloured	2·50	2·50
		a. Horiz. pair. Nos. 4078/4079	5·00	5·00
4079	**3191**	£1·55 multicoloured	2·50	2·50
Set of 6			10·50	10·50
First Day Cover				13·50
Presentation Pack (PO Pack No. 554)			13·50	
PHQ Cards (*set of 6*) (441)			4·00	12·00
Set of 3 Gutter Blocks of 4			21·00	

Nos. 4074/4075, 4076/4077 and 4078/4079 were each printed together, *se-tenant*, as horizontal pairs in sheets of 60 (2 panes 6×5).

Centenary of the RAF (Royal Air Force) (4th issue)

2018 (11 May.) Self-adhesive. Two phosphor bands. Gravure. Die-cut perf 14

4080	**3179**	(1st) multicoloured	3·00	3·00
4081	**3180**	(1st) multicoloured	3·00	3·00

Nos. 4080/4081 were issued in stamp booklets with 4×1st bright scarlet stamps, originally sold for £4·02.

3192 Barn Owl (*Tyto alba*)

3193 Little Owl (*Athene noctua*)

3194 Tawny Owl
(*Strix aluco*)

3195 Short-eared Owl
(*Asio flammeus*)

3196 Long-eared Owl
(*Asio otus*)

3197 Two Young Barn Owls
(*Tyto alba*)

3198 Little Owl Chicks
(*Athene noctua*)

3199 Tawny Owl Chick
(*Strix aluco*)

3200 Short-eared Owl Chick
(*Asio flammeus*)

3201 Long-eared Owl Chick
(*Asio otus*)

Owls

2018 (11 May) Two phosphor bands. Perf 14½×14.

4082	**3192**	(1st) multicoloured	1·00	1·00	□	□
		a. Horiz strip of 5. Nos. 4082/4086	4·50	4·50	□	□
4083	**3193**	(1st) multicoloured	1·00	1·00	□	□
4084	**3194**	(1st) multicoloured	1·00	1·00	□	□
4085	**3195**	(1st) multicoloured	1·00	1·00	□	□
4086	**3196**	(1st) multicoloured	1·00	1·00	□	□
4087	**3197**	(1st) multicoloured	1·00	1·00	□	□
		a. Horiz strip of 5. Nos. 4087/4091	4·50	4·50	□	□
4088	**3198**	(1st) multicoloured	1·00	1·00	□	□

4089	**3199**	(1st) multicoloured	1·00	1·00	□	□
4090	**3200**	(1st) multicoloured	1·00	1·00	□	□
4091	**3201**	(1st) multicoloured	1·00	1·00	□	□
Set of 10			9·00	9·00	□	
First Day Cover				12·50	□	
Presentation Pack (PO Pack No. 555)			12·00		□	
PHQ Cards (*set of 10*) (442)			6·75	11·00	□	□
Set of 2 Gutter Strips of 10			19·00		□	
Set of 2 Traffic Light Gutter Strips of 20			40·00		□	

Nos. 4082/4086 and 4087/4091 were each printed together, *se-tenant*, as horizontal strips of five stamps in sheets of 50 (2 panes 5×5).

3202 Royal Wedding

Royal Wedding

2018 (19 May) 'All-over' phosphor. Perf 14½×14.

MS4092 116×89 mm. **3202** (1st) Prince Harry and Ms. Meghan Markle×2; £1·55 Prince Harry and Ms. Meghan Markle (black and white photo)×2	7·00	7·00	□	
First Day Cover		8·50	□	
Presentation Pack (PO Pack No. M24)	7·50		□	

A souvenir pack containing Nos. **MS**3932 and **MS**4092 with silver foil cachet postmarks and imagery from the Royal Weddng was available from Royal Mail from 29 June 2018 for £24·99.

3203 Summer Exhibition
(Grayson Perry)

3204 Queen of the Sky
(Fiona Rae)

3205 St Kilda: The Great Sea Stacs
(Norman Ackroyd)

3206 Inverleith Allotments and
Edinburgh Castle (Barbara Rae)

3207 *Queuing at the RA*
(Yinka Shonibare)

3208 *Saying Goodbye*
(Tracey Emin)

3215 Private Godfrey (Arnold Ridley)   **3216** Chief Warden Hodges (Bill
('Do you think I might be excused?')   Pertwee) ('Put that light out!')

250th Anniversary of the Royal Academy of Arts, London

2018 (5 June) Two phosphor bands. Perf 14×14½.

4093	**3203**	(1st) multicoloured	1·00	1·00	☐ ☐
		a. Vert pair. Nos. 4093/4094	2·00	2·00	☐ ☐
4094	**3204**	(1st) multicoloured	1·00	1·00	☐ ☐
4095	**3205**	£1·25 multicoloured	1·90	1·90	☐ ☐
		a. Vert pair. Nos. 4095/4096	3·75	3·75	☐ ☐
4096	**3206**	£1·25 multicoloured	1·90	1·90	☐ ☐
4097	**3207**	£1·55 multicoloured	2·40	2·40	☐ ☐
		a. Vert pair. Nos. 4097/4098	4·75	4·75	☐ ☐
4098	**3208**	£1·55 multicoloured	2·40	2·40	☐ ☐
Set of 6			9·50	9·50	☐ ☐
First Day Cover				13·00	☐
Presentation Pack (PO Pack No. 556)			12·00		☐
PHQ Cards (*set of 6*) (443)			4·00	11·50	☐ ☐
Set of 3 Gutter Pairs (only 2 stamps in each gutter pair)			11·00		☐

Nos. 4093/4094, 4095/4096 and 4097/4098 were each printed together, *se-tenant*, as vertical pairs in sheets of 60 (2 panes 5×6).

50th Anniversary of *Dad's Army*
(BBC television sitcom 1968–1977)

2018 (26 June) One centre band (2nd) or two phosphor bands (others).

(a) Ordinary gum. Perf 14½. x 14

4099	**3209**	(2nd) multicoloured	90	90	☐ ☐
		a. Horiz pair. Nos. 4099/4100	1·75	1·75	☐ ☐
4100	**3210**	(2nd) multicoloured	90	90	☐ ☐
4101	**3211**	(1st) multicoloured	1·00	1·00	☐ ☐
		a. Horiz pair. Nos. 4101/4102	2·00	2·00	☐ ☐
4102	**3212**	(1st) multicoloured	1·00	1·00	☐ ☐
4103	**3213**	£1·45 multicoloured	2·25	2·25	☐ ☐
		a. Horiz pair. Nos. 4103/4104	4·50	4·50	☐ ☐
4104	**3214**	£1·45 multicoloured	2·25	2·25	☐ ☐
4105	**3215**	£1·55 multicoloured	2·40	2·40	☐ ☐
		a. Horiz pair. Nos. 4105/4106	4·75	4·75	☐ ☐
4106	**3216**	£1·55 multicoloured	2·40	2·40	☐ ☐
Set of 8			12·00	12·00	☐ ☐
First Day Cover				16·00	☐
Presentation Pack (PO Pack No. 557)			23·00		☐
PHQ Cards (*set of 8*) (444)			5·50	14·00	☐ ☐
Set of 4 Gutter Blocks of 4			24·00		☐

(b) Self-adhesive. Die-cut perf 14½×14.

4107	**3211**	(1st) multicoloured	1·75	1·75	☐ ☐
4108	**3212**	(1st) multicoloured	1·75	1·75	☐ ☐

Nos. 4099/4100, 4101/4102, 4103/4104 and 4105/4106 were each printed *se-tenant* as horizontal pairs in sheets of 60 (2 panes 6×5).

Nos. 4107/4108 were issued in stamp booklets with 4×1st bright scarlet stamps originally sold for £4·02.

Stamps as Nos. 4101/4102 but self-adhesive and perforated 14×14½ were issued in sheets of ten containing five stamps of each design with labels showing stills from the television series.

3209 Sergeant Wilson
(John Le Mesurier) ('Do you think
that's wise, sir?')

3210 Private Pike (Ian Lavender) ('I'll
tell Mum!')

3211 Captain Mainwaring (Arthur
Lowe) ('You stupid boy!')

3212 Lance Corporal Jones (Clive
Dunn) ('Don't panic! Don't panic!')

3217 South Front

3213 Private Walker (James Beck)
('It won't cost you much...')

3214 Private Frazer (John Laurie)
('We're doomed. Doomed!')

3218 West Front

3219 East Front

3220 Pond Gardens

3221 Maze

3222 Great Fountain Garden

3223 Hampton Court Palace

3224 Great Hall

3225 King's Great Bedchamber

Hampton Court Palace

2018 (31 July) Two phosphor bands.

(a) Ordinary gum. Perf 14½

4109	**3217**	(1st) multicoloured	1·00	1·00	
		a. Horiz strip of 3. Nos.			
		4109/4111	3·00	3·00	
4110	**3218**	(1st) multicoloured	1·00	1·00	
4111	**3219**	(1st) multicoloured	1·00	1·00	
4112	**3220**	£1·55 multicoloured	2·40	2·40	
		a. Horiz strip of 3. Nos.			
		4112/4114	7·25	7·25	
4113	**3221**	£1·55 multicoloured	2·40	2·40	
4114	**3222**	£1·55 multicoloured	2·40	2·40	
Set of 6			9·00	9·00	
First Day Cover				12·50	
Presentation Pack (Nos. 4109/4114 and					
MS4115) (PO Pack No.558)			19·00		
PHQ Cards (*set of 11*) (445)			7·50	22·00	
Set of 2 Gutter Strips of 6			18·00		
MS4115 156×74 mm. **3223** (1st) Great Hall;					
(1st) King's Great Bedchamber; £1·45					
Chapel Royal; £1·45 King's Staircase			6·50	6·50	
First Day Cover				8·25	

(b) Self-adhesive. Die-cut perf 14

4116	**3224**	(1st) multicoloured	1·75	1·75	
4117	**3225**	(1st) multicoloured	1·75	1·75	

Nos. 4109/4111 and 4112/4114 were each printed together, *se-tenant*, as horizontal strips of three stamps in sheets of 60 (2 panes 6×5).

Nos. 4116/4117 were issued in stamp booklets with 4×1st bright scarlet stamps, originally sold for £4·02.

The 11 PHQ cards show the individual stamps including those from No. **MS**4115 and the complete miniature sheet.

3226 Joseph Banks, Red-tailed Tropicbird and Red Passion Flower

3227 Chief Mourner of Tahiti and a Scene with a Canoe

3228 Captain James Cook and *Triumph of the Navigators*

3229 Drawings of the Observations of a Transit of Venus, 1769 and Sextant

3230 Scarlet Clianthus, and Portrait of a Maori Chief

3231 Blue-Black Grassquit and Self-Portrait of Sydney Parkinson

3232 *The Endeavour* Voyage

Captain Cook and the *Endeavour* Voyage (1768–71)

2018 (16 Aug.) One centre band (2nd) or two phosphor bands (others). Perf 14×14½ (Nos. 4118/4123) or 14 (No. **MS**4124).

4118	**3226**	(2nd) multicoloured	90	90	☐	☐
		a. Horiz pair. Nos.				
		4118/4119	1·75	1·75	☐	☐
4119	**3227**	(2nd) multicoloured	90	90	☐	☐
4120	**3228**	(1st) multicoloured	1·00	1·00	☐	☐
		a. Horiz pair. Nos.				
		4120/4121	2·00	2·00	☐	☐
4121	**3229**	(1st) multicoloured	1·00	1·00	☐	☐
4122	**3230**	£1·45 multicoloured	2·25	2·25	☐	☐
		a. Horiz pair. Nos.				
		4122/4123	4·50	4·50	☐	☐
4123	**3231**	£1·45 multicoloured	2·25	2·25	☐	☐
Set of 6			7·50	7·50	☐	
First Day Cover				10·50	☐	
Presentation Pack (Nos. 4118/4123 and						
MS4124) (PO Pack No.559)			17·00		☐	
PHQ Cards (*set of 11*) (446)			7·50	20·00	☐	☐
Set of 3 Gutter Blocks of 4			15·00		☐	

MS4124 125×89 mm. **3232** (1st) Chart of the discoveries made by Captain James Cook (Lieutenant Roberts) ('Charting a new course: New Zealand and Australia'); (1st) Boathouse and canoes on Raiatea, Society Islands (after Sydney Parkinson); £1·45 Arched rock with Maori clifftop fort, New Zealand ('Mapping New Zealand: a Maori clifftop fort'); £1·45 Repairing the *Endeavour* on the Endeavour River, Australia (after Sydney Parkinson) ... 6·50 ... 6·50 ☐ ☐

First Day Cover			8·25	☐	

Nos. 4118/4119, 4120/4121 and 4122/4123 were printed together, *se-tenant*, as horizontal pairs in sheets of 60 (2 panes 6×5).

Nos. 4118/**MS**4124 commemorate the 250th Anniversary of the Departure of the *Endeavour*.

The 11 PHQ cards show the ten individual stamps including those from No. **MS**4124 and the complete miniature sheet.

3233 Laurence Olivier in *The Dance of Death*

3234 Glenda Jackson in *King Lear*

3235 Albert Finney in *Hamlet*

3236 Maggie Smith in *Hedda Gabler*

3237 John Gielgud and Ralph Richardson in *No Man's Land*

3238 Sharon Benson in *Carmen Jones*

3239 Judi Dench and John Stride in *Romeo and Juliet*

3240 Richard Burton in *Henry V*

Bicentenary of The Old Vic, London

2018 (30 Aug.) Two phosphor bands. Perf 14½×14

4125	**3233**	(1st) multicoloured	1·00	1·00	☐	☐
		a. Horiz pair. Nos.				
		4125/4126	2·00	2·00	☐	☐
4126	**3234**	(1st) multicoloured	1·00	1·00	☐	☐
4127	**3235**	£1·25 multicoloured	1·90	1·90	☐	☐
		a. Horiz pair. Nos.				
		4127/4128	3·75	3·75	☐	☐
4128	**3236**	£1·25 multicoloured	1·90	1·90	☐	☐
4129	**3237**	£1·45 multicoloured	2·25	2·25	☐	☐
		a. Horiz pair. Nos.				
		4129/4130	4·50	4·50	☐	☐
4130	**3238**	£1·45 multicoloured	2·25	2·25	☐	☐
4131	**3239**	£1·55 multicoloured	2·40	2·40	☐	☐
		a. Horiz pair. Nos.				
		4131/4132	4·75	4·75	☐	☐
4132	**3240**	£1·55 multicoloured	2·40	2·40	☐	☐
Set of 8			13·50	13·50	☐	☐
First Day Cover				19·00	☐	
Presentation Pack (PO Pack No. 560)			17·00		☐	
PHQ Cards (*set of 8*) (447)			5·50	15·00	☐	☐
Set of 4 Gutter Pairs (only 2 stamps in						
each gutter pair)			14·00		☐	
Set of 4 Traffic Light Gutter Blocks						
(4 stamps per block)			28·00		☐	

Nos. 4125/4126, 4127/4128, 4129/4130 and 4131/4132 were each printed together, *se-tenant*, as horizontal pairs in sheets of 60 (2 panes 6×5).

3241 *100 Poppies*
(Zafer and Barbara Baran)

3242 *Anthem for Doomed Youth*
(poem by Wilfred Owen) (woodblock
print by Andrew Davidson)

3247 *Hermione Granger*
(Emma Watson)

3248 *Hogwarts Express*

3243 Second Lieutenant
Walter Tull (1888–1918)

3244 *We Are Making a New
World* (Paul Nash)

3249 *Harry Potter*
(Daniel Radcliffe)

3250 *Flying Ford Anglia*

3245 The Grave of the
Unknown Warrior,
Westminster Abbey, London

3246 Lieutenant Francis
Hopgood's Goggles

3251 *Ron Weasley*
(Rupert Grint)

3252 *Hagrid's Motorbike*

Centenary of the First World War (5th issue)

2018 (13 Sept.)

(a) Ordinary gum. Two phosphor bands. Perf 14½

4133	**3241**	(1st) multicoloured	1·00	1·00
4134	**3242**	(1st) multicoloured	1·00	1·00
4135	**3243**	(1st) multicoloured	1·00	1·00
4136	**3244**	£1·55 multicoloured	2·40	2·40
4137	**3245**	£1·55 multicoloured	2·40	2·40
4138	**3246**	£1·55 multicoloured	2·40	2·40
Set of 6			9·00	9·00
First Day Cover				12·50
Presentation Pack (PO Pack No. 561)			12·00	
PHQ Cards (*set of 6*) (448)			4·00	11·00
Set of 6 Gutter Pairs			18·00	

MS4138*a* 296x210 mm. Nos. 3626/3631,
   3711/3716,   3838/3843,   3983/3988
   and 4133/4138   65·00   65·00

(b) Self-adhesive. Die-cut perf 14½.

4139	**2774**	(1st) multicoloured	1·75	1·75
4140	**3241**	(1st) multicoloured	1·75	1·75

Nos. 4139/4140 were issued in stamp booklets with 4×1st bright
scarlet stamps, originally sold for £4·02.

  No. **MS**4138*a* was a special composite sheet sold for £32·94.

  No. 4139 was as T **2774**, the Poppy stamp issued in 2014
for the first Centenary of the First World War series, but self-
adhesive and printed in gravure.

  A souvenir pack containing the Poppy stamps Nos. 3626,
3711, 3838, 3983 and 4133 each affixed to a poem print was sold
by Royal Mail for £24·99.

3253 *Ginny Weasley*
(Bonnie Wright)

3254 *Triwizard Cup*

3255 *Neville Longbottom*
(Matthew Lewis)

3256 *Knight Bus*

3257 Hogwarts Professors and The Marauders Map

3258 Man and Girl posting Letters in Wall-mounted Post box

3259 Postal Worker emptying Post box

Harry Potter

2018 (16 Oct.) 'All-over' phosphor (No. **MS**4151 – stamps only) or two phosphor bands (others).

(a) Ordinary gum. Litho. Perf 14×14½

4141	**3247**	(1st) multicoloured	1·00	1·00		
		Horiz strip of 5.				
		Nos. 4141/4145	4·50	4·50		
4142	**3248**	(1st) multicoloured	1·00	1·00		
4143	**3249**	(1st) multicoloured	1·00	1·00		
4144	**3250**	(1st) multicoloured	1·00	1·00		
4145	**3251**	(1st) multicoloured	1·00	1·00		
4146	**3252**	(1st) multicoloured	1·00	1·00		
		Horiz strip of 5.				
		Nos. 4146/4150	4·50	4·50		
4147	**3253**	(1st) multicoloured	1·00	1·00		
4148	**3254**	(1st) multicoloured	1·00	1·00		
4149	**3255**	(1st) multicoloured	1·00	1·00		
4150	**3256**	(1st) multicoloured	1·00	1·00		
Set of 10			9·00	9·00		
First Day Cover				13·00		
Presentation Pack (Nos. 4141/4150 and						
MS4151) (PO Pack No. 562)			17·00			
PHQ Cards (set of 16) (449)			11·00	23·00		
Set of 2 Gutter Strips of 10			18·00			

(b) Self-adhesive. Litho. Die-cut perf 14×14½
(Nos. 4152/4153) or 14 (No. **MS**4153)

MS4151 202×74 mm. **3257** (1st) Pomona Sprout (Miriam Margolyes); (1st) Horace Slughorn (Jim Broadbent); (1st) Sybill Trelawney (Emma Thompson); (1st) Remus Lupin (David Thewlis); (1st) Severus Snape (Alan Rickman) 5·00 5·00

First Day Cover 6·75

(c) Self-adhesive. Gravure. Die-cut perf 14×14½

4152	**3247**	(1st) multicoloured	1·75	1·75		
4153	**3249**	(1st) multicoloured	1·75	1·75		

Nos. 4141/4145 and 4146/4150 were each printed together, se-tenant, as horizontal strips of five stamps in sheets of 50 (2 panes 5×5).

Nos. 4152/4153 were issued in stamp booklets with 4×1st bright scarlet stamps, originally sold for £4·02.

When placed under a UV light parts of the designs of Nos. 4141/4150 and 4152/4153 light up green, and No. **MS**4151 reveals additional inscriptions.

The 16 PHQ cards show the individual stamps including those from No. **MS**4151 and the complete miniature sheet.

A collectors sheet containing stamps as Nos. 4141/4150 but self-adhesive with labels showing Harry Potter film stills was sold for £7·70, a £1 premium over face value.

A Souvenir Stamp Art Folder containing pages of enlarged images of Nos. 4141/4150 with the stamps attached, cancelled with a special cachet postmark, and also a poster of the miniature sheet, were sold by Royal Mail for £24·99.

3260 Man and Girl posting Letters in Wall-mounted Post box

3261 Postal Worker emptying Post box

3262 Man and Boy approaching Rural Pillar Box

3263 Man approaching Post Box

3264 Woman with Dog posting Letter

3265 Pillar Box near Church

Christmas. Post Boxes

2018 (1 Nov.) One centre band (No. 4154) or two bands (others). Perf 14½×15

(a) Self-adhesive. Gravure

4154	**3258**	(2nd) multicoloured	90	90		
4155	**3259**	(1st) multicoloured	1·00	1·00		
4156	**3260**	(2nd Large) multicoloured	1·10	1·10		
4157	**3261**	(1st Large) multicoloured	1·40	1·40		
4158	**3262**	£1·25 multicoloured	1·90	1·90		
4159	**3263**	£1·45 multicoloured	2·25	2·25		
4160	**3264**	£1·55 multicoloured	2·40	2·40		
4161	**3265**	£2·25 multicoloured	3·50	3·50		
Set of 8			13·00	13·00		
First Day Cover				18·00		
Presentation Pack (PO Pack No. 563)			25·00			
PHQ Cards (set of 9) (450)			6·00	25·00		

(b) Ordinary gum. Litho

MS4162 190×74 mm. As Nos. 4154/4161		14·00	14·00		
First Day Cover			18·00		

The 2nd class, 1st class, £1·25, £1·45, £1·55 and £2·25 values were also issued in sheets of 20 containing eight 2nd class, eight 1st class and one each of the £1·25, £1·45, £1·55 and £2·25 values, each stamp accompanied by a se-tenant label.

The nine PHQ cards show the individual stamps and the complete miniature sheet.

3266 70th Birthday of Prince of Wales

70th Birthday of the Prince of Wales

2018 (14 Nov.) 'All-over' phosphor. Self-adhesive. Multicoloured. Die-cut perf 141/2x15

MS4163 203×74 mm. **3266** (1st) Prince Charles; (1st) Prince Charles with Camilla, Duchess of Cornwall; (1st) Prince Charles with Prince William and Prince Harry; £1·55 Prince Charles, Prince William and Prince Harry at Cirencester Park Polo Club; £1·55 Prince Charles at Castle of Mey; £1·55 Prince Charles with schoolchildren at

Llancaiach Fawr Manor	10·50	10·50	☐ ☐
First Day Cover		13·00	☐
Presentation Pack (PO Pack No. 564)	12·00		☐
PHQ Cards (*set of 7*) (451)	4·75	12·00	☐ ☐

Collectors Pack

2018 (14 Nov.) Comprises Nos. 4033/**MS**4043, 4050/**MS**4064, 4074/4079, 4082/4106, 4109/**MS**4115, 4118/4138, 4141/**MS**4151, 4154/4161 and **MS**4163

CP4163*a* Collectors Pack	£275	☐

Post Office Yearbook

2018 (14 Nov.) Comprises Nos. 4033/**MS**4043, 4050/**MS**4064, 4074/4079, 4082/4106, 4109/**MS**4115, 4118/4138, 4141/**MS**4151, 4154/4161 and **MS**4163

YB4163*a* Yearbook	£300	☐

Miniature Sheet Collection

2018 (14 Nov.) Comprises Nos. **MS**4043, **MS**4064, **MS**4092, **MS**4115, **MS**4124, **MS**4151, **MS**4162 and **MS**4163

MS4163*a* Miniature Sheet Collection	85·00	☐

3267 Pomona Sprout
(Miriam Margolyes)

3268 Horace Slughorn
(Jim Broadbent)

3269 Sybill Trelawney
(Emma Thompson)

3270 Remus Lupin
(David Thewlis)

3271 Severus Snape
(Alan Rickman)

Harry Potter (2nd issue)

2018 (4 Dec.) 'All-over' phosphor (stamps only). Self-adhesive. Die-cut perf 14

4164	**3267**	(1st) multicoloured	1·40	1·40	☐ ☐
4165	**3268**	(1st) multicoloured	1·40	1·40	☐ ☐
4166	**3269**	(1st) multicoloured	1·40	1·40	☐ ☐
4167	**3270**	(1st) multicoloured	1·40	1·40	☐ ☐
4168	**3271**	(1st) multicoloured	1·40	1·40	☐ ☐
Set of 5			6·25	6·25	☐ ☐

Nos. 4164/4168 were issued in No. **MS**4151 and in two booklet panes from the £13·97 Harry Potter booklet, No. DY27. The booklet panes are as No. **MS**4151 but in two panes with Marauder's Map margins.

3272 Stamp Classics

Stamp Classics

2019 (15 Jan.) Multicoloured. Phosphor frame. Perf 14×13½

MS4169   203×74 mm. **3272** (1st) Queen Victoria 1891 £1 green; (1st) King Edward VII 1910 2d. Tyrian plum; (1st) King George V 1913 'Seahorse' 2s.6d. brown; £1·55 King Edward VIII 1936 1½d. red-brown; £1·55 King George VI (and Queen Victoria) 1940 Penny Black Centenary ½d. green; £1·55 Queen Elizabeth II 1953 Coronation

2½d. carmine-red	13·50	13·50	☐ ☐
First Day Cover		12·50	☐
Presentation Pack (PO Pack No. 566)	12·00		☐
PHQ Cards (*set of 7*) (452)	4·75	22·00	☐ ☐

No. **MS**4169 commemorates the 150th Anniversary of the Royal Philatelic Society and the 50th Anniversary of Queen Elizabeth II opening the National Postal Museum, London.

3273 The Skull Sectioned

3274 A Sprig of Guelder-Rose

3275 Studies of Cats

3276 A Star-of-Bethlehem and Other Plants

3277 The Anatomy of the Shoulder and Foot

3278 The Head of Leda

3279 The Head of a Bearded Man

3280 The Skeleton

3281 The Head of St Philip

3282 A Woman in a Landscape

3283 A Design for an Equestrian Monument

3284 The Fall of Light on a Face

500th Death Anniversary of Leonardo da Vinci (1452–1519, artist)

2019 (13 Feb.) Two phosphor bands. Perf 14½

4170	**3273**	(1st) multicoloured	1·00	1·00	☐	☐
		a. Horiz strip of 6. Nos.				
		4170/4175	5·50	5·50	☐	☐
4171	**3274**	(1st) multicoloured	1·00	1·00	☐	☐
4172	**3275**	(1st) multicoloured	1·00	1·00	☐	☐
4173	**3276**	(1st) multicoloured	1·00	1·00	☐	☐
4174	**3277**	(1st) multicoloured	1·00	1·00	☐	☐
4175	**3278**	(1st) multicoloured	1·00	1·00	☐	☐
4176	**3279**	(1st) multicoloured	1·00	1·00	☐	☐
		a. Horiz strip of 6. Nos.				
		4176/4181	5·50	5·50	☐	☐
4177	**3280**	(1st) multicoloured	1·00	1·00	☐	☐
4178	**3281**	(1st) multicoloured	1·00	1·00	☐	☐
4179	**3282**	(1st) multicoloured	1·00	1·00	☐	☐
4180	**3283**	(1st) multicoloured	1·00	1·00	☐	☐
4181	**3284**	(1st) multicoloured	1·00	1·00	☐	☐
Set of 12			11·00	11·00		
First Day Cover				15·00	☐	
Presentation Pack (PO Pack No. 567)			14·00		☐	
PHQ Cards (set of 12) (453)			7·00	12·00	☐	☐
Set of 2 Gutter Strips of 12			22·00			

Nos. 4170/4175 and 4176/4181 were each printed together, se-tenant, as horizontal strips of six stamps in sheets of 60 (2 panes 6×5).

3285 Spider-Man

3286 Captain Marvel

3287 Hulk

3288 Doctor Strange

3289 Captain Britain

3290 Peggy Carter

3291 Iron Man

3292 Union Jack

3293 Black Panther

3294 Thor

3295 Marvel Heroes UK

3296 Thanos

3297 Thor, Doctor Strange and Iron Man ('He's strong.')

3298 Hulk, Iron Man, Black Panther and Spider-Man ('but we're stronger...')

3299 Captain Britain, Spider-Man, Iron Man, Hulk, Thor and Black Panther ('...together!')

3300 Captain Britain ('Fury, a portal is opening.')

Marvel (1st issue)

2019 (14 Mar.) Two phosphor bands

		(a) Ordinary gum. Litho. Perf 14½			
4182	**3285**	(1st) multicoloured	1·00	1·00	
		a. Horiz strip of 5. Nos. 4182/4186	4·50	4·50	
4183	**3286**	(1st) multicoloured	1·00	1·00	
4184	**3287**	(1st) multicoloured	1·00	1·00	
4185	**3288**	(1st) multicoloured	1·00	1·00	
4186	**3289**	(1st) multicoloured	1·00	1·00	
4187	**3290**	(1st) multicoloured	1·00	1·00	
		a. Horiz strip of 5. Nos. 4187/4191	4·50	4·50	
4188	**3291**	(1st) multicoloured	1·00	1·00	
4189	**3292**	(1st) multicoloured	1·00	1·00	
4190	**3293**	(1st) multicoloured	1·00	1·00	
4191	**3294**	(1st) multicoloured	1·00	1·00	
Set of 10			9·00	9·00	
First Day Cover				14·00	

Presentation Pack (Nos. 4182/4191 and **MS**4192) (PO Pack No. 568) ... 24·00

PHQ Cards (set of 16) (454) ... 9·00 24·00

Set of 2 Gutter Strips of 10 ... 22·00

(b) Self-adhesive. Litho

MS4192 203×74 mm. **3295** (1st) Thanos (Perf 14); (1st) Thor, Doctor Strange and Iron Man ('He's strong.') (Perf 14½×14); (1st) Hulk, Iron Man, Black Panther and Spider-Man ('but we're stronger...') (Perf 14); £1·25 Captain Britain, Spider-Man, Iron Man, Hulk, Thor and Black Panther ('...together!') (Perf 14); £1·45 Captain Britain ('Fury, a portal is opening.') (Perf 14½×14) ... 7·25 7·25

First Day Cover ... 10·00

(c) Self-adhesive booklet stamps. Gravure. Die-cut perf 14½.

4193	**3285**	(1st) multicoloured	1·75	1·75	
4194	**3287**	(1st) multicoloured	1·75	1·75	

Nos. 4182/4186 and 4187/4191 were each printed together, *se-tenant,* as horizontal strips of five stamps in sheets of 50 (2 panes 5×5).

Nos. 4193/4194 were issued in stamp booklets with 4×1st bright scarlet stamps, originally sold for £4·02.

Nos. 4182/4199 commemorate the 80th Anniversary of Marvel Comics.

The 16 PHQ cards show the 15 individual stamps, including those from No. **MS**4192, and the complete sheet.

A collector's sheet containing stamps as Nos. 4182/4191 but self-adhesive was sold for £7·70, a £1 premium above face value.

Marvel (2nd issue)

2019 (14 Mar.) Litho. Die-cut perf 14½×14 (Nos. 4196, 4199) or 14 (others)

4195	**3296**	(1st) multicoloured	1·25	1·25	
4196	**3297**	(1st) multicoloured	1·25	1·25	
4197	**3298**	(1st) multicoloured	1·25	1·25	
4198	**3299**	£1·25 multicoloured	2·50	2·50	
4199	**3300**	£1·45 multicoloured	2·75	2·75	
Set of 5			8·00	8·00	

Nos. 4195/4199 were issued in No. **MS**4192 and in two booklet panes from the £17·45 Marvel booklet. The booklet panes are as No. **MS**4192 but in two panes with enlarged margins.

3301 White-tailed Eagle (*Haliaeetus albicilla*)

3302 Merlin (*Falco columbarius*)

3303 Hobby (*Falco subbuteo*)

3304 Buzzard (*Buteo buteo*)

Golden Eagle
Aquila chrysaetos

3305 Golden Eagle
(*Aquila chrysaetos*)

Kestrel
Falco tinnunculus

3306 Kestrel
(*Falco tinnunculus*)

Goshawk
Accipiter gentilis

3307 Goshawk
(*Accipiter gentilis*)

Sparrowhawk
Accipiter nisus

3308 Sparrowhawk
(*Accipiter nisus*)

Red Kite
Milvus milvus

3309 Red Kite (*Milvus milvus*)

Peregrine Falcon
Falco peregrinus

3310 Peregrine Falcon
(*Falco peregrinus*)

Raspberry Pi microcomputer
helps to teach programming

3311 Raspberry Pi
Microcomputer

The Falkirk Wheel rotating boat
lift connects Scottish waterways

3312 The Falkirk Wheel
Rotating Boat Lift

Three-way catalytic converter
reduces pollutants in car exhaust

3313 Three-way Catalytic
Converter

Crossrail created 26 miles (42km)
of new rail tunnels under London

3314 Crossrail

Superconducting magnet allows
high-quality imaging in MRI

3315 Superconducting
Magnet in MRI Scanner

Synthetic bone-graft material
encourages new bone growth

3316 Synthetic Bone-graft

HARRIER JUMP JET
50TH ANNIVERSARY

3317 Harrier GR3

Birds of Prey

2019 (4 Apr.) Phosphor background

		(a) Ordinary gum. Litho. Perf 14×14½			
4200	**3301**	(1st) multicoloured	1·00	1·00	☐ ☐
		a. Horiz strip of 5. Nos.			
		4200/4204	4·50	4·50	☐ ☐
4201	**3302**	(1st) multicoloured	1·00	1·00	☐ ☐
4202	**3303**	(1st) multicoloured	1·00	1·00	☐ ☐
4203	**3304**	(1st) multicoloured	1·00	1·00	☐ ☐
4204	**3305**	(1st) multicoloured	1·00	1·00	☐ ☐
4205	**3306**	(1st) multicoloured	1·00	1·00	☐ ☐
		a. Horiz strip of 5. Nos.			
		4205/4209	4·50	4·50	☐ ☐
4206	**3307**	(1st) multicoloured	1·00	1·00	☐ ☐
4207	**3308**	(1st) multicoloured	1·00	1·00	☐ ☐
4208	**3309**	(1st) multicoloured	1·00	1·00	☐ ☐
4209	**3310**	(1st) multicoloured	1·00	1·00	☐ ☐
Set of 10			9·00	9·00	☐ ☐
First Day Cover				13·00	☐
Presentation Pack (PO Pack No. 569)			15·00		☐
PHQ Cards (*set of 10*) (455)			6·00	12·00	☐ ☐
Set of 2 Gutter Strips of 10			18·00		☐

		(b) Self-adhesive. Gravure. Die-cut perf 14×14½			
4210	**3304**	(1st) multicoloured	13·00	13·00	☐ ☐
4211	**3303**	(1st) multicoloured	13·00	13·00	☐ ☐

Nos. 4200/4204 and 4205/4209 were each printed together, *se-tenant*, as horizontal strips of five stamps in sheets of 50 (2 panes 5×5).

Nos. 4210/4211 were issued in stamp booklets with 4×1st bright scarlet stamps, originally sold for £4·20.

British Engineering

2019 (2 May) Two phosphor bands. Perf 14½×14 (Nos. 4212/4217) or 14 (No. **MS**4218)

4212	**3311**	(1st) multicoloured	1·00	1·00	☐ ☐
		a. Horiz pair. Nos.			
		4212/4213	2·00	2·00	☐ ☐
4213	**3312**	(1st) multicoloured	1·00	1·00	☐ ☐
4214	**3313**	£1·55 multicoloured	2·40	2·40	☐ ☐
		a. Horiz pair. Nos.			
		4214/4215	4·75	4·75	☐ ☐
4215	**3314**	£1·55 multicoloured	2·40	2·40	☐ ☐
4216	**3315**	£1·60 multicoloured	2·50	2·50	☐ ☐
		a. Horiz pair. Nos.			
		4216/4217	5·00	5·00	☐ ☐
4217	**3316**	£1·60 multicoloured	2·50	2·50	☐ ☐
Set of 6			10·50	10·50	☐ ☐
First Day Cover				14·50	☐
Presentation Pack (Nos. 4212/4217 and **MS**4218) (PO Pack No. 570)			21·00		☐
PHQ Cards (*set of 11*) (456)			6·50	20·00	☐ ☐
Set of 3 Gutter Pairs (only 2 stamps in each Gutter Pair)			11·00		☐
Set of 3 Traffic Light Gutter Blocks of 4			22·00		☐

MS4218   203×75 mm. **3317** (1st) Harrier
GR3: Short Take-off; (1st) Harrier GR3:
Conventional Flight; £1·55 Harrier
GR3: Transition to Landing; £1·55
Harrier GR3: Vertical Landing   6·75   6·75 ☐ ☐

First Day Cover   8·50 ☐

Nos. 4212/4213, 4214/4215 and 4216/4217 were each printed together, *se-tenant*, as horizontal pairs in sheets of 60 (2 panes 6×5).

The 11 PHQ cards show the ten individual stamps, including those from No. **MS**4218, and the complete sheet.

3318 *Queen Victoria*
(Heinrich von Angeli),1890

3319 Queen Victoria and
Benjamin Disraeli, 1878

3320 Queen Victoria with
Servant John Brown, 1876

3321 Queen Victoria wearing
her Robes of State, 1859

3322 Marriage of Queen
Victoria and Prince Albert, 1840

3323 Princess Victoria
aged 11, 1830

3324 The Legacy of Prince Albert

Birth Bicentenary of Queen Victoria (1st issue)

2019 (24 May). Two phosphor bands. Perf 14×14½ (Nos. 4219/4224) or 14 (No. **MS**4225).

4219	**3318**	(1st) multicoloured	1·00	1·00	☐ ☐
		a. Horiz pair. Nos. 4219/4220	2·00	2·00	☐ ☐
4220	**3319**	(1st) multicoloured	1·00	1·00	☐ ☐
4221	**3320**	£1·35 multicoloured	2·00	2·00	☐ ☐
		a. Horiz pair. Nos. 4221/4222	4·00	4·00	☐ ☐
4222	**3321**	£1·35 multicoloured	2·00	2·00	☐ ☐
4223	**3322**	£1·60 multicoloured	2·50	2·50	☐ ☐
		a. Horiz pair. Nos. 4223/4224	5·00	5·00	☐ ☐

4224	**3323**	£1·60 multicoloured	2·50	2·50	☐ ☐
Set of 6			10·00	10·00	☐
First Day Cover				13·50	☐

Presentation Pack (Nos. 4219/4224 and
MS4225) (PO Pack No. 571)   20·00   ☐
PHQ Cards (*set of 11*) (457)   6·50   22·00 ☐ ☐
Set of 3 Gutter Pairs   20·00   ☐

MS4225   146×74 mm. **3324** (1st) Model
Lodge, Kennington; (1st) Balmoral
Castle, Scotland; £1·55 The New
Crystal Palace, Sydenham; £1·55
Royal Albert Hall, London   6·75   6·75 ☐ ☐

First Day Cover   8·50 ☐

Nos. 4219/4220, 4221/4222 and 4223/4224 were each printed together, *se-tenant*, as horizontal pairs in sheets of 60 (2 panes 6×5).

The 11 PHQ cards show the individual stamps including those from No. **MS**4225 and the complete miniature sheet.

3325 Model Lodge, Kennington

3326 Balmoral Castle, Scotland

3327 The New Crystal Palace,
Sydenham

3328 Royal Albert Hall, London

Birth Bicentenary of Queen Victoria (2nd issue)

2019 (24 May). Two phosphor bands. Perf 14.

4226	**3325**	(1st) multicoloured	1·50	1·50	☐ ☐
4227	**3326**	(1st) multicoloured	1·50	1·50	☐ ☐
4228	**3327**	£1·55 multicoloured	3·00	3·00	☐ ☐
4229	**3328**	£1·55 multicoloured	3·00	3·00	☐ ☐
Set of 4			8·00	8·00	☐ ☐

Nos. 4226/4229 come from No. **MS**4225 and £17·20 premium booklets.

D-Day British soldiers are briefed before embarkation

3329 No. 4 Commando, 1st Special Service Brigade briefed by Commanding Officer Lieutenant Colonel R. Dawson before Embarkation

D-Day HMS *Warspite* shelling in support of beach landings

3330 HMS *Warspite* shelling German Gun Batteries in support of Landings on Sword Beach

3331 Paratroopers of British 6th Airborne Division synchronising Watches before take-off, 5 June

3332 Commandos of HQ 4th Special Service Brigade wade ashore on Juno Beach

3333 American A-20 Havoc Light Bomber

3334 East Yorkshire Regiment Troops take cover from Enemy Shell, 19 July 1944

3335 The Normandy Landings

● GOLD
3336 British 50th Division landing on Gold Beach

● SWORD
3337 British 3rd Division landing at Sword Beach

75th Anniversary of D-Day

2019 (6 June) Multicoloured. Two phosphor bands

(a) Ordinary gum. Litho. Perf 14½

4230	**3329**	(1st) multicoloured	1·00	1·00	☐	☐
		a. Vert pair. Nos. 4230/4231	2·00	2·00	☐	☐
4231	**3330**	(1st) multicoloured	1·00	1·00	☐	☐
4232	**3331**	£1·35 multicoloured	2·00	2·00	☐	☐
		a. Vert pair. Nos. 4232/4233	4·00	4·00	☐	☐
4233	**3332**	£1·35 multicoloured	2·00	2·00	☐	☐
4234	**3333**	£1·60 multicoloured	2·50	2·50	☐	☐
		a. Vert pair. Nos. 4234/4235	5·00	5·00	☐	☐
4235	**3334**	£1·60 multicoloured	2·50	2·50	☐	☐
Set of 6			10·00	10·00	☐	
First Day Cover				13·50	☐	
Presentation Pack (Nos. 4230/4235 and **MS**4236) (PO Pack No. 572)			19·00		☐	
PHQ Cards (*set of 12*) (458)			7·00	22·00	☐	☐
Set of 3 Gutter Pairs (only 2 stamps in each gutter pair)			11·00		☐	

MS4236 203×75 mm. **3335** (1st)×5 US 4th Infantry Division, Utah Beach; US troops going ashore at Omaha Beach; British 50th Division landing on Gold Beach; Canadian 3rd Division landing at Juno Beach; British 3rd Division landing at Sword Beach

			5·25	5·25	☐	☐
First Day Cover				7·00	☐	

(b) Self-adhesive. Gravure. Die-cut perf 14½

4237	**3336**	(1st) multicoloured	1·75	1·75	☐	☐
4238	**3337**	(1st) multicoloured	1·75	1·75	☐	☐

Nos. 4230/4231, 4232/4233 and 4234/4235 were each printed together, *se-tenant*, as vertical pairs in sheets of 60 (2 panes 5×6).

Nos. 4237/4238 were issued in stamp booklets with 4×1st bright scarlet stamps, originally sold for £4·20.

The 12 PHQ cards show each of the individual stamps including those from No. **MS**4236 and the complete miniature sheet.

3338 Burning the Clocks, Brighton

3339 'Obby 'Oss, Padstow, Cornwall

3340 World Gurning Championships, Egremont, Cumbria

3341 Up Helly Aa, Lerwick, Shetland

3342 Halloween, Londonderry

3343 Cheese Rolling, Cooper's Hill, Brockworth, Gloucestershire

3344 Horn Dance, Abbots Bromley, Staffordshire

3345 Bog Snorkelling, Llanwrtyd Wells, Wales

Curious Customs

2019 (9 July) One centre band (2nd) or two bands (others). Perf 14×14½

4239	**3338**	(2nd) multicoloured	90	90	☐	☐
		a. Horiz pair. Nos. 4239/4240	1·75	1·75	☐	☐
4240	**3339**	(2nd) multicoloured	90	90	☐	☐
4241	**3340**	(1st) multicoloured	1·00	1·00	☐	☐
		a. Horiz pair. Nos. 4241/4242	2·00	2·00	☐	☐
4242	**3341**	(1st) multicoloured	1·00	1·00	☐	☐
4243	**3342**	£1·55 multicoloured	2·40	2·40	☐	☐
		a. Horiz pair. Nos. 4243/4244	4·75	4·75	☐	☐
4244	**3343**	£1·55 multicoloured	2·40	2·40	☐	☐
4245	**3344**	£1·60 multicoloured	2·50	2·50	☐	☐
		a. Horiz pair. Nos. 4245/4246	5·00	5·00	☐	☐
4246	**3345**	£1·60 multicoloured	2·50	2·50	☐	☐
Set of 8			12·50	12·50	☐	
First Day Cover				16·50		☐
Presentation Pack (PO Pack No. 573)			15·00		☐	
PHQ Cards (*set of 8*) (459)			5·00	13·00	☐	☐
Set of 4 Gutter Pairs			25·00		☐	

Nos. 4239/4240, 4241/4242, 4243/4244 and 4245/4246 were each printed together, *se-tenant*, as horizontal pairs in sheets of 60 (2 panes 6×5).

3346 Autumn at Glen Affric, Inverness-shire, Scotland

3347 Autumn in the Acer Glade, The National Arboretum, Westonbirt, Gloucestershire

3348 Sherwood Forest, Nottinghamshire

3349 Coed y Brenin, Gwynedd, Wales

3350 Waterfall in Glenariff, County Antrim, Northern Ireland

3351 Beech in Autumn, Sidwood, Kielder Forest, Northumberland

Forests

2019 (13 Aug.) Two phosphor bands. Perf 14½

4247	**3346**	(1st) multicoloured	1·00	1·00	☐	☐
		a. Vert pair. Nos. 4247/4248	2·00	2·00	☐	☐
4248	**3347**	(1st) multicoloured	1·00	1·00	☐	☐
4249	**3348**	£1·55 multicoloured	2·40	2·40	☐	☐
		a. Vert pair. Nos. 4249/4250	4·75	4·75	☐	☐
4250	**3349**	£1·55 multicoloured	2·40	2·40	☐	☐
4251	**3350**	£1·60 multicoloured	2·50	2·50	☐	☐
		a. Vert pair. Nos. 4251/4252	5·00	5·00	☐	☐
4252	**3351**	£1·60 multicoloured	2·50	2·50	☐	☐
Set of 6			10·50	10·50	☐	☐
First Day Cover				14·50		☐
Presentation Pack (PO Pack No. 574)			13·00		☐	
PHQ Cards (*set of 6*) (460)			4·00	12·50	☐	☐
Set of 3 Gutter Pairs (only 2 stamps in each gutter pair)			12·00		☐	

Nos. 4247/4248, 4249/4250 and 4251/4252 were each printed together, *se-tenant*, as vertical pairs in sheets of 60 (2 panes 5×6).

Nos. 4247/4252 commemorate the Centenary of the Forestry Commission.

3352 *Honky Château*

3353 *Goodbye Yellow Brick Road*

3354 *Caribou*

3355 *Captain Fantastic and The Brown Dirt Cowboy*

3356 *Sleeping with The Past*

3357 *The One*

3358 *Made in England*

3359 *Songs from The West Coast*

3360 Elton John Live

Elton John

2019 (3 Sept.) Two phosphor bands

(a) Ordinary gum. Litho. Perf 14

4253	**3352**	(1st) multicoloured	1·00	1·00
		a. Horiz strip of 4. Nos. 4253/4256	3·75	3·75
4254	**3353**	(1st) multicoloured	1·00	1·00
4255	**3354**	(1st) multicoloured	1·00	1·00
4256	**3355**	(1st) multicoloured	1·00	1·00
4257	**3356**	£1·55 multicoloured	2·40	2·40
		a. Horiz strip of 4. Nos. 4257/4260	9·25	9·25
4258	**3357**	£1·55 multicoloured	2·40	2·40
4259	**3358**	£1·55 multicoloured	2·40	2·40
4260	**3359**	£1·55 multicoloured	2·40	2·40
Set of 8			12·50	12·50
First Day Cover				17·00

Presentation Pack (Nos. 4253/4260 and **MS**4261) (PO Pack No. 575)	23·00	
Goodbye Yellow Brick Road Character Pack (containing No. 4254×10)	11·00	
Captain Fantastic and The Brown Dirt Cowboy Character Pack (containing 4256×10)	12·00	
PHQ Cards (*set of 13*) (461)	7·50	25·00
Set of 2 Gutter Strips of 8	26·00	

MS4261 156×74 mm. **3360** Elton John Live (1st) Madison Square Garden, 2018; (1st) Dodger Stadium, 1975; £1·55 Hammersmith Odeon, 1973; £1·55 Buckingham Palace, 2012			6·75	6·75	
First Day Cover				8·50	

(b) Self-adhesive. Gravure. Die-cut perf 14

4262	**3353**	(1st) multicoloured	1·75	1·75
4263	**3355**	(1st) multicoloured	1·75	1·75

Nos. 4253/4256 and 4257/4260 were each printed together, *se-tenant*, as horizontal strips of four stamps in sheets of 48 (2 panes 4×6).

Nos. 4262/4263 were issued in stamp booklets with 4×1st bright scarlet stamps, originally sold for £4·20.

The 13 PHQ cards show the individual stamps, including those from No. **MS**4261, and the complete miniature sheet.

A *Goodbye Yellow Brick Road* fan sheet containing No. 4254×4 was sold for £7·50, a *Captain Fantastic and The Brown Dirt Cowboy* fan sheet containing No. 4256×4 was sold for £7·50 and an Album Collection fan sheet containing Nos. 4253/4260 was sold for £10·20.

3361 *Mary Rose*, 1511 (Geoff Hunt)

3362 HMS *Queen Elizabeth*, 2014 (Robert G Lloyd)

3363 HMS *Victory*, 1765 (Monamy Swaine)

3364 HMS *Dreadnought*, 1906 (H J Morgan)

3365 HMS *Warrior*, 1860 (Thomas Goldsworth Dutton)

3366 *Sovereign of the Seas*, 1637 (Paul Garnett)

3367 HMS *King George V*, 1939 (Robert G Lloyd)

3368 HMS *Beagle*, 1820 (John Chancellor)

Royal Navy Ships

2019 (19 Sept.) Two phosphor bands

(a) Ordinary gum. Litho. Perf 14

4264	**3361**	(1st) multicoloured	1·00	1·00	☐	☐
		a. Horiz pair. Nos. 4264/4265	2·00	2·00	☐	☐
4265	**3362**	(1st) multicoloured	1·00	1·00	☐	☐
4266	**3363**	£1·35 multicoloured	2·00	2·00	☐	☐
		a. Horiz pair. Nos. 4266/4267	4·00	4·00	☐	☐
4267	**3364**	£1·35 multicoloured	2·00	2·00	☐	☐
4268	**3365**	£1·55 multicoloured	2·40	2·40	☐	☐
		a. Horiz pair. Nos. 4268/4269	4·75	4·75	☐	☐
4269	**3366**	£1·55 multicoloured	2·40	2·40	☐	☐
4270	**3367**	£1·60 multicoloured	2·50	2·50	☐	☐
		a. Horiz pair. Nos. 4270/4271	5·00	5·00	☐	☐
4271	**3368**	£1·60 multicoloured	2·50	2·50	☐	☐
Set of 8			14·00	14·00	☐	☐
First Day Cover				20·00	☐	
Presentation Pack (PO Pack No. 576)			18·00		☐	
PHQ Cards (set of 8) (462)			5·00	16·00	☐	☐
Set of 4 Gutter Blocks of 4			28·00		☐	

(b) Self-adhesive. Gravure. Die-cut perf 14

4272	**3361**	(1st) multicoloured	13·00	13·00	☐	☐
4273	**3362**	(1st) multicoloured	13·00	13·00	☐	☐

Nos. 4264/4265, 4266/4267, 4268/4269 and 4270/4271 were each printed together, *se-tenant*, as horizontal pairs in sheets of 60 (2 panes 6×5).

Nos. 4272/4273 were issued in stamp booklets with 4×1st bright scarlet stamps, originally sold for £4·20.

3369 Cricket World Cup Winners (men)

3370 Cricket World Cup Winners (women)

ICC Cricket World Cup Winners

2019 (26 Sept.) Two phosphor bands. Perf 14½

MS4274 203×74 mm. **3369** (1st) England Captain Eoin Morgan lifting Cricket World Cup Trophy; (1st) Eoin Morgan (with trophy) and England team; £1·60 England players celebrating; £1·60 England players congratulating Ben Stokes (men)		6·75	6·75	☐	☐
MS4275 203×74 mm. **3370** (1st) England team after their victory ('CHAMPIONS'); (1st) England players congratulating Anya Shrubsole; £1·60 England Captain Heather Knight and teammates celebrating; £1·60 England team celebrating on balcony at Lord's Cricket Ground (women, 2017)		6·75	6·75	☐	☐
First Day Covers (2)			17·00	☐	
Presentation Pack (PO Pack No. M25)		16·00		☐	

3371 'Scrambled snake!'

3372 'Gruffalo crumble!'

3373 'All was quiet in the deep dark wood.'

3374 'A mouse took a stroll'

3375 'Roasted fox!'

3376 'Owl ice cream?'

3377 The Gruffalo

The Gruffalo (by Julia Donaldson, illustrated by Axel Scheffler)

2019 (10 Oct.) Two phosphor bands. Perf 14 (Nos. 4276/4281) or 14½ (No. **MS**4282)

4276	**3371**	(1st) multicoloured	1·00	1·00	☐	☐
		a. Horiz strip of 3. Nos. 4276/4278	3·00	3·00	☐	☐
4277	**3372**	(1st) multicoloured	1·00	1·00	☐	☐
4278	**3373**	(1st) multicoloured	1·00	1·00	☐	☐
4279	**3374**	£1·60 multicoloured	2·50	2·50	☐	☐
		a. Horiz strip of 3. Nos. 4279/4281	7·50	7·50	☐	☐
4280	**3375**	£1·60 multicoloured	2·50	2·50	☐	☐
4281	**3376**	£1·60 multicoloured	2·50	2·50	☐	☐
Set of 6			9·50	9·50	☐	
First Day Cover				13·00		☐
Presentation Pack (Nos. 4276/4281 and **MS**4282) (PO Pack No. 577)			19·00		☐	
PHQ Cards (*set of 11*) (463)			7·50	22·00	☐	☐
Set of 2 Gutter Strips of 12			22·00		☐	
MS4282 126×89 mm. **3377** (1st) Owl; (1st) Mouse; £1·55 Snake; £1·55 Fox			6·75	6·75	☐	☐
First Day Cover				10·00		☐

Nos. 4276/4278 and 4279/4281 were each printed together, *se-tenant*, as horizontal strips of three stamps in sheets of 60 (2 panes 6×5).

Stamps as those within No. **MS**4282 but self-adhesive were issued in sheets of ten containing three of each of the two 1st class designs and two of each of the two £1·55 designs, each stamp with a label.

The 11 PHQ cards show the individual stamps, including those from No. **MS**4282, and the complete miniature sheet.

Christmas. Nativity

2019 (5 Nov.) One centre band (No. 4283) or two bands (others). Perf 14½×15

		(a) Self-adhesive. Gravure				
4283	**3378**	(2nd) multicoloured	90	90	☐	☐
4284	**3379**	(1st) multicoloured	1·00	1·00	☐	☐
4285	**3380**	(2nd Large) multicoloured	1·25	1·25	☐	☐
4286	**3381**	(1st Large) multicoloured	1·60	1·60	☐	☐
4287	**3382**	£1·35 multicoloured	2·00	2·00	☐	☐
4288	**3383**	£1·55 multicoloured	2·40	2·40	☐	☐
4289	**3384**	£1·60 multicoloured	2·50	2·50	☐	☐
4290	**3385**	£2·30 multicoloured	3·50	3·50	☐	☐
Set of 8			13·50	13·50	☐	☐
First Day Cover				19·00		☐
Presentation Pack (PO Pack No. 578)			17·00		☐	
PHQ Cards (*set of 9*) (464)			6·00	28·00	☐	☐
		(b) Ordinary gum. Litho				
MS4291 179×74 mm. Nos. 4283/4290			14·50	14·50	☐	☐
First Day Cover				19·00		☐

The 2nd class, 1st class, £1·35, £1·55, £1·60 and £2·30 values were also issued in sheets of 20 containing eight 2nd class, eight 1st class and one each of the £1·35, £1·55, £1·60 and £2·30 values, each stamp accompanied by a *se-tenant* label.

The nine PHQ cards show the individual stamps and the complete miniature sheet.

3378 Angel and Shepherd

3379 Mary and Baby Jesus

3380 Angel and Shepherd

3381 Mary and Baby Jesus

3382 Joseph

3383 Baby Jesus in Manger

3384 Shepherds and Star

3385 Three Wise Men

3386 Count Dooku (Christopher Lee)

3387 Lando Calrissian (Billy Dee Williams)

3388 Sith Trooper

3389 Jannah (Naomi Ackie)

3390 Grand Moff Tarkin (Peter Cushing)

3391 Darth Maul (Ray Park)

3392 Zorii
(Kerri Russell)

3393 Wicket W. Warrick
(Warwick Davis)

3394 Poe Dameron
(Oscar Isaac)

3395 Queen Amidala (Natalie Portman)

3396 *Star Wars* Vehicles

Star Wars (5th issue)

2019 (26 Nov.) 'All-over' phosphor (No. **MS**4303 stamps only) or two phosphor bands (others)

(a) Ordinary gum. Litho. Perf 14½

4292	**3386**	(1st) multicoloured	1·00	1·00		
		a. Horiz strip of 5. Nos.				
		4292/4296	5·00	5·00		
4293	**3387**	(1st) multicoloured	1·00	1·00		
4294	**3388**	(1st) multicoloured	1·00	1·00		
4295	**3389**	(1st) multicoloured	1·00	1·00		
4296	**3390**	(1st) multicoloured	1·00	1·00		
4297	**3391**	(1st) multicoloured	1·00	1·00		
		a. Horiz strip of 5. Nos.				
		4297/4301	5·00	5·00		
4298	**3392**	(1st) multicoloured	1·00	1·00		
4299	**3393**	(1st) multicoloured	1·00	1·00		
4300	**3394**	(1st) multicoloured	1·00	1·00		
4301	**3395**	(1st) multicoloured	1·00	1·00		
Set of 10			9·00	9·00		
First Day Cover				14·50		
Presentation Pack (Nos. 4292/4301 and						
MS4303) (PO Pack No. 579)			19·00			
PHQ Cards (set of 16) (465)			11·50	20·00		
MS4302 210×297 mm. Nos. 3758/3769,						
4007/4014 and 4292/4301			40·00	40·00		

(b) Self-adhesive. Litho

MS4303 192×74 mm. **3396** (1st) Poe's X-wing fighter (41×30 mm) (Perf 14); (1st) Jedi starfighter (27×37 mm) (Perf 14); (1st) Slave 1 (27×37 mm) (Perf 14); (1st) TIE silencer (41×30 mm) (Perf 14); (1st) Podracers (60×21 mm) (Perf 14½×14); (1st) Speeder bikes (60×21 mm) (Perf 14½×14)   6·50   6·50

First Day Cover   8·75

(c) Self-adhesive. Gravure. Die-cut perf 14½

4304	**3394**	(1st) multicoloured	1·75	1·75	
4305	**3388**	(1st) multicoloured	1·75	1·75	

Nos. 4292/4296 and 4297/4301 were each printed together, *se-tenant*, as horizontal strips of five stamps in sheets of 50. Nos. 4304/4305 were issued in stamp booklets with 4×1st bright scarlet stamps, originally sold for £4·20.

A collectors sheet containing stamps as Nos. 4292/4301 but self-adhesive with labels showing film scenes was sold for £8·10, a £1·10 premium over face value.

Collectors Pack

2019 (26 Nov.) Comprises Nos. **MS**4169/**MS**4192, 4200/4209, 4212/**MS**4225, 4230/**MS**4236, 4239/**MS**4261, 4264/4271, **MS**4274/4290, 4292/4301 and **MS**4303.

CP4305*a*   Collectors Pack   £300

Post Office Yearbook

2019 (26 Nov.) Comprises Nos. **MS**4169/**MS**4192, 4200/4209, 4212/**MS**4225, 4230/**MS**4236, 4239/**MS**4261, 4264/4271, **MS**4274/4290, 4292/4301 and **MS**4303

YB4305*a*   Yearbook   £350

Miniature Sheet Collection

2019 (26 Nov.) Comprises Nos. **MS**4169, **MS**4192, **MS**4218, **MS**4225, **MS**4236, **MS**4261, **MS**4274/**MS**4275, **MS**4282, **MS**4291 and **MS**4303

MS4305*a*   Miniature Sheet Collection   85·00

3397 Poe's X-wing Fighter

3398 Jedi Starfighter

3399 Podracers

3400 Slave 1

3401 TIE Silencer

3402 Speeder Bikes

Star Wars (6th issue)

2019 (26 Nov.) 'All-over' phosphor (stamps only). Self-adhesive. Litho. Die-cut perf 14 (Nos. 4306/4307, 4309/4310) or 14½×14 (Nos. 4308, 4311)

4306	**3397**	(1st) multicoloured	1·50	1·50
4307	**3398**	(1st) multicoloured	1·50	1·50
4308	**3399**	(1st) multicoloured	1·50	1·50
4309	**3400**	(1st) multicoloured	1·50	1·50
4310	**3401**	(1st) multicoloured	1·50	1·50
4311	**3402**	(1st) multicoloured	1·50	1·50
Set of 6			8·25	8·25

Nos. 4306/4311 were issued in No. **MS**4303 and also in two booklet panes from the £17·65 *Star Wars* The Making of the Vehicles booklet.

The booklet panes are as No. **MS**4303 but in two panes with margins giving information about *Star Wars* vehicles.

3403 *Elite*, 1984

3404 *Worms*, 1995

3405 *Sensible Soccer*, 1992

3406 *Lemmings*, 1991

3407 *Wipeout*, 1995

3408 *Micro Machines*, 1991

3409 *Dizzy*, 1987

3410 *Populous*, 1989

3411 *Tomb Raider*

3412 *Tomb Raider*, 1996

3413 *Tomb Raider*, 2013

Video Games.

2020 (21 Jan). (a) Ordinary gum. Litho. Band at right (No. 4312), centre band (No. 4313) or two bands (others). Perf 14.

4312	**3403**	(2nd) multicoloured	90	90
		a. Vert pair. Nos. 4312/4313	1·75	1·75
4313	**3404**	(2nd) multicoloured	90	90
4314	**3405**	(1st) multicoloured	1·00	1·00
		a. Vert pair. Nos. 4314/4315	2·00	2·00
4315	**3406**	(1st) multicoloured	1·00	1·00
4316	**3407**	£1·55 multicoloured	2·40	2·40
		a. Vert pair. Nos. 4316/4317	4·75	4·75
4317	**3408**	£1·55 multicoloured	2·40	2·40
4318	**3409**	£1·60 multicoloured	2·50	2·50
		a. Vert pair. Nos. 4318/4319	5·00	5·00
4319	**3410**	£1·60 multicoloured	2·50	2·50
Set of 8			12·50	12·50
First Day Cover				17·00
Presentation Pack (Nos 4312/4319 and				
MS4320) (PO Pack No. 581)			23·00	
PHQ Cards (set of 13) (466)			8·75	25·00
Set of 4 Gutter Blocks of 4			26·00	

MS4320 126×90 mm. **3411** (1st) *Tomb Raider*, 1996; (1st) *Tomb Raider*, 2013; £1.55 *Adventures of Lara Croft*, 1998; £1.55 *Tomb Raider Chronicles*, 2000 .... 6·75 6·75 ☐ ☐
First Day Cover .... 9·25 ☐

(b) Self-adhesive. Gravure. Two phosphor bands. Die-cut perf 14

4321 **3412** (1st) multicoloured ...... 1·75 1·75 ☐ ☐
4322 **3413** (1st) multicoloured ...... 1·75 1·75 ☐ ☐

Nos. 4312/4313, 4314/4315, 4316/4317 and 4318/4319 were printed together, *se-tenant*, as vertical pairs in sheets of 60 (2 panes 5×6).

Nos. 4321/4322 were issued in stamp booklets with 4x1st bright scarlet stamps, originally sold for £4·20.

Stamps as within No. **MS**4320 but self-adhesive were also issued in sheets of ten printed in lithography containing three of each of the 1st class designs and two of each of the £1·55 designs, with *se-tenant* labels.

The 13 PHQ cards show the 12 individual stamps, including those from No. **MS**4320, and the complete miniature sheet. A Gamer collectors pack originally sold for £14·95 contained eight postcards each with stamp affixed packed in a silver case.

3414 Cat's Eye Nebula

3415 Enceladus

3416 Pulsars

3417 Black Holes

3418 Jupiter's Auroras

3419 Gravitational Lensing

3420 Comet 67P

3421 Cygnus A Galaxy

Visions of the Universe

2020 (11 Feb). One centre band (2nd) or two bands (others). Perf 14.

4323	**3414**	(2nd) multicoloured		90	90	☐ ☐
		a. Horiz pair. Nos. 4323/4324		1·75	1·75	☐ ☐
4324	**3415**	(2nd) multicoloured		90	90	☐ ☐
4325	**3416**	(1st) multicoloured		1·25	1·25	☐ ☐
		a. Horiz pair. Nos. 4325/4326		2·50	2·50	☐ ☐
4326	**3417**	(1st) multicoloured		1·25	1·25	☐ ☐
4327	**3418**	£1·55 multicoloured		2·40	2·40	☐ ☐
		a. Horiz pair. Nos. 4327/4328		4·75	4·75	☐ ☐
4328	**3419**	£1·55 multicoloured		2·40	2·40	☐ ☐
4329	**3420**	£1·60 multicoloured		2·50	2·50	☐ ☐
		a. Horiz pair. Nos. 4329/4330		5·00	5·00	☐ ☐
4330	**3421**	£1·60 multicoloured		2·50	2·50	☐ ☐
Set of 8				12·50	12·50	☐ ☐
First Day Cover					17·00	☐
Presentation Pack (PO Pack No. 582)				15·00		☐
PHQ Cards (set of 8) (467)				5·50	15·00	☐ ☐
Set of 4 Gutter Pairs				25·00		

Nos. 4323/4324, 4325/4326, 4327/4328 and 4329/4330 were each printed together, *se-tenant*, as horizontal pairs in sheets of 60 (2 panes 6×5).

London International Stamp Exhibition

2020 (10 Mar). Self-adhesive. Gravure. Two phosphor bands. Die-cut perf 14½×14 (with one elliptical hole in each vert side).

4331 **2938** (1st) Two Pence Blue ...... 1·25 1·25 ☐ ☐

No. 4331 comes from Booklet containing Nos. 3709, 3806 and 4331, each x2 which was originally sold for £4·20

3422 James Bond in *Casino Royale*

3423 James Bond in *Goldeneye*

3424 James Bond in *The Living Daylights*

3425 James Bond in *Live and Let Die*

3426 James Bond in *On Her Majesty's Secret Service*

3427 James Bond in *Goldfinger*

3429 Bell-Textron Jet Pack, *Thunderball*

3430 Aston Martin DB5, *Skyfall*

James Bond (1st issue)

2020 (17 Mar). (a) Ordinary gum. Litho. Two phosphor bands (Nos. 4332/4337) or 'all-over' phosphor (No. **MS**4338). Perf 14½ (Nos.4332/4337) or 14×14½ (£1·55) or 14 (1st) (No. **MS**4338).

4332	**3422**	(1st) multicoloured	1·25	1·25
		a. Horiz strip of 3. Nos. 4332/4334	3·75	3·75
4333	**3423**	(1st) multicoloured	1·25	1·25
4334	**3424**	(1st) multicoloured	1·25	1·25
4335	**3425**	£1·60 multicoloured	2·50	2·50
		a. Horiz strip of 3. Nos. 4335/4337	7·50	7·50
4336	**3426**	£1·60 multicoloured	2·50	2·50
4337	**3427**	£1·60 multicoloured	2·50	2·50
Set of 6			10·50	10·50
First Day Cover				13·50
Presentation Pack (Nos 4332/4337 and **MS**4338) (PO Pack No. 583)			·20·00	
PHQ Cards (set of 11) (468)			7·50	22·00
Set of 2 Gutter Strips of 6			22·00	

MS4338 202×74 mm. **3428** (1st) Bell-Textron Jet Pack, *Thunderball*; (1st) Aston Martin DB5, *Skyfall*; £1·55 Lotus Esprit Submarine, *The Spy Who Loved Me*; £1·55 Little Nellie, *You Only Live Twice*

	6·75	6·75
First Day Cover		9·25

(b) Self-adhesive. Gravure. 'All-over' phosphor. Die-cut perf 14

4339	**3429**	(1st) Bell-Textron Jet Pack, *Thunderball*	1·75	1·75
4340	**3430**	(1st) Aston Martin DB5, *Skyfall*	1·75	1·75

Nos. 4332/4334 and 4335/4337 were each printed together, *se-tenant*, as horizontal strips of three in sheets of 36 (2 panes 3×6).

Stamps from No. **MS**4338 have '007' perforations at top right, top left, bottom right or bottom left.

Nos. 4339/4340 were issued in stamp booklets with 4x1st bright scarlet stamps, originally sold for £4·20.

Nos. 4332/4337 were also issued in a collectors sheet containing Nos. 4332x3, 4333/4336 and No. 4337x3 with attached labels, originally sold for £12·60

The 11 PHQ cards show the 10 individual stamps, including those from No. **MS**4338, and the complete miniature sheet.

A (1st) Aston Martin stamp as from No. **MS**4338 but self-adhesive and perf 14×14½ was also issued in a collector's sheet containing ten stamps and ten labels, issued on 21 November 2020 and originally sold for £8·80.

3428 Q Branch

3431 Little Nellie, *You Only Live Twice*

3432 Lotus Esprit Submarine, *The Spy Who Loved Me*

James Bond (2nd issue)

2020 (17 Mar). Litho. 'All-over' phosphor. Perf 14 (1st) or 14×14½ (£1·55), all with '007' perforations at top right, top left, bottom right or bottom left.

4341	**3429**	(1st) multicoloured	1·25	1·25	☐ ☐
4342	**3430**	(1st) multicoloured	1·25	1·25	☐ ☐
4343	**3431**	£1·55 multicoloured	2·40	2·40	☐ ☐
4344	**3432**	£1·55 multicoloured	2·40	2·40	☐ ☐
Set of 4			7·25	7·25	☐ ☐

Nos. 4341/4344 were issued in No. **MS**4338 and in a booklet pane from £16·99 James Bond booklet, No. DY33.

3433 *The Progress of Rhyme* (John Clare)

3434 *Frost at Midnight* (Samuel Taylor Coleridge)

3435 *Auguries of Innocence* (William Blake)

3436 *The Lady of the Lake* (Walter Scott)

3437 *To a Skylark* (Percy Bysshe Shelley)

3438 *The Rainbow* (William Wordsworth)

3439 *Ode to the Snowdrop* (Mary Robinson)

3440 *The Fate of Adelaide* (Letita Elizabeth Landon)

3441 *Ode on a Grecian Urn* (John Keats)

3442 *She Walks in Beauty* (Lord Byron)

Romantic Poets

2020 (7 Apr.) Two phosphor bands. Perf 14.

4345	**3433**	(1st) black and orange-brown	1·25	1·25	☐ ☐
		a. Horiz strip of 5. Nos. 4345/4349	6·25	6·25	☐ ☐
4346	**3434**	(1st) black and orange-brown	1·25	1·25	☐ ☐
4347	**3435**	(1st) black and orange-brown	1·25	1·25	☐ ☐
4348	**3436**	(1st) black and orange-brown	1·25	1·25	☐ ☐
4349	**3437**	(1st) black and orange-brown	1·25	1·25	☐ ☐
4350	**3438**	(1st) black and orange-brown	1·25	1·25	☐ ☐
		a. Horiz strip of 5. Nos. 4350/4354	6·25	6·25	☐ ☐
4351	**3439**	(1st) black and orange-brown	1·25	1·25	☐ ☐
4352	**3440**	(1st) black and orange-brown	1·25	1·25	☐ ☐
4353	**3441**	(1st) black and orange-brown	1·25	1·25	☐ ☐
4354	**3442**	(1st) black and orange-brown	1·25	1·25	☐ ☐
Set of 10			11·50	11·50	☐ ☐
First Day Cover				14·00	☐
Presentation Pack (PO Pack No. 584)			13·00		☐
PHQ Cards (*set of 10*) (469)			6·75	20·00	☐
Set of 2 Gutter Strips of 10			24·00		☐

Nos. 4345/4349 and 4350/4354 were printed together, *se-tenant,* as horizontal strips of five in sheets of 50 (2 panes 5×5).

180th Anniversary of the Penny Black

2020 (6 May). As T **2848** but ordinary gum. Litho. Perf 14½x14 (with one elliptical hole in each vert side).
MS4355 122x141mm. (1st) Penny Black x25   28·00   28·00 ☐ ☐
No. **MS**4355 was issued in sheets of 25, originally sold for £19.

3443 Serviceman returning home to Oreston, South Devon, 1945

3444 Nurses celebrating VE Day, Liverpool, 1945

3445 Crowds celebrating VE day, Piccadilly, London, 1945

3446 Evacuee children returning home, London, 1945

3447 Troops march along Oxford Street, London, 1945

3448 Soldier and saliors leaving demobilisation centre with boxes of civilian clothes

3449 Liberated Allied prisoners of war, Aomori Camp, near Yokohama, Japan

3450 Navy personnel in VE Day celebration, Glasgow, 1945

3451 Memorials

75th Anniversary of the End of the Second World War (1st issue)

2020 (8 May.) One centre band (2nd) or two phosphor bands (others). Perf 14. (Nos. 4356/4363) or 14½ (No. **MS**4364).

4356	**3443**	(2nd) multicoloured	90	90	☐ ☐
		a. Vert pair. Nos. 4356/4357	1·75	1·75	☐ ☐
4357	**3444**	(2nd) multicoloured	90	90	☐ ☐
4358	**3445**	(1st) multicoloured	1·25	1·25	☐ ☐
		a. Vert pair. Nos. 4358/4359	2·50	2·50	☐ ☐
4359	**3446**	(1st) multicoloured	1·25	1·25	☐ ☐
4360	**3447**	£1·42 multicoloured	2·25	2·25	☐ ☐
		a. Vert pair. Nos. 4360/4361	4·50	4·50	☐ ☐
4361	**3448**	£1·42 multicoloured	2·25	2·25	☐ ☐
4362	**3449**	£1·63 multicoloured	2·50	2·50	☐ ☐
		a. Vert pair. Nos. 4360/4361	5·00	5·00	☐ ☐
4363	**3450**	£1·63 multicoloured	2·50	2·50	☐ ☐
Set of 8			12·50	12·50	☐ ☐
First Day Cover				17·00	☐
Presentation Pack (Nos. 4356/4352 and					
MS4364) (PO Pack No. 585)			22·00		☐
PHQ Cards (*set of 13*) (470)			8·75	25·00	☐ ☐
Set of 4 Gutter Strips of 4			26·00		☐

MS4364 202×74 mm. **3451** (1st) Hall of Names, Holocaust History Museum, Yad Vashem, Jerusalem; (1st) Runnymede Memorial; £1·63 Plymouth Naval Memorial; £1·63 Rangoon Memorial, Myanmar (all 60x30 mm)   7·00   7·00 ☐ ☐

First Day Cover   10·00 ☐

Nos. 4356/4357 and 4358/4359, 4360/4361 and 4362/4363 were printed together, *se-tenant*, as vertical pairs in sheets of 60 (2 panes 5×6).

The 13 PHQ cards show the ten individual stamps, including those from No. **MS**4364, and the complete miniature sheet.

3452 Hall of Names, Holocaust History Museum, Yad Vashem, Jerusalem

3453 Runnymede Memorial

3454 Plymouth Naval Memorial

3455 Rangoon Memorial, Myanmar

75th Anniversary of the End of the Second World War (2nd issue)

2020 (8 May.) Two phosphor bands Perf 14½.

4365	**3452**	(1st) multicoloured	1·75	1·75	☐ ☐
4366	**3453**	(1st) multicoloured	1·75	1·75	☐ ☐
4367	**3454**	£1·63 multicoloured	3·00	3·00	☐ ☐
4368	**3455**	£1·63 multicoloured	3·00	3·00	☐ ☐
Set of 4			9·50	9·50	☐ ☐

Nos. 4365/4368 were issued in No. **MS**4364 and In a booklet pane from the £19·80 75th Anniversary of the End of the Second World War booklet, No. DY34

3456 "That woman's tongue. If it was a bit longer she could shave with it." Ena Sharples and Elsie Tanner

3457 "Woman, Stanley, woman." Stan and Hilda Ogden

3458 "Vera, my little swamp duck." Jack and Vera Duckworth

3459 "Ken! Do something!" Deirdre and Ken Barlow

3460 "I can't abide to see people gossiping" Rita Sullivan and Norris Cole

3461 "Be nice if every day I have left would be like this" Hayley and Roy Cropper

3462 "I love you. We shouldn't be apart a minute longer." Wedding of Dev and Sunita Alahan

3463 "I always thought I'd be the person you'd cheat with, not on" Tracy Barlow and Steve McDonald

3465 Dover Lighthouse

3466 Bignor Mosaic

3467 Amphitheatre at Isca Fortress

3468 Ribchester Helmet

3464 Rovers Return Barmaids

3469 Bridgeness distance slab at eastern end of Antonine Wall

3470 Copper-alloy figurine of Warrior God, Cambridgeshire

Coronation Street

2020 (28 May.) One centre band (2nd) or two phosphor bands (others).

(a) Ordinary gum. Litho. Perf 14.

4369	**3456**	(2nd) multicoloured	90	90	☐	☐
		a. Horiz pair Nos. 4369/4370	1·75	1·75	☐	☐
4370	**3457**	(2nd) multicoloured	90	90	☐	☐
4371	**3458**	(1st) multicoloured	1·25	1·25	☐	☐
		a. Horiz pair Nos. 4371/4372	2·50	2·50	☐	☐
4372	**3459**	(1st) multicoloured	1·25	1·25	☐	☐
4373	**3460**	£1·42 multicoloured	2·25	2·25	☐	☐
		a. Horiz pair Nos. 4373/4374	4·50	4·50	☐	☐
4374	**3461**	£1·42 multicoloured	2·25	2·25	☐	☐
4375	**3462**	£1·63 multicoloured	2·50	2·50	☐	☐
		a. Horiz pair Nos. 4375/4376	5·00	5·00	☐	☐
4376	**3450**	£1·63 multicoloured	2·50	2·50	☐	☐
Set of 8			12·50	12·50	☐	☐
First Day Cover				17·00		☐
Presentation Pack (Nos. 4369/4376 and **MS**4377) (PO Pack No. 586)			23·00		☐	
PHQ Cards (*set of 13*) (471)			8·75	25·00	☐	☐
Set of 4 Gutter Pairs			26·00		☐	

MS4377 156×74 mm. **3464** (1st) Bet Lynch (Julie Goodyear); (1st) Raquel Watts (Sarah Lancashire); £1·42 Liz McDonald (Beverley Callard); £1·42 Gemma Winter (Dolly-Rose Campbell) (all 27x36 mm)

		6·50	6·50	☐	☐
First Day Cover			9·00		☐

(b) Self-adhesive. Gravure. Die-cut perf 14

4378	**3458**	(1st) multicoloured	1·75	1·75	☐	☐
4379	**3459**	(1st) multicoloured	1·75	1·75	☐	☐

Nos. 4369/4370 and 4373/4374 and 4375/4376 were printed together, *se-tenant,* as horizontal pairs in sheets of 60 (2 panes 6×5).

Nos. 4378/4379 were issued in stamp booklets with 4x1st bright scarlet stamps, originally sold for £4·56.

Stamps as Nos. 4371/4372 but self-adhesive were issued in collectors sheets containing five of each design, sold for £8·80

The 13 PHQ cards show the 12 individual stamps, including those from No. **MS**4377, and the complete miniature sheet.

3471 Gorgon's head from temple to Sulis Minerva, Bath

3472 Hadrian's Wall

Roman Britain

2020 (18 June.) One centre band (2nd) or two bands (others). Perf 14½x14.

4380	**3465**	(2nd) multicoloured	90	90	☐	☐
		a. Horiz pair Nos. 4380/4381	1·75	1·75	☐	☐
4381	**3466**	(2nd) multicoloured	90	90	☐	☐
4382	**3467**	(1st) multicoloured	1·25	1·25	☐	☐
		a. Horiz pair Nos. 4382/4383	2·50	2·50	☐	☐
4383	**3468**	(1st) multicoloured	1·25	1·25	☐	☐
4384	**3469**	£1·63 multicoloured	2·50	2·50	☐	☐
		a. Horiz pair Nos. 4384/4385	5·00	5·00	☐	☐
4385	**3470**	£1·63 multicoloured	2·50	2·50	☐	☐
4386	**3471**	£1·68 multicoloured	2·75	2·75	☐	☐
		a. Horiz pair Nos. 4386/4387	5·50	5·50	☐	☐
4387	**3472**	£1·68 multicoloured	2·75	2·75	☐	☐
Set of 8			13·50	13·50	☐	☐
First Day Cover				18·00		☐
Presentation Pack (PO Pack No. 587)			16·00		☐	
PHQ Cards (*set of 8*) (472)			5·50	22·00	☐	☐
Set of 4 Gutter Pairs (only 2 stamps in each gutter pair)			15·00		☐	

Set of 4 Traffic Light Gutter Blocks (4 stamps in each gutter Block)   28·00   ☐

Nos. 4380/4381, 4382/4383, 4384/4385 and 4386/4387 were each printed together, *se-tenant,* as horizontal pairs in sheets of 60 (2 panes 6x5).

3473 *Queen II, 1974*

3474 *Sheer Heart Attack, 1974*

3475 *A Night At The Opera, 1975*

3476 *News of the World, 1977*

3477 *The Game, 1980*

3478 *Greatest Hits, 1981*

3479 *The Works, 1984*

3480 *Innuendo, 1991*

3481 *Queen Live*

Queen (rock band) (1st issue)

2020 (9 July.) Two phosphor bands.
(a) Ordinary gum. Litho. Perf 14 (Nos. 4388/4395), 14½x14 (Queen Machin-size stamp from No. **MS**4396) or 14½ (other stamps from No. **MS**4396).

4388	**3473**	(1st) multicoloured	1·25	1·25	☐	☐
		a. Horiz strip Nos. 4388/4391	5·00	5·00	☐	☐
4389	**3474**	(1st) multicoloured	1·25	1·25	☐	☐
4390	**3475**	(1st) multicoloured	1·25	1·25	☐	☐
4391	**3476**	(1st) multicoloured	1·25	1·25	☐	☐
4392	**3477**	£1·63 multicoloured	2·50	2·50	☐	☐

		a. Horiz strip of 4 Nos. 4392/4395	10·00	10·00		
4393	**3478**	£1·63 multicoloured	2·50	2·50	☐	☐
4394	**3479**	£1·63 multicoloured	2·50	2·50	☐	☐
4395	**3480**	£1·63 multicoloured	2·50	2·50	☐	☐
Set of 8			13·50	13·50	☐	☐
First Day Cover				18·00		☐

Presentation Pack (Nos. 4388/4395 and **MS**4398) (PO Pack No. 588)   25·00   ☐
PHQ Cards (*set of 15*) (473)   9·50   25·00   ☐ ☐
Set of 2 Gutter Strips of 8   28·00   ☐

MS4396 202×74 mm. **3481** (1st) Freddie Mercury, Magic Tour, Wembley Stadium, 1986; (1st) Roger Taylor, Hyde Park Concert, 1976; (1st) Queen, Primrose Hill, London, 1974; £1·63 John Deacon, A Night at the Opera Tour, Hammersmith Odeon, 1975; £1·63 Brian May, Magic Tour, Nepstadion, Budapest, 1986   8·75   8·75   ☐ ☐
First Day Cover   11·00   ☐

(b) Self-adhesive. Gravure. Die-cut perf 14

4397	**3473**	(1st) multicoloured	1·75	1·75	☐	☐
4398	**3475**	(1st) multicoloured	1·75	1·75	☐	☐

Nos. 4388/4395 were printed together, *se-tenant,* as horizontal strips of four stamps in sheets of 24 (2 panes 4×6).

Nos. 4397/4398 were issued in stamp booklets with 4x1st bright scarlet stamps, originally sold for £4·56.

The 15 PHQ cards show the 14 individual stamps, including those from No. **MS**4396, and the complete miniature sheet.

Stamps as Nos. 4388x2, 4389, 4390x2 and 4391/4395 but self-adhesive were issued with labels in a Queen Album Cover collectors sheet originally sold for £13·15.

An Album Cover Collection fan sheet containing Nos. 4388/4395 was originally sold for £10·20.

A Night at the Opera fan sheet containing No. 4390x4 was orignally sold for £7·50.

3482 *Freddie Mercury, Magic Tour, Wembley Statium, 1986*

3483 *Roger Taylor, Hyde Park Concert, 1976*

3484 *John Deacon, A Night at the Opera, Hammersmith Odeon, 1986*

3485 *Brian May, Magic Tour, Nepstadion, Budapest, 1986*

Queen (rock band) (2nd issue)

2020 (9 July.) Two phosphor bands. Litho. Perf 14½

4399	**3482**	(1st) multicoloured	1·75	1·75	☐	☐
4400	**3483**	(1st) multicoloured	1·75	1·75	☐	☐
4401	**3484**	£1·63 multicoloured	3·00	3·00	☐	☐
4402	**3485**	£1·63 multicoloured	3·00	3·00	☐	☐
Set of 4			9·50	9·50	☐	☐

Nos. 4399/4402 were issued in No. **MS**4396 and a booklet pane from the £19·10 Queen premium booklet, No. DY35.

3486 Queen,
Primrose Hill,
London, 1974

Queen (rock band) (3rd issue)

2020 (9 July.) Two phosphor bands. Litho. Perf 14½x14 (with one elliptical hole in each vert side).

| 4403 | **3486** | (1st) multicoloured | 1·75 | 1·75 | ☐ ☐ |

Nos. **4399/4402** was issued in No. **MS**4396 and the Machin booklet pane from the £19·10 Queen premium booklet, No. DY35.

A stamp as No. 4403 but self-adhesive was issued in a Queen Live Collector Sheet containing ten stamps with labels, orginally sold for £8·80.

3487 Palace of Westminster from Old Palace Yard

3488 Palace of Westminster from River Thames

3489 Elizabeth Tower

3490 Commons Chamber

3491 Central Lobby

3492 Lords Chamber

3493 Palace of Westminster

Palace of Westminster

2020 (30 July.) Two phosphor bands Perf 14½.

4404	**3487**	(1st) multicoloured	1·25	1·25	☐ ☐
		a. Horiz strip of 3. Nos. 4404/4406	3·75	3·75	☐ ☐
4405	**3488**	(1st) multicoloured	1·25	1·25	☐ ☐
4406	**3489**	(1st) multicoloured	1·25	1·25	☐ ☐
		a. Horiz pair Nos. 4371/4372	2·50	2·50	☐ ☐
4407	**3490**	£1·68 multicoloured	2·75	2·75	☐ ☐
		a. Horiz strip of 3. Nos. 4407/4409	8·25	8·25	☐ ☐
4408	**3491**	£1·68 multicoloured	2·75	2·75	☐ ☐
4409	**3492**	£1·68 multicoloured	2·75	2·75	☐ ☐
Set of 6			11·00	11·00	☐
First Day Cover				14·50	☐
Presentation Pack (Nos. 4404/4409 and					
MS4410) (PO Pack No. 589)			21·00		☐
PHQ Cards (*set of 11*) (474)			7·50	20·00	☐ ☐
Set of 2 Gutter Strips of 6			23·00		☐

MS4410 203×74 mm. **3493** (1st) Norman Porch; (1st) Chapel of St Mary Undercroft; £1·63 St Stephen's Hall; £1·63 Royal Gallery

| | | | 7·50 | 7·50 | ☐ ☐ |
| *First Day Cover* | | | | 10·00 | ☐ |

Nos. 4404/4406 and 4407/4409 were each printed together, *se-tenant,* as horizontal strips of 3 in sheets of 36 (2 panes 3×6).

The 11 PHQ cards show the ten individual stamps, including those from No. **MS**4410, and the complete miniature sheet.

3494 *The Reichenbach Fall*

3495 *A Study in Pink*

3496 *The Great Game*

3497 *The Empty Hearse*

3498 *A Scandal in Belgravia*

3499 *The Final Problem*

3500 Sherlock Holmes Mysteries by Sir Arthur Conan Doyle

3501 *The Red-Headed League*   **3502** *The Adventure of the Speckled Band*

Sherlock

2020 (18 Aug.) Two phosphor bands.
(a) Ordinary gum. Litho. Perf 14½ (Nos. 4411/4416) or 14 (No. **MS**4417).

4411	**3494**	(1st) multicoloured	1·25	1·25	☐	☐

		a. Vert pair Nos. 4411/4412	2·50	2·50	☐	☐
4412	**3495**	(1st) multicoloured	1·25	1·25	☐	☐
4413	**3496**	£1·42 multicoloured	2·25	2·25	☐	☐
		a. Vert pair Nos. 4413/4414	4·50	4·50	☐	☐
4414	**3497**	£1·42 multicoloured	2·25	2·25	☐	☐
4415	**3498**	£1·68 multicoloured	2·75	2·75	☐	☐
		a. Vert pair Nos. 4415/4416	5·50	5·50	☐	☐
4416	**3499**	£1·68 multicoloured	2·75	2·75	☐	☐
		Set of 6	11·00	11·00	☐	
		First Day Cover		15·00		☐
		Presentation Pack (Nos. 4411/4416 and **MS**4417) (PO Pack No. 590)	22·00		☐	
		PHQ Cards (set of 11) (475)	7·50	20·00	☐	☐
		Set of 3 Gutter Pairs (only 2 stamps in each gutter pair)	12·50		☐	

MS4417 126x89 mm. **3500** (1st) *The Adventure of the Speckled Band;* (1st) *The Red-Headed League;* £1·68 *The Adventure of the Second Stain;* £1·68 *The Adventure of the Dancing Men*   8·00   8·00 ☐ ☐
First Day Cover   10·00 ☐

(b) Self-adhesive. Gravure. Die-cut perf 14

4418	**3501**	(1st) multicoloured	2·50	2·50	☐	☐
4419	**3502**	(1st) multicoloured	2·50	2·50	☐	☐

Nos. 4411/4412, 4413/4414 and 4415/4416 were printed together, *se-tenant,* in vertical pairs throughout the sheets.

Nos. 4411/4416 show scenes from the *Sherlock* television series, and show additional inscriptions when UV light is shone over the stamps.

Nos. 4412 and 4414 have the two phosphor bands at left and centre of the stamp, No. 4415 has them at left and just right of centre, and No. 4416 at left and centre right. Nos. 4411 and 4413 have the two phosphor bands at left and right of the stamps as usual.

Nos. 4418/4419 were issued in stamp booklets with 4x1st bright scarlet stamps, originally sold for £4·56.

Stamps as Nos. 4411/4416 but self-adhesive were issued in collector sheets with labels containing Nos. 4411x4, 4412x2 and one each of Nos. 4413/4416, originally sold for £11·95.

The 11 PHQ cards show the ten individual stamps, including those from No. **MS**4417, and the complete miniature sheet.

3503 Then with a terrifying roar, The water bursts in through the door. (*Rupert's Rainy Adventure*)

3504 The bath is rocked from side to side, And Pompey quite enjoys his ride. (*Rupert's Rainy Adventure*)

3505 Then Algy looks a trifle glum, "I'm going home" he tells his chum (*Rupert and the Mare's Nest*)

3506 The large bird says, "Our king will know; Climb on my back and off we'll go" (*Rupert and Mare's Nest*)

3507 "There's something puzzling all of you," Says Rupert. "So please tell me too" *(Rupert and the Lost Cuckoo)*

3508 "My cuckoo's back again -- hooray! He didn't really go away!" *(Rupert and the lost Cuckoo)*

3509 Though Rupert searches all around, There's not one spruce tree to be found. *(Rupert's Christmas Tree)*

3510 The tree is such a lovely sight, That Rupert's chums gazed with delight. *(Rupert's Christmas Tree)*

Rupert Bear

2020 (3 Sept.) Centre band (2nd) or two bands (others) Perf 14½x14.

4420	**3503**	(2nd) multicoloured	90	90	☐	☐
		a. Horiz pair. Nos. 4420/4421	1·75	1·75	☐	☐
4421	**3504**	(2nd) multicoloured	90	90	☐	☐
4422	**3505**	(1st) multicoloured	1·25	1·25	☐	☐
		a. Horiz pair Nos. 4422/4423	2·50	2·50	☐	☐
4423	**3506**	(1st) multicoloured	1·25	1·25	☐	☐
4424	**3507**	£1·45 multicoloured	2·25	2·25	☐	☐
		a. Horiz. pair. Nos. 4424/4425	4·50	4·50	☐	☐
4425	**3508**	£1·45 multicoloured	2·25	2·25	☐	☐
4426	**3509**	£1·70 multicoloured	2·75	2·75	☐	☐
		a. Horiz. pair. Nos. 4426/4427	4·50	4·50	☐	☐
4427	**3510**	£1·70 multicoloured	2·75	2·75	☐	☐
Set of 8			13·00	13·00	☐	☐
First Day Cover				17·00	☐	
Presentation Pack (PO Pack No. 591)			15·00		☐	
PHQ Cards (*set of 8*) (476)			7·00	22·00	☐	☐
Set of 4 Gutter Pairs (only 2 stamps in each gutter pair)			14·50		☐	
Set of 4 Traffic Light Blocks of four			27·00		☐	

Nos. 4420/4421 and 4422/4423, 4424/4425 and 4426/4427 were each printed together, *se-tenant*, as horizontal pairs in sheets of 60 (2 panes 6×5).

3511 Common Carder Bee *(bombus pascuorum)*

Painted Lady Butterfly *Vanessa cardui*

3512 Painted Lady Butterfly *(Vanessa cardui)*

Longhorn Beetle *Rutpela maculata*

3513 Longhorn Beetle *(Rutpela maculata)*

Elephant Hawk-moth *Deilephila elpenor*

3514 Elephant Hawk-Moth *(Deilephila elpenor)*

Marmalade Hoverfly *Eplsyrphus balteatus*

3515 Marmalade Hoverfly *(Episyrphus balteatus)*

Ruby-tailed Wasp *Chrysis ignita agg.*

3516 Ruby-tailed Wasp *(Chrysis ignita agg)*

Brilliant Bugs

2020 (1 Oct.) Two bands (other) Perf 14½x14.

4428	**3511**	(1st) multicoloured	1·25	1·25	☐	☐
		a. Vert. pair. Nos. 4428/4429	2·50	2·50	☐	☐
4429	**3512**	(1st) multicoloured	1·25	1·25	☐	☐
4430	**3513**	£1·45 multicoloured	2·25	2·25	☐	☐
		a. Vert. pair Nos. 4430/4431	4·50	4·50	☐	☐
4431	**3514**	£1·45 multicoloured	2·25	2·25	☐	☐
4432	**3515**	£1·70 multicoloured	2·75	2·75	☐	☐
		a. Vert. pair. Nos. 4432/4433	5·50	5·50	☐	☐
4433	**3516**	£1·70 multicoloured	2·75	2·75	☐	☐
Set of 6			11·00	11·00	☐	☐

First Day Cover		15·00	☐
Presentation Pack (PO Pack No. 477)	13·00		☐
PHQ Cards (set of 8)	4·00	18·00	☐ ☐
Set of 3 Gutter Pairs (only 2 stamps in gutter pair)	12·50		☐

Nos. 4428/4429 and 4430/4431, 4432/4433 were each printed together, *se-tenant*, as vertical pairs in sheets of 60 (2 panes 5×6).

3517 Adoration of the Magi (detail), St Andrew's Church, East Lexham

3518 Virgin and Child, St Andrew's Church, Coln Rogers

3519 Adoration of the Magi, St. Andrew's Church, Lexham

3520 Virgin and Child, St Andrew's Church, Coln Rogers

3521 Virgin and Child, Church of St James, Hollowell

3522 Virgin and Child, All Saints' Church, Otley

3523 The Holy Family (detail), St Columba's Church, Topcliffe

3524 Virgin and Child, Christ Church, Coalville

Christmas. Stained-glass Windows

2020 (3 Nov.) Centre band (2nd) or two bands (others) Perf 14½x15.

(a) Self-adhesive. Gravure

4434	**3517**	(2nd) multicoloured	90	90	☐ ☐
4435	**3518**	(1st) multicoloured	1·00	1·00	☐ ☐
4436	**3519**	(2nd Large) multicoloured	1·10	1·10	☐ ☐
4437	**3520**	(1st Large) multicoloured	1·40	1·40	☐ ☐
4438	**3521**	£1·45 multicoloured	2·25	2·25	☐ ☐
4439	**3522**	£1·70 multicoloured	2·75	2·75	☐ ☐
4440	**3523**	£2·50 multicoloured	3·75	3·75	☐ ☐
4441	**3524**	£2·55 multicoloured	4·00	4·00	☐ ☐
Set of 8			15·00	15·00	☐ ☐
First Day Cover				22·00	☐
Presentation Pack (PO Pack No. 593)			20·00		☐
PHQ Cards (set of 9)			6·25	25·00	☐ ☐

(b) Ordinary gum. Litho

MS4442 189×74 mm. As Nos.

4434/4441		17·00	17·00	☐ ☐
First Day Cover			22·00	☐

The 2nd class, 1st class, £1·45, £1·70, £2·50 and £2·55 values were also issued in sheets of 20 containing eight 2nd class, eight 1st class and one each of the £1·45, £1·70, £2·50 and £2·55 values, each stamp accompanied by a *se-tenant* label.

The nine PHQ cards show the individual stamps and the complete miniature sheet.

3525 Captain James T. Kirk (William Shatner), *The Original Series*, 1966–1969

3526 Captain Jean-Luc Picard (Patrick Stewart), *The Next Generation*, 1987–1994

3527 Captain Benjamin Sisko (Avery Brooks), *Deep Space Nine*, 1993–1999

3528 Captain Kathryn Janeway (Kate Mulgrew), *Voyager*, 1995–2001

3529 Captain Jonathan Archer (Scott Bakula), *Enterprise*, 2001–2005

3530 Captain Gabriel Lorca (Jason Isaacs), *Discovery*, 2017–

3531 Spock (Leonard Nimoy), *The Original Series*

3532 Deanna Troi (Marina Sirtis), *The Next Generation*

3533 Julian Bashir (Alexander Siddig), *Deep Space Nine*

3534 Malcom Reed (Dominic Keating), *Enterprise*

3535 Michael Burnham (Sonequa Martin-Greene), *Discovery*

3536 Ash Tyler/Voq (Shazad Latif), *Discovery*

3537 Star Trek. The Movies

Star Trek

2020 (13 Nov). Two phosphor bands.

(a) Ordinary gum. Litho. P 14½

4443	**3525**	(1st) multicoloured	1·25	1·25
		a. Horiz strip of 6. Nos.		
		4443/4448	7·50	7·50
4444	**3526**	(1st) multicoloured	1·25	1·25
4445	**3527**	(1st) multicoloured	1·25	1·25
4446	**3528**	(1st) multicoloured	1·25	1·25
4447	**3529**	(1st) multicoloured	1·25	1·25
4448	**3530**	(1st) multicoloured	1·25	1·25
4449	**3531**	(1st) multicoloured	1·25	1·25
		a. Horiz strip of 6. Nos.		
		4449/4454	7·50	7·50
4450	**3532**	(1st) multicoloured	1·25	1·25
4451	**3533**	(1st) multicoloured	1·25	1·25
4452	**3534**	(1st) multicoloured	1·25	1·25
4453	**3535**	(1st) multicoloured	1·25	1·25
4454	**3536**	(1st) multicoloured	1·25	1·25

Set of 12	13·50	13·50
First Day Cover		17·00
Presentation Pack (Nos. 4443/4454 and		
MS4455) (PO Pack No. 594)	23·00	
PHQ Cards (set of 19)	13·00	28·00
Set of 2 Gutter Strips of 12	28·00	

(b) Self-adhesive. Litho

MS4455 146×74 mm. (1st) Montgomery Scott (Simon Pegg), new Movie Series (60x21 mm) (Perf 14½); (1st) Praetor Shinzon (Tom Hardy), Next Generation Movie: *Nemesis* (60x21 mm) (Perf 14½); (1st) Tolian Soran (Malcom McDowell) Original Movie Series: *Generation* (27x37 mm) (Perf 14); (1st) Klingon Chancellor Gorkon (David Warner), Original Movie Series (27x37 mm) (Perf 14); (1st) Dr. Carol Marcus (Alice Eve), new Movie Series: *Star Trek Into Darkness* (27x37 mm) (Perf 14); (1st) Krall (Idris Elba), new Movie Series (27x37 mm) (Perf 14) sold for £4·56   7·50   7·50

First Day Cover		9·50

(c) Self-adhesive. Gravure. Die-cut perf 14½

4456	**3525**	(1st) multicoloured	1·75	1·75
4457	**3526**	(1st) multicoloured	1·75	1·75

Nos. 4443/4448 and 4449/4454 were printed together, *se-tenant,* as horizontal strips of five stamps in sheets of 60 (2 panes 6×5).

Nos. 4456/4457 were issued in stamp booklets with 4×1st bright scarlet stamps, originally sold for £4·56.

The 19 PHQ cards show the 18 individual stamps, including those from No. **MS**4455, and the complete miniature sheet.

A collectors sheet containing stamps as Nos. 4443/4454 but self-adhesive was originally sold for £8·70.

Collectors Pack

2020 (13 Nov.) Comprises Nos. 4312/**MS**4320, 4323/4330, 4332/**MS**4338, 4345/4354, 4356/**MS**4364, 4369/**MS**4377, 4380/**MS**4396, 4404/**MS**4417, 4420/4441 and 4443/**MS**4455.

CP4457a	Collectors Pack sold for £166	£325	

Post Office Yearbook

2020 (13 Nov.) Comprises Nos. 4312/**MS**4320, 4323/4330, 4332/**MS**4338, 4345/4354, 4356/**MS**4364, 4369/**MS**4377, 4380/**MS**4396, 4404/**MS**4417, 4420/4441 and 4443/**MS**4455

YB4455a	Yearbook sold for £186	£375	

Miniature Sheet Collection

2020 (13 Nov.) Comprises Nos. **MS**4320, **MS**4338, **MS**4364, **MS**4377, **MS**4396, **MS**4410, **MS**4417, **MS**4442 and **MS**4455

MS4455a	Miniature Sheet Collection	
	sold for £57	£110

Decimal Machin Definitives

These are now combined into a single section to facilitate identification. The section is divided up as follows:

1. Denominated stamps with ordinary gum and standard perforations..
2. NVI (No Value Indicated) stamps with ordinary gum and standard perforations.
3. NVI stamps with ordinary gum and one elliptical hole on each side.
4. Denominated stamps with ordinary gum and one elliptical hole on each vertical side.
5. NVI stamps with self-adhesive gum and elliptical perforations
6. Millennium Machins
7. NVI and denominated stamps with self-adhesive gum and elliptical perforations
8. Overseas booklet stamps
9. 'Pricing in Proportion' NVI stamps
10. 'Security' Machins and commemorative Machins issued since 2010

1. Denominated stamps with ordinary gum and standard perforations

356a

357 (Value redrawn)

1970 (17 June)–**72** 10p. and some printings of the 50p. were issued on phosphor paper. Perf 12

829	**356a**	10p. cerise	50	50	
830		20p. olive-green	60	20	
831		50p. ultramarine	1·25	25	
831b	**357**	£1 black (6.12.72)	2·25	40	
Set of 4			3·25	1·25	
First Day Cover (Nos. 829/831)				2·00	
First Day Cover (No. 831b)				2·50	
Presentation Pack (PO Pack No. 18) (Nos. 829/831)				8·00	
Presentation Pack (PO Pack No. 38) (Nos. 830/831, 790 or 831b)				12·50	

PRINTING PROCESSES

There is a basic distinction between stamps printed by photogravure, later, gravure, and those printed by lithography. Sorting the two is not as difficult as it sounds and with a little experience it should become easy to tell which method of production was employed for a particular stamp.

The tiny dots of the printing screen give uneven edges to the values on gravure stamps (right). Litho values have clean, clear outlines (left).

All you need is a reasonably good glass giving a magnification of ×4 or more (×10 is even better!).

The image on a gravure stamp is created from a pattern or 'screen', of minute dots which are not evident when looking at the stamp without a glass but show up quite clearly under magnification, especially in the Queen's face and around the margin of the stamp design where it meets the white background of the paper. Now look at the value; here also, what looks to the naked eye like a straight line is in fact made up of rows of tiny little dots.

'Screens' of dots are also used in the production of litho printed stamps but they are only required where the printer is attempting to produce shades and tints as is necessary in the Queen's head portion of the stamp. Where solid colour is used, as in the background of the majority of values, there is no need to resort to a screen of dots and the background is printed as a solid mass of colour. If you look at the margins or the values of stamps produced in this way you will not see any evidence of dots—just a clear clean break between the inked portion of the stamp and the unlinked white of the paper.

367

367a

Two types of the 3p., 10p. and 26p. (Nos. X930/X930c, X886/X886b and X971/X971b).

I

II

I

II

I

II

1971 (15 Feb)–**96**. T **367**

(a) Printed in photogravure by Harrison and Sons (except for some ptgs of Nos. X879 and X913 which were produced by Enschedé) with phosphor bands. Perf 15×14

X841	½p. turquoise-blue (2 bands)	10	10	
X842	½p. turquoise-blue (1 side band) (24.5.72)	55·00	25·00	
X843	½p. turquoise-blue (1 centre band) (14.12.77)	20	20	
X844	1p. crimson (2 bands)	10	10	
X845	1p. crimson (1 centre band) (14.12.77)	20	20	
X846	1p. crimson ('all-over' phosphor) (10.10.79)	20	20	
X847	1p. crimson (1 side band at left) (20.10.86)	80	80	
X848	1½p. black (2 bands)	20	20	

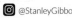

X849	2p. myrtle-green (face value as in Type **367**) (2 bands)	15	15	☐ ☐
X850	2p. myrtle-green (face value as in Type **367**) ('all-over' phosphor) *(10.10.79)*	25	25	☐ ☐
X851	2½p. magenta (1 centre band)	15	15	☐ ☐
X852	2½p. magenta (1 side band)	80	80	☐ ☐
X853	2½p. magenta (2 bands) *(21.5.75)*	20	20	☐ ☐
X854	2½p. rose-red (2 bands) *(26.8.81)*	30	30	☐ ☐
X855	3p. ultramarine (2 bands)	20	20	☐ ☐
X856	3p. ultramarine (1 centre band) *(10.9.73)*	15	15	☐ ☐
X857	3p. bright magenta (Type I) (2 bands) *(1.2.82)*	25	25	☐ ☐
X858	3½p. olive-grey (2 bands)	40	40	☐ ☐
X859	3½p. olive-grey (1 centre band) *(24.6.74)*	30	30	☐ ☐
X860	3½p. purple-brown (1 centre band) *(5.4.83)*	1·75	1·75	☐ ☐
X861	4p. ochre-brown (2 bands)	20	20	☐ ☐
X862	4p. greenish blue (2 bands) *(26.8.81)*	2·25	2·25	☐ ☐
X863	4p. greenish blue (1 centre band) *(3.9.84)*	1·25	1·25	☐ ☐
X864	4p. greenish blue (1 side band) *(8.1.85)*	4·50	4·50	☐ ☐
X865	4½p. grey-blue (2 bands) *(24.10.73)*	20	20	☐ ☐
X866	5p. pale violet (2 bands)	20	20	☐ ☐
X867	5p. claret (1 centre band) *(20.10.86)*	1·00	1·00	☐ ☐
X868	5½p. violet (2 bands) *(24.10.73)*	25	25	☐ ☐
X869	5½p. violet (1 centre band) *(17.3.75)*	25	25	☐ ☐
X870	6p. light emerald (2 bands)	25	25	☐ ☐
X871	6½p. greenish blue (2 bands) *(4.9.74)*	30	30	☐ ☐
X872	6½p. greenish blue (1 centre band) *(24.9.75)*	25	25	☐ ☐
X873	6½p. greenish blue (1 side band) *(26.1.77)*	80	80	☐ ☐
X874	7p. purple-brown (2 bands) *(15.1.75)*	25	25	☐ ☐
X875	7p. purple-brown (1 centre band) *(13.6.77)*	25	25	☐ ☐
X876	7p. purple-brown (1 side band) *(13.6.77)*	35	35	☐ ☐
X877	7½p. chestnut (2 bands)	25	25	☐ ☐
X878	8p. rosine (2 bands) *(24.10.73)*	25	25	☐ ☐

X879	8p. rosine (1 centre band) *(20.8.79)*	25	25	☐ ☐
X880	8p. rosine (1 side band) *(28.8.79)*	50	50	☐ ☐
X881	8½p. light yellowish green (2 bands) *(24.9.75)*	25	25	☐ ☐
X882	9p. yellow-orange and black (2 bands)	40	40	☐ ☐
X883	9p. deep violet (2 bands) *(25.2.76)*	25	25	☐ ☐
X884	9½p. purple (2 bands) *(25.2.76)*	30	30	☐ ☐
X885	10p. orange-brown and chestnut (2 bands) *(11.8.71)*	30	30	☐ ☐
X886	10p. orange-brown (Type I) (2 bands) *(25.2.76)*	30	30	☐ ☐
	b. Type II *(4.9.84)*	14·00	14·00	☐ ☐
X887	10p. orange-brown (Type I) ('all-over' phosphor) *(3.10.79)*	25	25	☐ ☐
X888	10p. orange-brown (Type I) (1 centre band) *(4.2.80)*	25	25	☐ ☐
X889a	10p. orange-brown (Type I) (1 side band) *(4.2.80)*	1·00	1·00	☐ ☐
X890	10½p. yellow (2 bands) *(25.2.76)*	35	35	☐ ☐
X891	10½p. blue (2 bands) *(26.4.78)*	40	40	☐ ☐
X892	11p. brown-red (2 bands) *(25.2.76)*	30	30	☐ ☐
X893	11½p. drab (1 centre band) *(14.1.81)*	30	30	☐ ☐
X894	11½p. drab (1 side band) *(26.1.81)*	35	35	☐ ☐
X895	12p. yellowish green (2 bands) *(4.2.80)*	40	40	☐ ☐
X896	12p. bright emerald (1 centre band) *(29.10.85)*	40	40	☐ ☐
X897	12p. bright emerald (1 side band) *(14.1.86)*	55	55	☐ ☐
X898	12½p. light emerald (1 centre band) *(27.1.82)*	30	30	☐ ☐
X899	12½p. light emerald (1 side band) *(1.2.82)*	30	30	☐ ☐
X900	13p. pale chestnut (1 centre band) *(28.8.84)*	30	30	☐ ☐
X901	13p. pale chestnut (1 side band) *(3.9.84)*	40	40	☐ ☐
X902	14p. grey-blue (2 bands) *(26.1.81)*	90	90	☐ ☐
X903	14p. deep blue (1 centre band) *(23.8.88)*	45	45	☐ ☐
X904	14p. deep blue (1 side band) *(5.9.88)*	4·00	4·00	☐ ☐
X905	15p. bright blue (1 centre band) *(26.9.89)*	50	50	☐ ☐
X906a	15p. bright blue (1 side band) *(2.10.89)*	2·50	2·50	☐ ☐
X907	15½p. pale violet (2 bands) *(1.2.82)*	30	30	☐ ☐

X908	16p. olive-drab (2 bands) *(5.4.83)*	90	90
X909	17p. grey-blue (2 bands) *(3.9.84)*	50	50
X910	17p. deep blue(1 centre band) *(4.9.90)*	70	70
X911*a*	17p. deep blue (1 side band) *(4.9.90)*	1·50	1·50
X912	18p. deep olive-grey (2 bands) *(20.10.86)*	60	60
X913	18p. bright green (1 centre band) *(10.9.91)*	50	50
X914	19p. bright orange-red (2 bands) *(5.9.88)*	1·00	1·00
X915	20p. dull purple (2 bands) *(25.2.76)*	80	80
X916	20p. brownish black (2 bands) *(2.10.89)*	2·00	2·00
X917	22p. bright orange-red (2 bands) *(4.9.90)*	90	90
X917*a*	25p. rose-red (2 bands) *(6.2.96)*	9·00	9·00
X918	26p. rosine (Type I) (2 bands) *(3.3.87)*	8·00	8·00
X919	31p. purple (2 bands) *(18.3.86)*	10·00	10·00
X920	34p. ochre-brown (2 bands) *(8.1.85)*	6·00	6·00
X921	50p. ochre-brown (2 bands) *(2.2.77)*	1·75	1·75
X922	50p. ochre (2 bands) *(20.3.90)*	3·75	3·75

(b) Printed in photogravure by Harrison and Sons on phosphorised paper. Perf 15×14

X924	½p. turquoise-blue *(10.12.80)*	20	20
X925	1p. crimson *(12.12.79)*	20	20
X926	2p. myrtle-green (face value as in Type **367**) *(12.12.79)*	20	20
X927	2p. deep green (smaller value as in Type **367a**) *(26.7.88)*	75	75
X928	2p. myrtle-green (smaller value as in Type **367a**) *(5.9.88)*	10.00	10.00
X929	2½p. rose-red *(14.1.81)*	20	20
X930	3p. bright magenta (Type I) *(22.10.80)*	20	20
	c. Type II *(10.10.89)*	2·00	2·00
X931	3½p. purple-brown *(30.3.83)*	30	30
X932	4p. greenish blue *(30.12.81)*	25	25
X933	4p. new blue *(26.7.88)*	35	35
X934	5p. pale violet *(10.10.79)*	30	30
X935	5p. dull red-brown *(26.7.88)*	25	25
X936	6p. yellow-olive *(10.9.91)*	25	25
X937	7p. brownish red *(29.10.85)*	1·50	1·50
X938	8½p. yellowish green *(24.3.76)*	65	50
X939	10p. orange-brown (Type I) *(11.79)*	35	35
X940	10p. dull orange (Type II) *(4.9.90)*	35	35
X941	11p. brown-red *(27.8.80)*	1·00	1·00
X942	11½p. ochre-brown *(15.8.79)*	40	40

X943	12p. yellowish green *(30.1.80)*	40	40
X944	13p. olive-grey *(15.8.79)*	55	55
X945	13½p. purple-brown *(30.1.80)*	80	80
X946	14p. grey-blue *(14.1.81)*	50	50
X947	15p. ultramarine *(15.8.79)*	60	60
X948	15½p. pale violet *(14.1.81)*	45	45
X949	16p. olive-drab *(30.8.83)*	40	40
X950	16½p. pale chestnut *(27.1.82)*	80	80
X951	17p. light emerald *(30.1.80)*	60	60
X952	17p. grey-blue *(30.3.83)*	55	55
X953	17½p. pale chestnut *(30.1.80)*	60	60
X954	18p. deep violet *(14.1.81)*	60	60
X955	18p. deep olive-grey *(28.8.84)*	60	60
X956	19p. bright orange-red *(23.8.88)*	80	60
X957	19½p. olive-grey *(27.1.82)*	1·90	1·90
X958	20p. dull purple *(10.10.79)*	1·00	1·00
X959	20p. turquoise-green *(23.8.88)*	75	75
X960	20p. brownish black *(26.9.89)*	65	65
X961	20½p. ultramarine *(30.3.83)*	1·10	1·10
X962	22p. blue *(22.10.80)*	70	70
X963	22p. yellow-green *(28.8.84)*	70	70
X964	22p. bright orange-red *(4.9.90)*	80	80
X965	23p. brown-red *(30.3.83)*	1·50	1·50
X966	23p. bright green *(23.8.88)*	1·25	1·25
X967	24p. violet *(28.8.84)*	1·60	1·60
X968	24p. Indian red *(26.9.89)*	2·00	2·00
X969	24p. chestnut *(10.9.91)*	80	80
X970	25p. purple *(14.1.81)*	90	90
X971	26p. rosine (Type I) *(27.1.82)*	90	90
	b. Type II *(4.8.87)*	6·00	6·00
X972	26p. drab *(4.9.90)*	1·50	1·50
X973	27p. chestnut *(23.8.88)*	1·00	1·00
X974	27p. violet *(4.9.90)*	1·00	1·00
X975	28p. deep violet *(20.3.83)*	1·00	1·00
X976	28p. ochre *(23.8.88)*	1·00	1·00
X977	28p. deep bluish grey *(10.9.91)*	1·00	1·00
X978	29p. ochre-brown *(27.1.82)*	1·10	1·10
X979	29p. deep mauve *(26.9.89)*	2·50	2·50
X980	30p. deep olive-grey *(26.9.89)*	1·25	1·25
X981	31p. purple *(30.8.83)*	2·00	2·00
X982	31p. ultramarine *(4.9.90)*	1·50	1·50
X983	32p. greenish blue *(23.8.88)*	1·70	1·70
X984	33p. light emerald *(4.9.90)*	1·25	1·25
X985	34p. ochre-brown *(28.8.84)*	1·50	1·50
X986	34p. deep bluish grey *(26.9.89)*	1·50	1·50
X987	34p. deep mauve *(10.9.91)*	1·75	1·75
X988	35p. sepia *(23.8.88)*	1·50	1·50
X989	35p. yellow *(10.9.91)*	1·50	1·50
X990	37p. rosine *(26.9.89)*	1·75	1·75

X991	39p. bright mauve			
	(10.9.91)	1·50	1·50	☐ ☐
X991*a*	50p. ochre *(21.1.92)*	9·00	9·00	☐ ☐

(c) Printed in photogravure by Harrison and Sons on ordinary paper. Perf 15×14

X992	50p. ochre-brown			
	(21.5.80)	2·00	2·00	☐ ☐
X993	50p. ochre *(13.3.90)*	4·00	4·00	☐ ☐
X994	75p. grey-black (smaller values as Type **367a**) *(26.7.88)*	4·75	4·75	☐ ☐

(d) Printed in lithography by John Waddington. Perf 14

X996	4p. greenish blue (2 bands)			
	(30.1.80)	20	20	☐ ☐
X997	4p. greenish blue (phosphorised paper) *(11.81)*	30	30	☐ ☐
X998	20p. dull purple (2 bands)			
	(21.5.80)	1·50	1·50	☐ ☐
X999	20p. dull purple (phosphorised paper) *(11.81)*	1·50	1·50	☐ ☐

(e) Printed in lithography by Questa. Perf 14 (Nos. X1000, X1003/X1004 and X1023) or 15×14 (others)

X1000	2p. emerald-green (face value as in Type **367**) (phosphorised paper) *(21.5.80)*	20	20	☐ ☐
	a. Perf 15×14 *(10.7.84)*	25	25	☐ ☐
X1001	2p. bright green and deep green (smaller value as in Type **367a**) (phosphorised paper) *(23.2.88)*	55	55	☐ ☐
X1002	4p. greenish blue (phosphorised paper) *(13.5.86)*	55	55	☐ ☐
X1003	5p. light violet (phosphorised paper) *(21.5.80)*	25	25	☐ ☐
X1004	5p. claret (phosphorised paper) *(27.1.82)*	40	40	☐ ☐
	a. Perf 15×14 *(21.2.84)*	45	45	☐ ☐
X1005	13p. pale chestnut (1 centre band) *(9.2.88)*	50	50	☐ ☐
X1006	13p. pale chestnut (1 side band) *(9.2.88)*	50	50	☐ ☐
X1007	14p. deep blue (1 centre band) *(11.10.88)*	2·00	2·00	☐ ☐
X1008	17p. deep blue (1 centre band) *(19.3.91)*	55	55	☐ ☐
X1009	18p. deep olive-grey (phosphorised paper) *(9.2.88)*	55	55	☐ ☐
X1010	18p. deep olive-grey (2 bands) *(9.2.88)*	7·50	7·50	☐ ☐
X1011	18p. bright green (1 centre band) *(27.10.92)*	55	55	☐ ☐

X1012	18p. bright green (1 side band) *(27.10.92)*	90	90	☐ ☐
X1013	19p. bright orange-red (phosphorised paper) *(11.10.88)*	1·50	1·50	☐ ☐
X1014	20p. dull purple (phosphorised paper) *(13.5.86)*	1·25	1·25	☐ ☐
X1015	22p. yellow-green (2 bands) *(9.2.88)*	8·00	8·00	☐ ☐
X1016	22p. bright orange-red (phosphorised paper) *(19.3.91)*	75	75	☐ ☐
X1017	24p. chestnut (phosphorised paper) *(27.10.92)*	70	70	☐ ☐
X1018	24p. chestnut (2 bands) *(27.10.92)*	1·75	1·75	☐ ☐
X1019	33p. light emerald (phosphorised paper) *(19.3.91)*	2·00	2·00	☐ ☐
X1020	33p. light emerald (2 bands) *(25.2.92)*	1·25	1·25	☐ ☐
X1021	34p. bistre-brown (2 bands) *(9.2.88)*	8·00	8·00	☐ ☐
X1022	39p. bright mauve (2 bands) *(27.10.92)*	2·00	2·00	☐ ☐
X1023	75p. black (face value as Type **367**) (ordinary paper) *(30.1.80)*	2·25	2·25	☐ ☐
	a. Perf 15×14 *(21.2.84)*	2·75	2·75	☐ ☐
X1024	75p. brownish grey and black (smaller value as Type **367a**) (ordinary paper) *(23.2.88)*	9·00	9·00	☐ ☐

(f) Printed in lithography by Walsall. Perf 14

X1050	2p. deep green (phosphorised paper) *(9.2.93)*	1·50	1·50	☐ ☐
X1051	14p. deep blue (1 side band) *(9.2.93)*	3·25	3·25	☐ ☐
X1052	19p. bright orange-red (2 bands) *(25.4.89)*	90	90	☐ ☐
X1053	24p. chestnut (phosphorised paper) *(9.2.93)*	90	90	☐ ☐
X1054	29p. deep mauve (2 bands) *(2.10.89)*	3·00	3·00	☐ ☐
X1055	29p. deep mauve (phosphorised paper) *(17.4.90)*	3·00	3·00	☐ ☐
X1056	31p. ultramarine (phosphorised paper) *(17.9.90)*	1·75	1·75	☐ ☐
X1057	33p. light emerald (phosphorised paper) *(16.9.91)*	1·75	1·75	☐ ☐
X1058	39p. bright mauve (phosphorised paper) *(16.9.91)*	2·00	2·00	☐ ☐

Presentation Pack (PO Pack No. 26) (contains ½p. (X841), 1p. (X844), 1½p. (X848), 2p. (X849), 2½p. (X851), 3p. (X855), 3½p. (X858), 4p. (X861), 5p. (X866), 6p. (X870), 7½p. (X877), 9p. (X882)) | 9·00 | ☐

Presentation Pack (Scandinavia 71)
  (contents as above)   25·00 ☐

Presentation Pack (PO Pack No. 37) (contains ½p. (X841), 1p. (X844), 1½p. (X848), 2p. (X849), 2½p. (X851), 3p. (X855 or X856), 3½p. (X858 or X859), 4p. (X861), 4½p. (X865), 5p. (X866), 5½p. (X868 or X869), 6p. (X870), 7½p. (X877), 8p. (X878), 9p. (X882), 10p. (X885))   30·00 ☐

Later issues of this pack included the 6½p. (X871) or the 6½p. (X872) and 7p. (X874).

Presentation Pack (PO Pack No. 90) (contains ½p. (X841), 1p. (X844), 1½p. (X848), 2p. (X849), 2½p. (X851), 3p. (X856), 5p. (X866), 6½p. (X872), 7p. (X874 or X875), 7½p. (X877), 8p. (X878), 8½p. (X881), 9p. (X883), 9½p. (X884), 10p. (X886), 10½p. (X890), 11p. (X892), 20p. (X915), 50p. (X921))   5·00 ☐

Presentation Pack (PO Pack No. 129a) (contains 2½p. (X929), 3p. (X930), 4p. (X996), 10½p. (X891), 11½p. (X893), 11½p. (X942), 12p. (X943), 13p. (X944), 13½p. (X945), 14p. (X946), 15p. (X947), 15½p. (X948), 17p. (X951), 17½p. (X953), 18p. (X954), 22p. (X962), 25p. (X970), 75p. (X1023))   15·00 ☐

Presentation Pack (PO Pack No. 1) (contains ½p. (X924), 1p. (X925), 2p. (X1000), 3p. (X930), 3½p. (X931), 4p. (X997), 5p. (X1004), 10p. (X888), 12½p. (X898), 16p. (X949), 16½p. (X950), 17p. (X952), 20p. (X999), 20½p. (X961), 23p. (X965), 26p. (X971), 28p. (X975), 31p. (X981), 50p. (X992), 75p. (X1023))   32·00 ☐

Presentation Pack (PO Pack No. 5) (contains ½p. (X924), 1p. (X925), 2p. (X1000a), 3p. (X930), 4p. (X997), 5p. (X1004a), 10p. (X939), 13p. (X900), 16p. (X949), 17p. (X952), 18p. (X955), 20p. (X999), 22p. (X963), 24p. (X967), 26p. (X971), 28p. (X975), 31p. (X981), 34p. (X985), 50p. (X992), 75p. (X1023a))   25·00 ☐

Presentation Pack (PO Pack No. 9) (contains 1p. (X925), 2p. (X1000a), 3p. (X930), 4p. (X997), 5p. (X1004a), 7p. (X937), 10p. (X939), 12p. (X896), 13p. (X900), 17p. (X952), 18p. (X955), 20p. (X999), 22p. (X963), 24p. (X967), 26p. (X971), 28p. (X975), 31p. (X981), 34p. (X985), 50p. (X992), 75p. (X1023a))   30·00 ☐

Presentation Pack (PO Pack No. 15) (contains 14p. (X903), 19p. (X956), 20p. (X959), 23p. (X966), 27p. (X973), 28p. (X976), 32p. (X983), 35p. (X988))   9·00 ☐

Presentation Pack (PO Pack No. 19) (contains 15p. (X905), 20p. (X960), 24p. (X968), 29p. (X979), 30p. (X980), 34p. (X986), 37p. (X990))   7·00 ☐

Presentation Pack (PO Pack No. 22) (contains 10p. (X940), 17p. (X910), 22p. (X964), 26p. (X972), 27p. (X974), 31p. (X982), 33p. (X984))   7·00 ☐

Presentation Pack (PO Pack No. 24) (contains 1p. (X925), 2p. (X927), 3p. (X930), 4p. (X933), 5p. (X935), 10p. (X940), 17p. (X910), 20p. (X959), 22p. (X964), 26p. (X972), 27p. (X974), 30p. (X980), 31p. (X982), 32p. (X983), 33p. (X984), 37p. (X990), 50p. (X993), 75p. (X994))   30·00 ☐

Presentation Pack (PO Pack No. 25) (contains 6p. (X936), 18p. (X913), 24p. (X969), 28p. (X977), 34p. (X987), 35p. (X989), 39p. (X991))   7·00 ☐

First Day Covers

15 Feb. 1971	½p., 1p., 1½p., 2p., 2½p., 3p., 3½p., 4p., 5p., 6p., 7½p., 9p. (Nos. X841, X844, X848/X849, X851, X855, X858, X861, X866, X870, X877, X882) (Covers carry 'POSTING DELAYED BY THE POST OFFICE STRIKE 1971' cachet)	2·50 ☐
11 Aug. 1971	10p. (No. X885)	1·00 ☐
24 Oct. 1973	4½p., 5½p., 8p. (Nos. X865, X868, X878)	1·00 ☐
4 Sept. 1974	6½p. (No. X871)	1·00 ☐

15 Jan. 1975	7p. (No. X874)	1·00 ☐
24 Sept. 1975	8½p. (No. X881)	1·00 ☐
25 Feb. 1976	9p., 9½p., 10p., 10½p., 11p., 20p. (Nos. X883/X884, X886, X890, X892, X915)	2·50 ☐
2 Feb. 1977	50p. (No. X921)	1·00 ☐
26 Apr. 1978	10½p. (No. X891)	1·00 ☐
15 Aug. 1979	11½p., 13p., 15p. (Nos. X942, X944, X947)	1·00 ☐
30 Jan. 1980	4p., 12p., 13½p., 17p., 17½p., 75p. (Nos. X996, X943, X945, X951, X953, X1023)	2·00 ☐
22 Oct. 1980	3p., 22p. (Nos. X930, X962)	1·00 ☐
14 Jan. 1981	2½p., 11½p., 14p., 15½p., 18p., 25p (Nos. X929, X893, X946, X948, X954, X970)	1·25 ☐
27 Jan. 1982	5p., 12½p., 16½p., 19½p., 26p., 29p. (Nos. X1004, X898, X950, X957, X971, X978)	2·00 ☐
30 Mar. 1983	3½p., 16p., 17p., 20½p., 23p., 28p., 31p. (Nos. X931, X949, X952, X961, X965, X975, X981)	2·75 ☐
28 Aug. 1984	13p., 18p., 22p., 24p., 34p. (Nos. X900, X955, X963, X967, X985)	2·00 ☐
29 Oct. 1985	7p., 12p. (Nos. X937, X896)	2·00 ☐
23 Aug. 1988	14p., 19p., 20p., 23p., 27p., 28p., 32p., 35p. (Nos. X903, X956, X959, X966, X973, X976, X983, X988)	3·50 ☐
26 Sept. 1989	15p., 20p., 24p., 29p., 30p., 34p., 37p. (Nos. X905, X960, X968, X979/X980, X986, X990)	3·00 ☐
4 Sept. 1990	10p., 17p., 22p., 26p., 27p., 31p., 33p. (Nos. X940, X910, X964, X972, X974, X982, X984)	3·00 ☐
10 Sept. 1991	6p., 18p., 24p., 28p., 34p., 35p., 39p. (Nos. X936, X913, X969, X977, X987, X989, X991)	3·25 ☐

For similar stamps, but with elliptical perforations see Nos. Y1667/Y1803 in 1993.

PHOSPHOR BANDS. See notes above No. 561.

Phosphor bands are applied to the stamps, after the design has been printed, by a separate cylinder. On issues with 'all-over' phosphor the 'band' covers the entire stamp. Parts of the stamp covered by phosphor bands, or the entire surface for 'all-over' phosphor versions, appear matt.

Nos. X847, X852, X864, X873, X876, X880, X889, X894, X897, X899, X901, X906, X911, X1006 and X1012 exist with the phosphor band at the left or right of the stamp.

PHOSPHORISED PAPER. First introduced as an experiment for a limited printing of the 1s.6d. value (No. 743c) in 1969, this paper has the phosphor, to activate the automatic sorting machinery, added to the paper coating before the stamps were printed. Issues on this paper have a completely shiny surface. Although not adopted after this first trial further experiments on the 8½p. in 1976 led to this paper being used for new printings of current values.

508

1977 (2 Feb.)–**87 T 508** Ordinary paper

1026	£1 bright yellow-green and blackish olive	3·00	25	□ □
1026b	£1·30 pale drab and deep greenish blue (3.8.83)	5·50	6·00	□ □
1026c	£1·33 pale mauve and grey-black (28.8.84)	7·50	8·00	□ □
1026d	£1·41 pale drab and deep greenish blue (17.9.85)	8·50	8·50	□ □
1026e	£1·50 pale mauve and grey-black (2.9.86)	6·00	5·00	□ □
1026f	£1·60 pale drab and deep greenish blue (15.9.87)	6·50	7·00	□ □
1027	£2 light emerald and purple-brown	9·00	50	□ □
1028	£5 salmon and chalky blue	22·00	3·00	□ □
Set of 8		60·00	32·00	□ □

Presentation Pack (Nos. 1026, 1027/1028) (PO Pack No. 91 (small size))	38·00	□
Presentation Pack (Nos. 1026, 1027/1028) (PO Pack No. 13 (large size))	£170	□
Presentation Pack (PO Pack No. 14) (No. 1026f)	22·00	□
Set of 8 Gutter Pairs	£125	□
Set of 8 Traffic Light Gutter Pairs	£150	□

First Day Covers

2 Feb. 1977	Nos. 1026, 1027/1028	10·00	□
3 Aug. 1983	No. 1026b	6·50	□
28 Aug. 1984	No. 1026c	8·50	□
17 Sept. 1985	No. 1026d	9·00	□
2 Sept. 1986	No. 1026e	5·50	□
15 Sept. 1987	No. 1026f	7·50	□

See also No. U3920

2. NVI (No Value Indicated) stamps with ordinary gum and standard perforations.

913

914

Booklet Stamps

1989 (22 Aug.)–**92**

(a) Printed in photogravure by Harrison and Sons. Perf 15 × 14

1445	**913**	(2nd) bright blue (1 centre band)	1·25	1·25	□ □
1446		(2nd) bright blue (1 side band) (20.3.90)	2·00	2·00	□ □
1447	**914**	(1st) brownish black (phosphorised paper)	1·50	1·50	□ □
1448		(1st) brownish black (2 bands) (20.3.90)	2·50	2·50	□ □

(b) Printed in lithography by Walsall. Perf 14

1449	**913**	(2nd) bright blue (1 centre band)	1·25	1·00	□ □
1450	**914**	(1st) blackish brown (2 bands)	1·60	1·60	□ □

(c) Printed in lithography by Questa. Perf 15 × 14

1451	**913**	(2nd) bright blue (1 centre band) (19.9.89)	1·25	1·00	□ □
1451a		(2nd) bright blue (1 side band) (25.2.92)	1·75	1·75	□ □
1452	**914**	(1st) brownish black (phosphorised paper) (19.9.89)	1·75	1·75	□ □
First Day Cover (Nos. 1445, 1447)				4·50	□

For similar stamps showing changed colours see Nos. 1511/1516, for those with elliptical perforations Nos. 1664/1671 and for self-adhesive versions Nos. 2039/2040, 2295, U2941/U2942, U2945, U2948, U3001/U3002 and U3271.

No. 1451a exists with the phosphor band at the left or right of the stamp.

Booklet Stamps

1990 (7 Aug.)–**92** As Types **913/914**, but colours changed

(a) Photo Harrison. Perf 15 × 14

1511	**913**	(2nd) deep blue (1 centre band)	1·50	1·50	□ □
1512	**914**	(1st) bright orange-red (phosphorised paper)	1·50	1·50	□ □

(b) Litho Questa. Perf 15 × 14

1513	**913**	(2nd) deep blue (1 centre band)	1·75	1·75	□ □
1514	**914**	(1st) bright orange-red (phosphorised paper)	1·75	1·75	□ □
1514a		(1st) bright orange-red (2 bands) (25.2.92)	2·00	2·00	□ □

(c) Litho Walsall. Perf 14

1515	**913**	(2nd) deep blue (1 centre band)	1·75	2·00	□ □
1516	**914**	(1st) bright orange-red (phosphorised paper)	1·75	2·00	□ □
		c. Perf 13	4·00	4·00	□ □
First Day Cover (Nos. 1515/1516)				3·00	□

For similar stamps with elliptical perforations see Nos. 1664/1671.

3. NVI stamps with ordinary gum and one elliptical hole on each side.

1093a

1993 (6 Apr.)–**2017**. As Types **913/914** and **1093a**, but Perf 14 (No. 1665) or 15 × 14 (others) (both with one elliptical hole in each vertical side)

(a) Gravure

Harrison (No. 1666), Questa (Nos. 1664a, 1667a), Walsall (No. 1665), Harrison (later De La Rue), Questa or Walsall (No. 1667), Harrison (later De La Rue), Enschedé, Questa or Walsall (Nos. 1664, 1668, 1669) or ISP Walsall (No. 1668s)

1664	**913**	(2nd) bright blue (1 centre band) (7.9.93)	1·25	1·25	□ □
		a. Perf 14 (1.12.98)	1·25	1·25	□ □
1665		(2nd) bright blue (1 side band) (13.10.98)	1·75	1·75	□ □

1666	**914**	(1st) bright orange-red (phosphorised paper)	1·75	1·50	☐ ☐
1667		(1st) bright orange-red (2 phosphor bands) *(4.4.95)*	1·50	1·25	☐ ☐
		a. Perf 14 *(1.12.98)*	1·75	1·75	☐ ☐
1668		(1st) gold (2 phosphor bands) *(21.4.97)*	1·60	1·60	☐ ☐
1668s		(1st) brownish black (2 phosphor bands) *(5.6.17)*	3·50	3·50	☐ ☐
1669	**1093a**	(E) deep blue (2 phosphor bands) *(19.1.99)*	2·25	2·25	☐ ☐

(b) Litho Questa or Walsall (No. 1670), Questa, Enschedé or Walsall (No. 1671), De La Rue or Walsall (No. 1672)

1670	**913**	(2nd) bright blue (1 centre band)	1·25	90	☐ ☐
1671	**914**	(1st) bright orange-red (2 phosphor bands)	1·25	1·00	☐ ☐
1672		(1st) gold (2 phosphor bands) *(8.1.08)*	1·60	1·60	☐ ☐

First Day Covers

21 Apr. 1997	(1st) (No 1668), and 26p. (Y1692)	3·25	☐
19 Jan. 1999	(E) (No 1669)	2·75	☐

Nos. 1664, 1667, 1669 and 1670/1671 also come from sheets.

No. 1665 exists with the phosphor band at the left or right of the stamp and was only issued in booklets.

No. 1668 was issued by Harrison in booklets and Walsall in sheets and booklets for the Queen's Golden Wedding on 21 April 1997. The gold colour was later adopted for the (1st) class rate, replacing bright orange-red. As such, it appeared in a number of prestige booklets.

For No. 1668 in presentation pack see Pack No. 38 listed below, No. Y1667 etc.

No. 1668s was issued on 5 June 2017 in the £15·14 50th Anniversary of the Machin Definitive Prestige booklet.

No. 1669 was valid for the basic European airmail rate, initially 30p.

No. 1672 was only issued in £7·40 or £7·15 stamp booklets.

For self-adhesive versions in these colours see Nos. 2039/2040 and 2295/2298.

1390

Profile on Print. Booklet Stamps

1999 (16 Feb.)

(a) Embossed and litho Walsall. Self-adhesive. Die-cut perf 14 × 15

2077	**1390**	(1st) grey (face value) (Queen's head in colourless relief) (phosphor background around head)	1·50	1·50	☐ ☐

(b) Recess Enschedé. Perf 14 × 14½

2078	**1390**	(1st) grey-black (2 phosphor bands)	1·50	1·50	☐ ☐

(c) Typo Harrison. Perf 14 × 15

2079	**1390**	(1st) black (2 phosphor bands)	1·50	1·50	☐ ☐
Set of 3			4·00	4·00	☐ ☐

Nos. 2077/2079 were only issued in £7·54 the Profile on Print stamp booklet No. DX22.

4. Denominated stamps with ordinary gum and one elliptical hole on each vertical side.

II Normal figures of face value

III Open '4' and open lower curve of '5'

1993–2011 As Nos. X841 etc, but perf 14 (No. Y1678) or 15 × 14 (others) (both with one elliptical hole in each vertical side)

(a) Gravure

Enschedé: 20p. (Y1684), 29p., 35p. (Y1698), 36p., 38p. (Y1706), 41p. (Y1712), 43p. (Y1716)

Harrison: 20p. (Y1686), 25p. (Y1689), 26p. (Y1692), 35p. (Y1699), 41p. (Y1713), 43p. (Y1717)

Walsall: 10p. (Y1676), 19p. (Y1683), 38p. (Y1707), 43p. (Y1717)

Enschedé or Harrison (later De La Rue): 4p., 6p., 25p. (Y1690), 31p., 39p. (Y1708), £1 (Y1743)

Enschedé, or Harrison (later De La Rue Questa or Walsall): 1p., 2p.

Enschedé, Harrison (later De La Rue) or Walsall: 5p., 10p. (Y1676), 30p., 37p. (Y1703), 42p., 50p. (Y1726), 63p.

Harrison (later De La Rue) or Questa: 19p. (Y1682), 20p. (Y1685), 26p. (Y1691)

De La Rue or Walsall: 20p. (Y1687), 38p. (Y1707), 39p. (Y1709), 40p. (Y1710), 50p. (Y1727), 64p., 65p., 68p.

De La Rue: 7p., 8p., 9p., 12p., 14p., 15p., 16p., 17p., 22p., 33p., 34p., 35p. (Y1700), 37p. (Y1704/Y1705), 41p. (Y1714), 43p. (Y1718), 44p., 45p., 48p., 49p., 56p., 60p., 62p., 67p., 72p., 78p., 81p., 88p., 90p., 97p., £1 (Y1744), £1·46, £1·50, £2, £3, £5

Enschedé or De La Rue: 35p. (Y1701), 40p. (Y1711), 46p., 47p., 54p.

Y1667	**367**	1p. crimson (2 bands) *(8.6.93)*	20	20	☐ ☐
Y1668		2p. deep green (2 bands) *(11.4.95)*	20	20	☐ ☐
Y1669		4p. new blue (2 bands) *(14.12.93)*	20	20	☐ ☐
Y1670		5p. dull red-brown (2 bands) (Type II) *(8.6.93)*	25	25	☐ ☐
Y1671		6p. yellow-olive (2 bands) *(27.4.93)*	30	30	☐ ☐
Y1672		7p. grey (2 bands) *(20.4.99)*	2·75	2·75	☐ ☐
Y1673		7p. bright magenta (2 bands) *(1.4.04)*	30	30	☐ ☐
Y1674		8p. yellow (2 bands) *(25.4.00)*	35	35	☐ ☐
Y1675		9p. yellow-orange (2 bands) *(5.4.05)*	30	30	☐ ☐
Y1676		10p. dull orange (2 bands) *(8.6.93)*	35	35	☐ ☐
		a. Perf 14 *(13.10.98)*	1·75	1·75	☐ ☐

Y1677	12p. greenish blue (2 bands) *(1.8.06)*	70	70	☐ ☐
Y1678	14p. rose-red (2 bands) *(1.8.06)*	70	70	☐ ☐
Y1679	15p. bright magenta (2 bands) *(1.4.08)*	65	65	☐ ☐
Y1680	16p. pale cerise (2 bands) *(27.3.07)*	65	65	☐ ☐
Y1681	17p. brown-olive (2 bands) *(31.3.09)*	75	75	☐ ☐
Y1682	19p. bistre (1 centre band) *(26.10.93)*	50	50	☐ ☐
Y1683	19p. bistre (1 side band) *(15.2.00)*	90	90	☐ ☐
Y1684	20p. turquoise-green (2 bands) *(14.12.93)*	80	80	☐ ☐
Y1685	20p. bright green (1 centre band) *(25.6.96)*	60	60	☐ ☐
Y1686	20p. bright green (1 side band) *(23.9.97)*	1·10	1·10	☐ ☐
Y1687	20p. bright green (2 bands) *(20.4.99)*	60	60	☐ ☐
Y1688	22p. drab (2 bands) *(31.3.09)*	80	80	☐ ☐
Y1689	25p. rose-red (phosphorised paper) *(26.10.93)*	70	70	☐ ☐
Y1690	25p. rose-red (2 bands) *(20.12.94)*	70	70	☐ ☐
Y1691	26p. red-brown (2 bands) *(25.6.96)*	70	70	☐ ☐
Y1692	26p. gold (2 bands) *(21.4.97)*	90	90	☐ ☐
Y1693	29p. grey (2 bands) *(26.10.93)*	90	90	☐ ☐
Y1694	30p. deep olive-grey (2 bands) *(27.7.93)*	90	90	☐ ☐
Y1695	31p. deep mauve (2 bands) *(25.6.96)*	1·00	1·00	☐ ☐
Y1696	33p. grey-green (2 bands) *(25.4.00)*	1·25	1·25	☐ ☐
Y1697	34p. yellow-olive (2 bands) *(6.5.03)*	4·75	4·75	☐ ☐
Y1698	35p. yellow (2 bands) *(17.8.93)*	1·25	1·25	☐ ☐
Y1699	35p. yellow (phosphorised paper) *(1.11.93)*	7·50	7·50	☐ ☐
Y1700	35p. sepia (2 bands) *(1.4.04)*	1·25	1·25	☐ ☐
Y1701	35p. yellow-olive (1 centre band) *(5.4.05)*	1·25	1·25	☐ ☐
Y1702	36p. bright ultramarine (2 bands) *(26.10.93)*	1·25	1·25	☐ ☐
Y1703	37p. bright mauve (2 bands) *(25.6.96)*	1·00	1·00	☐ ☐
Y1704	37p. grey-black (2 bands) *(4.7.02)*	1·50	1·50	☐ ☐
Y1705	37p. brown-olive (1 centre band) *(28.3.06)*	1·50	1·50	☐ ☐
Y1706	38p. rosine (2 bands) *(26.10.93)*	1·50	1·50	☐ ☐
Y1707	38p. ultramarine (2 bands) *(20.4.99)*	1·50	1·50	☐ ☐
	a. Perf 14 *(15.2.00)*	5·50	5·50	☐ ☐
Y1708	39p. bright magenta (2 bands) *(25.6.96)*	1·25	1·25	☐ ☐
Y1709	39p. grey (2 bands) *(1.4.09)*	1·50	1·50	☐ ☐
Y1710	40p. deep azure (2 bands) *(25.4.00)*	1·25	1·25	☐ ☐
Y1711	40p. turquoise-blue (2 bands) *(1.4.04)*	1·25	1·25	☐ ☐
Y1712	41p. grey-brown (2 bands) *(26.10.93)*	1·50	1·50	☐ ☐
Y1713	41p. drab (phosphorised paper) *(1.11.93)*	7·50	7·50	☐ ☐
Y1714	41p. rosine (2 bands) *(25.4.00)*	1·50	1·50	☐ ☐
Y1715	42p. deep olive-grey (2 bands) *(4.7.02)*	1·25	1·25	☐ ☐
Y1716	43p. deep olive-brown (2 bands) *(25.6.96)*	1·40	1·40	☐ ☐
Y1717	43p. sepia (2 bands) *(8.7.96)*	4·75	4·75	☐ ☐
	a. Perf 14 *(13.10.98)*	1·50	1·50	☐ ☐
Y1718	43p. emerald (2 bands) *(1.4.04)*	1·75	1·75	☐ ☐
Y1719	44p. grey-brown (2 bands) *(20.4.99)*	4·00	4·00	☐ ☐
Y1720	44p. deep bright blue (2 bands) *(28.3.06)*	1·50	1·50	☐ ☐
Y1721	45p. bright mauve (2 bands) *(25.4.00)*	1·50	1·50	☐ ☐
Y1722	46p. yellow (2 bands) *(5.4.05)*	1·50	1·50	☐ ☐
Y1723	47p. turquoise-green (2 bands) *(4.7.02)*	1·75	1·75	☐ ☐
Y1724	48p. bright mauve (2 bands) *(27.3.07)*	1·75	1·75	☐ ☐
Y1725	49p. red-brown (2 bands) *(28.3.06)*	2·00	2·00	☐ ☐
Y1726	50p. ochre (2 bands) *(14.12.93)*	1·50	1·50	☐ ☐
Y1727	50p. grey (2 bands) *(27.3.07)*	1·50	1·50	☐ ☐
Y1728	54p. red-brown (Type II) *(27.3.07)*	1·50	1·50	☐ ☐
Y1729	56p. yellow-olive (2 bands) *(1.4.08)*	1·75	1·75	☐ ☐
Y1730	60p. light emerald (2 bands) *(30.3.10)*	1·75	1·75	☐ ☐
Y1731	62p. rosine (2 bands) *(31.3.09)*	1·75	1·75	☐ ☐
Y1732	63p. light emerald (2 bands) *(25.6.96)*	1·50	1·50	☐ ☐
Y1733	64p. turquoise-green (2 bands) *(20.4.99)*	1·75	1·75	☐ ☐
Y1734	65p. greenish blue (2 bands) *(25.4.00)*	1·75	1·75	☐ ☐
Y1735	67p. bright mauve (2 bands) *(30.3.10)*	1·75	1·75	☐ ☐
Y1736	68p. grey-brown (2 bands) *(4.7.02)*	2·00	2·00	☐ ☐
Y1737	72p. rosine (2 bands) *(28.3.06)*	2·25	2·25	☐ ☐
Y1738	78p. emerald (2 bands) *(27.3.07)*	2·25	2·25	☐ ☐
Y1739	81p. turquoise-green (2 bands) *(1.4.08)*	2·00	2·00	☐ ☐
Y1740	88p. bright magenta (2 bands) *(30.3.10)*	2·00	2·00	☐ ☐
Y1741	90p. ultramarine (2 bands) *(31.3.09)*	2·25	2·25	☐ ☐
Y1742	97p. violet (2 bands) *(30.3.10)*	2·50	2·50	☐ ☐
Y1743	£1 bluish violet (2 bands) *(22.8.95)*	2·50	2·50	☐ ☐
Y1744	£1 magenta (2 bands) *(5.6.07)*	2·00	2·00	☐ ☐
Y1745	£1·46 greenish-blue (2 bands) *(30.3.10)*	3·25	3·25	☐ ☐

Y1746	£1·50 brown-red (2 bands) *(1.7.03)*	3·50	3·50	☐ ☐
Y1747	£2 deep blue-green (2 bands) *(1.7.03)*	5·00	5·00	☐ ☐
Y1748	£3 deep mauve (2 bands) *(1.7.03)*	7·00	7·00	☐ ☐
Y1749	£5 azure (2 bands) *(1.7.03)*	12·00	12·00	☐ ☐

(b) Litho Cartor 1p. (Y1761), 5p. (Y1765),10p. (Y1767), 16p., 17p., 20p. (Y1773), 22p., 50p., 54p., 60p. (Y1785), 62p., 67p., 90p., 97p.), De La Rue 48p., Cartor, Questa or De La Rue 10p. (Y1767), Questa or Walsall 25p., 35p., 41p., Walsall 37p., 60p. (Y1784), 63p., Questa (others), Cartor or De La Rue 5p. (Y1762)

Y1760 **367**	1p. lake (2 bands) *(8.7.96)*	35	35	☐ ☐
Y1761	1p. reddish purple (2 bands) *(17.9.09)*	2·50	2·50	☐ ☐
Y1762	5p. chocolate (2 bands) *(12.2.09)*	3·50	3·50	☐ ☐
Y1764	5p. lake-brown (Type II) *(22.3.11)*	2·50	2·50	☐ ☐
Y1765	5p. red-brown (2 bands) (Type III) *(7.1.10)*	4·00	4·00	☐ ☐
Y1766	6p. yellow-olive (2 bands) *(26.7.94)*	8·00	8·00	☐ ☐
Y1767	10p. dull orange (2 bands) *(25.4.95)*	2·00	2·00	☐ ☐
Y1768	10p. pale brownish orange *(7.1.10)*	2·50	2·50	☐ ☐
Y1769	16p. pale cerise (2 bands) *(13.1.09)*	2·50	2·50	☐ ☐
Y1770	17p. bistre (2 bands) *(18.8.09)*	2·50	2·50	☐ ☐
Y1771	19p. bistre (1 side band at left) *(26.7.94)*	1·25	1·25	☐ ☐
Y1772	20p. bright yellow-green (1 centre band) *(8.7.96)*	2·00	2·00	☐ ☐
Y1773	20p. light green (2 bands) *(7.1.10)*	3·00	3·00	☐ ☐
Y1774	22p. olive-brown (2 bands) *(18.8.09)*	3·50	3·50	☐ ☐
Y1775	25p. red (2 bands) *(1.11.93)*	85	85	☐ ☐
Y1776	26p. chestnut (2 bands) *(8.7.96)*	65	65	☐ ☐
Y1777	30p. olive-grey (2 bands) *(25.4.95)*	2·50	2·50	☐ ☐
Y1778	35p. yellow (2 bands) *(1.11.93)*	90	90	☐ ☐
Y1779	37p. bright mauve (2 bands) *(8.7.96)*	2·50	2·50	☐ ☐
Y1780	41p. drab (2 bands) *(1.11.93)*	1·40	1·40	☐ ☐
Y1781	48p. bright mauve (2 bands) *(12.2.09)*	2·75	2·75	☐ ☐
Y1782	50p. grey (2 bands) *(13.1.09)*	3·50	3·50	☐ ☐
Y1783	54p. chestnut (2 bands) (Type III) *(7.1.10)*	3·50	3·50	☐ ☐
Y1784	60p. dull blue-grey (2 bands) *(9.8.94)*	1·50	1·50	☐ ☐
Y1785	60p. emerald (2 bands) *(13.5.10)*	6·00	6·00	☐ ☐
Y1786	62p. rosine (2 bands) *(18.8.09)*	3·75	3·75	☐ ☐
Y1787	63p. light emerald (2 bands) *(8.7.96)*	3·25	3·25	☐ ☐
Y1788	67p. bright mauve (2 bands) *(22.3.11)*	10·00	10·00	☐ ☐
Y1789	90p. bright blue (2 bands) *(17.9.09)*	4·75	4·75	☐ ☐
Y1790	97p. bluish violet (2 bands) *(22.3.11)*	10·00	10·00	☐ ☐

(c) Recess Enschedé or De La Rue

Y1800 **367**	£1·50 red *(9.3.99)*	4·50	2·00	☐ ☐
Y1801	£2 dull blue *(9.3.99)*	5·00	2·25	☐ ☐
Y1802	£3 dull violet *(9.3.99)*	7·00	3·00	☐ ☐
Y1803	£5 brown *(9.3.99)*	12·00	5·00	☐ ☐
PHQ Card (No. Y1725) (D7)		50	8·00	☐ ☐

PHQ Cards (Nos. 1664, 1668, Y1667/Y1668, Y1670, Y1675/Y1676, Y1679/Y1680, Y1687, Y1724, Y1727, Y1729, Y1739, Y1744, Y1746/ Y1749, 2357a, 2358, 2359, 2652/2653) (D30) — 7·00 ☐

Presentation Pack (PO Pack No. 30) (contains 19p. (Y1682), 25p. (Y1689), 29p. (Y1693), 36p. (Y1702), 38p. (Y1706), 41p. (Y1712)) — 6·00 ☐

Presentation Pack (PO Pack No. 34) (contains 1p. (Y1667), 2p. (Y1668), 4p. (Y1669), 5p. (Y1671), 6p. (Y1671), 10p. (Y1676), 19p. (Y1682), 20p. (Y1684), 25p. (Y1690), 29p. (Y1693), 30p. (Y1694), 35p. (Y1698), 36p. (Y1702), 38p. (Y1706), 41p. (Y1712), 50p. (Y1726), 60p. (Y1730), £1 (Y1743)) — 35·00 ☐

Presentation Pack (PO Pack No. 35) (contains 20p. (Y1685), 26p. (Y1691), 31p. (Y1695), 37p. (Y1703), 39p. (Y1708), 43p. (Y1716), 63p. (Y1732)) — 8·00 ☐

Presentation Pack (PO Pack No. 38) (contains 1st (1668), 26p. (Y1692)) — 6·00 ☐

Presentation Pack (PO Pack No. 41) (contains 2nd (1664), 1st (1667), 1p. (Y1667), 2p. (Y1668), 4p. (Y1669), 5p. (Y1670), 6p. (Y1671), 10p. (Y1676), 20p. (Y1685), 26p. (Y1691), 30p. (Y1694), 31p. (Y1695), 37p. (Y1703), 39p. (Y1708), 43p. (Y1717), 50p. (Y1726), 63p. (Y1732), £1 (Y1743)) — 18·00 ☐

Presentation Pack (PO Pack Nos. 43 or 43A) (contains £1·50 (Y1800), £2 (Y1801), £3 (Y1802), £5 (Y1803)) — 38·00 ☐

Presentation Pack (PO Pack No. 44) contains 7p. (Y1672), 19p. (Y1682), 38p. (Y1707), 44p. (Y1719), 64p. (Y1733)) — 9·50 ☐

Presentation Pack (PO Pack No. 49) (contains 8p. (Y1674), 33p. (Y1696), 40p. (Y1710), 41p. (Y1714), 45p. (Y1721), 65p. (Y1734)) — 8·50 ☐

Presentation Pack (PO Pack No. 57) (contains 2nd (1664), 1st (1667), E (1669), 1p. (Y1667), 2p. (Y1668), 4p. (Y1669), 5p. (Y1670), 8p. (Y1674), 10p. (Y1676), 20p. (Y1687), 33p. (Y1696), 40p. (Y1710), 41p. (Y1714), 45p. (Y1721), 50p. (Y1726), 65p. (Y1734), £1 (Y1743)) — 16·00 ☐

Presentation Pack (PO Pack No. 58) (contains 37p. (Y1704), 42p. (Y1715), 47p. (Y1723), 68p. (Y1736)) — 6·50 ☐

Presentation Pack (PO Pack No. 62) (contains £1·50 (Y1746), £2 (Y1747), £3 (Y1748), £5 (Y1749)) — 25·00 ☐

Presentation Pack (PO Pack No. 67) (contains 7p. (Y1673), 1st (1668), 35p. (Y1700), 39p. (Y1709), 40p. (Y1711), 43p. (Y1718), Worldwide postcard (2357a)) — 10·00 ☐

Presentation Pack (PO Pack No. 71) (contains 1p. (Y1667), 2p. (Y1668), 5p. (Y1670), 9p. (Y1675), 10p. (Y1676), 20p. (Y1687), 35p. (Y1701), 40p. (Y1711), 42p. (Y1715), 46p. (Y1722), 47p. (Y1723), 50p. (Y1726), 68p. (Y1736), £1 (Y1743), 2nd (2039), 1st (2295), Worldwide postcard (2357a), Europe up to 40 grams (2358), Worldwide up to 40 grams (2359)) — 50·00 ☐

Presentation Pack (PO Pack No. 72) (contains 37p. (Y1705), 44p. (Y1720), 49p. (Y1725), 72p. (Y1737)) — 11·00 ☐

Presentation Pack (PO Pack No. 75) (contains 16p. (Y1680), 48p. (Y1724), 50p. (Y1727), 54p. (Y1728), 78p. (Y1738)) — 10·00 ☐

Presentation Pack (PO Pack No.77) (contains 1p. (Y1667), 2p. (Y1668), 5p. (Y1670), 10p. (Y1676), 14p. (Y1678), 16p. (Y1679), 20p. (Y1687), 46p. (Y1722), 48p. (Y1724), 50p. (Y1727), 54p. (Y1728), 78p. (Y1738), £1 (Y1744), 2nd (1664), 1st (1668), 2nd Large (2652), 1st Large (2653), Worldwide postcard (2357*a*), Europe up to 40 grams (2358), Worldwide up to 40 grams (2359)) — 45·00 ☐

Presentation Pack (PO Pack No. 78) (contains 15p. (Y1679), 56p. (Y1729), 81p. (Y1739)) — 5·00 ☐

Presentation Pack (PO Pack No. 84) (contains 17p. (Y1681), 22p. (Y1688), 62p. (Y1731), 90p. (Y1741)) — 8·50 ☐

Presentation Pack (PO Pack No. 86) (contains 60p. (Y1730), 67p. (Y1735), 88p. (Y1740), 97p. (Y1742), £1·46 (Y1745), Europe up to 20 grams (2357*b*), Worldwide up to 20 grams (2358*a*), Recorded Signed for 1st (U3045), Recorded Signed for 1st Large (U3046)) — 28·00 ☐

Presentation Pack (PO Pack No. 88) (contains 1p. (Y1667), 2p. (Y1668), 5p. (Y1670), 9p. (Y1675), 10p. (Y1676), 20p. (Y1687), 50p. (Y1727), 60p. (Y1730), 67p. (Y1735), 88p. (Y1740), 97p. (Y1742), £1 (Y1744), £1·46 (Y1745), Worldwide postcard (2357*a*), Europe up to 20 grams (2357*b*), Europe up to 40 grams (2358), Worldwide up to 20 grams (2358*a*), Worldwide up to 40 grams (2359*a*), 2nd (1664), 1st (1668), 2nd Large (2652), 1st Large (2653), Recorded Signed for 1st (U2981), Recorded Signed for 1st Large (U2982)) — 50·00 ☐

For PO Pack No. 37 see below No. 1977.

For PO Pack No. 74 containing Nos. Y1677/Y1678 see below No. 2657.

First Day Covers

26 Oct. 1993	19p., 25p., 29p., 36p., 38p., 41p. (Nos. Y1682, Y1689, Y1693, Y1702, Y1706, Y1712)	6·00	☐
9 Aug. 1994	60p. (No. Y1784)	2·00	☐
22 Aug. 1995	£1 (No. Y1743)	3·00	☐
25 June 1996	20p., 26p., 31p., 37p., 39p., 43p., 63p. (Nos. Y1685, Y1691, Y1695, Y1703, Y1708, Y1716, Y1732)	8·00	☐
9 Mar. 1999	£1·50, £2, £3, £5 (Nos. Y1800/ Y1803)	15·00	☐
20 Apr. 1999	7p., 38p., 44p., 64p. (Nos. Y1672, Y1707, Y1719, Y1733)	5·00	☐
25 Apr. 2000	8p., 33p., 40p., 41p., 45p., 65p. (Nos. Y1674, Y1696, Y1710, Y1714, Y1721, Y1734)	5·00	☐
4 July 2002	37p., 42p., 47p., 68p., (Nos. Y1704, Y1715, Y1723, Y1736)	5·00	☐
6 May 2003	34p. (No. Y1697)	4·50	☐
1 July 2003	£1·50, £2, £3, £5 (Nos. Y1746/ Y1749)	25·00	☐
1 Apr. 2004	7p., 35p., 39p., 40p., 43p., Worldwide postcard (Nos. Y1673, Y1700, Y1709, Y1711, Y1718, 2357*a*)	9·00	☐
5 Apr. 2005	9p., 35p., 46p. (Nos. Y1675, Y1701, Y1722)	2·25	☐
28 Mar. 2006	37p., 44p., 49p., 72p. (Nos. Y1705, Y1720, Y1725, Y1737)	4·25	☐
27 Mar. 2007	16p., 48p., 50p., 54p., 78p. (Nos. Y1680, Y1724, Y1727/ Y1728, Y1738)	6·00	☐
1 Apr. 2008	15p., 56p., 81p. (Nos. Y1679, Y1729, Y1739)	4·50	☐
31 Mar. 2009	17p., 22p., 62p., 90p., (Nos. Y1681, Y1688, Y1731, Y1741)	6·00	☐
30 Mar. 2010	60p., 67p., 88p., 97p., £1·46, Europe up to 20 grams, Worldwide up to 20 grams (Nos. Y1730, Y1735, Y1740, Y1742, Y1745, 2357*b*, 2358*a*)	20·00	☐

For Nos. Y1677/Y1678 on first day cover see under Nos. 2650/2657.

Nos. Y1743/Y1749 are printed in Iriodin ink which gives a shiny effect to the solid part of the background behind the Queen's head.

Nos. Y1699 and Y1713 were only issued in coils and Nos. Y1676, Y1683, Y1678, Y1686, Y1707, Y1717 and Y1660/Y1689 only in booklets.

No. Y1771 exists with the phosphor band at the left or right of the stamp, but Nos. Y1683 and Y1686 exist with band at right only.

See also No. **MS**2146.

For self-adhesive versions of the 42p. and 68p. see Nos. 2297/2298.

1917

70th Anniversary of the Year of Three Kings. Miniature Sheet

2006 (31 Aug.) Sheet 127×72 mm containing No. Y1748. Multicoloured. Two phosphor bands. Perf 15×14 (with one elliptical hole in each vertical side)

MS2658	**1917** £3 deep mauve	5·25	5·25	☐ ☐
First Day Cover			5·50	☐

5. NVI stamps with self-adhesive gum and elliptical perforations

1116

Self-adhesive Booklet Stamp

1993 (19 Oct.) Litho Walsall. Two phosphor bands. Die-cut perf 14×15 (with one elliptical hole in each vertical side)

1789	**1116** (1st) orange-red	1·50	1·50	☐ ☐
First Day Cover			2·50	☐
Presentation Pack (booklet pane of 20) (PO Pack No. 29)		18·00		☐
PHQ Card (D6)		40	2·50	☐ ☐

For similar 2nd and 1st designs printed in gravure by Enschedé see Nos. 1976/1977.

1301

1302

Self-adhesive Coil Stamps

1997 (18 Mar.) Gravure Enschedé. One centre phosphor band (2nd) or two phosphor bands (1st). Perf 14×15 die-cut (with one elliptical hole in each vertical side)

1976	**1301** (2nd) bright blue	1·40	1·40	☐ ☐
1977	**1302** (1st) bright orange-red	1·40	1·40	☐ ☐
Set of 2		2·75	2·75	☐ ☐
First Day Cover			3·00	☐
Presentation Pack (PO Pack No. 37)		3·50		☐

Nos. 1976/1977, which were priced at 20p. and 26p., were each sold in rolls of 100 with the stamps separate on the backing paper.

Machin stamps printed in gold were issued on 21 April 1997 for the Royal Golden Wedding. These are listed as definitives under Nos. 1668 (1st) and Y1692 26p.

Self-adhesive stamps

1998 (6 Apr.–22 June) Gravure Enschedé, Questa or Walsall. Designs as Types **913/914**. One centre phosphor band (2nd) or two phosphor bands (1st). Perf 15×14 die-cut (with one elliptical hole in each vertical side)

2039	(2nd) bright blue	1·00	1·00	☐ ☐
	b. Perf 14½×14			
	die-cut (22.6.98)	£300		☐
2040	(1st) bright orange-red	1·25	1·25	☐ ☐
	b. Perf 14½×14			
	die-cut (22.6.98)	£300		☐
Set of 2		2·00	2·00	☐ ☐

Nos. 2039/2040 were initially priced at 20p. and 26p., and were available in coils of 200 (Enschedé), sheets of 100 (Enschedé, Questa or Walsall) or self-adhesive booklets (Questa or Walsall).

See also Nos. 2295/2298.

6. Millennium Machins

1437

New Millennium

2000 (6 Jan–23 May.) Photo De La Rue, Questa or Walsall (No. 2124); Questa or Walsall (No. 2124d). Two phosphor bands. Perf 15×14 (with one elliptical hole in each vertical side)

2124	**1437**	(1st) olive-brown	1·25	1·25	☐ ☐
		d. Perf 14 (23.5.2000)	1·25	1·25	☐ ☐
First Day Cover				2·00	☐
Presentation Pack (PO Pack No. 48)			2·50		☐
PHQ Card (23 May) (D16)			40	2·50	☐ ☐

No. 2124 comes from sheets or stamp booklets and No. 2124d from booklets only.

See also No. **MS**2147 for this stamp on phosphorised paper.

1459

Stamp Show 2000 International Stamp Exhibition, (1st issue) London. Jeffrey Matthews Colour Palette Miniature Sheet

2000 (22 May) Sheet 124×70 mm. Containing stamps as T **367** with two labels. Phosphorised paper. Perf 15×14 (with one elliptical hole in each vertical side)

MS2146	**1459**	4p. new blue; 5p. dull red-brown; 6p. yellow-olive; 10p. dull orange; 31p. deep mauve; 39p. deep bright magenta; 64p. turqoise-green; £1 bluish violet	15·00	15·00 ☐ ☐

First Day Cover		15·00	☐
Exhibition Card (wallet, sold at £4·99, containing one mint sheet and one cancelled on postcard)		30·00	☐

The £1 value is printed in Iriodin ink which gives a shiny effect to the solid part of the background behind the Queen's head.

1459a

Stamp Show 2000 International Stamp Exhibition, (2nd issue) London. Her Majesty's Stamps Miniature Sheet

2000 (23 May) Sheet 121×89 mm. Phosphorised paper. Perf 15×14 (with one elliptical hole in each vertical side of stamps as T **1437**)

MS2147	**1459a**	(1st) olive-brown (Type **1437**)×4; £1 slate-green (as Type **163**)	9·00	9·00 ☐ ☐
First Day Cover			9·25	☐
Presentation Pack (PO Pack No. M03)		40·00		☐
PHQ Cards (set of 2) (PSM03)		80	15·00	☐ ☐

The £1 value is an adaptation of the 1953 Coronation 1s.3d. stamp. It is shown on one of the PHQ cards with the other depicting the complete miniature sheet.

See also No. 2380 for T **163** from £7·46 stamp booklet.

7. NVI and denominated stamps with self-adhesive gum and elliptical perforations

2002 (5 June–4 July) Self-adhesive. Photo Questa, Walsall, De La Rue or Enschedé (No. 2295) or Walsall (others). Two phosphor bands. Perf 15×14 die-cut (with one elliptical hole in each vertical side)

2295	**914**	(1st) gold	1·25	1·25	☐ ☐
2296	**1093a**	(E) deep blue (04.07.02)	2·25	2·25	☐ ☐
2297	**367a**	42p. deep olive-grey (04.07.02)	5·00	5·00	☐ ☐
2298		68p. grey-brown (04.07.02)	5·75	5·75	☐ ☐
Set of 4			13·00	13·00	☐ ☐
PHQ Card (No. 2295) Walsall (27.3.03) (D22)			40	1·10	☐ ☐

Further printings of No. 2295 in sheets of 100 appeared on 4 July 2002 produced by Enschedé and on 18 March 2003 printed by Walsall.

8. Overseas Booklet Stamps

1655

2003 (27 Mar.)–**10** Self-adhesive. Two phosphor bands. Perf 15 × 14 die-cut with one elliptical hole in each vertical side

2357a	(Worldwide postcard) grey-black, rosine and ultramarine *(1.4.04)*	1·90	1·90	☐ ☐
2357b	(Europe up to 20 grams) deep blue-green, new blue and rosine *(30.3.10)*	2·00	2·00	☐ ☐
2358 **1655**	(Europe up to 40 grams) new blue and rosine	2·00	2·00	☐ ☐
2358a	(Worldwide up to 20 grams) deep mauve, new blue and rosine *(30.3.10)*	2·25	2·25	☐ ☐
2359	(Worldwide up to 40 grams) rosine and new blue	3·00	3·00	☐ ☐
Set of 5		11·00	11·00	☐ ☐
First Day Cover (Nos. 2358, 2359)			5·00	☐
Presentation Pack (Nos. 2358, 2359) (PO Pack No. 60)			5·00	☐
PHQ Card (No. 2358) (D23)		40	5·00	☐ ☐

Nos. 2358 and 2359 were intended to pay postage on mail up to 40 grams to either Europe (52p.) or to foreign destinations outside Europe (£1·12). No. 2357a was intended to pay postcard rate to foreign destinations (43p.).

Operationally they were only available in separate booklets of four, initially sold at £2·08, £4·48 and £1·72, with the surplus self-adhesive paper around each stamp removed. Single examples of the stamps were available from philatelic outlets as sets of two or in presentation packs.

Nos. 2357b and 2358a were intended to pay postage on mail up to 20 grams to either Europe (initially 56p., or to foreign destinations outside Europe (90p.).

They were only available in separate booklets of four (Nos. MI3 and MJ3) initially sold at £2·24 and £3·60, increasing to £2·40 and £3·88 from 6 April 2010, with the surplus self-adhesive paper around each stamp removed.

For first day covers and presentation packs for Nos. 2357a/2357b and 2358a and PHQ cards for Nos. 2357a, 2358 and 2359 see below Nos. Y1667/Y1803.

9. Pricing in Proportion NVI stamps

1915

1916

2006 (1 Aug.–12 Sept.) Perf 15 × 14 (with one elliptical hole in each vertical side)

(a) Ordinary gum. Gravure De La Rue (No. 2651 also Enschedé or Walsall from prestige booklets)

(i) As T **1915**

2650	(2nd) bright blue (1 centre band)	1·00	1·00	☐ ☐
2651	(1st) gold (2 bands)	1·25	1·25	☐ ☐

(ii) As T **1916**

2652	(2nd Large) bright blue (2 bands)	1·50	1·50	☐ ☐
2653	(1st Large) gold (2 bands)	1·90	1·90	☐ ☐

(b) Self-adhesive. Gravure Walsall

(i) As T **1915**

2654	(2nd) bright blue (1 centre band) *(12.9.06)*	1·00	1·00	☐ ☐
2655	(1st) gold (2 bands) *(12.9.06)*	1·25	1·25	☐ ☐

(ii) As T **1916**

2656	(2nd Large) bright blue (2 bands) *(15.8.06)*	1·50	1·50	☐ ☐
2657	(1st gold (2 bands) *(15.8.06)*	1·90	1·90	☐ ☐
First Day Cover (Nos. Y1677/Y1678, 2650/2653)			5·75	☐
Presentation Pack (Nos. Y1677/Y1678, 2650/2653) (PO Pack No. 74)			6·00	☐

No. 2654 was issued in booklets of 12 sold at £2·76.

No. 2655 was available in booklets of six or 12, sold at £1·92 or £3·84.

Nos. 2656/2657 were issued in separate booklets of four, sold at £1·48 or £1·76.

Nos. 2650/2653 were also issued in the £7·66 The Machin. The Making of a Masterpiece booklet, No. DX39 and No. 2651 from the £15·14 50th Anniversary of the Machin Definitive Prestige booklet, DY21, issued 5 June 2017.

All these booklets had the surplus self-adhesive paper around each stamp removed.

For PHQ cards for Nos. 2652/2653 see below No. Y1803.

10. Security Machins

2132a

2132b

2132c

2132d

2009 (17 Feb)–**19**. Self-adhesive. Designs as Types **367**, **913/914** or Types **2132a/2132d**. One centre band (U2995, U3065, U3095) or two bands (others). U-shaped slits (Nos. U2920/U3059). Die-cut perf 14½ × 14 (with one elliptical hole in each vertical side)

(a) Self-adhesive. As T **367**. Iridescent overprint. Printed in gravure

U2920	1p. crimson *(3.1.13)*	40	35	☐ ☐
U2921	2p. deep green *(3.1.13)*	40	35	☐ ☐
U2922	5p. dull red-brown *(3.1.13)*	45	40	☐ ☐
U2923	10p. dull orange *(3.1.13)*	60	50	☐ ☐
U2924	20p. bright green *(3.1.13)*	70	60	☐ ☐
U2911	50p. grey	2.00	1.50	☐ ☐
U2925	50p. slate *(3.1.13)*	1·50	1·25	☐ ☐
U2926	68p. deep turquoise-green *(29.3.11)*	2·25	2·00	☐ ☐
U2927	76p. bright rose *(29.3.11)*	2·00	1·75	☐ ☐
U2928	78p. bright mauve *(27.3.13)*	2·00	1·75	☐ ☐
U2929	81p. emerald *(26.3.14)*	2·25	2·00	☐ ☐
U2930	87p. yellow-orange *(25.4.12)*	4·25	4·00	☐ ☐
U2931	88p. orange-yellow *(27.3.13)*	2·25	2·00	☐ ☐
U2932	97p. bluish-violet *(26.3.14)*	2·50	2·25	☐ ☐
U2912	£1 magenta	3·50	2·75	☐ ☐
U2934	£1 bistre-brown *(3.1.13)*	2·25	2·00	☐ ☐
U2935	£1·05 grey-olive *(22.3.16)*	2·75	2·50	☐ ☐
U2936	£1·10 yellow-olive *(29.3.11)*	3·25	3·00	☐ ☐
U2937	£1·17 orange-red *(21.3.17)*	2·75	2·50	☐ ☐
U2938	£1·25 emerald *(20.3.18)*	2·75	2·50	☐ ☐
U2939	£1·28 emerald *(25.4.12)*	4·00	3·75	☐ ☐

U2940	£1·33 orange-yellow		
	(24.3.15)	2·75	2·50
U2940*a*	£1·35 bright mauve *(19.3.19)*	2·50	2·25
U2941	£1·40 grey-green *(21.3.17)*	3·00	2·75
U2942	£1·42 deep rose-red		
	(17.3.20)	2·50	2·50
U2943	£1·45 lavender-grey *(20.3.18)*	3·25	3·00
U2945	£1·47 lavender-grey *(26.3.14)*	3·50	3·25
U2913	£1·50 brown-red	3·25	3·00
U2946	£1·52 bright mauve *(24.3.15)*	3·00	2·75
U2947	£1·55 greenish blue *(20.3.18)*	3·00	2·75
U2948	£1·57 yellow-olive *(21.3.17)*	3·25	3·00
U2949	£1·60 orange-yellow		
	(19.3.19)	3·00	2·75
U2949*a*	£1·63 orange-red *(17.3.20)*	2·75	2·75
U2950	£1·65 grey-olive *(29.3.11)*	3·75	3·50
U2951	£1·68 yellow-olive *(17.3.20)*	3·00	3·00
U2953	£1·88 dull ultramarine		
	(27.3.13)	3·75	3·50
U2954	£1·90 bright mauve *(25.4.12)*	4·00	3·75
U2955	£2 deep blue-green	3·75	3·50
U2956	£2·15 greenish-blue *(26.3.14)*	4·25	4·00
U2957	£2·25 deep violet *(24.3.15)*	3·75	3·50
U2958	£2·27 bistre *(21.3.17)*	4·00	3·75
U2959	£2·30 grey-olive *(19.3.19)*	3·50	3·25
U2960	£2·42 bluish violet*(17.3.20)*	3·75	3·75
U2961	£2·45 bluish green*(24.3.15)*	4·00	3·75
U2962	£2·55 deep rose-red *(21.3.17)*	4·50	4·25
U2963	£2·65 bluish violet *(20.3.18)*	4·50	4·25
U2964	£2·80 bluish green *(19.3.19)*	4·25	4·00
U2965	£2·97 bright magenta *(17.3.20)*	4·50	4·50
U2966	£3 deep mauve	5·00	4·75
U2968	£3·15 turquoise-blue *(24.3.15)*	5·00	4·75
U2969	£3·30 bright magenta *(24.3.15)*	5·25	5·00
U2970	£3·45 grey-green *(19.3.19)*	5·00	4·75
U2971	£3·60 yellow-orange *(19.3.19)*	5·25	5·00
U2972	£3·66 pale ochre *(17.3.20)*	5·25	5·25
U2973	£3·82 emerald *(17.3.20)*	5·50	5·50
U2974	£5 azure	8·00	7·75
Set of 54		£170	£160

Presentation Pack (Nos. U2975/U2978 and U2911/U2912) (PO Pack 82) *(17.2.09)*   7·50

Presentation Pack (Nos. U2913/U2916) (PO Pack No. 83) *(17.2.09)*   23·50

Presentation Pack (Nos. U2926/U2927, U2936, U2950 and U3055/U3059) (PO Pack No. 90) *(29.3.11)*   15·00

Presentation Pack (Nos. U2930, U2939, U2954, U3271 and U3276) (PO Pack No. 94) *(25.4.12)*   10·50

Presentation Pack (Nos. U2920/U2955, U2934, U2997 and U3002) (PO Pack No. 96) *(3.1.13)*   7·50

Presentation Pack (Nos. U2928, U2931, U2953, U3049 and U3050) (PO Pack No. 97) *(27.3.13)*   14·00

Presentation Pack (Nos. U2929, U2932, U2945 and U2956) (PO Pack No. 99) *(26.3.14)*   10·00

Presentation Pack (Nos. U2940, U2946, U2957, U2961 and U2968/U2969) (PO Pack No. 101) *(24.3.15)*   22·00

Presentation Pack (No. U2935) (PO Pack No. 103) *(22.3.16)*   3·00

Presentation Pack (Nos. U2937, U2941, U2948, U2958 and U2962) (PO Pack No. 106) *(21.3.17)*   17·00

Presentation Pack (Nos. U2938, U2943, U2947 and U2963) (PO Pack No. 108) *(20.3.18)*   12·50

Presentation Pack (Nos. U2940*a*, U2949, U2959, U2964, U2970 and U2971) (PO Pack No. 110) *(19.3.19)*   21·00

Presentation Pack (Nos. U2942, U2949*a*, U2951, U2960, U2965, U2972 and U2973) (PO Pack No. 112) *(17.3.20)*   25·00

First Day Covers

17 Feb. 2009   (Nos. U2975/U2978 and U2911/U2912)   12·00

---

17 Feb. 2009	(Nos. U2913/U2916)	20·00
29 Mar. 2011	(Nos. U2926/U2927, U2936 and U2950)	10·50
25 Apr. 2012	(Nos. U2930, U2939, U2954 and U3276)	14·00
3 Jan. 2013	(Nos. U2920/U2925, U2934, U2997 and U3002)	10·00
27 Mar. 2013	(Nos. U2928, U2931, U2953, U3049 and U3050)	16·00
26 Mar. 2014	(Nos. U2929, U2932, U2945 and U2956)	14·00
24 Mar. 2015	(Nos. U2940, U2946, U2957, U2961 and U2968/U2969)	25·00
22 Mar. 2016	(No. U2935)	3·25
21 Mar. 2017	(Nos. U2937, U2941, U2948, U2958 and U2962)	17·00
20 Mar. 2018	(Nos. U2938, U2943, U2947 and U2963)	14·00
19 Mar. 2019	(Nos. U2940*a*, U2949, U2959, U2964, U2970 and U2971)	23·00
17 Mar. 2020	(Nos. U2942, U2949*a*, U2951, U260, U2965, U2972 and U2973)	28·00

(b) **Self-adhesive.** As Types **913/914**, **1916** or Types **2132a/2132d**. Iridescent overprint. Printed in gravure

U2995	(2nd) bright blue *(1.7.10)*	1·50	1·25
U2996	(1st) gold *(20.5.10)*	3·50	3·50
U3271	(1st) slate-blue *(6.2.12)*	1·75	1·50
U2997	(1st) vermilion *(3.1.13)*	2·00	1·75
U3744	(1st) bright lilac *(9.9.15)*	2·00	2·00
U2998	(1st) bright scarlet *(11.4.17)*	1·60	1·40
U3000	(2nd Large) bright blue		
	(26.1.11)	1·75	1·50
U3001	(1st Large) gold *(3.11.10)*	6·00	6·00
U3276	(1st Large) slate-blue		
	(25.4.12)	2·50	2·25
U3002	(1st Large) vermilion		
	(3.1.13)	2·75	2·50
U3003	(1st Large) bright scarlet		
	(11.4.17)	2·00	1·75
U3045	(1st) (Recorded Signed for) bright orange-red and lemon		
	(17.11.09)	4·00	3·75
U3049	(Royal Mail Signed for 1st) bright orange-red and lemon *(27.3.13)*	4·25	3·75
U3046	(Recorded Signed for 1st Large) bright orange-red and lemon *(17.11.09)*	4·25	4·00
U3050	(Royal Mail Signed for 1st Large) bright orange-red and lemon *(27.3.13)*	4·75	4·25
U3051	(Special Delivery up to 100g) blue and silver *(26.10.10)*	12·00	10·50
U3052	(Special Delivery up to 500g) blue and silver *(26.10.10)*	13·00	11·50

Presentation Pack (Nos. U3051/U3052) (PO Pack No. 89) *(26.10.10)*   24·00

First Day Covers

17 Nov. 2009	(Nos. U3045/U3046)	6·75
26 Oct. 2010	(Nos. U3051/U3052)	22·00

(c) **Self-adhesive.** Designs as T **367**. No iridescent overprint. Printed in gravure

U3055	1p. crimson *(8.3.11)*	80	80
U3056	2p. deep green *(8.3.11)*	50	50
U3057	5p. dull red-brown		
	(8.3.11)	60	60
U3058	10p. dull orange *(8.3.11)*	70	70
U3059	20p. bright green *(8.3.11)*	1·00	1·00
Set of 5		3·25	3·25

First Day Cover (Nos. U3055/U3059)   3·50

(d) Ordinary gum. Designs as Types 367 and 913/914.
Iridescent overprint. Printed in gravure

U3065	(2nd) bright blue *(13.5.10)*	4·75	4·75	☐ ☐
U3066	(1st) gold *(13.5.10)*	4·75	4·75	☐ ☐
U3279	(1st) slate-blue *(31.5.12)*	3·75	3·75	☐ ☐
U3067	(1st) vermilion *(5.6.17)*	3·75	3·75	☐ ☐
U3060	68p. turquoise-green *(10.1.12)*	4·00	4·00	☐ ☐
U3061	£1 magenta *(5.6.17)*	6·00	7·00	☐ ☐

(e) Ordinary gum. As Types 367 and 913/914.
Iridescent overprint. Printed in litho

U3070	1p. crimson *(9.5.13)*	1·00	1·00	☐ ☐
U3071	2p. deep green *(9.5.13)*	1·00	1·00	☐ ☐
U3072	5p. red-brown *(26.3.13)*	1·00	1·00	☐ ☐
U3074	10p. dull orange *(26.3.13)*	1·25	1·25	☐ ☐
U3075	20p. bright green *(26.3.13)*	1·50	1·50	☐ ☐
U3150	(2nd) bright blue *(17.12.15)*	2·25	2·25	☐ ☐
U3155	(1st) gold *(9.9.11)*	5·25	5·25	☐ ☐
U3156	(1st) vermilion *(9.5.13)*	2·00	2·00	☐ ☐
U3157	(1st) bright scarlet *(15.2.17)*	2·50	2·50	☐ ☐
U3747	(1st) bright lilac *(21.4.16)*	3·50	3·50	☐ ☐
U3077	50p. slate *(19.9.13)*	1·75	1·75	☐ ☐
U3078	76p. bright rose *(9.9.11)*	9·50	9·50	☐ ☐
U3079	81p. deep turquoise-green *(19.2.15)*	8·00	8·00	☐ ☐
U3080	87p. yellow-orange *(26.3.13)*	6·00	6·00	☐ ☐
U3081	97p. bluish violet *(19.2.15)*	3·75	3·75	☐ ☐
U3082	£1 sepia *(15.4.14)*	2·25	2·25	☐ ☐
U3083	£1·05 grey-olive *(28.7.16)*	2·75	2·75	☐ ☐
U3084	£1·17 bright orange *(23.1.18)*	3·50	3·50	☐ ☐
U3089	£1·25 emerald *(4.12.18)*	2·75	2·75	☐ ☐
U3094	£1·33 orange yellow *(14.5.15)*	3·00	3·00	☐ ☐
U3096	£1·35 bright purple *(11.2.20)*	3·00	3·00	☐ ☐
U3099	£1·40 grey-green *(14.12.17)*	3·50	3·50	☐ ☐
U3104	£1·45 lavender-grey *(14.3.19)*	5·00	5·00	☐ ☐
U3109	£1·55 greenish-blue *(13.2.19)*	4·00	4·00	☐ ☐
U3110	£1·63 bright orange *(8.5.20)*	4·50	4·50	☐ ☐

No. U3045 originally sold for £1·14, U3046 for £1·36, U3047 for £5·05 and U3048 for £5·50.

No. U3049 was originally sold for £1·55 (£1·70 from 2 April 2013) and U3050 was originally sold for £1·85 (£2 from 2 April 2013).

Nos. U3271, U3276 and U3279 have an iridescent overprint reading 'DIAMOND JUBILEE', and Nos. U3744 and U3747 have an iridescent overprint 'LONG TO REIGN OVER US' The others have an iridescent overprint with the words 'ROYAL MAIL' repeated throughout.

Nos. U3070/U3086 all come from premium booklets as follows:

U3067	£15·14 50th Anniversary the Machin Definitive
U3060	£11·47 Roald Dahl
U3061	£15·14 50th Anniversary the Machin Definitive
U3070	£11·11 Football Heroes, £14·60 Inventive Britain, £13·96 First World War Centenary (2nd issue), £17·45 Marvel, £6·10 Visions of the Universe, £19·10 Queen (rock band)
U3071	£11·11 Football Heroes, £13·97 Classic Locomotives, £14·60 Inventive Britain, £18·69 RAF Centenary, £17·20 Queen Victoria Bicentenary, £16·10 Visions of the Universe, £16·99 James Bond, £18·35 *Star Trek*
U3072	£13·77 *Dr. Who*, £11·11 Football Heroes, £11·19 Merchant Navy, £13·97 Classic Locomotives, £13·96 First World War Centenary (3rd issue), £14·47 Battle of Waterloo Bicentenary, £15·37 Beatrix Potter, £13·95 *Game of Thrones*, £18·69 RAF Centenary, £13·10 Leonardo da Vinci, £16·10 visions of the Universe, £19·80 75th Anniversary of the End of the Second World War
U3074	£13·77 *Dr. Who*, £11·11 Football Heroes, £11·39 Buckingham Palace, £11·30 First World War Centenary (1st issue), Battle of Waterloo Bicentenary, £15·37 Beatrix Potter, £13·10 Leonardo da Vinci, £16·10 Visions of the Universe
U3075	£13·77 *Dr. Who*, £11·39 Buckingham Palace, £11·30 First World War Centenary (1st issue), £13·95 *Game of Thrones*, £17·45 Marvel
U3150	£16·99 *Star Wars*, £16·99 James Bond, £18·35 *Star Trek*
U3155	£9·97 Aerial Post Centenary
U3156	£11·11 Football Heroes, £16·99 *Star Wars*, £15·11 90th Birthday of Queen Elizabeth II, £15·65 First World War Centenary (5th issue)
U3157	£14·58 Windsor Castle
U3747	£15·11 90th Birthday of Queen Elizabeth II
U3077	£11·19 Merchant Navy, £14·47 Battle of Waterloo Bicentenary, £17·20 Queen Victoria Bicentenary, £19·80 75th Anniversary of the End of the Second World War, £18·35 *Star Trek*
U3067	£15·59 50th Anniversary of the Machin Definitive
U3060	£11·47 Roald Dahl's Children's Stories
U3078	£9·97 Aerial Post Centenary
U3079	£14·60 Inventive Britain
U3080	£13·77 *Dr. Who*
U3081	£14·60 Inventive Britain
U3082	£11·39 Buckingham Palace, £11·30 First World War Centenary (1st issue), £14·47 Battle of Waterloo Bicentenary
U3061	£15·59 50th Anniversary of the Machin Definitive
U3083	£15·37 Beatrix Potter
U3084	£13·95 *Game of Thrones*, £18·69 RAF Centenary
U3089	£15·50 *Harry Potter*, £17·45 Marvel
U3094	£13·96 First World War Centenary (2nd issue)
U3099	£15·99 *Star Wars*. The Making of the Droids, Aliens and Creatures
U3104	£17·45 Marvel
U3109	£13·10 Leonardo da Vinci
U3096	£16·10 Visions of the Universe

For presentation pack containing Nos. U3045/U3046 see after No. Y1803.

Variations in the source and date codes incorporated into the iridescent overprint are outside the scope of this catalogue. Please refer to the *Great Britain Concise Catalogue* for further information.

EXHIBITION SOUVENIR

2268

London 2010 Festival of Stamps (3rd issue).
Jeffery Matthews Colour Palette. Miniature Sheet

2010 (8 May) Sheet 104×95 mm. Containing stamps as T **367** with a label. Two phosphor bands. Perf 15×14 (with one elliptical hole in each vertical side)

MS3073 **2268** 1p. reddish purple; 2p. deep grey-green; 5p. reddish-brown; 9p. bright orange; 10p. orange; 20p. light green; 60p. emerald; 67p. bright mauve; 88p. bright magenta; 97p. bluish violet; £1·46 turquoise-blue   40·00   40·00 ☐ ☐

3086 £1 gold foil Machin

50th Anniversary of the Machin Definitive

2017 (5 June) Two narrow phosphor bands. Perf 14 x 14½
3966   **3086**   £1 gold   4·50   5·50 ☐ ☐
No. 3966 was issued only in No. **MS**3964 and in £15·59 booklet No. DY21.

2408

Birth Centenary of Arnold Machin (sculptor).
Miniature Sheet

2011 (14 Sept.) Sheet 124×71 mm. Containing stamps as No. U3066. Two phosphor bands. Perf 14½×14 (with one elliptical hole in each vertical side)

MS3222 **2408** (1st) gold×10   13·00   13·50 ☐ ☐
First Day Cover   15·00   ☐

3041a

65th Anniversary of Accession of Queen Elizabeth II

2017 (6 Feb.) T **3041a**. Two phosphor bands. Iridescent overprint reading '65TH ANNIVERSARY OF ACCESSION'. Gravure. Perf 14 × 14½
U3920 **3041a**   £5 ultramarine   10·00   10·00 ☐ ☐
First Day Cover   12·00   ☐
Presentation Pack (PO Pack No. 105)   11·00   ☐

REGIONAL ISSUES

PERFORATION AND WATERMARK. All the following Regional stamps are perforated 15 × 14, unless otherwise stated.

For the listing of First Day Covers see the end of this section.

> **'Emblem' Regional Colours:** The colour descriptions of the 'Emblem' Regionals have been altered in many cases to show the perceived colours of the stamp, rather than the colours in which they are printed. Where the Queen's head has been printed in a black screen this appears as grey, which is the colour given in the description.

1 England

EN **1** Three Lions   EN **2** Crowned Lion with Shield of St George   EN **3** Oak Tree   EN **4** Tudor Rose

2001 (23 Apr.)–**02** Printed in gravure by De La Rue or Questa (Nos. EN1/EN2), De La Rue (others). One centre phosphor band (2nd) or two phosphor bands (others). Perf 15 × 14 (with one elliptical hole in each vertical side)

EN1	EN **1**	(2nd) slate-green and silver	1·25	1·00
EN2	EN **2**	(1st) lake-brown and silver	1·50	1·00
EN3	EN **3**	(E) olive-green and silver	2·00	2·00
EN4	EN **4**	65p. deep reddish lilac and silver	2·10	2·10
EN5		68p. deep reddish lilac and silver *(4.7.02)*	2·10	2·10

Presentation Pack (PO Pack No. 54) (Nos. EN1/EN4) — 7·00

PHQ Cards (*set of 4*) (Nos. EN1/EN4) (D20) — 1·25   7·00

Nos. EN1/EN3 were initially sold at 19p., 27p. and 36p., the latter representing the basic European airmail rate.

Combined Presentation Packs for England, Northern Ireland, Scotland and Wales

Presentation Pack (PO Pack No. 59) (contains 68p. from England, Northern Ireland, Scotland and Wales (Nos. EN5, NI93, S99, W88)) — 8·50

Presentation Pack (PO Pack No. 68) (contains 40p. from England, Northern Ireland, Scotland and Wales (Nos. EN9, NI97, S112, W101)) — 6·50

Presentation Pack (PO Pack No. 70) (contains 42p. from England, Northern Ireland, Scotland and Wales (Nos. EN10, NI98, S113, W102)) — 6·25

Presentation Pack (PO Pack No. 73) (contains 44p. and 72p. from England, Northern Ireland, Scotland and Wales (Nos. EN11, EN17, NI99, NI102, S114, S120, W103 and W109)) — 10·00

Presentation Pack (PO Pack No. 76) (contains 48p. and 78p. from England, Northern Ireland, Scotland and Wales (Nos. EN12, EN18, NI124, NI128, S115, S121, W104 and W110)) — 10·00

Presentation Pack (PO Pack No. 79) (contains 50p. and 81p. from England, Northern Ireland, Scotland and Wales (Nos. EN13, EN19, NI125, NI129, S116, S122, W105 and W111)) — 10·00

Presentation Pack (PO Pack No. 81) (contains 2nd, 1st, 50p. and 81p. from England, Northern Ireland, Scotland and Wales (Nos. EN6/EN7, EN13, EN19, NI122/NI123, NI125, NI129, S109/S110, S116, S122, W98/W99, W105 and W111)) — 40·00

Presentation Pack (PO Pack No. 85) (contains 56p. and 90p. from England, Northern Ireland, Scotland and Wales (Nos. EN14, EN120, NI126, NI130, S117, S123, W106 and W112)) — 13·00

Presentation Pack (PO Pack No. 87) (contains 60p. and 97p. from England, Northern Ireland, Scotland and Wales (Nos. EN15, EN21, NI127, NI131, S118, S124, W107 and W113)) — 14·00

Presentation Pack (PO Pack No. 91) (contains 68p. and £1·10 from England, Northern Ireland, Scotland and Wales (Nos. EN31, EN41, NI100, NI111, S132, S138, W123 and W129)) — 15·00

Presentation Pack (PO Pack No. 95) (contains 87p. and £1·28 from England, Northern Ireland, Scotland and Wales (Nos. EN32, EN43, NI103, S133, S143, W124 and W134)) — 18·00

Presentation Pack (PO Pack No. 98) (contains 88p. from England, Northern Ireland, Scotland and Wales (Nos. EN33, NI104, S134, and W125)) — 8·50

Presentation Pack (PO Pack No 100) (contains 97p. from England, Northern Ireland, Scotland and Wales (Nos. EN 34, NI105, S135 and W126) — 8·50

Presentation Pack (PO Pack No 102) (contains £1 and £1·33 from England, Northern Ireland, Scotland and Wales (Nos. EN35, EN44, NI106, NI114, S136, S144, W127 and W135)), — 18·00

Presentation Pack (PO Pack No 104) (contains £1·05 from England, Northern Ireland, Scotland and Wales (Nos. EN36, NI107, S137 and W128)) — 10·00

Presentation Pack (PO Pack No 107) (contains £1·17 and £1·40 from England, Northern Ireland, Scotland and Wales (Nos. EN54, EN59, NI159, NI164, S161, S166, W151 and W156)) — 22·00

Presentation Pack (PO Pack No 109) (contains 2nd, 1st, £1·25 and £1·45 from England, Northern Ireland, Scotland and Wales) (Nos. EN52/EN53, EN55, EN61, NI157/NI158, NI160, NI166, S159/S160, S162, S168, W149/W150, W152, W158)) — 25·00

Presentation Pack (PO Pack No. 111) (contains £1·35 and £1·55 from England, Northern Ireland, Scotland and Wales) (Nos. EN56, EN62, NI161, NI167, S163, S169, W153, W159) — 26·00

Presentation Pack (PO Pack No. 113) (contains £1·42 and £1·63 from England, Northern Ireland, Scotland and Wales) (Nos. EN60a, EN63, NI164a, NI168, S166a, S170, W156a, W160) — 28·00

2003 (14 Oct.)–**17** As Nos. EN1/EN3 and EN4 but with white borders. One centre phosphor band (2nd) or two phosphor bands (others). Perf 15 × 14 (with one elliptical hole in each vertical side)

(a) Printed in gravure by Walsall or De La Rue (2nd), 40p., 42p.) or De La Rue (others)

EN6	EN **1**	(2nd) slate-green and silver	1·25	1·00
EN7	EN **2**	(1st) lake-brown and silver	1·50	1·25
EN8	EN **3**	(E) olive-green and silver	2·00	2·00
EN9		40p. olive-green and silver *(11.5.04)*	1·25	1·25
EN10		42p. olive-green and silver *(5.4.05)*	1·75	1·75

EN11	44p. olive-green and silver *(28.3.06)*	1·25	1·25	☐ ☐
EN12	48p. olive-green and silver *(27.3.07)*	1·00	1·00	☐ ☐
EN13	50p. olive-green and silver *(1.4.08)*	1·25	1·25	☐ ☐
EN14	56p. olive-green and silver *(31.3.09)*	1·25	1·25	☐ ☐
EN15	60p. olive-green and silver *(31.3.10)*	1·50	1·50	☐ ☐
EN16 **EN 4**	68p. deep reddish lilac and silver	1·75	1·75	☐ ☐
EN17	72p. deep reddish lilac and silver *(28.3.06)*	1·75	1·75	☐ ☐
EN18	78p. deep reddish lilac and silver *(27.3.07)*	2·00	2·00	☐ ☐
EN19	81p. deep reddish lilac and silver *(1.4.08)*	2·00	2·00	☐ ☐
EN20	90p. deep reddish lilac and silver *(31.3.09)*	2·25	2·25	☐ ☐
EN21	97p. deep reddish lilac and silver *(31.3.10)*	2·50	2·50	☐ ☐

(b) Printed in lithography by Enschedé (booklets) (1st) or Cartor (sheets) (1st) or Cartor (others)

EN29 **EN 1**	(2nd) slate-green and grey *(3.1.13)*	1·25	1·00	☐ ☐
EN30 **EN 2**	(1st) lake-brown and silver *(20.9.07)*	1·50	1·50	☐ ☐
EN30*b*	(1st) lake-brown and grey	2·00	1·75	☐ ☐
EN31 **EN 3**	68p. olive-green and silver *(29.3.11)*	1·75	1·75	☐ ☐
EN32	87p. olive-green and silver *(25.4.12)*	2·25	2·25	☐ ☐
EN33	88p. olive-green and silver *(27.3.13)*	2·25	2·25	☐ ☐
EN34	97p. olive-green and silver *(26.3.14)*	2·40	2·40	☐ ☐
EN35	£1·00 olive-green and silver *(24.3.15)*	2·40	2·40	☐ ☐
EN36	£1·05 olive-green and grey *(22.3.16)*	2·75	2·75	☐ ☐
EN41 **EN 4**	£1·10 deep reddish lilac and silver *(29.3.11)*	2·50	2·50	☐ ☐
EN43	£1·28 deep reddish lilac and silver *(25.4.12)*	2·60	2·60	☐ ☐
EN44	£1·33 deep reddish lilac and silver *(24.3.15)*	2·75	2·75	☐ ☐

Presentation Pack (PO Pack No. 63) (Nos. EN6/EN8, EN16) — 6·00 ☐

PHQ Cards (*set of* 4) (Nos. EN6/EN8, EN16) (D24) — 1·25 — 6·50 ☐ ☐

Nos. EN6/EN8 were initially sold at 20p., 28p. and 38p., the latter representing the basic European airmail rate.

Stamps as No. EN30 but self-adhesive were issued on 23 April 2007 in sheets of 20 with *se-tenant* labels. These sheets were printed in lithography by Cartor and perforated 15×14 without the elliptical holes. The labels show either English scenes or personal photographs.

No. EN30 was first issued in £7·66 British Army Uniforms stamp booklet, No. DX40, but was issued in sheets in January 2013.

Stamps as Nos. EN30, NI95, S131 and W122 but self-adhesive were issued on 29 September 2008 in sheets of 20 containing five of each design with *se-tenant* labels. These sheets were printed in lithograhy by Cartor and perforated 15×14 with one elliptical hole in each vertical side.

EN **5**

Celebrating England

2007 (23 Apr.) Sheet 123×70 mm. Printed in gravure by De La Rue. Two phosphor bands. Perf 15×14 (with one elliptical hole in each vertical side) (1st) or 15×14½ (78p.)

MSEN50 **EN 5** (1st) No. EN7; (1st) St George's flag; 78p. St George; 78p. Houses of Parliament, London	4·00	4·00	☐ ☐
First Day Cover		4·50	☐
Presentation Pack (PO Pack No. M15)	5·00		☐
PHQ Cards (*set of* 5) (CGB2)	2·00	8·00	☐ ☐

No. **MS**EN50 was on sale at post offices throughout the UK.

The five PHQ cards show the four individual stamps and the complete miniature sheet.

Stamps as the 1st class St George's flag stamp within No. **MS**EN50 but self-adhesive were issued on 23 April 2009 in sheets of 20 with *se-tenant* labels showing English castles. These sheets were printed in lithography by Cartor.

EN **6** St George's Flag

England Flag

2013 (9 May)–**14**. Printed in lithography by Cartor or Enschedé. Two phosphor bands. Perf 14½×14 (with one elliptical hole in each vert side).

EN51 **EN 6** (1st) multicoloured	4·50	4·50	☐ ☐
a. Grey Queen's head	3·50	3·50	☐ ☐

No. EN51 silver Queen's head was issued in £11·11 Football Heroes, DY 7 and £16·49 Centenary of the First World War (3rd issue) No. DY18 booklets. No. EN51a was issued in the £13·97 Classic Locomotives booklets, No. DY9.

EN **7** Three Lions of England   EN **8** Crowned Lion, supporting the Shield of St George   EN **9** English Oak Tree   EN **10** English Tudor Rose

2017 (21 Mar.)–**19** As previous set but with value indicated in revised typeface. One centre band (No. EN52) or two phosphor bands (others). Perf 15×14 (with one elliptical hole in each vertical side).

EN52 **EN 7** (2nd) multicoloured *(20.3.18)*	1·00	75	☐ ☐
EN53 **EN 8** (1st) multicoloured *(20.3.18)*	1·25	75	☐ ☐

EN54	EN **9**	£1·17 multicoloured *(21.3.17)*	2·75	2·75	☐ ☐
EN55		£1·25 multicoloured *(20.3.18)*	2·75	2·75	☐ ☐
EN56		£1·35 multicoloured *(19.3.19)*	3·00	3·00	☐ ☐
EN60	EN **10**	£1·40 multicoloured *(21.3.17)*	3·00	3·00	☐ ☐
EN60*a*	EN **9**	£1·42 multicoloured *(17.3.20)*	2·50	2·50	☐ ☐
EN61		£1·45 multicoloured *(20.3.18)*	3·25	3·25	☐ ☐
EN62		£1·55 multicoloured *(19.3.19)*	3·25	3·25	☐ ☐
EN63		£1·63 multicoloured *(19.3.20)*	2·75	2·75	☐ ☐

Numbers have been left for possible additions to the above definitive series.

2 Northern Ireland

N **1**   N **2**   N **3**   N **4**

1958–67 Wmk **179**

NI1	N **1**	3d. lilac *(18.8.58)*	15	15	☐ ☐
		p. One centre phosphor band *(9.6.67)*	25	25	☐ ☐
NI2		4d. blue *(7.2.66)*	15	15	☐ ☐
		p. Two phosphor bands *(10.67)*	15	15	☐ ☐
NI3	N **2**	6d. purple *(29.9.58)*	50	50	☐ ☐
NI4		9d. bronze-green (2 phosphor bands) *(1.3.67)*	40	40	☐ ☐
NI5	N **3**	1s.3d. green *(29.9.58)*	50	50	☐ ☐
NI6		1s.6d. blue (2 phosphor bands) *(1.3.67)*	40	40	☐ ☐

1968–69 One centre phosphor band (Nos. NI8/NI9) or two phosphor bands (others). No wmk

NI7	N **1**	4d. blue *(27.6.68)*	25	25	☐ ☐
NI8		4d. sepia *(4.9.68)*	25	25	☐ ☐
NI9		4d. vermilion *(26.2.69)*	30	30	☐ ☐
NI10		5d. blue *(4.9.68)*	40	40	☐ ☐
NI11	N **3**	1s.6d. blue *(20.5.69)*	1·50	1·50	☐ ☐

Presentation Pack (comprises Nos. NI1p, NI4/NI6, NI8/NI10) (PO Pack No. 25)

		3·50		☐

Decimal Currency

1971–93 T N **4**. No wmk

(a) Printed in photogravure with phosphor bands

NI12	N **4**	2½p. bright magenta (1 centre band)	45	45	☐ ☐
NI13		3p. ultramarine (2 bands)	30	30	☐ ☐
NI14		3p. ultramarine (1 centre band) *(23.1.74)*	20	20	☐ ☐
NI15		3½p. olive-grey (2 bands) *(23.1.74)*	20	20	☐ ☐
NI16		3½p. olive-grey (1 centre band) *(6.11.74)*	40	40	☐ ☐

NI17		4½p. grey-blue (2 bands) *(6.11.74)*	30	30	☐ ☐
NI18		5p. reddish violet (2 bands)	90	90	☐ ☐
NI19		5½p. violet (2 bands) *(23.1.74)*	25	25	☐ ☐
NI20		5½p. violet (1 centre band) *(21.5.75)*	25	25	☐ ☐
NI21		6½p. greenish blue (1 centre band) *(14.1.76)*	20	20	☐ ☐
NI22		7p. purple-brown (1 centre band) *(18.1.78)*	30	30	☐ ☐
NI23		7½p. chestnut (2 bands)	1·25	1·25	☐ ☐
NI24		8p. rosine (2 bands) *(23.1.74)*	40	40	☐ ☐
NI25		8½p. yellow-green (2 bands) *(14.1.76)*	40	40	☐ ☐
NI26		9p. deep violet (2 bands) *(18.1.78)*	40	40	☐ ☐
NI27		10p. orange-brown (2 bands) *(20.10.76)*	40	40	☐ ☐
NI28		10p. orange-brown (1 centre band) *(23.7.80)*	40	40	☐ ☐
NI29		10½p. steel-blue (2 bands) *(18.1.78)*	50	50	☐ ☐
NI30		11p. scarlet (2 bands) *(20.10.76)*	50	50	☐ ☐

(b) Printed in photogravure on phosphorised paper

NI31		12p. yellowish green *(23.7.80)*	50	50	☐ ☐
NI32		13½p. purple-brown *(23.7.80)*	60	60	☐ ☐
NI33		15p. ultramarine *(23.7.80)*	60	60	☐ ☐

(c) Printed in lithography. Perf 14 (11½p., 12½p., 14p. (No. NI38), 15½p., 16p., 18p., (No. NI45), 19½p., 20½p., 22p. (No. NI53), 26p. (No. NI60), 28p. (No. NI62)) or 15 × 14 (others)

NI34		11½p. drab (1 side band) *(8.4.81)*	85	85	☐ ☐
NI35		12p. bright emerald (1 side band) *(7.1.86)*	90	90	☐ ☐
NI36		12½p. light emerald (1 side band) *(24.2.82)*	50	50	☐ ☐
		a. Perf 15 × 14 *(28.2.84)*	3·50	3·50	☐ ☐
NI37		13p. pale chestnut (1 side band) *(23.10.84)*	60	60	☐ ☐
NI38		14p. grey-blue (phosphorised paper) *(8.4.81)*	60	60	☐ ☐
NI39		14p. deep blue (1 centre band) *(8.11.88)*	50	50	☐ ☐
NI40		15p. bright blue (1 centre band) *(28.11.89)*	60	60	☐ ☐
NI41		15½p. pale violet (phosphorised paper) *(24.2.82)*	80	80	☐ ☐
NI42		16p. drab (phosphorised paper) *(27.4.83)*	1·00	1·00	☐ ☐
		a. Perf 15 × 14 *(28.2.84)*	5·00	5·00	☐ ☐
NI43		17p. grey-blue (phosphorised paper) *(23.10.84)*	80	80	☐ ☐
NI44		17p. deep blue (1 centre band) *(4.12.90)*	60	60	☐ ☐

NI45	18p. deep violet (phosphorised paper) (8.4.81)	80	80	☐	☐
NI46	18p. deep olive-grey (phosphorised paper) (6.1.87)	80	80	☐	☐
NI47	18p. bright green (1 centre band) (3.12.91)	80	80	☐	☐
	a. Perf 14 (31.12.92)*	6·50	6·50	☐	☐
NI48	18p. bright green (1 side band) (10.8.93)	1·50	1·50	☐	☐
NI49	19p. bright orange-red (phosphorised paper) (8.11.88)	80	80	☐	☐
NI50	19½p. olive-grey (phosphorised paper) (24.2.82)	1·50	1·50	☐	☐
NI51	20p. brownish black (phosphorised paper) (28.11.89)	80	80	☐	☐
NI52	20½p. ultramarine (phosphorised paper) (27.4.83)	2·75	2·75	☐	☐
NI53	22p. blue (phosphorised paper) (8.4.81)	80	80	☐	☐
NI54	22p. yellow-green (phosphorised paper) (23.10.84)	80	80	☐	☐
NI55	22p. bright orange-red (phosphorised paper) (4.12.90)	80	80	☐	☐
NI56	23p. bright green (phosphorised paper) (8.11.88)	80	80	☐	☐
NI57	24p. Indian red (phosphorised paper) (28.11.89)	90	90	☐	☐
NI58	24p. chestnut (phosphorised paper) (3.12.91)	80	80	☐	☐
NI59	24p. chestnut (2 bands) (10.8.93)	1·50	1·50	☐	☐
NI60	26p. rosine (phosphorised paper) (24.2.82)	90	90	☐	☐
	a. Perf 15 × 14 (27.1.87)	2·00	2·00	☐	☐
NI61	26p. drab (phosphorised paper) (4.12.90)	1·10	1·10	☐	☐
NI62	28p. deep violet-blue (phosphorised paper) (27.4.83)	1·00	1·00	☐	☐
	a. Perf 15 × 14 (27.1.87)	1·40	1·40	☐	☐
NI63	28p. deep bluish grey (phosphorised paper) (3.12.91)	90	90	☐	☐
NI64	31p. bright purple (phosphorised paper) (23.10.84)	1·40	1·40	☐	☐
NI65	32p. greenish blue (phosphorised paper) (8.11.88)	1·75	1·75	☐	☐
NI66	34p. deep bluish grey (phosphorised paper) (28.11.89)	1·40	1·40	☐	☐
NI67	37p. rosine (phosphorised paper) (4.12.90)	1·50	1·50	☐	☐
NI68	39p. bright mauve (phosphorised paper) (3.12.91)	1·50	1·50	☐	☐

* Earliest known date of use.
Nos. NI48 and NI59 were only issued in stamp booklets.

Presentation Pack (PO Pack No. 29) (contains 2½p. (NI12), 3p. (NI13), 5p. (NI18), 7½p. (NI23))	2·00		☐
Presentation Pack (PO Pack No. 61) (contains 3p. (NI14), 3½p. (NI15), 5½p. (NI19), 8p. (NI24) later with 4½p. (NI17) added)	3·00		☐
Presentation Pack (PO Pack No. 84) (contains 6½p. (NI21), 8½p. (NI25), 10p. (NI27), 11p. (NI30))	1·50		☐
Presentation Pack (PO Pack No. 129d) (contains 7p. (NI22), 9p. (NI26), 10½p. (NI29), 11½p. (NI34), 12p. (NI31), 13½p. (NI32), 14p. (NI38), 15p. (NI33), 18p. (NI45), 22p. (NI53))	7·00		☐
Presentation Pack (PO Pack No. 4) (contains 10p. (NI28), 12½p. (NI36), 16p. (NI42), 20½p. (NI52), 26p. (NI60), 28p. (NI62))	15·00		☐
Presentation Pack (PO Pack No. 8) (contains 10p. (NI28), 13p. (NI37), 16p. (NI42a), 19p. (NI43), 22p. (NI54), 26p. (NI60), 28p. (NI62), 31p. (NI64))	12·50		☐
Presentation Pack (PO Pack No. 12) (contains 12p. (NI35), 13p. (NI37), 17p. (NI43), 18p. (NI46), 22p. (NI54), 26p. (NI60a), 28p. (NI62a), 31p. (NI64))	16·00		☐

Combined Presentation Packs for Northern Ireland, Scotland and Wales

Presentation Pack (PO Pack No. 17) (contains 14p., 19p., 23p., 32p. from Northern Ireland, Scotland and Wales (Nos. NI39, NI49, NI56, NI65, S54, S62, S67, S77, W40, W50, W57, W66))	12·50		☐
Presentation Pack (PO Pack No. 20) (contains 15p., 20p., 24p., 34p. from Northern Ireland, Scotland and Wales (Nos. NI40, NI51, NI57, NI66, S56, S64, S69, S78, W41, W52, W58, W67))	12·00		☐
Presentation Pack (PO Pack No. 23) (contains 17p., 22p., 26p., 37p. from Northern Ireland, Scotland and Wales (Nos. NI44, NI55, NI61, NI67, S58, S66, S73, S79, W45, W56, W62, W68))	12·00		☐
Presentation Pack (PO Pack No. 26) (contains 18p., 24p., 28p., 39p. from Northern Ireland, Scotland and Wales (Nos. NI47, NI58, NI63, NI68, S60, S70, S75, S80, W48, W59, W64, W69))	12·00		☐

1993 (7 Dec.)–**2000**

(a) Printed in lithography by Questa. Perf 15 × 14 (with one elliptical hole in each vertical side)

NI69	N **4**	19p. bistre (1 centre band)	80	80	☐	☐
NI70		19p. bistre (1 side band) (26.7.94)	1·25	1·25	☐	☐
NI71		20p. bright green (1 centre band) (23.7.96)	1·25	1·25	☐	☐
NI72		25p. red (2 bands)	75	75	☐	☐
NI73		26p. red-brown (2 bands) (23.7.96)	1·50	1·50	☐	☐
NI74		30p. deep olive-grey (2 bands)	1·10	1·10	☐	☐
NI75		37p. bright mauve (2 bands) (23.7.96)	2·25	2·25	☐	☐
NI76		41p. grey-brown (2 bands)	1·50	1·50	☐	☐
NI77		63p. light emerald (2 bands) (23.7.96)	3·50	3·50	☐	☐

(b) Printed in photogravure by Walsall (19p., 20p., 26p. (No. NI81b), 38p., 40p., 63p., 64p., 65p.), Harrison or Walsall (26p. (No. NI81), 37p.). Perf 14 (No. NI80) or 15 × 14 (others) (both with one elliptical hole in each vertical side)

NI78	N **4**	19p. bistre (1 centre band) (8.6.99)	2·50	2·50	☐	☐

NI79	20p. bright green (1 centre band) (1.7.97)	2·50	2·50	☐ ☐
NI80	20p. bright green (1 side band) (13.10.98)	3·00	3·00	☐ ☐
NI81	26p. chestnut (2 bands) (1.7.97)	1·60	1·60	☐ ☐
	b. Perf 14 (13.10.98)	3·00	3·00	☐ ☐
NI82	37p. bright mauve (2 bands) (1.7.97)	1·90	1·90	☐ ☐
NI83	38p. ultramarine (2 bands) (8.6.99)	5·50	5·50	☐ ☐
NI84	40p. deep azure (2 bands) (25.4.00)	3·50	3·50	☐ ☐
NI85	63p. light emerald (2 bands) (1.7.97)	3·50	3·50	☐ ☐
NI86	64p. turquoise-green (2 bands) (8.6.99)	6·50	6·50	☐ ☐
NI87	65p. greenish blue (2 bands) (25.4.00)	3·00	3·00	☐ ☐

Nos. NI70, NI80 and NI81b were only issued in stamp booklets. No. NI70 exists with the phosphor band at the left or right of the stamp.

Presentation Pack (PO Pack No. 47) (contains 19p., 26p., 38p., 64p. (Nos. NI78, NI81, NI83 NI86)) ...... 15·00 ☐

Presentation Pack (PO Pack No. 52) (contains 1st, 40p., 65p. (Nos. NI84, NI87, NI88b)) ...... 16·00 ☐

Combined Presentation Packs for Northern Ireland, Scotland and Wales

Presentation Pack (PO Pack No. 31) (contains 19p., 25p., 30p., 41p. from Northern Ireland, Scotland and Wales (Nos. NI69, NI72, NI74, NI76, S81, S84, S86, S88, W70, W73, W75, W77)) ...... 20·00 ☐

Presentation Pack (PO Pack No. 36) (contains 20p., 26p., 37p., 63p. from Northern Ireland, Scotland and Wales (Nos. NI71, NI73, NI75, NI77, S83, S85, S87, S89, W72, W74 W76, W78)) ...... 16·00 ☐

Presentation Pack (PO Pack No. 42) (contains 20p. (1 centre band), 26p., 37p., 63p. from Northern Ireland, Scotland and Wales (Nos. NI79, NI81/NI82, NI85, S90/S93, W79/W82)) ...... 18·00 ☐

N **5**

2000 (15 Feb.–25 Apr.) T N **4** redrawn with '1st' face value as T N **5**. Two phosphor bands. Perf 14 (with one elliptical hole in each vertical side)

NI88	N **5**	(1st) bright orange-red	1·60	1·60	☐ ☐
		b. Perf 15 × 14 (25.4.00)	7·00	7·00	☐ ☐

No. NI88 was only issued in £7·50 Special by Design stamp booklets. No. NI88b was issued in sheets on 25 April.

N **6** Basalt Columns, Giant's Causeway

N **7** Aerial View of Patchwork Fields

N **8** Linen Pattern

N **9** Vase Pattern from Belleck

2001 (6 Mar.)–**02** Printed in lithography by De La Rue (68p.), De La Rue or Walsall (E), Walsall or Enschedé (2nd) or Walsall (others). One centre phosphor band (2nd) or two phosphor bands (others). Perf 15×14 (with one elliptical hole in each vertical side)

NI89	N **6**	(2nd) black, slate and drab	1·25	1·25	☐ ☐
NI90	N **7**	(1st) black, bright green, and greenish black	1·50	1·50	☐ ☐
NI91	N **8**	(E) olive-grey and black	2·25	2·25	☐ ☐
NI92	N **9**	65p. olive-bistre and black	2·25	2·25	☐ ☐
NI93		68p. olive-bistre and black (4.7.02)	2·75	2·75	☐ ☐

Presentation Pack (Nos. NI89/NI92) (PO Pack No. 53) ...... 6·00 ☐

PHQ Cards (*set of* 4) (Nos. NI89/NI92) (D19) ...... 1·25 7·50 ☐ ☐

Nos. NI89, NI90 and NI91 were initially sold at 19p., 27p. and 36p., the latter representing the basic European airmail rate.

For combined presentation packs for all four Regions, see under England.

2003 (14 Oct.)–**17** As Nos. NI89/NI91 and NI93 but with white borders. One centre phosphor band (2nd) or two phosphor bands (others). Perf 15×14 (with one elliptical hole in each vertical side)

(a) Printed in lithography by Walsall (No. NI98), De La Rue, Enschedé or Cartor/ISP Cartor (No. NI95), Cartor (Nos. NI101, NI106/NI107, NI112, NI114) or De La Rue (others)

NI94	N **6**	(2nd) black, slate and drab	1·25	1·25	☐ ☐
NI95	N **7**	(1st) black, bright green, and greenish black	1·50	1·50	☐ ☐
NI96	N **8**	(E) olive-grey and black	2·25	2·25	☐ ☐
NI97		40p. olive-grey and black (11.5.04)	1·60	1·60	☐ ☐
NI98		42p. bluish grey and black (5.4.05)	2·25	2·25	☐ ☐
NI99		44p. olive-grey and black (28.3.06)	1·40	1·40	☐ ☐
NI100	N **9**	68p. olive-bistre and black	2·50	2·50	☐ ☐
NI101	N **8**	68p. olive-grey and black (29.3.11)	2·00	2·00	☐ ☐
NI102	N **9**	72p. olive-bistre and black (28.3.06)	2·75	2·75	☐ ☐
NI103	N **8**	87p. olive-grey and black (25.4.12)	2·25	2·25	☐ ☐
NI104		88p. olive-grey and black (27.3.13)	2·25	2·25	☐ ☐
NI105		97p. olive-grey and black (26.3.14)	2·50	2·50	☐ ☐
NI106		£1 olive-grey and black (24.3.15)	2·50	2·50	☐ ☐
NI107		£1·05 olive-grey and black (22.3.16)	2·75	2·75	☐ ☐
NI111	N **9**	£1·10 olive-bistre and black (29.3.11)	2·50	2·50	☐ ☐
NI113	N **9**	£1·28 olive-bistre and black (25.4.12)	2·75	2·75	☐ ☐
NI114		£1·33 olive-bistre and black (24.3.15)	2·75	2·75	☐ ☐

(b) Printed in gravure by De La Rue

NI122	N **6**	(2nd) black, slate and drab (20.9.07)	1·25	1·25	☐ ☐
NI123	N **7**	(1st) black, bright green, and greenish black (20.9.07)	1·50	1·50	☐ ☐
NI124	N **8**	48p. olive-grey and black (27.3.07)	1·25	1·25	☐ ☐
NI125		50p. olive-grey and black (1.4.08)	1·25	1·25	☐ ☐
NI126		56p. olive-grey and black (31.3.09)	1·25	1·25	☐ ☐

NI127	60p. olive-grey and black				
	(30.3.10)	1·40	1·40	☐	☐
NI128 N **9**	78p. olive-bistre				
	and black *(27.3.07)*	1·60	1·60	☐	☐
NI129	81p. olive-bistre				
	and black *(1.4.08)*	2·00	2·00	☐	☐
NI130	90p. olive-bistre				
	and black *(31.3.09)*	2·25	2·25	☐	☐
NI131	97p. olive-bistre				
	and black *(30.3.10)*	2·50	2·50	☐	☐
Presentation Pack (Nos. NI94/NI96,					
NI100) (PO Pack No. 66)		7·50		☐	
PHQ Cards (*set of 4*) (Nos. NI94/NI96,					
NI100)(D27)		1·25	10·00	☐	☐

Nos. NI94/NI96 were initially sold at 20p., 28p. and 38p., the latter representing the basic European airmail rate.

The Enschedé printing of No. NI95 comes from £7·66 British Army Uniforms stamp booklet, No. DX40.

Stamps as NI95 but self-adhesive were issued on 11 March 2008 in sheets of 20 with *se-tenant* labels. These sheets were printed in lithography by Cartor and perforated 15×14 without the ellipitcal holes. The labels show either Northern Ireland scenes or personal photographs.

Stamps as No. NI95 but self-adhesive were issued again on 17 March 2009 in sheets of 20 with *se-tenant* labels showing Northern Ireland castles. These sheets were printed in lithography by Cartor.

Stamps as Nos. EN30, NI95, S131 and W122 but self-adhesive were issued on 29 September 2008 in sheets of 20 containing five of each design with *se-tenant* labels.

N **10**

Celebrating Northern Ireland

2008 (11 Mar.) Sheet 123×70 mm. Printed in lithography by De La Rue. Two phosphor bands. Perf 15×14½ (with one elliptical hole in each vertical side) (1st) or 15×14½ (78p.)

MSNI152 N **10** (1st) Carrickfergus Castle;					
(1st) Giant's Causeway; 78p. St Pat-					
rick; 78p. Queen's Bridge and *Angel*					
of Thanksgiving sculpture, Belfast	4·00	4·00		☐	☐
First Day Cover			4·75		☐
Presentation Pack (PO Pack No. 410)	5·00			☐	
PHQ Cards (*set of 5*) (CGB3)		1·50	7·00	☐	☐

No. **MS**NI152 was on sale at post offices throughout the UK.

The five PHQ cards depict the complete miniature sheet and the four stamps within it.

N **11**

50th Anniversary of the Country Definitives (1st issue)

2008 (29 Sept.) Sheet 124×70 mm. Containing designs as Nos. NI1, NI3, NI5, S1, S3, S5, W1, W3 and W5 (regional definitives of 1958) but inscribed 1st and printed in gravure by De La Rue on pale cream. Two phosphor bands. Perf 15×14 (with one elliptical hole in each vertical side)

MSNI153 N **11** (1st) As No. W1; (1st) As No.				
S1; (1st) As No. W5; (1st) As No. S5;				
As No. NI1; (1st) As No. W3; (1st) As No.				
S3; (1st) As No. NI3; (1st) As No. NI5	7·00	7·00	☐	☐
First Day Cover		9·25		☐
Presentation Pack (PO Pack No. 80)	10·00		☐	
PHQ Cards (*set of 10*) (D29)	3·00	12·50	☐	☐

No. **MS**NI153 was on sale at post offices throughout the UK.

The ten PHQ cards show the nine individual stamps and the complete sheet.

50th Anniversary of the Country Definitives (2nd issue)

2008 (29 Sept.) As Nos. NI1, NI3 and NI5 (definitives of 1958) but inscribed 1st and printed in lithography by De La Rue. Two phosphor bands. Perf 15×14½ (with one elliptical hole in each vertical side)

NI154 N **1**	(1st) deep lilac	1·60	1·60	☐	☐
NI155 N **3**	(1st) green	1·60	1·60	☐	☐
NI156 N **2**	(1st) deep claret	1·60	1·60	☐	☐
Set of 3		4·25	4·25	☐	☐

Nos. NI154/NI156 were only issued in the £9·72 The Regional Definitives booklet.

N **12** Basalt Columns, Giant's Causeway N **13** Aerial View of Patchwork Fields N **14** Linen Slip Case Pattern N **15** Parian China Vase Pattern from Belleek

2017 (21 Mar.)–**19** As previous set but value indicated in revised typeface. One centre band (No. NI157) or two phosphor bands (others). Perf 15×14 (with one elliptical hole in each vertical side)

NI157	N **12**	(2nd) multicoloured				
		(20.3.18)	1·00	75	☐	☐
NI158	N **13**	(1st) multicoloured				
		(20.3.18)	1·25	75	☐	☐
NI159	N **14**	£1·17 multicoloured				
		(21.3.17)	2·75	2·75	☐	☐
NI160		£1·25 multicoloured				
		(20.3.18)	2·75	2·75	☐	☐
NI161		£1·35 multicoloured				
		(19.3.19)	2·75	2·75	☐	☐
NI164	N **15**	£1·40 multicoloured				
		(21.3.17)	3·00	3·00	☐	☐
NI164*a*	N **14**	£1·42 multicoloured				
		(17.3.20)	2·50	2·50	☐	☐
NI166		£1·45 multicoloured				
		(20.3.18)	3·25	3·25	☐	☐
NI167		£1·55 multicoloured				
		(19.3.19)	3·25	3·25	☐	☐
NI168		£1·63 multicoloured				
		(17.3.20)	2·75	2·75	☐	☐

Numbers have been left for possible additions to the above definitive series.

3 Scotland

S **1**   S **2**   S **3**   S **4**

1958–67 Wmk **179**

S1	S **1**	3d. lilac *(18.8.58)*	15	15	
		p. Two phosphor bands *(21.9.63)*	7·50	6·00	
		pa. One side band *(30.4.65)*	25	25	
		pd. One centre phosphor band *(9.11.67)*	15	15	
S2		4d. blue *(7.7.66)*	20	20	
		p. Two phosphor bands	20	20	
S3	S **2**	6d. purple *(29.9.58)*	25	25	
		p. Two phosphor bands *(29.1.63)*	25	25	
S4		9d. bronze-green (2 phosphor bands) *(1.3.67)*	40	40	
S5	S **3**	1s.3d. green *(29.9.58)*	40	40	
		p. Two phosphor bands *(29.1.63)*	50	50	
S6		1s.6d. blue (2 phosphor bands) *(1.3.67)*	60	60	

No. S1pa. exists with the phosphor band at the left or right of the stamp.

1967–70 One centre phosphor band (Nos. S7, S9/S10) or two phosphor bands (others). No wmk

S7	S **1**	3d. lilac *(16.5.68)*	15	15	
S8		4d. blue *(28.11.67)*	30	30	
S9		4d. sepia *(4.9.68)*	15	15	
S10		4d. vermilion *(26.2.69)*	15	15	
S11		5d. blue *(4.9.68)*	25	25	
S12	S **2**	9d. bronze-green *(28.9.70)*	4·00	4·00	
S13	S **3**	1s.6d. blue *(12.12.68)*	1·25	1·25	

Presentation Pack (containing Nos. S3, S5p., S7, S9/S13) (PO Pack No. 23)   8·00

Decimal Currency

1971 (7 July)–**93** T S **4**. No wmk

(a) Printed in gravure by Harrison and Sons with phosphor bands. Perf 15 × 14

S14	S **4**	2½p. bright magenta (1 centre band)	25	20	
S15		3p. ultramarine (2 bands)	25	15	
S16		3p. ultramarine (1 centre band) *(23.1.74)*	15	15	
S17		3½p. olive-grey (2 bands) *(23.1.74)*	20	20	
S18		3½p. olive-grey (1 centre band) *(6.11.74)*	20	20	
S19		4½p. grey-blue (2 bands) *(6.11.74)*	25	25	
S20		5p. reddish violet (2 bands)	90	90	
S21		5½p. violet (2 bands) *(23.1.74)*	25	25	
S22		5½p. violet (1 centre band) *(21.5.75)*	20	25	
S23		6½p. greenish blue (1 centre band) *(14.1.76)*	20	25	
S24		7p. purple-brown (1 centre band) *(18.11.78)*	25	25	
S25		7½p. chestnut (2 bands)	90	90	
S26		8p. rosine (2 bands) *(23.1.74)*	35	35	
S27		8½p. yellow-green (2 bands) *(14.1.76)*	35	35	
S28		9p. deep violet (2 bands) *(18.1.78)*	35	35	
S29		10p. orange-brown (2 bands) *(20.10.76)*	35	35	
S30		10p. orange-brown (1 centre band) *(23.7.80)*	35	35	
S31		10½p. steel-blue (2 bands) *(18.1.78)*	45	45	
S32		11p. scarlet (2 bands) *(20.10.76)*	40	40	

(b) Printed in gravure by Harrison and Sons on phosphorised paper. Perf 15 × 14

S33	12p. yellowish green *(23.7.80)*	45	45	
S34	13½p. purple-brown *(23.7.80)*	60	60	
S35	15p. ultramarine *(23.7.80)*	50	50	

(c) Printed in lithography by John Waddington. One side phosphor band (11½p., 12p., 12½p., 13p.) or phosphorised paper (others). Perf 14

S36	11½p. drab *(8.4.81)*	55	55	
S37	12p. bright emerald *(7.1.86)*	1·25	1·25	
S38	12½p. light emerald *(24.2.82)*	45	45	
S39	13p. pale chestnut *(23.10.84)*	75	75	
S40	14p. grey-blue *(8.4.81)*	45	45	
S41	15½p. pale violet *(24.2.82)*	50	50	
S42	16p. drab *(27.4.83)*	50	50	
S43a	17p. grey-blue *(23.10.84)*	1·10	1·10	
S44	18p. deep violet *(8.4.81)*	70	70	
S45	19½p. olive-grey *(24.2.82)*	1·25	1·25	
S46	20½p. ultramarine *(27.4.83)*	2·25	2·25	
S47	22p. blue *(8.4.81)*	75	75	
S48	22p. yellow-green *(23.10.84)*	2·25	2·25	
S49	26p. rosine	70	70	
S50	28p. deep violet-blue	70	70	
S51	31p. bright purple	1·50	1·50	

(d) Printed in lithography by Questa. Perf 15 × 14

S52	12p. bright emerald (1 side band) *(29.4.86)*	1·25	1·25	
S53	13p. pale chestnut (1 side band) *(4.11.86)*	70	70	
S54	14p. deep blue (1 centre band) *(8.11.88)*	45	45	
S55	14p. deep blue (1 side band) *(21.3.89)*	50	50	
S56	15p. bright blue (1 centre band) *(28.11.89)*	50	50	

S57	17p. grey-blue (phosphorised paper) *(29.4.86)*	2·40	2·40	☐ ☐
S58	17p. deep blue (1 centre band) *(4.12.90)*	70	70	☐ ☐
S59	18p. deep olive-grey (phosphorised paper) *(6.1.87)*	70	70	☐ ☐
S60	18p. bright green (1 centre band) *(3.12.91)*	60	60	☐ ☐
	a. Perf 14 *(26.9.92)**	1·00	1·00	☐ ☐
S61	18p. bright green (1 side band) *(10.8.93)*	1·40	1·40	☐ ☐
S62	19p. bright orange-red (phosphorised paper) *(8.11.88)*	50	50	☐ ☐
S63	19p. bright orange-red (2 bands) *(21.3.89)*	1·40	1·40	☐ ☐
S64	20p. brownish black (phosphorised paper) *(28.11.89)*	70	70	☐ ☐
S65	22p. yellow-green (phosphorised paper) *(27.1.87)*	1·10	1·10	☐ ☐
S66	22p. bright orange-red (phosphorised paper) *(4.12.90)*	60	60	☐ ☐
S67	23p. bright green (phosphorised paper) *(8.11.88)*	80	80	☐ ☐
S68	23p. bright green (2 bands) *(21.3.89)*	9·00	9·00	☐ ☐
S69	24p. Indian red (phosphorised paper) *(28.11.89)*	1·00	1·00	☐ ☐
S70	24p. chestnut (phosphorised paper) *(3.12.91)*	75	75	☐ ☐
	a. Perf 14 *(10.92)**	8·00	8·00	☐ ☐
S71	24p. chestnut (2 bands) *(10.8.93)*	1·40	1·40	☐ ☐
S72	26p. rosine (phosphorised paper) *(27.1.87)*	2·25	2·25	☐ ☐
S73	26p. drab (phosphorised paper) *(4.12.90)*	1·00	1·00	☐ ☐
S74	28p. deep violet-blue (phosphorised paper) *(27.1.87)*	1·00	1·00	☐ ☐
S75	28p. deep bluish grey (phosphorised paper) *(3.12.91)*	1·00	1·00	☐ ☐
	a. Perf 14 *(18.12.93)**	9·00	9·00	☐ ☐
S76	31p. bright purple (phosphorised paper) *(29.4.86)*	1·50	1·50	☐ ☐
S77	32p. greenish blue (phosphorised paper) *(8.11.88)*	1·00	1·00	☐ ☐
S78	34p. deep bluish grey (phosphorised paper) *(28.11.89)*	1·25	1·25	☐ ☐
S79	37p. rosine (phosphorised paper) *(4.12.90)*	1·25	1·25	☐ ☐
S80	39p. bright mauve (phosphorised paper) *(3.12.91)*	1·50	1·50	☐ ☐
	a. Perf 14 *(11.92)*	12·50	12·50	☐ ☐

* Earliest known date of use.

Nos. S55, S61, S63, S68 and S71 were only issued in stamp booklets.

Presentation Pack (PO Pack No. 27) (contains 2½p. (S14), 3p. (S15), 5p. (S20), 7½p. (S25))	2·00	☐
Presentation Pack (PO Pack No. 62) (contains 3p. (S16), 3½p. (S17), 5½p. (S21), 8p. (S26), later with 4½p. (S19) added)	2·00	☐
Presentation Pack (PO Pack No. 85) (contains 6½p. (S23), 8½p. (S27), 10p. (S29), 11p. (S32))	1·50	☐
Presentation Pack (PO Pack No. 129b) (contains 7p. (S24), 9p. (S28), 10½p. (S31), 11½p. (S36), 12p. (S33), 13½p. (S34), 14p. (S40), 15p. (S35), 18p. (S44), 22p. (S47))	6·00	☐
Presentation Pack (PO Pack No. 2) (contains 10p. (S30), 12½p. (S38), 16p. (S42), 20½p. (S46), 26p. (S49), 28p. (S50))	14·00	☐
Presentation Pack (PO Pack No. 6) (contains 10p. (S30), 13p. (S39), 16p. (S42), 17p. (S43), 22p. (S48), 26p. (S49), 28p. (S50), 31p. (S51))	12·00	☐
Presentation Pack (PO Pack No. 10) (contains 12p. (S52), 13p. (S53), 17p. (S57), 18p. (S59), 22p. (S65), 26p. (S72), 28p. (S74), 31p. (S76))	15·00	☐

For combined packs containing values from all three Regions see under Northern Ireland.

1993 (7 Dec.)**–98**

(a) Printed in lithography by Questa. Perf 15 × 14 (with one elliptical hole in each vertical side)

S81	S **4**	19p. bistre (1 centre band)	70	70	☐ ☐
S82		19p. bistre (1 side band) *(25.4.95)*	2·00	2·00	☐ ☐
S83		20p. bright green (1 centre band) *(23.7.96)*	1·25	1·25	☐ ☐
S84		25p. red (2 bands)	80	80	☐ ☐
S85		26p. red-brown (2 bands) *(23.7.96)*	1·40	1·40	☐ ☐
S86		30p. deep olive-grey (2 bands)	1·25	1·25	☐ ☐
S87		37p. bright mauve (2 bands) *(23.7.96)*	1·75	1·75	☐ ☐
S88		41p. grey-brown (2 bands)	1·25	1·25	☐ ☐
S89		63p. light emerald (2 bands) *(23.7.96)*	2·50	2·50	☐ ☐

(b) Printed in gravure by Walsall (20p., 26p. (No. S91a), 63p.), Harrison or Walsall (26p. (No. S91), 37p.). Perf 14 (No. S90a) or 15 × 14 (others) (both with one elliptical hole in each vertical side)

S90	S **4**	20p. bright green (1 centre band) *(1.7.97)*	1·00	1·00	☐ ☐
S90a		20p. bright green (1 side band) *(13.10.98)*	3·00	3·00	☐ ☐
S91		26p. chestnut (2 bands) *(1.7.97)*	1·40	1·40	☐ ☐
		a. Perf 14 *(13.10.98)*	3·00	3·00	☐ ☐
S92		37p. bright mauve (2 bands) *(1.7.97)*	1·60	1·60	☐ ☐
S93		63p. light emerald (2 bands) *(1.7.97)*	3·50	3·50	☐ ☐

Nos. S82, S90a and S91a were only issued in stamp booklets.

For combined presentation packs for all three Regions, see under Northern Ireland.

S **5** Scottish Flag   S **6** Scottish Lion   S **7** Thistle   S **8** Tartan

1999 (8 June)–**2002** Printed in gravure by De La Rue (68p.), De La Rue, Questa or Walsall (2nd, 1st) or Walsall (others). One centre phosphor band (2nd) or two phosphor bands (others). Perf 15×14 (with one elliptical hole in each vertical side)

S94	S **5**	(2nd) new blue, blue and silver	1·25	1·25	☐ ☐
S95	S **6**	(1st) yellow, deep rose-red, rose-red and silver	1·50	1·50	☐ ☐
S96	S **7**	(E) bright lilac, deep lilac and silver	2·25	2·25	☐ ☐
S97	S **8**	64p. greenish yellow, bright magenta, new blue, grey-black and silver	5·50	5·50	☐ ☐
S98		65p. greenish yellow, bright magenta, new blue, grey-black and silver (25.4.00)	2·00	2·00	☐ ☐
S99		68p. greenish yellow, bright magenta, new blue, grey-black and silver (4.7.02)	2·25	2·25	☐ ☐

Presentation Pack (contains 2nd, 1st, E, 64p., (Nos. S94/S97) (PO Pack No. 45)	9·50		☐
Presentation Pack (contains 65p.) (No. S98)) (PO Pack No. 50)	10·00		☐
Presentation Pack (contains 2nd, 1st, E, 65p. (Nos. S94/S96, S98) (PO Pack No. 55)	15·00		☐
PHQ Cards (Nos. S94/S97) (D12)	1·25	10·00	☐ ☐

Nos. S94, S95 and S96 were initially sold at 19p., 26p. and 30p., the latter representing the basic European airmail rate.

For combined presentation packs for all four Regions, see under England.

S **9**

2000 (15 Feb.) T S **4** redrawn with '1st' face value as T S **9**. Two phosphor bands. Perf 14 (with one elliptical hole in each vertical side)

S108	S **9**	(1st) bright orange-red	1·60	1·60	☐ ☐

No. S108 was only issued in £7·50 Special by Design stamp booklets.

2003 (14 Oct.)–**16** As Nos. S94/S96 and S99 but with white borders. One centre phosphor band (2nd) or two phosphor bands (others). Perf 15×14 (with one elliptical hole in each vertical side)

(a) Printed in gravure by Walsall or De La Rue (42p.) or De La Rue (others)

S109	S **5**	(2nd) new blue, blue and silver	1·25	1·25	☐ ☐
S110	S **6**	(1st) yellow, deep rose-red, rose-red and silver	1·50	1·50	☐ ☐
S111	S **7**	(E) bright lilac, deep lilac and silver	2·10	2·10	☐ ☐
S112		40p. bright lilac and silver (11.5.04)	1·40	1·40	☐ ☐
S113		42p. bright lilac and silver (5.4.05)	1·75	1·75	☐ ☐

S114	44p. bright lilac, deep lilac and silver (28.3.06)	1·40	1·40	☐ ☐
S115	48p. bright lilac, deep lilac and silver (27.3.07)	1·25	1·25	☐ ☐
S116	50p. bright lilac, deep lilac and silver (1.4.08)	1·25	1·25	☐ ☐
S117	56p. bright lilac, deep lilac and silver (31.3.09)	1·40	1·40	☐ ☐
S118	60p. bright lilac, deep lilac and silver (30.3.10)	1·50	1·50	☐ ☐
S119 S **8**	68p. bright magenta, greenish yellow, new blue, grey-black and silver	1·60	1·60	☐ ☐
S120	72p. bright magenta, greenish yellow, new blue, grey-black and silver (28.3.06)	1·75	1·75	☐ ☐
S121	78p. bright magenta, greenish yellow, new blue, grey-black and silver (27.3.07)	1·75	1·75	☐ ☐
S122	81p. bright magenta, greenish yellow, new blue, grey-black and silver (1.4.08)	2·00	2·00	☐ ☐
S123	90p. bright magenta, greenish yellow, new blue, grey-black and silver (31.3.09)	2·25	2·25	☐ ☐
S124	97p. bright magenta, greenish yellow, new blue, grey-black and silver (30.3.10)	2·40	2·40	☐ ☐

(b) Printed in lithography by Enschedé or Cartor (1st) or Cartor (others)

S130	S **5**	(2nd) new blue, blue and silver (27.6.12)	1·25	1·25	☐ ☐
		a. new blue, blue and grey (5.16)	1·75	1·50	☐ ☐
S131	S **6**	(1st) yellow, deep rose-red, rose-red and silver (20.9.07)	1·50	1·50	☐ ☐
		a. yellow, deep rose-red, rose-red and grey (5.16)	2·00	2·00	☐ ☐
S132	S **7**	68p. bright lilac, deep lilac and silver (29.3.11)	1·90	1·90	☐ ☐
S133		87p. bright lilac, deep lilac and silver (25.4.12)	2·25	2·25	☐ ☐
S134		88p. bright lilac, deep lilac and silver (27.3.13)	2·25	2·25	☐ ☐
S135		97p. bright lilac, deep lilac and silver (26.3.14)	2·40	2·40	☐ ☐
S136		£1 bright lilac, deep lilac and silver (24.3.15)	2·40	2·40	☐ ☐
S137		£1·05 bright lilac, deep lilac and grey (22.3.16)	2·60	2·60	☐ ☐

S138 S **8** £1·10 silver, greenish
yellow, bright
magenta, new
blue and black
(29.3.11)   2·40   2·40 ☐ ☐

S143 £1·28 silver, greenish
yellow, bright
magenta, new blue
and black *(25.4.12)*   2·60   2·60 ☐ ☐

S144 £1·33 silver, greenish
yellow, bright
magenta, new blue
and black *(24.3.15)*   2·75   2·75 ☐ ☐

Presentation Pack (Nos. S109/S111,
S119) (PO Pack No. 64)   6·00   ☐

PHQ Cards (*set of* 4) (Nos. S109/S111,
S119) (D25)   1·25   6·50 ☐ ☐

Nos. S109/S111 were initially sold at 20p., 28p. and 38p., the latter representing the basic European airmail rate.

No. S131 was issued in £7·66 British Army Uniforms stamp booklet, No. DX40, printed by Enschedé and also on 27 June 2012 in sheets.

Stamps as No. S131 but self-adhesive were issued on 30 November 2007 in sheets of 20 with *se-tenant* labels. These sheets were printed by Cartor in lithography, and perforated 15×14 without the elliptical holes. The labels show either Scottish scenes or personal photographs.

Stamps as Nos. EN30, NI95, S131 and W122 but self-adhesive were issued on 29 September 2008 in sheets of 20 containing five of each design with *se-tenant* labels.

S **9a**

Opening of New Scottish Parliament Building

2004 (5 Oct.) Sheet 123×70 mm. Printed in gravure by De La Rue. One centre phosphor band (2nd) or two phosphor bands (others). Perf 15×14 (with one elliptical hole in each vertical side)

MSS152 S **9a** Nos. S109, S110×2 and
S112×2   5·00   5·00 ☐ ☐

First Day Cover   5·50 ☐

S **10**

Celebrating Scotland

2006 (30 Nov.) Sheet 124×71 mm. Printed in photogravure by De La Rue. Two phosphor bands. Perf 15×14 (with one elliptical hole in each vertical side) (1st) or 14×14 (72p.)

MSS153 S **10** (1st) As No. S110;
(1st) Scottish Flag; 72p. St Andrew;
72p. Edinburgh Castle   4·00   4·00 ☐ ☐

First Day Cover   4·25 ☐

Presentation Pack (PO Pack No. M14)   5·25   ☐

PHQ Cards (*set of* 5) (CGB1)   1·50   4·00 ☐ ☐

No. **MS**S153 was on sale at post offices throughout the UK.

The five PHQ cards depict the complete miniature sheet and the four stamps within it.

Stamps as the 1st class Scottish flag stamp within No. **MS**S153 but self-adhesive were issued on 30 November 2009 in sheets of 20 with *se-tenant* labels showing Scottish castles. These sheets were printed in lithography by Cartor.

50th Anniversary of the Country Definitives

2008 (29 Sept.) As Nos. S1, S3 and S5 (definitives of 1958) but inscribed 1st and printed in lithography by De La Rue. Two phosphor bands. Perf 15×14½ (with one elliptical hole in each vertical side)

S154 S **1**   (1st) deep lilac   1·60   1·60 ☐ ☐
S155 S **3**   (1st) green   1·60   1·60 ☐ ☐
S156 S **2**   (1st) deep claret   1·60   1·60 ☐ ☐
Set of 3   4·25   4·25 ☐ ☐

Nos. S154/S156 come from £9·72 The Regional Definitives stamp booklets.

S **11**

250th Birth Anniversary of Robert Burns (Scottish poet)

2009 (22 Jan.) Sheet 145×74 mm. Printed in gravure by Enschedé. One centre band (2nd) or two phosphor bands (others). Perf 14½ (size 34×34 mm) or 15×14 (with one elliptical hole in each vertical side) (others).

MSS157 S **11** (2nd) No. S109; (1st) 'A Man's
a Man for a' that' and Burns
ploughing (detail) (James Sargent
Storer) (34×34 mm); (1st) No. S110;
(1st) Portrait of Burns (Alexander
Nasmyth) (34×34 mm); 50p. No.
S116; 81p. No. S122   5·00   5·00 ☐ ☐

First Day Cover   5·50 ☐

Presentation Pack (PO Pack No. 422)   6·00   ☐

PHQ Cards (*set of* 3) (319)   90   7·00 ☐ ☐

No. **MS**S157 was on sale at post offices throughout the UK. The three PHQ cards show the two 34×34 mm Robert Burns stamps and the complete miniature sheet.

S **12** *Saltire*

Scotland Flag

2013 (9 May)–**14**. Printed in lithography by Cartor or Enschedé. Two phosphor bands. Perf 14½×14 (with one elliptical hole in each vert side)

S158	S **12**	(1st) multicoloured				
		(Queen's head silver)	4·75	4·75	☐ ☐
		a. Queen's head grey			
		(20.2.14)	3·50	3·50	☐ ☐

No. S158 was only issued in £11·11 Football Heroes and £13·97 Classic Locomotives booklets, Nos. DY7 and DY9.

No. S158a. was issued in £13·97 Classic Locomotives and £16·49 Centenary of the First World War (3rd issue) booklets.

S **13** Saltire   S **14** Lion Rampant   S **15** Thistle   S **16** Tartan of Scotland

2017 (21 Mar.) As previous set but with value indicated in revised typeface. One centre band (No. S159) or two phosphor bands (others). Perf 15×14 (with one elliptical hole in each vertical side)

S159	S **13**	(2nd) multicoloured				
		(20.3.18)	1·00	75	☐ ☐
S160	S **14**	(1st) multicoloured				
		(20.3.18)	1·25	75	☐ ☐
S161	S **15**	£1·17 multicoloured				
		(21.3.17)	2·75	2·75	☐ ☐
S162	S **15**	£1·25 multicoloured				
		(20.3.18)	2·75	2·75	☐ ☐
S163		£1·35 multicoloured				
		(19.3.19)	2·75	2·75	☐ ☐
S166	S **16**	£1·40 multicoloured				
		(21.3.17)	3·00	3·00	☐ ☐
S166a	S **15**	£1·42 multicoloured				
		(17.3.20)	2·50	2·50	☐ ☐
S168	S **16**	£1·45 multicoloured				
		(20.3.18)	3·25	3·25	☐ ☐
S169		£1·55 multicoloured				
		(19.3.19)	3·25	3·25	☐ ☐
S170		£1·63 multicoloured				
		(17.3.20)	2·75	2·75	☐ ☐

Numbers have been left for possible additions to this definitive series.

S **17**

700th Anniversary of the Declaration of Arbroath

2020 (6 Apr). Sheet 133×70 mm. Printed in lithography by ISP Cartor. One centre band (2nd) or two phos-phor bands (others). Perf 15×14 (with one elliptical hole in each vertical side).

MSS180 S **17** Nos. S159/S160, S166a and		
S170	7·00	☐
Commemorative Cover	9·00	☐

4 Wales

W **1**   W **2**   W **3**

1958–67 Wmk 179

W1	W **1**	3d. lilac (18.8.58)	15	15	☐ ☐
		p. One centre phosphor band (16.5.67)	20	15	☐ ☐
W2		4d. blue (7.2.66)	20	20	☐ ☐
		p. Two phosphor bands (10.67)	20	20	☐ ☐
W3	W **2**	6d. purple (29.9.58)	35	35	☐ ☐
W4		9d. bronze-green (two phosphor bands)			
		(1.3.67)	35	35	☐ ☐
W5	W **3**	1s.3d. green (29.9.58)	40	40	☐ ☐
W6		1s.6d. blue (two phosphor bands) (1.3.67)	40	40	☐ ☐

1967–69 One centre phosphor band (Nos. W7, W9/10) or two phosphor bands (others). No wmk

W7	W **1**	3d. lilac (6.12.67)	15	15	☐ ☐
W8		4d. blue (21.6.68)	15	15	☐ ☐
W9		4d. sepia (4.9.68)	15	15	☐ ☐
W10		4d. vermilion (26.2.69)	15	15	☐ ☐
W11		5d. blue (4.9.68)	15	15	☐ ☐
W12	W **3**	1s.6d. blue (1.8.69)	2·75	2·75	☐ ☐
Presentation Pack (comprises Nos. W4, W6/W7, W9/W11) (PO Pack No. 24)			5·50		☐

W **4** With 'p'   W **5** Without 'p'

Decimal Currency

1971–92 T W **4**. No wmk

(a) Printed in photogravure with phosphor bands

W13	W **4**	2½p. bright magenta (1 centre band)	20	20	☐ ☐
W14		3p. ultramarine (2 bands)	25	20	☐ ☐
W15		3p. ultramarine (1 centre band) (23.1.74)	25	25	☐ ☐
W16		3½p. olive-grey (2 bands) (23.1.74)	20	30	☐ ☐
W17		3½p. olive-grey (1 centre band) (6.11.74)	20	20	☐ ☐
W18		4½p. grey-blue (2 bands) (6.11.74)	25	25	☐ ☐
W19		5p. reddish violet (2 bands)	80	80	☐ ☐
W20		5½p. violet (2 bands) (23.1.74)	25	25	☐ ☐
W21		5½p. violet (1 centre band) (21.5.75)	25	25	☐ ☐
W22		6½p. greenish blue (1 centre band) (14.1.76)	20	20	☐ ☐
W23		7p. purple-brown (1 centre band) (18.1.78)	25	25	☐ ☐
W24		7½p. chestnut (2 bands)	1·75	1·75	☐ ☐
W25		8p. rosine (2 bands) (23.1.74)	30	30	☐ ☐

W26	8½p. yellow-green (2 bands) *(14.1.76)*	35	35	☐	☐
W27	9p. deep violet (2 bands) *(18.1.78)*	35	35	☐	☐
W28	10p. orange-brown (2 bands) *(20.10.76)*	35	35	☐	☐
W29	10p. orange-brown (1 centre band) *(23.7.80)*	35	35	☐	☐
W30	10½p. steel-blue (2 bands) *(18.1.78)*	45	45	☐	☐
W31	11p. scarlet (2 bands) *(20.10.76)*	40	40	☐	☐

(b) Printed in photogravure on phosphorised paper

W32	12p. yellowish-green *(27.3.80)*	45	45	☐	☐
W33	13½p. purple-brown *(27.3.80)*	55	55	☐	☐
W34	15p. ultramarine *(27.3.80)*	55	55	☐	☐

(c) Printed in lithography. Perf 14 (11½p., 12½p., 14p. (No. W39), 15½p., 16p., 18p. (No. W46), 19½p., 20½p., 22p. (No. W54), 26p. (No. W61), 28p. (No. W63)) or 15 × 14 (others)

W35	11½p. drab (1 side band) *(8.4.81)*	70	70	☐	☐
W36	12p. bright emerald (1 side band) *(7.1.86)*	1·00	1·00	☐	☐
W37	12½p. light emerald (1 side band) *(24.2.82)*	50	50	☐	☐
	a. Perf 15 × 14 *(10.1.84)*	2·75	2·75	☐	☐
W38	13p. pale chestnut (1 side band) *(23.10.84)*	50	50	☐	☐
W39	14p. grey-blue (phosphorised paper) *(8.4.81)*	55	55	☐	☐
W40	14p. deep blue (1 centre band) *(8.11.88)*	55	55	☐	☐
W41	15p. bright blue (1 centre band) *(28.11.89)*	60	60	☐	☐
W42	15½p. pale violet (phosphorised paper) *(24.2.82)*	70	70	☐	☐
W43	16p. drab (phosphorised paper) *(27.4.83)*	1·10	1·10	☐	☐
	a. Perf 15 × 14 *(10.1.84)*	1·10	1·10	☐	☐
W44	17p. grey-blue (phosphorised paper) *(23.10.84)*	80	80	☐	☐
W45	17p. deep blue (1 centre band) *(4.12.90)*	60	60	☐	☐
W46	18p. deep violet (phosphorised paper) *(8.4.81)*	80	80	☐	☐
W47	18p. deep olive-grey (phosphorised paper) *(6.1.87)*	80	80	☐	☐
W48	18p. bright green (1 centre band) *(3.12.91)*	55	55	☐	☐
	b. Perf 14 *(12.1.93)**	7·50	7·50	☐	☐
W49	18p. bright green (1 side band) *(25.2.92)*	1·75	1·75	☐	☐
W50	19p. bright orange-red (phosphorised paper) *(8.11.88)*	70	70	☐	☐
W51	19½p. olive-grey (phosphorised paper) *(24.2.82)*	1·25	1·25	☐	☐
W52	20p. brownish black (phosphorised paper) *(28.11.89)*	70	70	☐	☐
W53	20½p. ultramarine (phosphorised paper) *(27.4.83)*	2·50	2·50	☐	☐
W54	22p. blue (phosphorised paper) *(8.4.81)*	80	80	☐	☐

W55	22p. yellow-green (phosphorised paper) *(23.10.84)*	80	80	☐	☐
W56	22p. bright orange-red (phosphorised paper) *(4.12.90)*	80	80	☐	☐
W57	23p. bright green (phosphorised paper) *(8.11.88)*	80	80	☐	☐
W58	24p. Indian red (phosphorised paper) *(28.11.89)*	90	90	☐	☐
W59	24p. chestnut (phosphorised paper) *(3.12.91)*	70	70	☐	☐
	b. Perf 14 *(14.9.92)**	7·00	7·00	☐	☐
W60	24p. chestnut (2 bands) *(25.2.92)*	90	90	☐	☐
W61	26p. rosine (phosphorised paper) *(24.2.82)*	80	80	☐	☐
	a. Perf 15 × 14 *(27.1.87)*	3·00	3·00	☐	☐
W62	26p. drab (phosphorised paper) *(4.12.90)*	1·25	1·25	☐	☐
W63	28p. deep violet-blue (phosphorised paper) *(27.4.83)*	90	90	☐	☐
	a. Perf 15 × 14 *(27.1.87)*	1·25	1·25	☐	☐
W64	28p. deep bluish grey (phosphorised paper) *(3.12.91)*	80	80	☐	☐
W65	31p. bright purple (phosphorised paper) *(23.10.84)*	1·00	1·00	☐	☐
W66	32p. greenish blue (phosphorised paper) *(8.11.88)*	1·25	1·25	☐	☐
W67	34p. deep bluish grey (phosphorised paper) *(28.11.89)*	1·25	1·25	☐	☐
W68	37p. rosine (phosphorised paper) *(4.12.90)*	1·25	1·25	☐	☐
W69	39p. bright mauve (phosphorised paper) *(3.12.91)*	1·25	1·25	☐	☐

* Earliest known date of use.

Nos. W49 and W60 were only issued in stamp booklets. The former exists with the phosphor band at the left or right of the stamp.

Presentation Pack (PO Pack No. 28) (contains 2½p. (W13), 3p. (W14), 5p. (W19), 7½p. (W24))	2·00	☐
Presentation Pack (PO Pack No. 63) (contains 3p. (W15), 3½p. (W16), 5½p. (W20), 8p. (W25), later with 4½p. (W18) added)	2·25	☐
Presentation Pack (PO Pack No. 86) (contains 6½p. (W22), 8½p. (W26), 10p. (W28), 11p. (W31))	1·40	☐
Presentation Pack (PO Pack No. 129c) (contains 7p. (W23), 9p. (W27), 10½p. (W30), 11½p. (W35), 12p. (W32), 13½p. (W33), 14p. (W39), 15p. (W34), 18p. (W46), 22p. (W54))	6·00	☐
Presentation Pack (PO Pack No. 3) (contains 10p. (W29), 12½p. (W37), 16p. (W43), 20½p. (W53), 26p. (W61), 28p. (W63))	14·00	☐
Presentation Pack (PO Pack No. 7) (contains 10p. (W29), 13p. (W38), 16p. (W43a), 17p. (W44), 22p. (W55), 26p. (W61), 28p. (W63), 31p. (W65))	12·00	☐
Presentation Pack (PO Pack No. 11) (contains 12p. (W36), 13p. (W38), 17p. (W44), 18p. (W47), 22p. (W55), 26p. (W61a), 28p. (W63a), 31p. (W65))	15·00	☐

For combined packs containing values from all three Regions see under Northern Ireland.

1993 (7 Dec.)–**96** Printed in lithography by Questa. Perf 15×14 (with one elliptical hole in each vertical side)

W70	**W 4**	19p. bistre (1 centre band)	60	60	☐ ☐
W71		19p. bistre (1 side band)			
		(25.4.95)	1·90	1·90	☐ ☐
W72		20p. bright green (1 centre band) (23.7.96)	1·00	1·00	☐ ☐
W73		25p. red (2 bands)	75	75	☐ ☐
W74		26p. red-brown (2 bands)			
		(23.7.96)	1·25	1·25	☐ ☐
W75		30p. deep olive-grey (2 bands)	80	80	☐ ☐
W76		37p. bright mauve (2 bands) (23.7.96)	1·60	1·60	☐ ☐
W77		41p. grey-brown (2 bands)	1·40	1·40	☐ ☐
W78		63p. light emerald (2 bands) (23.7.96)	3·50	3·50	☐ ☐

No. W71 was only issued in stamp booklets.

For combined presentation packs for all three Regions see under Northern Ireland.

1997 (1 July)–**98** Printed in photogravure by Walsall (20p., 26p. (No. W80a), 63p.), Harrison or Walsall (26p. (No. W80), 37p.) Perf 14 (No. W79a) or 15×14 (others) (both with one elliptical hole in each vertical side)

W79	**W 5**	20p. bright green (1 centre band)	80	80	☐ ☐
W79a		20p. bright green (1 side band)			
		(13.10.98)	3·25	3·25	☐ ☐
W80		26p. chestnut (2 bands)	1·40	1·40	☐ ☐
		a. Perf 14 (13.10.98)	3·25	3·25	☐ ☐
W81		37p. bright mauve (2 bands)	1·75	1·75	☐ ☐
W82		63p. light emerald (2 bands)	3·50	3·50	☐ ☐

Presentation Pack (Nos. W79 and W80/W82) (PO Pack No. 39)   12·00   ☐

Nos. W79a and W80a were only issued in stamp booklets.

W **6** Leek   W **7** Welsh Dragon   W **8** Daffodil   W **9** Prince of Wales Feathers

1999 (8 June)–**2002** Printed in gravure by De La Rue (68p.), Walsall or De La Rue (1st), (2nd), (No. W83) or Walsall (others). One phosphor band (2nd) or two phosphor bands (others). Perf 14 (No. W83a) or 15×14 (others) (both with one elliptical hole in each vertical side)

W83	**W 6**	(2nd) orange-brown, yellow-orange and black (1 centre band)	1·10	1·10	☐ ☐
		a. orange-brown, yellow-orange and black (1 side band)			
		(18.9.00)	2·25	2·25	☐ ☐
W84	**W 7**	(1st) blue-green, greenish yellow, silver and black	1·75	1·75	☐ ☐
W85	**W 8**	(E) greenish blue, deep greenish blue and grey-black	2·10	2·10	☐ ☐
W86	**W 9**	64p. violet, gold, silver and black	5·50	5·50	☐ ☐
W87		65p. violet, gold, silver and black (25.4.00)	2·50	2·50	☐ ☐
W88		68p. violet, gold, silver and black (4.7.02)	2·25	2·25	☐ ☐

Presentation Pack (contains 2nd, 1st, E, 64p.) (Nos. W83, W84/W86) (PO Pack No. 46)   9·00   ☐

Presentation Pack (contains 65p.) (No. W87) (PO Pack No. 51)   10·00   ☐

Presentation Pack (contains 2nd, 1st, E, 65p.) (Nos. W83, W84/W85, W87) (PO Pack No. 56)   16·00   ☐

PHQ Cards (Nos. W83, W84/W86) (D13)   1·25   10·00   ☐ ☐

Nos. W83, W84 and W85 were initially sold at 19p., 26p. and 30p., the latter representing the basic European airmail rate.

No. W83a was only issued in the £7 Treasury of Trees stamp booklet, No. DX26

For combined presentation packs for all four Regions, see under England.

W **10**

2000 (15 Feb.) T W **4** redrawn with 'laf/st' face value as T W **10**. Two phosphor bands. Perf 14 (with one elliptical hole in each vertical side)

W97	**W 10**	(1st) bright orange-red	1·60	1·60	☐ ☐

No. W97 was only issued in £7·50 Special by Design stamp booklets.

2003 (14 Oct.)–**16** As Nos. W83, W84/W85 and W88, but with white borders. One centre phosphor band (2nd) or two phosphor bands (others). Perf 15×14 (with one elliptical hole in each vertical side)

(a) Printed in gravure by Walsall or De La Rue (42p.) or De La Rue (others)

W98	**W 6**	(2nd) orange-brown, deep orange-brown and black	1·10	1·10	☐ ☐
W99	**W 7**	(1st) blue-green, greenish yellow, silver and black	1·60	1·60	☐ ☐
W100	**W 8**	(E) greenish blue, deep greenish blue and grey-black	2·25	2·25	☐ ☐
W101		40p. greenish blue, deep greenish blue and grey-black			
		(11.5.04)	1·40	1·40	☐ ☐
W102		42p. greenish blue, deep greenish blue and grey-black			
		(5.4.05)	2·00	2·00	☐ ☐
W103		44p. greenish blue, deep greenish blue and grey-black			
		(28.3.06)	1·60	1·60	☐ ☐
W104		48p. greenish blue, deep greenish blue and grey-black			
		(27.3.07)	1·10	1·10	☐ ☐

W105	50p. greenish blue, deep greenish blue and grey-black *(1.4.08)*	1·40	1·40	☐	☐
W106	56p. greenish blue, deep greenish blue and grey-black *(31.3.09)*	1·50	1·50	☐	☐
W107	60p. greenish blue, deep greenish blue and grey-black *(30.3.10)*	1·75	1·75	☐	☐
W108 W **9**	68p. violet, gold, silver and black	1·60	1·60	☐	☐
W109	72p. violet, gold, silver and black *(28.3.06)*	1·60	1·60	☐	☐
W110	78p. violet, gold, silver and black *(27.3.07)*	2·00	2·00	☐	☐
W111	81p. violet, gold, silver and black *(1.4.08)*	2·25	2·25	☐	☐
W112	90p. violet, gold, silver and black *(31.3.09)*	2·40	2·40	☐	☐
W113	97p. violet, gold, silver and black *(30.3.10)*	2·50	2·50	☐	☐

(b) Printed in lithography by Enschedé or Cartor (W122 1st) or Cartor (others)

W121 W **6**	(2nd) orange-brown, deep orange-brown and black *(1.13)*	1·40	1·40	☐	☐
W122 W **7**	(1st) blue-green, greenish yellow and black *(20.9.07)*	1·60	1·60	☐	☐
W123 W **8**	68p. greenish blue, deep greenish blue and black *(29.3.11)*	1·75	1·75	☐	☐
W124	87p. greenish blue, deep greenish blue and black *(25.4.12)*	2·25	2·25	☐	☐
W125	88p. greenish blue, deep greenish blue and black *(27.3.13)*	2·25	2·25	☐	☐
W126	97p. greenish blue, deep greenish blue and black *(26.3.14)*	2·50	2·50	☐	☐
W127	£1 greenish blue, deep greenish blue and black *(24.3.15)*	2·50	2·50	☐	☐
W128	£1·05 greenish blue, deep greenish blue and black *(22.3.16)*	2·75	2·75	☐	☐
W129 W **9**	£1·10 violet, gold, silver and black *(29.3.11)*	2·50	2·50	☐	☐
W134	£1·28 violet, gold, silver and black *(25.4.12)*	2·75	2·75	☐	☐
W135	£1·33 violet, gold, silver and black *(24.3.15)*	2·75	2·75	☐	☐

Presentation Pack (Nos. W98/W100, W108) (PO Pack No. 65)	5·00		☐
PHQ Cards (set of 4) (Nos. W98/W100, W108) (D26)	1·50	10·00	☐ ☐

Nos. W98/W100 were initially sold at 20p., 28p. and 38p., the latter representing the basic European airmail rate.

No. W122 was first issued in the £7·66 British Army Uniforms stamp booklets, No. DX40, and No. **MS**W125. It was issued in sheets in January 2013.

Stamps as W122 but self-adhesive were issued on 1 March 2007 in sheets of 20 with *se-tenant* labels. These sheets were printed in lithography and perforated 15 × 14 without the elliptical holes. The labels show either Welsh scenes or personal photographs.

Stamps as Nos. EN30, NI95, S131 and W122 but self-adhesive were issued on 29 September 2008 in sheets of 20 containing five of each design with *se-tenant* labels.

W **10a**

Opening of New Welsh Assembly Building, Cardiff

2006 (1 Mar.) Sheet 123 × 70 mm. Printed in gravure by De La Rue. One centre phosphor band (2nd) or two phosphor bands (others). Perf 15 × 14 (with one elliptical hole on each vertical side)

MSW143 W **10a** Nos. W98, W99 × 2 and W108 × 2	4·50	4·50	☐ ☐
First Day Cover		5·00	☐

50th Anniversary of the Country Definitives

2008 (29 Sept.) As Nos. W1, W3 and W5 (definitives of 1958) but inscribed 1st and printed in lithography by De La Rue. Two phosphor bands. Perf 15 × 14½ (with one elliptical hole on each vertical side)

W144 W **1**	(1st) deep lilac	1·60	1·60	☐	☐
W145 W **3**	(1st) green	1·60	1·60	☐	☐
W146 W **2**	(1st) deep claret	1·60	1·60	☐	☐
Set of 3		4·25	4·25	☐	☐

Nos. W144/W146 were only issued in the £9·72 The Regional Definitives stamp booklet.

W **11**

Celebrating Wales miniature sheet

2009 (26 Feb.) Sheet 123 × 70 mm. Printed in lithography by De La Rue. Two phosphor bands. Perf 15 × 14 (with one elliptical hole on each vertical side (1st) or 14½ × 14 (81p.)

MSW147 W **10a** (1st) Red dragon; (1st) No. W120; 81p. St. David; 81p. National Assembly for Wales, Cardiff	4·25	4·25	☐ ☐
First Day Cover		5·25	☐
Presentation Pack (PO Pack No. 424)	5·00		☐
PHQ Cards (set of 5) (CGB4)	1·50	8·00	☐ ☐

No. **MS**W125 was on sale at post offices throughout the UK.

The five PHQ cards show the four individual stamps and the complete miniature sheet.

Stamps as the 1st class red Dragon stamp from No. **MS**W147 but self-adhesive were issued on 1 March 2010 in sheets of 20 with *se-tenant* labels showing Welsh castles. These sheets were printed in lithography by Cartor.

W **12** Red Dragon

Welsh Flag

2013 (9 May)–**14**. Printed in lithography by Cartor or Enschedé. Two phosphor bands. Perf 14½×14 (with one elliptical hole in each vert side)

W148 W **12**   (1st) multicoloured   4·00   4·00 ☐ ☐

No. W148 was only issued in the £11·11 Football Heroes, £13·97 Classic Locomotives and £16·49 Centenary of the First World War (3rd Issue) booklets.

W **13** Leek   W **14** Dragon   W **15** Daffodil   W **16** Prince of Wales Feathers

2017 (21 Mar.)–**19** As previous set but with value indicated in revised typeface. One centre band (No. W149) or two phosphor bands (others). Perf 15×14 (with one elliptical hole in each vertical side)

W149	W **13**	(2nd) multicoloured				
		(20.3.18)	1·00	75	☐	☐
W150	W **14**	(1st) multicoloured				
		(20.3.18)	1·25	75	☐	☐
W151	W **15**	£1·17 multicoloured				
		(21.3.17)	2·75	2·75	☐	☐
W152	W **15**	£1·25 multicoloured				
		(20.3.18)	2·75	2·75	☐	☐
W153		£1·35 multicoloured				
		(19.3.19)	2·75	2·75	☐	☐
W156	W **16**	£1·40 multicoloured				
		(21.3.17)	3·00	3·00	☐	☐
W156*a*	W **15**	£1·42 multicoloured				
		(17.3.20)	2·50	2·50	☐	☐
W158	W **16**	£1·45 multicoloured				
		(20.3.18)	3·25	3·25	☐	☐
W159		£1·55 multicoloured				
		(19.3.19)	3·25	3·25	☐	☐
W160		£1·63 multicoloured				
		(17.3.20)	2·75	2·75	☐	☐

Numbers have been left for possible additions to the above definitive series.

5 Isle of Man

Regional Issues

1   2   3

1958–68 Wmk **179**. Perf 15×14

1	**1**	2½d. red *(8.6.64)*	70	70	☐	☐
2	**2**	3d. lilac *(18.8.58)*	50	50	☐	☐
		p. One centre phosphor band *(27.6.68)*	20	20	☐	☐

3		4d. blue *(7.2.66)*	1·00	1·00	☐	☐
		p. Two phosphor bands *(5.7.67)*	30	30	☐	☐

1968–69 One centre phosphor band (Nos. 5/6) or two phosphor bands (others). No wmk

4	**2**	4d. blue *(24.6.68)*	25	25	☐	☐
5		4d. sepia *(4.9.68)*	30	30	☐	☐
6		4d. vermilion *(26.2.69)*	45	45	☐	☐
7		5d. blue *(4.9.68)*	45	45	☐	☐

Decimal Currency

1971 (7 July) One centre phosphor band (2½p.) or two phosphor bands (others). No wmk

8	**3**	2½p. magenta	30	30	☐	☐
9		3p. ultramarine	30	30	☐	☐
10		5p. violet	70	70	☐	☐
11		7½p. chestnut	80	80	☐	☐
Presentation Pack (PO Pack No. 30)			2·50		☐	

For comprehensive listings of the Independent Administration issues of the Isle of Man, see Stanley Gibbons *Collect Channel Islands and Isle of Man Stamps*.

6 Channel Islands General Issue

C **1** Gathering Vraic   C **2** Islanders gathering Vraic

Third Anniversary of Liberation

1948 (10 May) Wmk T **127**. Perf 15×14

C1	C **1**	1d. red	25	55	☐	☐
C2	C **2**	2½d. blue	25	60	☐	☐
First Day Cover				35·00		☐

7 Guernsey

(a) War Occupation Issues

Stamps issued under British authority during the German Occupation.

1   2   3

1941–44 Rouletted

(a) White paper. No wmk

1*d*	**1**	½d. green	5·00	3·50	☐	☐
2		1d. red	3·25	2·00	☐	☐
3*a*		2½d. blue	15·00	10·00	☐	☐

(b) Dark bluish French bank-note paper. Wmk loops

4	**1**	½d. green	32·00	25·00	☐	☐
5		1d. red	18·00	25·00	☐	☐

(b) Regional Issues

1958–67 Wmk **179**. Perf 15×14

6	**2**	2½d. red *(8.6.64)*	40	40	☐	☐

7	**3**	3d. lilac *(18.8.58)*	30	30	☐ ☐
		p. One centre phosphor band *(24.5.67)*	30	30	☐ ☐
8		4d. blue *(7.2.66)*	40	40	☐ ☐
		p. Two phosphor bands *(24.10.67)*	20	20	☐ ☐

1968–69 One centre phosphor band (Nos. 10/11) or two phosphor bands (others). No wmk

9	**3**	4d. blue *(16.4.68)*	20	20	☐ ☐
10		4d. sepia *(4.9.68)*	20	20	☐ ☐
11		4d. vermilion *(26.2.69)*	20	20	☐ ☐
12		5d. blue *(4.9.68)*	30	30	☐ ☐

For comprehensive listings of the Independent Postal Administration issues of Guernsey, see Stanley Gibbons *Collect Channel Islands and Isle of Man Stamps.*

8 Jersey

(a) War Occupation Issues

Stamps issued under British authority during the German Occupation.

5

6 Old Jersey Farm

7 Portelet Bay

8 Corbière Lighthouse

9 Elizabeth Castle

10 Mont Orgueil Castle

11 Gathering Vraic (seaweed)

1941–42 White paper. No wmk. Perf 11

| 1 | **5** | ½d. green | 8·00 | 6·00 | ☐ ☐ |
| 2 | | 1d. red | 8·00 | 5·00 | ☐ ☐ |

1943 No wmk. Perf 13½

3	**6**	½d. green	12·00	12·00	☐ ☐
4	**7**	1d. red	3·00	50	☐ ☐
5	**8**	1½d. brown	8·00	5·75	☐ ☐
6	**9**	2d. orange	7·50	2·00	☐ ☐
7a	**10**	2½d. blue	1·00	1·75	☐ ☐
8	**11**	3d. violet	3·00	2·75	☐ ☐
Set of 6			30·00	21·00	☐ ☐

(b) Regional Issues

12

13

1958–67 Wmk **179**. Perf 15 × 14

9	**12**	2½d. red *(8.6.64)*	45	45	☐ ☐
10	**13**	3d. lilac *(18.8.58)*	30	30	☐ ☐
		p. One centre phosphor band *(9.6.67)*	20	20	☐ ☐
11		4d. blue *(7.2.66)*	25	25	☐ ☐
		p. Two phosphor bands *(5.9.67)*	20	20	☐ ☐

1968–69 One centre phosphor band (4d. values) or two phosphor bands (5d.). No wmk

12	**13**	4d. sepia *(4.9.68)*	20	20	☐ ☐
13		4d. vermilion *(26.2.69)*	20	20	☐ ☐
14		5d. blue *(4.9.68)*	20	20	☐ ☐

For comprehensive listings of the Independent Postal Adminstration issues of Jersey, see Stanley Gibbons *Collect Channel Islands and Isle of Man Stamps.*

REGIONAL FIRST DAY COVERS

PRICES for First Day Covers listed below are for stamps, as indicated, used on illustrated envelopes and postmarked with operational cancellations (before 1964) or with special First Day of Issue cancellations (1964 onwards). First Day postmarks of 8 June 1964 and 7 February 1966 were of the machine cancellation 'envelope' type.

£sd Issues

18 Aug. 1958

Guernsey 3d. (No. 7)	20·00	☐
Isle of Man 3d. (No. 2)	32·00	☐
Jersey 3d. (No. 10)	20·00	☐
Northern Ireland 3d. (No. NI1)	30·00	☐
Scotland 3d. (No. S1)	17·00	☐
Wales 3d. (No. W1)	12·00	☐

29 Sept. 1958

Northern Ireland 6d., 1s.3d. (Nos. NI3, NI5)	35·00	☐
Scotland 6d., 1s.3d. (Nos. S3, S5)	25·00	☐
Wales 6d., 1s.3d. (Nos. W3, W5)	25·00	☐

8 June 1964

Guernsey 2½d. (No. 6)	30·00	☐
Isle of Man 2½d. (No. 1)	45·00	☐
Jersey 2½d. (No. 9)	30·00	☐

7 Feb. 1966

Guernsey 4d. (No. 8)	8·00	☐
Isle of Man 4d. (No. 3)	15·00	☐
Jersey 4d. (No. 11)	10·00	☐
Northern Ireland 4d. (No. NI2)	7·00	☐
Scotland 4d. (No. S2)	7·00	☐
Wales 4d. (No. W2)	7·00	☐

1 Mar. 1967

Northern Ireland 9d., 1s.6d. (Nos. NI4, NI6)	4·00	☐
Scotland 9d., 1s.6d. (Nos. S4, S6)	6·00	☐
Wales 9d., 1s.6d. (Nos. W4, W6)	4·00	☐

4 Sept. 1968

| Guernsey 4d., 5d. (Nos. 10, 12) | 3·00 | ☐ |
| Isle of Man 4d., 5d. (Nos. 5, 7) | 4·00 | ☐ |

Jersey 4d., 5d. (Nos. 12, 14)	3·00 ☐	
Northern Ireland 4d., 5d. (Nos. NI8, NI10)	3·00 ☐	
Scotland 4d., 5d. (Nos. S9, S11)	3·00 ☐	
Wales 4d., 5d. (Nos. W9, W11)	3·00 ☐	

Decimal Issues

7 July 1971

Isle of Man 2½p., 3p., 5p., 7½p. (Nos. 8/11)	3·50 ☐
Northern Ireland 2½p., 3p., 5p., 7½p. (Nos. NI12/NI13, NI18, NI23)	2·50 ☐
Scotland 2½p., 3p., 5p., 7½p. (Nos. S14/S15, S20, S25)	1·50 ☐
Wales 2½p., 3p., 5p., 7½p. (Nos. W13/W14, W19, W24)	2·00 ☐

23 Jan. 1974

Northern Ireland 3p., 3½p., 5½p., 8p. (Nos. NI14/NI15, NI19, NI24)	2·00 ☐
Scotland 3p., 3½p., 5½p., 8p. (Nos. S16/S17, S21, S26)	1·25 ☐
Wales 3p., 3½p., 5½p., 8p. (Nos. W15/W16, W20, W25)	1·50 ☐

6 Nov. 1974

Northern Ireland 4½p. (No. NI17)	80 ☐
Scotland 4½p. (No. S19)	1·00 ☐
Wales 4½p. (No. W18)	80 ☐

14 Jan. 1976

Northern Ireland 6½p., 8½p. (Nos. NI21, NI25)	80 ☐
Scotland 6½p., 8½p. (Nos. S23, S27)	1·00 ☐
Wales 6½p., 8½p. (Nos. W22, W26)	80 ☐

20 Oct. 1976

Northern Ireland 10p., 11p. (Nos. NI27, NI30)	90 ☐
Scotland 10p., 11p. (Nos. S29, S32)	1·00 ☐
Wales 10p., 11p. (Nos. W28, W31)	80 ☐

18 Jan. 1978

Northern Ireland 7p., 9p., 10½p. (Nos. NI22, NI26, NI29)	90 ☐
Scotland 7p., 9p., 10½p. (Nos. S24, S28, S31)	1·00 ☐
Wales 7p., 9p., 10½p. (Nos. W23, W27, W30)	1·00 ☐

23 July 1980

Northern Ireland 12p., 13½p., 15p. (Nos. NI31/NI33)	1·50 ☐
Scotland 12p., 13½p., 15p. (Nos. S33/S35)	1·50 ☐
Wales 12p., 13½p., 15p. (Nos. W32/W34)	2·00 ☐

8 April 1981

Northern Ireland 11½p., 14p., 18p., 22p. (Nos. NI34, NI38, NI45, NI53)	1·25 ☐
Scotland 11½p., 14p., 18p., 22p. (Nos. S36, S40, S44, S47)	1·50 ☐
Wales 11½p., 14p., 18p., 22p. (Nos. W35, W39, W46, W54)	2·00 ☐

24 Feb. 1982

Northern Ireland 12½p., 15½p., 19½p., 26p. (Nos. NI36, NI41, NI50, NI60)	2·00 ☐
Scotland 12½p., 15½p., 19½p., 26p. (Nos. S38, S41, S45, S49)	1·75 ☐
Wales 12½p., 15½p., 19½p., 26p. (Nos. W37, W42, W51, W61)	2·50 ☐

27 April 1983

Northern Ireland 16p., 20½p., 28p. (Nos. NI42, NI52, NI62)	2·00 ☐

Scotland 16p., 20½p., 28p. (Nos. S42, S46, S50)	2·00 ☐
Wales 16p., 20½p., 28p. (Nos. W43, W53, W63)	2·50 ☐

23 Oct. 1984

Northern Ireland 13p., 17p., 22p., 31p. (Nos. NI37, NI43, NI54, NI64)	2·25 ☐
Scotland 13p., 17p., 22p., 31p. (Nos. S39, S43, S48, S51)	2·00 ☐
Wales 13p., 17p., 22p., 31p. (Nos. W38, W44, W55, W65)	3·00 ☐

7 Jan. 1986

Northern Ireland 12p. (No. NI35)	90 ☐
Scotland 12p. (No. S37)	1·00 ☐
Wales 12p. (No. W36)	1·00 ☐

6 Jan. 1987

Northern Ireland 18p. (No. NI46)	90 ☐
Scotland 18p. (No. S59)	1·00 ☐
Wales 18p. (No. W47)	1·00 ☐

8 Nov. 1988

Northern Ireland 14p., 19p., 23p., 32p. (Nos. NI39, NI49, NI56, NI65)	2·50 ☐
Scotland 14p., 19p., 23p., 32p. (Nos. S54, S62, S67, S77)	2·00 ☐
Wales 14p., 19p., 23p., 32p. (Nos. W40, W50, W57, W66)	3·00 ☐

28 Nov. 1989

Northern Ireland 15p., 20p., 24p., 34p. (Nos. NI40, NI51, NI57, NI66)	3·00 ☐
Scotland 15p., 20p., 24p., 34p. (Nos. S56, S64, S69, S78)	2·50 ☐
Wales 15p., 20p., 24p., 34p. (Nos. W41, W52, W58, W67)	4·00 ☐

4 Dec. 1990

Northern Ireland 17p., 22p., 26p., 37p. (Nos. NI44, NI55, NI61, NI67)	3·00 ☐
Scotland 17p., 22p., 26p., 37p. (Nos. S58, S66, S73, S79)	2·50 ☐
Wales 17p., 22p., 26p., 37p. (Nos.W45, W56, W62, W68)	4·00 ☐

3 Dec. 1991

Northern Ireland 18p., 24p., 28p., 39p. (Nos. NI47, NI58, NI63, NI68)	3·00 ☐
Scotland 18p., 24p., 28p., 39p. (Nos. S60, S70, S75, S80)	2·50 ☐
Wales 18p., 24p., 28p., 39p. (Nos. W48, W59, W64, W69)	4·25 ☐

7 Dec. 1993

Northern Ireland 19p., 25p., 30p., 41p. (Nos. NI69, NI72, NI74, NI76)	4·00 ☐
Scotland 19p., 25p., 30p., 41p. (Nos. S81, S84, S86, S88)	3·50 ☐
Wales 19p., 25p., 30p., 41p. (Nos. W70, W73, W75, W77)	3·75 ☐

23 July 1996

Northern Ireland 20p. (1 centre band), 26p., 37p., 63p. (Nos. NI71, NI73, NI75, NI77)	5·00 ☐
Scotland 20p. (1 centre band), 26p., 37p., 63p. (Nos. S83, S85, S87, S89)	4·00 ☐
Wales 20p., 26p., 37p., 63p. (Nos. W72, W74, W76, W78)	6·00 ☐

1 July 1997

Wales 20p. (1 centre band), 26p., 37p., 63p. (Nos. W79 and W80/W82)	6·00 ☐

8 June 1999

Northern Ireland 38p., 64p. (Nos. NI83, NI86)	10·00 ☐

Scotland 2nd, 1st, E, 64p. (Nos S94/S97) 3·50 ☐
Wales 2nd, 1st, E, 64p. (Nos. W83, W84/
W86) 3·00 ☐

25 Apr. 2000
Northern Ireland 1st, 40p., 65p.
(Nos. NI84, NI87, NI88b) 12·50 ☐
Scotland 65p. (No. S98) 2·50 ☐
Wales 65p. (No. W87) 3·00 ☐

6 Mar. 2001
Northern Ireland 2nd, 1st, E, 65p.
(Nos. NI89/NI92) 2·75 ☐

23 Apr. 2001
England 2nd, 1st, E, 65p. (Nos. EN1/EN4) 2·00 ☐

4 July 2002
England 68p. (No. EN5) 1·50 ☐
Northern Ireland 68p. (No. NI93) 2·50 ☐
Scotland 68p. (No. S99) 2·00 ☐
Wales 68p. (No. W88) 2·50 ☐

14 Oct. 2003
England 2nd, 1st, E, 68p.
(Nos. EN6/EN8, EN16) 5·50 ☐
Northern Ireland 2nd, 1st, E, 68p.
(Nos. NI94/NI96, NI100) 3·25 ☐
Scotland 2nd, 1st, E, 68p.
(Nos. S109/S111, S119) 2·00 ☐
Wales 2nd, 1st, E, 68p.
(Nos. W98/W100, W108) 3·25 ☐

11 May 2004
England 40p. (No. EN9) 2·00 ☐
Northern Ireland 40p. (No. NI97) 1·75 ☐
Scotland 40p. (No. S112) 1·50 ☐
Wales 40p. (No. W101) 1·75 ☐

5 Apr. 2005
England 42p. (No. EN10) 2·00 ☐
Northern Ireland 42p. (No. NI98) 2·25 ☐
Scotland 42p. (No. S113) 1·75 ☐
Wales 42p. (No. W102) 2·00 ☐

28 Mar. 2006
England 44p., 72p. (Nos. EN11, EN17) 3·50 ☐
Northern Ireland 44p., 72p.
(Nos. NI99, NI102) 3·50 ☐
Scotland 44p., 72p. (Nos. S114, S120) 3·00 ☐
Wales 44p., 72p. (Nos. W103, W109) 3·25 ☐

27 Mar. 2007
England 48p., 78p. (Nos. EN12, EN18) 3·00 ☐
Northern Ireland 48p., 78p.
(Nos. NI124, NI128) 2·50 ☐
Scotland 48p., 78p. (Nos. S115, S121) 3·00 ☐
Wales 48p., 78p. (Nos. W104, W110) 3·50 ☐

1 Apr. 2008
England 50p., 81p. (Nos. EN13, EN19) 3·00 ☐
Northern Ireland 50p., 81p.
(Nos. NI125, NI129) 3·00 ☐
Scotland 50p., 81p. (Nos. S116, S122) 3·25 ☐
Wales 50p., 81p. (Nos. W105, W111) 3·75 ☐

31 Mar. 2009
England 56p., 90p. (Nos. EN14, EN20) 3·50 ☐
Northern Ireland 56p., 90p.
(Nos. NI126, NI130) 3·50 ☐
Scotland 56p., 90p. (Nos. S117, S123) 3·50 ☐
Wales 56p., 90p. (Nos. W106, W112) 4·00 ☐

31 Mar. 2010
England 60p., 97p. (Nos. EN15, EN21) 4·00 ☐
Northern Ireland 60p., 97p.
(Nos. NI127, NI131) 4·00 ☐
Scotland 60p., 97p. (Nos. S118, S124) 3·75 ☐
Wales 60p., 97p. (Nos. W107, W113) 4·00 ☐

29 Mar. 2011
England 68p., £1·10 (Nos. EN31, EN41) 4·50 ☐
Northern Ireland 68p., £1·10
(Nos. NI100, NI111) 4·25 ☐
Scotland 68p., £1·10
(Nos. S132, S138) 4·25 ☐
Wales 68p., £1·10
(Nos. W123, W129) 4·25 ☐

25 Apr. 2012
England 87p., £1·28 (Nos. EN32, EN43) 4·75 ☐
Northern Ireland 87p., £1·28
(Nos. NI103, NI113) 5·00 ☐
Scotland 87p., £1·28 (Nos. S133, S143) 4·50 ☐
Wales 87p., £1·28 (Nos. W124, W134) 5·00 ☐

27 Mar. 2013
England 88p. (No. EN33,) 2·25 ☐
Northern Ireland 88p., (No. NI104) 2·25 ☐
Scotland 88p. (Nos. S134) 2·00 ☐
Wales 88p. (No. W125) 2·25 ☐

26 Mar. 2014
England 97p. (No. EN34,) 2·25 ☐
Northern Ireland 97p., (No. NI105) 2·25 ☐
Scotland 97p., (Nos. S135) 2·25 ☐
Wales 97p., (No. W126) 2·50 ☐

24 Mar. 2015
England £1, £1·33 (Nos. EN35, EN44) 5·50 ☐
Northern Ireland £1, £1·33
(Nos. NI106, NI114) 5·00 ☐
Scotland £1, £1·33 (Nos. S136, S144) 5·25 ☐
Wales £1, £1·33 (Nos. W127, W135) 5·25 ☐

22 Mar. 2016
England £1·05 (No. EN36) 2·50 ☐
Northern Ireland £1·05 (No. NI107) 2·50 ☐
Scotland £1·05 (No. S137) 2·50 ☐
Wales £1·05 (No. W128) 2·75 ☐

21 Mar. 2017
England £1·17, £1·40
(No. EN54, EN60) 6·00 ☐
Northern Ireland £1·17, £1·40
(No. NI159, NI164) 6·00 ☐
Scotland £1·17, £1·40
(No. S161, S166) 5·00 ☐
Wales £1·17, £1·40
(No. W151, W156) 6·00 ☐

20 Mar. 2018
England 2nd, 1st, £1·25, £1·45 (Nos.
EN52/EN53, EN55, EN61) 9·00 ☐
Northern Ireland 2nd, 1st, £1·25, £1·45
(Nos. NI157/NI58, NI160, NI166) 9·00 ☐
Scotland 2nd, 1st, £1·25, £1·45
(Nos. S159/S160, S162, S168) 9·00 ☐
Wales 2nd, 1st, £1·25, £1·45
(Nos. W149/W150, W152, W158) 9·00 ☐

19 Mar. 2019
England £1·35, £1·55 (Nos. EN56,
EN62) 7·00 ☐
Northern Ireland £1·35, £1·55
(Nos. NI161, NI167) 7·00 ☐
Scotland £1·35, £1·55 (Nos. S163, S169) 7·00 ☐
Wales £1·35, £1·55 (Nos. W153, W159) 7·00 ☐

17 Mar. 2020
England £1·42, £1·63 (Nos. EN60a,
EN63) 7·00 ☐
Northern Ireland £1·42, £1·63
(Nos. NI164a, NI168) 7·00 ☐
Scotland £1·42, £1·63 (Nos. S166a,
S170) 7·00 ☐
Wales £1·42, £1·63 (Nos. W156a,
W160) 7·00 ☐

POSTAGE DUE STAMPS

PERFORATION. All postage due stamps to No. D101 are perf 14×15.

D **1**

D **2**

1914–22 Wmk T **100** (Royal Cypher ('Simple')) sideways

D1	D **1**	½d. green	50	25
D2		1d. red	50	25
D3		1½d. brown	48·00	20·00
D4		2d. black	50	25
D5		3d. violet	9·00	75
D6wi		4d. green	40·00	5·00
D7		5d. brown	7·00	3·50
D8		1s. blue	40·00	5·00
Set of 8			£130	32·00

1924–31 Wmk T **111** (Block G V R) sideways

D10	D **1**	½d. green	1·25	75
D11		1d. red	60	25
D12		1½d. brown	48·00	22·00
D13		2d. black	1·00	25
D14		3d. violet	1·50	25
D15		4d. green	15·00	4·25
D16		5d. brown	65·00	45·00
D17		1s. blue	8·50	50
D18	D **2**	2s.6d. purple/yellow	85·00	1·75
Set of 9			£200	70·00

1936–37 Wmk T **125** (E 8 R) sideways

D19	D **1**	½d. green	15·00	10·50
D20		1d. red	2·00	1·75
D21		2d. black	15·00	12·00
D22		3d. violet	2·00	2·00
D23		4d. green	65·00	35·00
D24a		5d. brown	40·00	28·00
D25		1s. blue	25·00	8·50
D26	D **2**	2s.6d. purple/yellow	£325	12·00
Set of 8			£450	£100

1937–38 Wmk T **127** (G VI R) sideways

D27	D **1**	½d. green	13·00	3·75
D28		1d. red	3·00	50
D29		2d. black	2·75	30
D30		3d. violet	11·00	30
D31		4d. green	£110	10·00
D32		5d. brown	17·00	75
D33		1s. blue	80·00	75
D34	D **2**	2s.6d. purple/yellow	85·00	1·25
Set of 8			£290	16·00

1951–52 Colours changed and new value (1½d.). Wmk T **127** (G VI R) sideways

D35	D **1**	½d. orange	3·50	3·50
D36		1d. blue	1·50	75
D37		1½d. green	2·00	2·00
D38		4d. blue	50·00	22·00
D39		1s. brown	28·00	5·25
Set of 5			75·00	30·00

1954–55 Wmk T **153** (Mult Tudor Crown and E 2 R) sideways

D40	D **1**	½d. orange	7·00	5·25
D41		2d. black	26·00	23·00
D42		3d. violet	75·00	60·00
D43		4d. blue	26·00	32·00
D44		5d. brown	20·00	20·00
D45	D **2**	2s.6d. purple/yellow	£150	5·75
Set of 6			£250	£130

1955–57 Wmk T **165** (Mult St Edward's Crown and E 2 R) sideways

D46	D **1**	½d. orange	2·75	3·25
D47		1d. blue	5·00	1·50
D48		1½d. green	8·50	7·00
D49		2d. black	45·00	3·50
D50		3d. violet	6·00	1·50
D51		4d. blue	25·00	6·00
D52		5d. brown	26·00	20·00
D53		1s. brown	65·00	2·25
D54	D **2**	2s.6d. purple/yellow	£200	8·25
D55		5s. red/yellow	£150	32·00
Set of 10			£475	75·00

1959–63 Wmk T **179** (Mult St Edward's Crown) sideways

D56	D **1**	½d. orange	15	1·25
D57		1d. blue	15	50
D58		1½d. green	2·50	2·50
D59		2d. black	1·10	50
D60		3d. violet	30	30
D61		4d. blue	30	30
D62		5d. brown	45	60
D63		6d. purple	50	30
D64		1s. brown	90	30
D65	D **2**	2s.6d. purple/yellow	3·00	50
D66		5s. red/yellow	8·25	1·00
D67		10s. blue/yellow	11·50	6·00
D68		£1 black/yellow	40·00	8·00
Set of 13			65·00	20·00

1968–69 Design size 22½×19 mm. No wmk

D69	D **1**	2d. black	75	1·00
D70		3d. violet	1·00	1·00
D71		4d. blue	1·00	1·00
D72		5d. orange-brown	8·00	11·00
D73		6d. purple	2·25	1·75
D74		1s. brown	4·00	2·50
Set of 6			15·00	16·00

1968–69 Design size 21½×17½ mm. No wmk

D75	D **1**	4d. blue	7·00	6·75
D76		8d. red	50	1·00

D **3**

D **4**

Decimal Currency

1970–75 No wmk

D77	D **3**	½p. turquoise-blue	15	2·50
D78		1p. reddish purple	15	15
D79		2p. myrtle-green	20	15
D80		3p. ultramarine	20	15
D81		4p. yellow-brown	25	15
D82		5p. violet	25	15
D83		7p. red-brown	35	1·00
D84	D **4**	10p. red	30	30
D85		11p. green	50	1·00
D86		20p. brown	60	25
D87		50p. ultramarine	2·00	1·25

D88	£1 black	4·00	1·00	☐ ☐
D89	£5 orange-yellow and black	25·00	1·50	☐ ☐
Set of 13		30·00	8·00	☐ ☐
Presentation Pack (Nos. D77/D82, D84, D86/D88) (PO Pack No. 36)		28·00		☐
Presentation Pack (Nos. D77/D88) (PO Pack No. 93)		9·00		☐

D 5   D 6   D 7

1982 No wmk

D90	D 5	1p. lake	10	30	☐ ☐
D91		2p. bright blue	30	30	☐ ☐
D92		3p. deep mauve	15	30	☐ ☐
D93		4p. deep blue	15	25	☐ ☐
D94		5p. sepia	20	25	☐ ☐
D95	D 6	10p. light brown	30	40	☐ ☐
D96		20p. olive-green	50	60	☐ ☐
D97		25p. deep greenish blue	80	90	☐ ☐
D98		50p. grey-black	1·75	1·75	☐ ☐
D99		£1 red	3·00	1·25	☐ ☐
D100		£2 turquoise-blue	5·00	4·25	☐ ☐
D101		£5 dull orange	10·00	2·25	☐ ☐
Set of 12			19·00	10·00	☐ ☐
Set of 12 Gutter Pairs			38·00		☐
Presentation Pack (PO Pack No. 135)			24·00		☐

1994 (15 Feb.) Perf 15×14 (with one elliptical hole on each vertical side)

D102	D 7	1p. red, yellow and black	10	75	☐ ☐
D103		2p. magenta, purple and black	10	75	☐ ☐
D104		5p. yellow, red-brown and black	15	50	☐ ☐
D105		10p. yellow, emerald and black	30	75	☐ ☐
D106		20p. blue-green, violet and black	75	1·50	☐ ☐
D107		25p. cerise, rosine and black	1·50	2·00	☐ ☐
D108		£1 violet, magenta and black	7·00	7·00	☐ ☐
D109		£1·20 greenish blue, blue-green and black	8·00	9·00	☐ ☐
D110		£5 greenish black, blue-green and black	20·00	20·00	☐ ☐
Set of 9			35·00	35·00	☐ ☐
First Day Cover				45·00	☐
Presentation Pack (PO Pack No. 32)			38·00		☐

ROYAL MAIL POSTAGE LABELS

ROYAL MAIL POST & GO STAMPS

These imperforate labels were issued as an experiment by the Post Office. Special microprocessor-controlled machines were installed at post offices in Cambridge, London, Shirley (Southampton) and Windsor to provide an after-hours sales service to the public. The machines printed and dispensed the labels according to the coins inserted and the buttons operated by the customer. Values were initially available in ½p. steps to 16p. and in addition, the labels were sold at philatelic counters in two packs containing either three values (3½p., 12½p., 16p.) or 32 values (½p. to 16p.).

From 28 August 1984 the machines were adjusted to provide values up to 17p. After 31 December 1984 labels including ½p. values were withdrawn. The machines were taken out of service on 30 April 1985.

Machine postage-paid impression in red on phosphorised paper with grey-green background design. No watermark. Imperforate.

1984 (1 May–28 Aug.)

Set of 32 (½p. to 16p.)	15·00	22·00 □ □
Set of 3 (3½p., 12½p., 16p.)	2·50	3·00 □ □
Set of 3 on *First Day Cover* (1.5)		6·50 □
Set of 2 (16½p., 17p.) (28.8)	4·00	3·00 □ □

Following trials of a number of self-service machines capable of dispensing postage labels, Royal Mail began installing 'Post and Go' machines in larger post offices in October 2008. In addition to postage labels, the machines dispense stamps with a pre-printed background and an inkjet printed indicator of the service required, together with a four-part code.

The first machines were sited at the Galleries post office in Bristol and came into use on 8 October 2008. They dispensed five different stamps, dependent on the service; the code at the foot of the stamp referring to the branch in which the machine is sited, the machine number within the branch, and the session and transaction numbers.

The five original stamps were later complemented by values for 40g., 60g. and 100g. Unused stocks of earlier designs, such as Birds and Farmyard Animals also began to appear carrying the new service indicators and those seen have now been listed, although the set prices shown are generally for the values available at the time each design was released.

By the end of 2016 Post & Go machines could be found in most large post offices, nationwide.

> Collectors should note that the listings are for the different values available from Post & Go machines, not the different designs provided in the special packs available from Tallents House. These packs are listed as separate items below each set.

FT **1**

2008 (8 Oct.)–**12** T FT **1**. Olive-brown background. Self-adhesive. Two phosphor bands. Gravure Walsall, thermally printed service indicator Two phosphor bands. Perf 14 × 14½

FS1a	(1st Class up to 100g)	3.25	3·25	□ □
FS2a	(1st Large up to 100g)	3·50	3·50	□ □
FS3a	(Europe up to 20g)	4·00	4·00	□ □
FS3cb	(Euro 20g World 10g)	5·50	5·50	□ □
FS3dc	(Europe up to 60g)	8·50	8·50	□ □
FS3ea	(Europe up to 100g)	8·50	8·50	□ □
FS4a	(Worldwide up to 10g)	6·00	6·00	□ □
FS5a	(Worldwide up to 20g)	4·75	4·75	□ □
FS5e	(Worldwide up to 40g)	13·00	13·00	□ □
FS5fc	(Worldwide up to 60g)	9·25	9·25	□ □
FS5ga	(Worldwide up to 100g)	9·25	9·25	□ □
FS1a/FS3a, FS4a, FS5a, FS5e *Set of 6*		32·00	32·00	□ □
Special Pack (Nos. FS1/FS5) (31.3.09)		£100		□

The special pack contains separate stamps. These are reproductions of the first 'Post and Go' stamps printed at the Galleries Post Offices, Bristol. They differ from machine printed stamps in having the service indicator and branch code printed in gravure.

It is possible to obtain *se-tenant* strips of mixed values from Post and Go machines but we do not list these.

See also Nos. FS77a/FS84*b*

FT **2** Blue Tit

Birds of Britain (1st series)

2010 (17 Sept.) Multicoloured. Self-adhesive. Two phosphor bands. Designs printed in gravure by Walsall, thermally printed service indicator. Perf 14 × 14½

FS6	(1st Class up to 100g)	6·50	6·50	☐	☐
FS7	(1st Large up to 100g)	7·00	7·00	☐	☐
FS8	(Europe up to 20g)	8·50	8·50	☐	☐
FS8a	(Europe up to 60g)	80·00	80·00	☐	☐
FS9	(Worldwide up to 10g)	14·00	14·00	☐	☐
FS10	(Worldwide up to 20g)	10·00	10·00	☐	☐
FS10a	(Worldwide up to 40g)	40·00	40·00	☐	☐
FS10b	(Worldwide up to 60g)	80·00	80·00	☐	☐
FS6/FS8, FS9, FS10 Set of 5		40·00	40·00	☐	☐
First Day Cover (No. FS6 in 6 designs)			20·00		☐
Special Pack (No. FS6 in sheetlet of 6 gravure designs)		20·00			☐

Nos. FS6/FS10b were each available in six different designs: FT **2**, Goldfinch, Wood Pigeon, Robin, House Sparrow and Starling.

Nos. FS6/FS10 were available from Post and Go terminals in 30 post offices.

Stamps from the special pack and first day cover sold by Tallents House differ from machine printed stamps in having the service indicator and branch code printed in gravure.

Nos. FS8a, FS10a and FS10b resulted from the late use of old stock.

FT **3** Blackbird

Birds of Britain (2nd series)

2011 (24 Jan.) Multicoloured. Self-adhesive. Two phosphor bands. Designs printed in gravure by Walsall, thermally printed service indicator. Perf 14 × 14½

FS11	(1st class up to 100g)	3·50	3·50	☐	☐
FS12	(1st Large up to 100g)	3·75	3·75	☐	☐
FS13	(Europe up to 20g)	4·25	4·25	☐	☐
FS13a	(Europe up to 60g)	20·00	20·00	☐	☐
FS14	(Worldwide up to 10g)	8·50	8·50	☐	☐
FS15	(Worldwide up to 20g)	4·25	4·25	☐	☐
FS15a	(Worldwide up to 40g)	20·00	20·00	☐	☐
FS15b	(Worldwide up to 60g)	20·00	20·00	☐	☐
FS11/FS13, FS14, FS15 Set of 5		20·00	20·00	☐	☐
First Day Cover (No. FS11 in 6 designs)			20·00		☐
Special Pack (No. FS11 in sheetlet of 6 gravure designs)		35·00			☐

Nos. FS11/FS15b were each available in 6 different designs: FT **3**, two Magpies, Long-tailed Tit, Chaffinch, Collared Dove and Greenfinch.

Stamps from the special pack and first day cover sold by Tallents House differ from machine printed stamps in having the service indicator and branch code printed in gravure.

No. FS13a, FS15a and FS15b resulted from the late use of old stock.

FT **4** Mallard

Birds of Britain (3rd series)

2011 (19 May) Multicoloured. Self-adhesive. Two phosphor bands. Designs printed in gravure by Walsall, thermally printed service indicator. Perf 14 × 14½

FS16	(1st Class up to 100g)	2·50	2·50	☐	☐
FS17	(1st Large up to 100g)	3·00	3·00	☐	☐
FS18	(Europe up to 20g)	3·50	3·50	☐	☐
FS18a	(Europe up to 60g)	27·00	27·00	☐	☐
FS19	(Worldwide up to 10g)	5·00	5·00	☐	☐
FS20	(Worldwide up to 20g)	4·00	4·00	☐	☐
FS20a	(Worldwide up to 40g)	10·00	10·00	☐	☐
FS20b	(Worldwide up to 60g)	27·00	27·00	☐	☐
FS16/FS18, FS19, FS20 Set of 5		15·00	15·00	☐	☐
First Day Cover (No. FS16 in 6 designs)			8·75		☐
Special Pack (No. FS16 in sheetlet of 6 gravure designs)		8·00			☐

Nos. FS16/FS20b were each available in six different designs: FT **4**, Greylag Goose, Kingfisher, Moorhen, Mute Swan, and Great Crested Grebe.

Stamps from the special pack sold by Tallents House differ from machine printed stamps in having the service indicator and branch code printed in gravure.

Nos. FS18a, FS20a and FS20b resulted from the late use of old stock.

FT **5** Puffin

Birds of Britain (4th series)

2011 (16 Sept.) Multicoloured. Self-adhesive. Two phosphor bands. Designs printed in gravure by Walsall, thermally printed service indicator. Perf 14 × 14½

FS21	(1st class up to 100g)	2·25	2·25	☐	☐
FS22	(1st Large up to 100g)	2·75	2·75	☐	☐
FS23	(Europe up to 20g)	3·25	3·25	☐	☐
FS23a	(Europe up to 60g)	8·00	8·00	☐	☐
FS24	(Worldwide up to 10g)	4·75	4·75	☐	☐
FS25	(Worldwide up to 20g)	3·75	3·75	☐	☐
FS26	(Worldwide up to 40g)	7·50	7·50	☐	☐
FS26a	(Worldwide up to 60g)	8·50	8·50	☐	☐
FS21/FS23, FS24/FS26 Set of 6		20·00	20·00	☐	☐
First Day Cover (FS21 in 6 designs)			7·25		☐
Special Pack (No. FS21 in sheetlet of 6 gravure designs)		9·00			☐

Nos. FS21/FS26a were each available in six different designs: FT **5**, Gannet, Oystercatcher, Ringed Plover, Cormorant and Arctic Tern.

Stamps from the special pack sold by Tallents House differ from machine printed stamps in having the service indicator and branch code printed in gravure.

Nos. FS23a, and FS26a resulted from the late use of old stock.

FT **6** Welsh Mountain Badger Face

British Farm Animals (1st series). Sheep

2012 (24 Feb.) Multicoloured. Self-adhesive Two phosphor bands. Designs printed in gravure by Walsall, thermally printed service indicator. Perf 14×14½.

FS27	(1st Class up to 100g)	2·75	2·75	☐	☐
FS28	(1st Large up to 100g)	3·25	3·25	☐	☐
FS29	(Europe up to 20g)	3·25	3·25	☐	☐
FS29a	(Euro 20g World 10g)	10·00	10·00	☐	☐
FS29b	(Europe up to 60g)	12·00	12·00	☐	☐
FS30	(Worldwide up to 10g)	5·25	5·25	☐	☐
FS31	(Worldwide up to 20g)	4·00	4·00	☐	☐
FS32	(Worldwide up to 40g)	5·75	5·75	☐	☐
FS32b	(Worldwide up to 60g)	13·00	13·00	☐	☐
FS27/FS29, FS30/FS32 Set of 6		22·00	22·00	☐	☐
First Day Cover (FS27 in 6 designs)			8·75	☐	
Special Pack (FS27 in strip of 6 designs)					
(P&G 6)		8·00		☐	

Nos. FS27/FS32b were each available in six different designs: FT 6; Dalesbred; Jacob; Suffolk; Soay; Leicester Longwool.

Nos. FS29a, FS29b and FS32b resulted from the late use of old stock.

FT **7** Berkshire

British Farm Animals (2nd series). Pigs

2012 (24 Apr.) Multicoloured. Self-adhesive. Two phosphor bands. Designs printed in gravure by Walsall, thermally printed service indicator. Perf 14×14½.

FS33	(1st class up to 100g)	2·75	2·75	☐	☐
FS34	(1st Large up to 100g)	3·25	3·25	☐	☐
FS35	(Europe up to 20g)	3·25	3·25	☐	☐
FS35a	(Euro 20g World 10g)	8·75	8·75	☐	☐
FS35b	(Europe up to 60g)	13·00	13·00	☐	☐
FS36	(Worldwide up to 10g)	5·25	5·25	☐	☐
FS37	(Worldwide up to 20g)	4·00	4·00	☐	☐
FS38	(Worldwide up to 40g)	5·75	5·75	☐	☐
FS38b	(Worldwide up to 60g)	13·00	13·00	☐	☐
FS33/FS35, FS36/FS38 Set of 6		22·00	22·00	☐	☐
First Day Cover (No. FS33 in 6 designs)			8·50	☐	
Special Pack (FS33 in strip of 6 designs)					
(P&G 7)		8·00		☐	

Nos. FS33/FS38b were each available in six different designs: FT **7**; Gloucestershire Old Spot; Oxford Sandy and Black; Welsh; Tamworth; British Saddleback.

Nos. FS35a, FS35b and FS38b resulted from the late use of old stock.

FT **8** Union Flag

Union Flag

2012 (21 May) T FT **8**. Multicoloured. Self-adhesive. Two phosphor bands. Designs printed in gravure by Walsall, thermally printed service indicator. Perf 14×14½

FS39	(1st Class up to 100g)	2·75	2·75	☐	☐
FS40	(1st Large up to 100g)	3·25	3·25	☐	☐
FS41	(Europe up to 20g)	3·50	3·50	☐	☐
FS41a	(Euro 20g World 10g)	3·50	3·50	☐	☐
FS41b	(Europe up to 60g)	9·75	9·75	☐	☐
FS41c	(Europe up to 100g)	9·50	9·50	☐	☐
FS42	(Worldwide up to 10g)	5·25	5·25	☐	☐
FS43	(Worldwide up to 20g)	4·50	4·50	☐	☐
FS44	(Worldwide up to 40g)	6·00	6·00	☐	☐
FS44b	(Worldwide up to 60g)	10·50	10·50	☐	☐
FS44c	(Worldwide up to 100g)	10·50	10·50	☐	☐
FS39/FS41, FS42/FS44 Set of 6		23·00	23·00	☐	☐
First Day Cover (No. FS39 only)			2·50	☐	
Special Pack (No. FS39 only) (P&G 8)		3·00		☐	

FT **9** Irish Moiled

British Farm Animals (3rd series). Cattle

2012 (28 Sept.) Multicoloured. Self-adhesive. Two phosphor bands. Designs printed in gravure by Walsall, thermally printed service indicator. Perf 14×14½

FS45	(1st Class up to 100g)	4·00	4·00	☐	☐
FS46	(1st Large up to 100g)	4·75	4·75	☐	☐
FS47	(Europe up to 20g)	5·00	5·00	☐	☐
FS47a	(Euro 20g World 10g)	10·00	10·00	☐	☐
FS47b	(Europe up to 60g)	12·00	12·00	☐	☐
FS48	(Worldwide up to 10g)	6·00	6·00	☐	☐
FS49	(Worldwide up to 20g)	5·25	5·25	☐	☐
FS50	(Worldwide up to 40g)	7·00	7·00	☐	☐
FS50b	(Worldwide up to 60g)	13·00	13·00	☐	☐
FS45/FS47, FS48/FS50 Set of 6		29·00	29·00	☐	☐
First Day Cover (No. FS45 in 6 designs)			8·50	☐	
Special Pack (FS45 in strip of 6 designs)					
(P&G 9)		8·00		☐	

Nos. FS45/FS50b were each available in six different designs: FT **9**; Welsh Black; Highland; White Park; Red Poll; Aberdeen Angus.

Nos. FS47a, FS47b and FS50b resulted from the late use of old stock.

FT **10** Robin

Christmas Robin

2012 (6 Nov.) T FT **10**. With date code in background. Multicoloured. Self-adhesive. Two phosphor bands. Designs printed in gravure by Walsall, thermally printed service indicator. Perf 14×14½

FS51	(1st Class up to 100g)	2·75	2·75	☐	☐
FS52	(1st Large up to 100g)	3·25	3·25	☐	☐
FS53	(Europe up to 20g)	3·50	3·50	☐	☐
FS53c	(Euro 20g World 10g)	5·00	5·00	☐	☐
FS53da	(Euro 20g up to 60g)	9·00	9·00	☐	☐
FS53e	(Europe up to 100g)	13·00	13·00	☐	☐
FS54	(Worldwide up to 10g)	4·00	4·00	☐	☐
FS55	(Worldwide up to 20g)	4·50	4·50	☐	☐
FS56	(Worldwide up to 40g)	5·75	5·75	☐	☐
FS56da	(Worldwide up to 60g)	9·75	9·75	☐	☐
FS56e	(Worldwide up to 100g)	14·00	14·00	☐	☐
FS51/FS53, FS54/FS56 Set of 6		22·00	22·00	☐	☐

Nos. FS53ca, FS53da, FS53e, FS56da and FS56e resulted from the late use of old stock.

Nos. FS57 and FS58 are vacant.

FT **11** Lesser Silver Water Beetle

FT **13** Minnow

Freshwater Life (1st series). Ponds

2013 (22 Feb.) Multicoloured. Self-adhesive. Two phosphor bands. Designs printed in gravure by Walsall, thermally printed service indicator. Perf 14 × 14½

FS59	(1st Class up to 100g)	2·25	2·25	
FS60	(1st Large up to 100g)	2·50	2·50	
FS61	(Europe up to 20g)	3·25	3·25	
FS61a	(Euro 20g World 10g)	7·50	7·50	
FS61b	(Europe up to 60g)	9·00	9·00	
FS61c	(Europe up to 100g)	30·00	30·00	
FS62	(Worldwide up to 10g)	3·25	3·25	
FS63	(Worldwide up to 20g)	3·50	3·50	
FS64	(Worldwide up to 40g)	4·25	4·25	
FS64b	(Worldwide up to 60g)	9·50	9·50	
FS64c	(Worldwide up to 100g)	30·00	30·00	
FS59/FS61, FS62/FS64 Set of 6		16·00	16·00	
First Day Cover (FS59 in 6 designs)			9·50	
Special Pack (FS59 in strip of 6 designs)				
(P&G 11)		8·00		

Nos. FS59/FS64b were each available in six different designs: FT **11**, Three-spined Stickleback, Smooth Newt, Fairy Shrimp, Emperor Dragonfly and Glutinous Snail.

Nos. FS61a, FS61b and FS64b resulted from the late use of old stock.

FT **12** Perch

Freshwater Life (2nd series). Lakes

2013 (25 June) Multicoloured. Self-adhesive. Two phosphor bands. Designs printed in gravure by Walsall, thermally printed service indicator. Perf 14 × 14½

FS65	(1st Class up to 100g)	2·75	2·75	
FS66	(1st Large up to 100g)	3·25	3·25	
FS67	(Europe up to 20g)	3·75	3·75	
FS67a	(Euro 20g World 10g)	6·50	6·50	
FS67b	(Europe up to 60g)	8·25	8·25	
FS67c	(Europe up to 100g)	24·00	24·00	
FS68	(Worldwide up to 10g)	3·75	3·75	
FS69	(Worldwide up to 20g)	4·00	4·00	
FS70	(Worldwide up to 40g)	4·75	4·75	
FS70b	(Worldwide up to 60g)	8·75	8·75	
FS70c	(Worldwide up to 100g)	24·00	24·00	
FS65/FS67, FS68/FS70 Set of 6		19·00	19·00	
First Day Cover (FS65 in 6 designs)			9·50	
Special Pack (FS65 in strip of 6 designs)				
(P&G 12)		8·00		

Nos. FS65/FS70b were each available in six different designs: FT **12**, European Eel, Crucian Carp, Caddis Fly Larva, Arctic Char and Common Toad.

Nos. FS67a, FS67b and FS70b resulted from the late use of old stock.

Freshwater Life (3rd series). Rivers

2013 (20 Sept.) Multicoloured. Self-adhesive. Two phosphor bands. Designs printed in gravure by Walsall, thermally printed service indicator. Perf 14 × 14½

FS71	(1st Class up to 100g)	2·25	2·25	
FS72	(1st Large up to 100g)	2·50	2·50	
FS73	(Europe up to 20g)	3·25	3·25	
FS73a	(Euro 20g World 10g)	6·50	6·50	
FS73b	(Europe up to 60g)	7·50	7·50	
FS73c	(Europe up to 100g)	24·00	24·00	
FS74	(Worldwide up to 10g)	3·35	3·35	
FS75	(Worldwide up to 20g)	3·50	3·50	
FS76	(Worldwide up to 40g)	4·25	4·25	
FS76b	(Worldwide up to 60g)	8·00	8·00	
FS76c	(Worldwide up to 100g)	24·00	24·00	
FS71/FS73, FS74/FS76 Set of 6		16·00	16·00	
First Day Cover (FS71 in 6 designs)			9·50	
Special Pack (FS71 in strip of 6 designs)				
(P&G 13)		10·00		

Nos. FS71/FS76b were each available in six different designs: FT **13**, Atlantic Salmon, White-clawed Crayfish, River Lamprey, Blue-winged Olive Mayfly Larva and Brown Trout.

Nos. FS73a, FS73b and FS76b resulted from the late use of old stock.

NOTE: From FS77 onwards all Post & Go stamps incorporated a year code, unless otherwise stated.

2013 (19 Nov.) T FT **1** with date code in background. Olive-brown background, Self-adhesive. Two phosphor bands. Designs printed in gravure by Walsall, thermally printed service indicator. Perf 14 × 14½

FS77a	(1st Class up to 100g)	2·50	2·50	
FS78a	(1st Large up to 100g)	3·00	3·00	
FS79	(Europe up to 20g)	5·50	5·50	
FS79ba	(Euro 20g World 10g)	3·25	3·25	
FS80a	(Europe up to 60g)	6·00	6·00	
FS80c	(Europe up to 100g)	4·25	4·25	
FS80d	(Europe 100g World 20g)	4·25	4·25	
FS81a	(Worldwide up to 10g)	—	—	
FS82a	(Worldwide up to 20g)	3·75	3·75	
FS82b	(World 100g Zone 1-3)	5·75	5·75	
FS83a	(Worldwide up to 40g)	—	—	
FS84a	(Worldwide up to 60g)	7·00	7·00	
FS84c	(Worldwide up to 100g)	5·75	5·75	
FS84d	(World 100g Zone 2)	5·75	5·75	
FS77a, FS78a, FS79ba, FS80c, FS82a,				
FS84c Set of 6		20·00	20·00	

2013 (17 Nov.) Union Flag T FT **8** with date code in background. Multicoloured. Self-adhesive. Two phosphor bands. Designs printed in gravure by Walsall; thermally printed service indicator. Perf 14 × 14½

FS85a	(1st Class up to 100g)	4·00	4·00	☐ ☐
FS86a	(1st Large up to 100g)	4·25	4·25	☐ ☐
FS87	(Europe up to 20g)	—	—	☐ ☐
FS87a	(Euro 20g World 10g)	4·50	4·50	☐ ☐
FS88	(Europe up to 60g)	20·00	20·00	☐ ☐
FS88a	(Europe up to 100g)	5·50	5·50	☐ ☐
FS89	(Worldwide up to 10g)	—	—	☐ ☐
FS90a	(Worldwide up to 20g)	4·75	4·75	☐ ☐
FS91	(Worldwide up to 40g)	—	—	☐ ☐
FS92	(Worldwide up to 60g)	21·00	21·00	☐ ☐
FS92a	(Worldwide up to 100g)	6·75	6·75	☐ ☐
FS85a, FS86a, FS87a, FS88a, FS90a, FS92a *Set of 6*		27·00	27·00	☐ ☐

FT **14**

2013 (20 Nov.) T FT **14** with date code in background. New blue background. Self-adhesive. One phosphor band (over the Queen's head). Designs printed in gravure by Walsall, thermally printed service indicator. Perf 14 × 14½

FS93a	(2nd Class up to 100g)	2·50	2·50	☐ ☐
FS94a	(2nd Large up to 100g)	2·75	2·75	☐ ☐
Special Pack (FS93/FS94) *(20.02.13)*				
(P&G 10)			10·00	☐

Post & Go stamps as T FT **14** were issued by Tallents House on 20 February 2013 in packs and on first day covers (price £7 per pack or £3 per first day cover.) They were also sold at Spring Stampex 2013 from machines, but were not made available through post offices until November 2013.

FT **15** Primrose

British Flora (1st series). Spring Blooms

2014 (19 Feb.) Multicoloured. Self-adhesive. Two phosphor bands. Designs printed in gravure by ISP Walsall, thermally printed service indicator. Perf 14 × 14½

FS95	(1st Class up to 100g)	4·50	4·50	☐ ☐
FS96	(1st Large up to 100g)	5·25	5·25	☐ ☐
FS97	(Europe up to 20g)	5·50	5·50	☐ ☐
FS97b	(Euro 20g World 10g)	6·00	6·00	☐ ☐
FS98a	(Europe up to 60g)	7·50	7·50	☐ ☐
FS98b	(Europe up to 100g)	11·50	11·50	☐ ☐
FS99	(Worldwide up to 10g)	6·50	6·50	☐ ☐
FS100	(Worldwide up to 20g)	5·75	5·75	☐ ☐
FS101	(Worldwide up to 40g)	7·50	7·50	☐ ☐
FS102a	(Worldwide up to 60g)	8·50	8·50	☐ ☐
FS102b	(Worldwide up to 100g)	12·50	12·50	☐ ☐
FS95/FS97, FS99/FS101 *Set of 6*		32·00	32·00	☐ ☐
First Day Cover (FS95 in 6 designs)			9·50	☐
Special Pack (FS95 in strip of 6 designs)				
(P&G 14)			8·00	☐

Nos. FS95/FS102b were each available in six different designs: FT **15**, Snowdrop, Lesser Celandine, Dog Violet, Wild Daffodil and Blackthorn.

OPEN VALUE LABELS In February 2014, 'Open Value labels', previously dispensed from Post & Go machines printed on white self-adhesive paper began to appear on the same illustrated background designs as Post & Go stamps. These show a service indicator '1L' (1st Letter), '2SP' (2nd Small Parcel), etc and the price. These are outside the scope of this catalogue, but on 7 July 2014 Royal Mail released a special pack (P&G 15) containing five such labels in the Machin Head design, as Types FT **1** and FT **14** (*Price* £8).

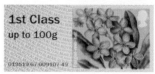

FT **16** Forget-me-not

British Flora (2nd series). Symbolic Flowers

2014 (17 Sept.) Multicoloured. Self-adhesive. Two phosphor bands. Designs printed in gravure by ISP Walsall, thermally printed service indicator. Perf 14 × 14½

FS103	(1st Class up to 100g)	3·00	3·00	☐ ☐
FS104	(1st Large up to 100g)	3·25	3·25	☐ ☐
FS104b	(Europe up to 20g)	25·00	25·00	☐ ☐
FS105	(Euro 20g World 10g)	3·50	3·50	☐ ☐
FS106	(Europe up to 60g)	6·75	6·75	☐ ☐
FS106b	(Europe up to 100g)	10·00	10·00	☐ ☐
FS107	(Worldwide up to 20g)	4·50	4·50	☐ ☐
FS108	(Worldwide up to 60g)	7·25	7·25	☐ ☐
FS108b	(Worldwide up to 100g)	11·00	11·00	☐ ☐
FS103/FS108 *Set of 6*		26·00	26·00	☐ ☐
First Day Cover (FS103 in 6 designs)			9·50	☐
Special Pack (FS103 in strip of 6 designs)				
(P&G 16)			8·00	☐

Nos. FS103/FS108b were each available in six different designs: FT **16**, Common Poppy, Dog Rose, Spear Thistle, Heather and Cultivated Flax.

The Poppy design was released as a single design roll in the run-up to Remembrance Sunday in October 2014, October 2015, October 2016, October 2017 and October 2018..

FT **17** Common Ivy

British Flora (3rd series). Winter Greenery

2014 (13 Nov.) Multicoloured. Self-adhesive. One phosphor band (FS109/FS110) or two phosphor bands (others). Designs printed in gravure by ISP Walsall, thermally printed service indicator. Perf 14 × 14½

FS109	(2nd Class up to 100g)	3·50	3·50	☐ ☐
FS110	(2nd Large up to 100g)	4·00	4·00	☐ ☐
FS111	(1st Class up to 100g)	3·50	3·50	☐ ☐
FS112	(1st Large up to 100g)	4·00	4·00	☐ ☐
FS113	(Euro 20g World 10g)	4·00	4·00	☐ ☐
FS113c	(Europe up to 20g)	25·00	25·00	☐ ☐
FS114	(Europe up to 60g)	4·50	4·50	☐ ☐
FS114c	(Europe up to 100g)	10·00	10·00	☐ ☐
FS115	(Worldwide up to 20g)	4·25	4·25	☐ ☐
FS116	(Worldwide up to 60g)	5·75	5·75	☐ ☐
FS116c	(Worldwide up to 100g)	11·00	11·00	☐ ☐
FS109/FS116 *Set of 8*		30·00	30·00	☐ ☐
First Day Cover (FS109/FS112 in 4 designs)			9·50	☐

Special Pack (FS109/FS112 in 4 designs)
(P&G 17)   7·00   ☐

Nos. FS109/FS110 were each available as FT **17** or Mistletoe. Nos. FS111/FS116c were all available as Butcher's Broom and Holly.

FT **18** *Falcon*

Working Sail

2015 (18 Feb.) Multicoloured. Self-adhesive. Two phosphor bands. Designs printed in gravure by ISP Walsall, thermally printed service indicator. Perf 14 × 14½

FS117	(1st Class up to 100g)	3·75	3·75	☐ ☐
FS118	(1st Large up to 100g)	4·25	4·25	☐ ☐
FS119	(Euro 20g World 10g)	4·50	4·50	☐ ☐
FS120	(Europe up to 60g)	7·50	7·50	☐ ☐
FS121	(Europe up to 100g)	14·00	14·00	☐ ☐
FS122	(Worldwide up to 20g)	5·25	5·25	☐ ☐
FS123	(Worldwide up to 60g)	8·25	8·25	☐ ☐
FS124	(Worldwide up to 100g)	15·00	15·00	☐ ☐
FS117/FS120, FS122, FS123 *Set of 6*		30·00	30·00	☐ ☐
First Day Cover (FS117 in 6 designs)			9·50	☐

Special Pack (FS117 in strip of
6 designs) (P&G 18)   8·00   ☐

Nos. FS117/FS124 were each available in six different designs: FT **18**; *Briar, Harry, Margaret, Stag* and *Nell Morgan.*

FT **19** Lion

Heraldic Beasts

2015 (13 May) Multicoloured. Self-adhesive. Two phosphor bands. Designs printed in gravure by ISP Walsall, thermally printed service indicator. Perf 14 × 14½

FS125	(1st Class up to 100g)	3·75	3·75	☐ ☐
FS126	(1st Large up to 100g)	4·25	4·25	☐ ☐
FS127	(Euro 20g World 10g)	4·50	4·50	☐ ☐
FS128	(Europe up to 100g)	5·50	5·50	☐ ☐
FS129	(Worldwide up to 20g)	5·25	5·25	☐ ☐
FS130	(Worldwide up to 100g)	6·75	6·75	☐ ☐
FS125/FS130, *Set of 6*		27·00	27·00	☐ ☐
First Day Cover (FS125 in 6 designs)			9·50	☐

Special Pack (FS125 in strip of
6 designs) (P&G 19)   8·00   ☐

Nos. FS125/FS130 were each available in six different designs: FT **19**; Unicorn, Yale, Dragon, Falcon and Griffin.

FT **20** *Dover*

Sea Travel

2015 (16 Sept.) Multicoloured. Self-adhesive. Two phosphor bands. Designs printed in gravure by ISP Walsall, thermally printed service indicator. Perf 14 × 14½

FS131	(1st Class up to 100g)	3·75	3·75	☐ ☐
FS132	(1st Large up to 100g)	4·25	4·25	☐ ☐
FS133	(Euro 20g World 10g)	4·50	4·50	☐ ☐
FS134	(Europe up to 100g)	5·50	5·50	☐ ☐
FS135	(Worldwide up to 20g)	5·25	5·25	☐ ☐
FS136	(Worldwide up to 100g)	6·75	6·75	☐ ☐
FS131/FS136, *Set of 6*		27·00	27·00	☐ ☐
First Day Cover (FS131 in 6 designs)			9·50	☐

Special Pack (FS131 in strip of
6 designs) (P&G 20)   8·00   ☐

Nos. FS131/FS136 were each available in six different designs: FT **20**; Hong Kong, Sydney, Ha Long Bay, New York City and Venice.

Nos. FS137/FS142, Poppies, are omitted from this listing as they fall outside the scope of *Collect British Stamps*, A full listing will be found in the *Great Britain Concise Catalogue.*

FT **22** Mountain Hare

Winter Fur and Feathers

2015 (16 Nov.) Multicoloured. Self-adhesive. One phosphor band (FS143/FS144) or two phosphor bands (others). Designs printed in gravure by ISP Walsall, thermally printed service indicator. Perf 14 × 14½

FS143	(2nd Class up to 100g)	2·25	2·25	☐ ☐
FS144	(2nd Large up to 100g)	3·00	3·00	☐ ☐
FS145	(1st Class up to 100g)	3·75	3·75	☐ ☐
FS146	(1st Large up to 100g)	4·25	4·25	☐ ☐
FS147	(Euro 20g World 10g)	4·50	4·50	☐ ☐
FS148	(Europe up to 100g)	5·50	5·50	☐ ☐
FS149	(Worldwide up to 20g)	5·25	5·25	☐ ☐
FS150	(Worldwide up to 100g)	6·75	6·75	☐ ☐
FS143/FS150, *Set of 8*		28·00	28·00	☐ ☐
First Day Cover (FS143/FS146 in 4 designs)			8·00	☐

Special Pack (FS143/FS146 in 4 designs)
(P&G 21)   7·25   ☐

Nos. FS143/FS144 were each available as FT **22** or Redwing. Nos. FS145/FS146 were all available as Red Fox or Red Squirrel.

FT **23** Post boy, 1640s

Royal Mail Heritage: Transport

2016 (17 Feb.) Multicoloured. Self-adhesive. Two phosphor bands. Designs printed in gravure by ISP Walsall, thermally printed service indicator. Perf 14 × 14½

FS151	(1st Class up to 100g)	3·25	3·25	☐ ☐
FS152	(1st Large up to 100g)	3·50	3·50	☐ ☐
FS153	(Euro 20g World 10g)	3·75	3·75	☐ ☐
FS154	(Europe up to 100g)	4·50	4·50	☐ ☐
FS155	(Worldwide up to 20g)	4·25	4·25	☐ ☐
FS156	(Worldwide up to 100g)	6·25	6·25	☐ ☐
FS151/FS156 *Set of 6*		23·00	23·00	☐ ☐
First Day Cover (FS151 in 6 designs)			9·50	☐

Special Pack (FS151 in strip of 6 designs)
(P&G 22)   10·00   ☐

Nos. FS151/FS156 were each available in six different designs: FT **23**; Mail Coach, 1790s; Falmouth Packet, 1820s; Travelling Post Office, 1890s; Airmail, 1930s and Royal Mail Minivan, 1970s.

2016 (5 Aug.) As T FT **14** with background text reading, alternately, '2ndCLASS' in large lettering and 'ROYALMAIL' in small lettering, with year code. New blue background. Self-adhesive. One phosphor band (over the Queen's head). Designs printed in gravure by Walsall, thermally printed service indicator. Perf 14×14½

FS157	(2nd Class up to 100g)	2·50	2·50	☐ ☐
FS158	(2nd Large up to 100g)	2·75	2·75	☐ ☐

FT **24** Seven-spot Ladybird

Ladybirds

2016 (14 Sept.) Multicoloured. Self-adhesive. Two phosphor bands. Designs printed in gravure by ISP Walsall, thermally printed service indicator. Perf 14×14½

FS159	(1st Class up to 100g)	2·50	2·50	☐ ☐
FS160	(1st Large up to 100g)	2·75	2·75	☐ ☐
FS161	(Euro 20g World 10g)	3·00	3·00	☐ ☐
FS162	(Europe up to 100g)	3·75	3·75	☐ ☐
FS163	(Worldwide up to 20g)	3·50	3·50	☐ ☐
FS164	(Worldwide up to 100g)	5·75	5·75	☐ ☐
FS159/FS164 *Set of* 6		20·00	20·00	☐ ☐
First Day Cover (FS159 in 6 designs)			9·50	☐
Special Pack (FS159 in strip of 6 designs) (P&G 23)			9·00	☐

Nos. FS159/FS164 were each available in six different designs: FT **24**; Fourteen-spot Ladybird; Orange Ladybird; Heather Ladybird; Striped Ladybird and Water Ladybird.

FT **25** Hedgehog

Hibernating Animals

2016 (14 Nov.) Multicoloured. Self-adhesive. One phosphor band (FS163/FS164) or two phosphor bands (others). Designs printed in gravure by ISP Walsall, thermally printed service indicator. Perf 14×14½

FS165	(2nd Class up to 100g)	2·50	2·50	☐ ☐
FS166	(2nd Large up to 100g)	2·75	2·75	☐ ☐
FS167	(1st Class up to 100g)	2·75	2·75	☐ ☐
FS168	(1st Large up to 100g)	3·00	3·00	☐ ☐
FS169	(Euro 20g World 10g)	3·25	3·25	☐ ☐
FS170	(Europe up to 100g)	4·50	4·50	☐ ☐
FS171	(Worldwide up to 20g)	4·25	4·25	☐ ☐
FS172	(Worldwide up to 100g)	6·00	6·00	☐ ☐
FS165/FS172 *Set of* 8		25·00	25·00	☐ ☐
First Day Cover (FS165/FS168 in 4 designs)			8·00	☐
Special Pack (FS165/FS168 in 4 designs) (P&G 24)			9·00	☐

Nos. FS165/FS166 were each available as FT **25** or Grass Snake.

Nos. FS167/FS172 were all available as Dormouse or Brown Long-eared Bat.

FT **26** Travelling Post Office: bag exchange

Royal Mail Heritage: Mail by Rail

2017 (15 Feb.) Multicoloured. Self-adhesive. Two phosphor bands. Designs printed in gravure by ISP Walsall, thermally printed service indicator. Perf 14×14½

FS173	(1st Class up to 100g)	2·50	2·50	☐ ☐
FS174	(1st Large up to 100g)	2·75	2·75	☐ ☐
FS175	(Euro 20g World 10g)	3·00	3·00	☐ ☐
FS176	(Europe up to 100g)	3·75	3·75	☐ ☐
FS177	(Worldwide up to 20g)	3·50	3·50	☐ ☐
FS178	(Worldwide up to 100g)	5·75	5·75	☐ ☐
FS173/FS178 *Set of* 6		20·00	20·00	☐ ☐
First Day Cover (FS173 in 6 designs)			7·50	☐
Special Pack (FS173 in strip of 6 designs) (P&G 25)			9·00	☐

Nos. FS173/FS178 were each available in six different designs: FT **26**; Post Office (London) Railway; Night Mail: Poster; Travelling Post Office: Loading; Travelling Post Office: sorting and Travelling Post Office: on the move.

FT **27** Machin Commemorative Head

Machin Anniversary 1967–2017

2017 (5 June) Self-adhesive. Two phosphor bands. Designs printed in gravure by ISP Walsall, thermally printed service indicator. Perf 14×14½

FS179	(1st Class up to 100g)	2·25	2·25	☐ ☐
FS180	(1st Large up to 100g)	2·75	2·75	☐ ☐
FS181	(Euro 20g World 10g)	3·00	3·00	☐ ☐
FS182	(Europe up to 100g)	3·50	3·50	☐ ☐
FS183	(Worldwide up to 20g)	3·25	3·25	☐ ☐
FS184	(Worldwide up to 100g)	5·25	5·25	☐ ☐
FS179/FS184 *Set of* 6		19·00	19·00	☐ ☐
First Day Cover (FS179 in 6 designs)			7·50	☐
Special Pack (FS179 in strip of 6 designs) (P&G 26)			10·00	☐

Nos. FS179/FS184 were each available in six different colours: orange-brown, light olive, violet, deep sepia, bright emerald and drab.

FT **28** First UK Aerial Mail, 1911

Royal Mail Heritage: Mail by Air

2017 (13 Sept.) Multicoloured. Self-adhesive. Two phosphor bands. Designs printed in gravure by ISP Walsall, thermally printed service indicator. Perf 14×14½

FS185	(1st Class up to 100g)	2·25	2·25	☐ ☐
FS186	(1st Large up to 100g)	2·75	2·75	☐ ☐
FS187	(Euro 20g World 10g)	3·00	3·00	☐ ☐
FS188	(Europe up to 100g)	3·50	3·50	☐ ☐
FS189	(Worldwide up to 20g)	3·25	3·25	☐ ☐
FS190	(Worldwide up to 100g)	5·25	5·25	☐ ☐
FS185/FS190 *Set of* 6		18·00	18·00	☐ ☐
First Day Cover (FS185 in 6 designs)			7·50	☐
Special Pack (FS185 in strip of 6 designs) (P&G 27)			6·50	☐

Nos. FS185/FS190 were each available in six different designs: FT **28**; Military Mail Flight, 1919; International Airmail, 1933; Domestic Airmail, 1934; Flying Boat Airmail, 1937 and Datapost Service, 1980s.

British Flora (3rd Series). Winter Greenery (reissued)

2017 (13 Nov.) FS109/FS110 reissued with blue background text reading, alternatively, '2ndCLASS' in large lettering and 'ROYALMAIL' in small lettering. One phosphor band at right. Designs printed gravure by ISP Walsall, thermally printed service indicator. Perf 14×14½.

FS191	(2nd Class up to 100g)	2·10	2·10	☐	☐
FS192	(2nd Large up to 100g)	2·25	2·25	☐	☐

Nos. FS191/FS192 were each available as FT **17** or Mistletoe.

Nos. FS111/FS113, FS114c/FS115 and FS116c were also reissued (as Nos. FS193/FS198) with the 'ROYALMAIL' background text in a different shade. These are outside the scope of this catalogue.

FT **29** The Iron Throne – Ice

Game of Thrones

2018 (23 Jan.) Multicoloured. Self-adhesive. One phosphor band at right (FS199/FS200) or two phosphor bands (others). Designs printed gravure by ISP Walsall, thermally printed service indicator. Perf 14×14½.

FS199	(2nd Class up to 100g)	5·25	5·25	☐	☐
FS200	(2nd Large up to 100g)	5·50	5·50	☐	☐
FS201	(1st Class up to 100g)	5·25	5·25	☐	☐
FS202	(1st Large up to 100g)	5·75	5·75	☐	☐
FS203	(Euro 20g World 10g)	6·00	6·00	☐	☐
FS204	(Europe up to 100g)	6·25	6·25	☐	☐
FS205	(Worldwide up to 20g)	6·25	6·25	☐	☐
FS206	(Worldwide up to 100g)	7·00	7·00	☐	☐
FS199/FS206 *Set of* 8		45·00	45·00	☐	☐
First Day Cover (FS199 and FS201)			4·00		☐
Special Pack (FS199 and FS201) (P&G 28)		5·00		☐	

Nos. FS199/FS200 were each available in one blue design, FT **29**.

Nos. FS201/FS206 were each available in one yellow-orange design depicting The Iron Throne – Fire.

FT **30** Packet *Antelope*, 1780

Royal Mail Heritage: Mail by Sea

2018 (14 Feb.) Multicoloured. Self-adhesive. Two phosphor bands. Designs printed gravure by ISP Walsall, thermally printed service indicator. Perf 14×14½.

FS207	(1st Class up to 100g)	2·25	2·25	☐	☐
FS208	(1st Class up to 100g)	2·75	2·75	☐	☐
FS209	(Euro 20g World 10g)	3·00	3·00	☐	☐
FS210	(Europe up to 100g)	3·50	3·50	☐	☐
FS211	(Worldwide up to 20g)	3·25	3·25	☐	☐
FS212	(Worldwide up to 100g)	5·25	5·25	☐	☐
FS207/FS212 *Set of* 6		18·00	18·00	☐	☐
First Day Cover (FS207 in 6 designs)			7·50		☐
Special Pack (FS207 in strip of 6 designs)					
(P&G 29)		6·50		☐	

Nos. FS207/FS212 were each available in six different designs: FT **30**, SS *Great Western*, 1838; SS *Britannia*, 1887; RMS *Olympic*, 1911; RMS *Queen Mary*, 1936; RMS *St Helena*, 1990.

1st Class up to 100g

FT **31** Pentacycle, 1882

Royal Mail Heritage: Mail by Bike

2018 (12 Sept.) Multicoloured, Self-adhesive. Two phosphor bands. Designs printed gravure by ISP Walsall, thermally printed service indicator. Perf 14×14½.

FS213	(1st Class up to 100g)	2·25	2·25	☐	☐
FS214	(1st Large up to 100g)	2·75	2·75	☐	☐
FS215	(Euro 20g World 10g)	3·00	3·00	☐	☐
FS216	(Europe up to 100g)	3·50	3·50	☐	☐
FS217	(Worldwide up to 20g)	3·25	3·25	☐	☐
FS218	(Worldwide up to 100g)	5·25	5·25	☐	☐
FS213/FS218 *Set of* 6		18·00	18·00	☐	☐
First Day Cover (FS213 in 6 designs)			7·50		☐
Special Pack (FS213 in strip of 6 designs)					
(P&G 30)		9·50		☐	

Nos. FS213/FS218 were each available in six different designs: FT **31**; Motorcycle and trailer, 1902; Tricycle and basket, 1920; Bicycle, 1948; Motorcycle, 1965; Quad bike, 2002.

Stanley Gibbons Regent Binder

The classic Springback binder, a favourite of our collectors for housing their collections.

Size: 267 x 293mm

Leaves and Pages for these binders can be found on our website

Binder Colour	product code	price
●	RREG-BLU	£29.95
●	RREG-RED	£29.95

STANLEY GIBBONS
THE HOME OF STAMP COLLECTING

To order, call **01425 472 363**
email **orders@stanleygibbons.com**
or visit **stanleygibbons.com**

STANLEY GIBBONS | 399 Strand | London | WC2R 0LX
www.stanleygibbons.com

 @StanleyGibbons   /StanleyGibbonsGroup   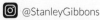 @StanleyGibbons

OFFICIAL STAMPS

Various stamps of Queen Victoria and King Edward VII overprinted in Black.

I.R.	**I. R.**	**O.W.**
OFFICIAL	**OFFICIAL**	**OFFICIAL**
(O **1**)	(O **2**)	(O **3**)

ARMY **ARMY**

OFFICIAL	**OFFICIAL**	**GOVT PARCELS**
(O **4**)	(O **5**)	(O **7**)

BOARD

OF

EDUCATION	**OFFICIAL**	**OFFICIAL**
(O **8**)	(O **9**)	(O **10**)

R.H. **ADMIRALTY**

1 Inland Revenue

Overprinted with T O **1** or T O **2** (5s., 10s., £1)

1882–1901 Queen Victoria

O2	52	½d. green	90·00	40·00	
O5		½d. blue	£110	35·00	
O13	71	½d. vermilion	15·00	7·00	
O17		½d. green	20·00	15·00	
O3	57	1d. lilac (Die II)	8·00	6·00	
O6	64	2½d. lilac	£525	£180	
O14	74	2½d. purple on blue	£175	30·00	
O4	43	6d. grey (Plate 18)	£575	£140	
O18	79	6d. purple on red	£625	£150	
O7	65	1s. green	£6000	£1900	
O15	82	1s. green	£1000	£375	
O19		1s. green and red	£4250	£1800	
O9	59	5s. red	£12000	£2500	
O10	60	10s. blue	£11500	£3750	
O11	61	£1 brown (Wmk Crowns)	£60000	£22000	
O12		£1 brown (Wmk Orbs)	£85000	£30000	
O16		£1 green	£12500	£2500	

1902–04 King Edward VII

O20	83	½d. blue-green	32·00	4·50	
O21		1d. red	22·00	3·00	
O22	86	2½d. blue	£1000	£275	
O23	83	6d. purple	£500000	£300000	
O24	93	1s. green and red	£3750	£900	
O25	95	5s. red	£38000	£10000	
O26	96	10s. blue	£85000	£45000	
O27	97	£1 green	£50000	£18000	

2 Office of Works
Overprinted with T O **3**

1896–1902 Queen Victoria

O31	71	½d. vermilion	£350	£150	
O32		½d. green	£475	£225	
O33	57	1d. lilac (Die II)	£500	£150	
O34	78	5d. dull purple and blue	£4000	£1400	
O35	81	10d. dull purple and red	£7250	£2250	

1902–03 King Edward VII

O36	83	½d. blue-green	£575	£180	
O37		1d. red	£575	£180	
O38	85	2d. green and red	£2000	£450	
O39	86	2½d. blue	£3500	£675	
O40	92	10d. purple and red	£40000	£7000	

3 Army
Overprinted with T O **4** (½d., 1d.) or T O **5** (2½d., 6d.)

1896–1901 Queen Victoria

O41	71	½d. vermilion	8·00	3·00	
O42		½d. green	10·00	15·00	
O43	57	1d. lilac (Die II)	8·00	7·00	
O44	74	2½d. purple on blue	50·00	35·00	
O45	79	6d. purple on red	£110	60·00	

Overprinted with T O **4**

1902 King Edward VII

O48	83	½d. blue-green	6·00	2·50	
O49		1d. red	6·00	2·50	
O50		6d. purple	£175	80·00	

4 Government Parcels
Overprinted with T O **7**

1883–1900 Queen Victoria

O69	57	1d. lilac (Die II)	£100	30·00	
O61	62	1½d. lilac	£400	£100	
O65	72	1½d. purple and green	£170	30·00	
O70	73	2d. green and red	£250	50·00	
O71	77	4½d. green and red	£400	£275	
O62	63	6d. green	£3500	£1400	
O66	79	6d. purple on red	£275	75·00	
O63	64	9d. green	£2750	£1200	
O67	80	9d. purple and blue	£425	£120	
O64	44	1s. brown (Plate 13)	£1750	£300	
O64c		1s. brown (Plate 14)	£3500	£600	
O68	82	1s. green	£700	£275	
O72		1s. green and red	£650	£275	

1902 King Edward VII

O74	83	1d. red	75·00	22·00	
O75	85	2d. green and red	£225	60·00	
O76	83	6d. purple	£275	60·00	
O77	91	9d. purple and blue	£650	£175	
O78	93	1s. green and red	£1350	£300	

5 Board of Education
Overprinted with T O **8**

1902 Queen Victoria

O81	78	5d. dull purple and blue	£5750	£1500	
O82	82	1s. green and red	£12000	£6000	

1902–04 King Edward VII

O83	83	½d. blue-green	£180	45·00	
O84		1d. red	£180	45·00	
O85	86	2½d. blue	£5000	£475	
O86	89	5d. purple and blue	£30000	£8500	
O87	93	1s. green and red	£160000		

6 Royal Household
Overprinted with T O **9**

1902 King Edward VII

O91	83	½d. blue-green	£375	£200	
O92		1d. red	£325	£175	

7 Admiralty
Overprinted with T O **10**

1903 King Edward VII

O101	**83**	½d. blue-green	30·00	15·00	☐	☐
O102		1d. red	20·00	10·00	☐	☐
O103	**84**	1½d. purple and green	£325	£150	☐	☐
O104	**85**	2d. green and red	£350	£160	☐	☐
O105	**86**	2½d. blue	£475	£150	☐	☐
O106	**87**	3d. purple on yellow	£425	£160	☐	☐

Prestige and Sponsored Booklets
– a Simplified listing

On 1 December 1969 a new style of large-size booklet was issued, entitled Stamps for Cooks, sponsored by the Milk Marketing Board and containing recipes and stamps to a value of £1. The booklet contained one pane in a *se-tenant* combination that was not available from any other source, ensuring that sales to stamp collectors were high, even if those to cooks were probably rather limited!

In spite of this success, however, it was 1972 before a second sponsored booklet, The Story of Wedgwood was issued, providing the only source of the ½p. Machin definitive with one phosphor band at left. Nearly eight years were to pass before the same company sponsored a second Story of Wedgwood booklet, followed two years later by Stanley Gibbons with Story of Stanley Gibbons.

From then on, sponsored large-size booklets became an annual event, generally containing at least one stamp which was not available from any other source. In 1989 Royal Mail themselves became the 'sponsors' of each new booklet, which were by then widely known among collectors simply as 'Prestige Booklets'. Their frequency of issue increased steadily, until in 2009 four such booklets were issued.

In 2011, with the issue of the Morris & Co booklet, Royal Mail introduced an additional charge, over and above the face value of the stamps contained in them to cover the costs of manufacturing these booklets and with this change the Stanley Gibbons catalogue number prefix was altered from 'DX' to 'DY'.

This simplified checklist provides a complete listing of the Prestige and Sponsored booklets issued to the end of 2017.

DX**3**

ZP1a	£1 Stamps for Cooks *(1.2.69)*	6·50	☐
DX1	£1 The Story of Wedgwood *(24.5.72)*	60·00	☐
DX2	£3 The Story of Wedgwood *(16.4.80)*	3·75	☐
DX3	£4 Story of Stanley Gibbons *(19.5.82)*	5·00	☐
DX4	£4 Story of the Royal Mint *(14.9.83)*	5·00	☐
DX5	£4 The Story of our Christian Heritage *(4.9.84)*	13·00	☐
DX6	£5 The Story of The Times *(8.1.85)*	8·50	☐
DX7	£5 The Story of British Rail *(18.3.86)*	10·00	☐
DX8	£5 The Story of P&O *(3.3.87)*	10·00	☐
DX9	£5 The Story of The Financial Times *(9.2.88)*	16·00	☐
DX10	£5 The Scots Connection *(21.3.89)*	10·00	☐
DX11	£5 London Life *(20.3.90)*	12·50	☐

DX12	£6	Alias Agatha Christie	
		(19.3.91)	9·00
DX13	£6	Cymru-Wales *(25.2.92)*	9·00
DX14	£6	Tolkien, the Centenary	
		(27.10.92)	9·00
DX15	£5·64	The Story of Beatrix Potter	
		(10.8.93)	15·00
DX16	£6·04	Northern Ireland *(26.7.94)*	12·00
DX17	£6	The National Trust *(25.4.95)*	12·00
DX18	£6·48	European Football	
		Championship *(14.5.96)*	9·00
DX19	£6·15	Celebrating 75 years of the	
		BBC *(23.9.97)*	13·50
DX20	£7·49	The Wilding Definitives	
		(10.3.98)	11·00
DX21	£6·16	Breaking Barriers *(13.10.98)*	18·00
DX22	£7·54	Profile on Print *(16.2.99)*	25·00
DX23	£6·99	World Changers *(21.9.99)*	17·00
DX24	£7·50	Special by Design *(15.2.00)*	20·00
DX25	£7·03	The Life of the Century	
		(4.8.00)	15·00
DX26	£7·00	A Treasury of Trees *(18.9.00)*	17·00
DX27	£6·76	Unseen & Unheard	
		(22.10.01)	20·00
DX28	£7·29	A Gracious Accession	
		(6.2.02)	22·50
DX29	£6·83	Across the Universe	
		(24.9.02)	24·00
DX30	£6·99	Microcosmos *(25.2.03)*	26·00
DX31	£7·46	A Perfect Coronation	
		(2.6.03)	38·00
DX32	£7·44	Letters by Night *(16.3.04)*	15·00
DX33	£7·23	The Glory of the Garden	
		(25.5.04)	20·00
DX34	£7·43	The Brontë Sisters *(24.2.05)*	15·00
DX35	£7·26	Battle of Trafalgar *(18.10.05)*	16·00
DX36	£7·40	Isambard Kingdom Brunel	
		(23.2.06)	15·00
DX37	£7·44	Victoria Cross *(21.9.06)*	15·00
DX38	£7·49	World of Invention *(1.3.07)*	18·00
DX39	£7·66	The Machin, the Making of	
		a Masterpiece *(5.6.07)*	18·00
DX40	£7·66	British Army Uniforms	
		(20.9.07)	16·00
DX41	£7·40	Ian Fleming's James Bond	
		(8.1.08)	16·00
DX42	£7·15	Pilot to Plane, RAF	
		Uniforms *(18.9.08)*	15·00
DX43	£9·72	50th Anniversary of	
		Country Definitives *(29.9.08)*	24·00
DX44	£7·68	British Design Classics	
		(13.1.09)	24·00
DX45	£7·75	Charles Darwin *(12.2.09)*	40·00
DX46	£8·18	Treasures of the Archive	
		(18.8.09)	22·00
DX47	£7·93	Royal Navy Uniforms	
		(17.9.09)	20·00
DX48	£8·06	Classic Album Covers	
		(7.1.10)	35·00
DX49	£7·72	The Royal Society *(25.2.10)*	17·00
DX50	£11·15	King George V *(8.5.10)*	28·00
DX51	£9·76	Britain Alone *(13.5.10)*	20·00
DX52	£9·05	WWF, For a Living Planet	
		(22.3.11)	25·00
DY1	£9·99	Morris & Co *(5.5.11)*	15·00
DY2	£9·97	First United Kingdom	
		Aerial Post *(9.9.11)*	40·00
DY3	£11·47	Roald Dahl *(10.1.12)*	20·00
DY4	£12·77	The Diamond Jubilee	
		(31.5.12)	20·00
DY5	£10·71	Olympic and Paralympic	
		Games *(27.7.12)*	35·00

DY6	£13·77	50 Years of *Doctor Who*	
		(26.3.13)	24·00
DY7	£11·11	Football Heroes *(9.5.13)*	26·00
DY8	£11·19	Merchant Navy *(19.9.13)*	18·00
DY9	£13·97	Classic Locomotives	
		(20.2.14)	35·00
DY10	£11·39	Buckingham Palace	
		(15.4.14)	16·00
DY11	£11·30	Centenary of the First	
		World War *(28.7.14)*	16·00
DY12	£14·50	Inventive Britain *(19.2.15)*	22·00
DY13	£13·96	Centenary of the	
		First World War (2nd issue)	
		(14.5.15)	22·00
DY14	£14·47	Bicentenary of the Battle of	
		Waterloo *(18.6.15)*	26·00
DY15	£16·99	The Making of *Star Wars*	
		The British Story *(17.12.15)*	26·00
DY16	£16·36	500 Years of Royal Mail	
		(18.2.16)	25·00
DY17	£15·11	90th Birthday of Queen	
		Elizabeth II *(21.4.16)*	26·00
DY18	£16·49	Centenary of the First	
		World War (3rd issue)	
		(21.6.16)	28·00
DY19	£15·37	The Tale of Beatrix Potter	
		(28.7.16)	24·00
DY20	£14·58	Windsor Castle *(15.2.17)*	24·00
DY21	£15·14	50th Anniversary of the	
		Machin Definitive *(5.6.17)*	30·00
DY22	£15·41	Centenary of the First	
		World War (4th issue)	
		(31.7.17)	24·00
DY23	£15·99	*Star Wars*. The Making	
		of the Droids, Aliens and	
		Creatures *(14.12.17)*	24·00
DY24	£13·95	*Game of Thrones* *(23.1.18)*	22·00
DY25	£18·69	Centenary of the RAF	
		(20.3.18)	30·00
DY26	£15·65	Centenary of the First	
		World War (5th issue)	
		(13.9.18)	24·00
DY27	£15·50	Harry Potter *(4.12.18)*	24·00
DY28	£13·10	500th Death Anniversary	
		of Leonardo da Vinci	
		(13.2.19)	22·00
DY29	£17·45	Marvel *(14.3.19)*	26·00
DY30	£17·20	Birth Bicentenary of Queen	
		Victoria *(24.5.19)*	25·00
DY31	£17·65	*Star Wars* the Making of	
		the Vehicles *(26.11.19)*	25·00
DY32	£16·10	Visions of the Universe.	
		Bicentenary of the Royal	
		Astronomical Society	
		(11.2.20)	26·00
DY33	£16·99	James Bond *(17.3.20)*	25·00
DY34	£19·80	75th Anniversary of the	
		Second World War *(8.5.20)*	25·00
DY35	£19·10	Queen (rock band) *(9.7.20)*	25·00
DY36	£18·35	*Star Trek* *(13.11.20)*	25·00

Philatelic, Numismatic and Philatelic Medallic Covers

On 2 June 1993 Royal Mail and the Royal Mint prepared a commemorative cover to celebrate the 40th anniversary of the Coronation of Her Majesty The Queen. The cover bore the Royal Mint's Coronation Anniversary Crown and the £10 'Britannia' stamp, issued on 2 March 1993 (No. 1658).

On 1 March 1994 a similar cover was produced for the 25th Anniversary of the Investiture of HRH The Prince of Wales. The cover bore the set of five stamps issued on that date

(Nos. 1810/1814), showing paintings by Prince Charles, and a commemorative medal struck by the Royal Mint.

So began a series of Philatelic Numismatic Covers (PNC) and Philatelic Medallic Covers (PMC) produced by Royal Mail and the Royal Mint.

This listing comprises only those jointly produced covers sold by the Philatelic Bureau. Privately sponsored covers incorporating coins or medals including those sponsored by the Royal Mint alone, are outside its scope.

No.	Date	Issue	Stamps	Coin/Medal	Price
RMC1	2.6.93	Coronation 40th Anniversary	1658	£5 Coin	18·00
RMC2	1.3.94	Prince of Wales Investiture 25th Anniversary	1810/1814	Medal	22·00
RMC3	27.7.94	Bank of England 300th Anniversary	1671×4 + label	£2 Coin	18·00
RMC4	20.5.95	R. J. Mitchell Birth Centenary	1671×4 + label	Medal	14·00
RMC5	15.8.95	End of Second World War 50th Anniversary	1873, 1875	£2 Coin	14·00
RMC6	29.10.95	William Wyon Birth Bicentenary	Y1743	Medal	14·00
RMC7	21.4.96	Queen's 70th Birthday	1671×4 + label	£5 Coin	17·00
RMC8	8.6.96	European Football Championship	1925/1929	£2 Coin	18·00
RMC9	1.10/3.11.96	Classic Sports Cars	1945/1949	Medal	17·00
RMC10	28.1.97	King Henry VIII 450th Death Anniversary	1965/1971	£1 Coin	14·00
RMC11	30.6.97	Transfer of Hong Kong to Chinese Rule	1671×4 + label	Hong Kong $5 Coin	22·00
RMC12	23.8.97	British Aircraft Designers	1984/1988	£2 Coin	14·00
RMC13	20.11.97	Royal Golden Wedding	2011/2014	£5 Coin	17·00
RMC14	24.2.98	Order of the Garter 650th Anniversary	2026/2030	£1 Coin	£100
RMC15	5.7.98	NHS 50th Anniversary	2046/2049	50p. Coin	25·00
RMC16	25.8.98	Notting Hill Carnival	2055/2058	50p. Coin	14·00
RMC17	14.11.98	HRH Prince of Wales 50th Birthday	1671×4 + label	£5 Coin	17·00
RMC18	12.5.99	Berlin Airlift 50th Anniversary	1671×4 + label	Medal	14·00
RMC19	1.7.99	New Scottish Parliament Building	S94/S97	£1 Coin	35·00
RMC20	1.10.99	Rugby World Cup, Wales	1671×4 + label	£2 Coin	14·00
RMC21	31.12.99	Millennium	**MS**2123	£5 Coin	12·00
RMC22	4.4.00	National Botanic Garden of Wales	2124×4 + label	£1 Coin	16·00
RMC23	14.8.00	150 Years of Public Libraries	2116, 2121, 2100	50p. Coin	14·00
RMC24	4.8.00	Queen Mother's 100th Birthday	**MS**2161	£5 Coin	17·00
RMC25	1.1.01	*Archers* Radio Programme 50th Anniversary	2107/2108, 2110	Medal	14·00
RMC26	24.5.01	RN Submarine Service Centenary	2202/2205	Medal	17·00
RMC27	20.6.01	Queen Victoria Death Centenary	2133a×2 + label	£5 Coin	17·00
RMC28	2.10.01	Northern Ireland	NI89/NI92	£1 Coin	10·00
RMC29	6.2.02	Golden Jubilee	2253/2257	£5 Coin	15·00
RMC29a	6.2.02	Golden Jubilee	2258/2259	£5 Coin and £5 note	40·00
RMC30	31.5.02	World Cup Football, Japan & Korea	2291, **MS**2292	£1 Coin	11·00
RMC31	16.7.02	17th Commonwealth Games, Manchester	2299/2303	4×£2 Coins	£160
RMC32	11.12.02	Queen Mother Commemoration	2280/2283	£5 Coin	17·00
RMC33	25.2.03	Discovery of DNA 50th Anniversary	2343/2347	£2 Coin	14·00
RMC34	2.6.03	Coronation 50th Anniversary	2368/2377	£5 Coin	17·00
RMC35	27.8.03	Extreme Endeavours	2360/2365	£1 Coin	14·00
RMC36	7.10.03	British Museum 250th Anniversary	2404/2409	Medal	14·00
RMC37	13.1.04	Classic Locomotives	2417/2422	£2 Coin	14·00
RMC38	6.4.04	Entente Cordiale Centenary	2446/2447 + France 50c., 75c.	£5 Coin	20·00
RMC39	13.4.04	Ocean Liners	2448/2453	Medal	14·00
RMC40	25.5.04	RHS Bicentenary	2456/2461	Medal	14·00
RMC41	30.11.04	Scotland Definitive	S109/S110, S112/S119	£1 Coin	25·00
RMC42	24.2.05	Charlotte Brontë 150th Death Anniversary	2518/2523	50p. Coin	15·00
RMC43	1.3.05	Wales Definitive	W98/W9, W101/W108	£1 Coin	16·00
RMC44	21.4.05	World Heritage Sites	2532/2535 + Australia 2×50c. & 2×$1	50p. Coin + Australia 50c.	40·00
RMC45	5.7.05	End of the War 60th Anniversary	**MS**2547	Medal and £2 Coin	22·50
RMC46	18.10.05	Battle of Trafalgar Bicentenary	2574/2579	2×£5 Coins	40·00
RMC47	23.2.06	Brunel Birth Bicentenary	2607/2612	2×£2 Coins	17·00
RMC48	17.3.06	Northern Ireland Definitive	NI94/NI95, NI98, NI100	£1 Coin	18·00
RMC49	21.4.06	Queen's 80th Birthday	2620/2627	£5 Coin	19·00
RMC50	6.6.06	World Cup Football	2628/2633	Medal	16·00
RMC51	18.7.06	National Portrait Gallery 150th Anniversary	2640/2649	Medal	16·00
RMC52	21.9.06	Victoria Cross 150th Anniversary	2659/2664	2×50p. Coins	20·00
RMC53	16.1.07	Act of Union 300th Anniversary	6×1st as 2570 but litho	£2 Coin	16·00
RMC54	13.2.07	*The Sky at Night* 50th Anniversary	2709/2714	Medal	16·00
RMC55	22.3.07	Abolition of the Slave Trade Bicentenary	2728/2733	£2 Coin	35·00
RMC56	23.4.07	England Definitive	EN6/EN7, EN12, EN18	£1 Coin	21·00
RMC57	5.6.07	First Machin Stamps 40th Anniversary	2741	Medal	16·00
RMC58	3.7.07	British Motor Racing	2744/2749	Medal	16·00

No.	Date	Issue	Stamps	Coin/Medal	Price
RMC59	26.7.07	Scouting Centenary	2758/2763	50p. Coin	20·00
RMC60	20.11.07	Diamond Wedding	2780/2786	£5 Coin	28·00
RMC61	1.4.08	Territorial Army Centenary	2774/2776	Medal	16·00
RMC62	13.5.08	St Paul's Cathedral 300th Anniversary	**MS**2847	Medal	16·00
RMC63	5.6.08	First Machin Coin 40th Anniversary	2741	Medal	16·00
RMC64	17.7.08	Farnborough A Celebration of Aviation	2855/2860	Medal	16·00
RMC65	24.7.08	1908 Olympic Games, London Centenary	1668x4	£2 Coin	28·00
RMC66	29.9.08	Country Definitives 50th Anniversary and £1 Coin 25th Anniversary	**MS**NI153	£1 Coin	18·00
RMC67	6.11.08	Armistice 90th Anniversary	2883/2885	Medal	16·00
RMC68	13.11.09	Mini car 50th Anniversary	2889x2	Medal	17·00
RMC69	22.1.09	Robert Burns 250th Birth Anniversary	**MS**S157	£2 Coin	32·00
RMC70	12.2.09	Charles Darwin Birth Bicentenary	2898/2903	£2 Coin	35·00
RMC71	2.3.09	First Concorde Test Flight 40th Anniversary	2891x2	Medal	17·00
RMC72	21.4.09	Accession of Henry VIII 500th Anniversary and Accession of Elizabeth I 450th Anniversary	2925, 2929 2×£5	Coins	35·00
RMC73	19.5.09	Royal Botanic Gardens, Kew 250th Anniversary	**MS**2941	50p. Coin	£275
RMC74	1.9.09	Fire and Rescue Service	2958/2963	Medal	17·00
RMC75	18.9.09	Big Ben 150th Anniversary	2805 + label	Medal	17·00
RMC76	22.10.09	Countdown to London 2012 Olympic Games I The countdown begins...	2981/2990	£5 Coin	20·00
RMC77	1.12.09	High value Security Definitives	U2913/U2916	£1 Coin	24·00
RMC78	2.2.10	Girlguiding Centenary	**MS**3025	50p. Coin	20·00
RMC79	25.2.10	Royal Society 350th Anniversary	3026/3035	Medal	20·00
RMC80	11.3.10	Battersea Cats and Dogs Home 150th Anniversary	3036/3045	Medal	20·00
RMC81	21.4.10	City of London	As 1st St George's flag stamp from **MS**EN50 but self-adhesive+label	£1 Coin	27·00
RMC82	13.5.10	Dunkirk	**MS**3086	Medal	20·00
RMC83	27.7.10	Countdown to London 2012 Olympic Games II The Games spring to life...	3097/3106	£5 Coin	24·00
RMC84	1.8.10	Florence Nightingale	2805 + label	£2 Coin	32·00
RMC85	12.10.10	Olympic and Paralympic Sports I. Athletics – Track	2983	50p. Coin	13·00
RMC86	12.10.10	Olympic and Paralympic Sports II Cycling	3101	50p. Coin	13·00
RMC87	30.11.10	Olympic and Paralympic Sports III Football	3104	50p. Coin	13·00
RMC88	30.11.10	Olympic and Paralympic Sports IV Boccia	2985	50p. Coin	13·00
RMC89	11.1.11	F.A.B. The Genius of Gerry Anderson	**MS**3142	Medal	20·00
RMC90	1.2.11	Olympic and Paralympic Sports V Weightlifting	2989	50p. Coin	13·00
RMC91	1.2.11	Olympic and Paralympic Sports VI Hockey	3103	50p. Coin	13·00
RMC92	17.3.11	City of Belfast	NI123	£1 Coin	28·00
RMC93	22.3.11	WWF 50th Anniversary	**MS**3172	50p. Coin	22·00
RMC94	24.3.11	Olympic and Paralympic Sports VII Shooting	3098	50p. Coin	13·00
RMC95	24.3.11	Olympic and Paralympic Sports VIII Goalball	3105	50p. Coin	13·00
RMC96	21.4.11	Royal Wedding	**MS**3180	£5 Coin	32·00
RMC97	26.5.11	Olympic and Paralympic Sports IX Taekwondo	3100	50p. Coin	13·00
RMC98	26.5.11	Olympic and Paralympic Sports X Boxing	3106	50p. Coin	13·00
RMC99	14.6.11	Thomas the Tank Engine	3187/3192	Medal	20·00
RMC100	27.7.11	Countdown to London 2012 Olympic Games IV The final push to the line	3195/3204	£5 Coin	22·00
RMC101	27.7.11	Olympic and Paralympic Sports XI Wrestling	3199	50p. Coin	13·00
RMC102	27.7.11	Olympic and Paralympic Sports XII Handball	3204	50p. Coin	13·00
RMC103	23.8.11	Restoration of the Monarchy	3207/3214	£5 Coin	22·00
RMC104	22.9.11	Olympic and Paralympic Sports XIII Basketball	2990	50p. Coin	13·00
RMC105	22.9.11	Olympic and Paralympic Sports XIV Modern Pentathlon	3099	50p. Coin	13·00
RMC106	6.10.11	500th Anniversary of Launch of *Mary Rose*	2925 and *Mary Rose* stamp from **MS**2930	£2 Coin	60·00
RMC107	8.11.11	Christmas 400th Anniversary of the King James Bible	3237/3243	£2 coin	60·00
RMC108	29.11.11	Olympic and Paralympic Sports XV Canoeing	2981	50p. coin	13·00
RMC109	29.11.11	Olympic and Paralympic Sports XVI Archery	2982	50p. coin	13·00
RMC110	30.11.11	City of Edinburgh	S110 + label	£1 coin	22·00
RMC111	5.1.12	Olympic and Paralympic Games	3250/3253	£2 coin	24·00
RMC112	12.1.12	Olympic and Paralympic Sports XVII Aquatics	2984	50p. coin	13·00
RMC113	12.1.12	Olympic and Paralympic Sports XVIII Rowing	3097	50p. coin	13·00
RMC114	28.2.12	Olympic and Paralympic Sports XIX Sailing	3195	50p. coin	13·00
RMC115	28.2.12	Olympic and Paralympic Sports XX Badminton	2988	50p. coin	13·00
RMC116	1.3.12	City of Cardiff	W99+label	£1 coin	22·00
RMC117	1.4.12	Olympic and Paralympic Sports XXI Judo	2986	50p. coin	13·00
RMC118	1.4.12	Olympic and Paralympic Sports XXII Triathlon	3203	50p. coin	13·00
RMC119	6.5.12	Olympic and Paralympic Sports XXIII Wheelchair rugby	3198	50p. coin	13·00
RMC120	6.5.12	Olympic and Paralympic Sports XXIV Volleyball	3197	50p. coin	13·00
RMC121	31.5.12	Diamond Jubilee	3319/3326	£5 coin	20·00
RMC122	12.6.12	Olympic and Paralympic Sports XXV Equestrian	2987	50p. coin	13·00
RMC123	12.6.12	Olympic and Paralympic Sports XXVI Table Tennis	3102	50p. coin	13·00
RMC124	19.6.12	Charles Dickens Birth Bicentenary	3330/3335	£2 coin	28·00
RMC125	27.7.12	Olympic and Paralympic Sports XXVII Wheelchair Tennis	3200	50p. coin	13·00
RMC126	27.7.12	Olympic and Paralympic Sports XXVIII Fencing	3201	50p. coin	13·00

No.	Date	Issue	Stamps	Coin/Medal	Price
RMC127	27.7.12	Countdown to London 2012 Olympic Games IV. Crossing the Finishing Line	MS3341	£5 coin and £5 silver proof coin	20.00
RMC128	28.8.12	Olympic and Paralympic Sports XXIX Gymnastics	3202	50p. coin	13.00
RMC129	28.8.12	Olympic and Paralympic Sports XXX Athletics – Field	3196	50p. coin	13.00
RMC130	9.1.13	150th Anniversary of the London Underground	3423/3428	2×£2 Coins	40.00
RMC131	30.5.13	60th Anniversary of the Coronation. Six Decades of Royal Portraits	3491/3496	£2 Coin	26.00
RMC132	10.10.13	Dinosaurs	3532/3541	Medal	38.00
RMC133	22.11.13	Birth Centenary of Benjamin Britten	3459	50p. Coin	40.00
RMC134	7.1.14	Classic Children's TV	3552/3563	Medal	30.00
RMC135	15.4.14	Buckingham Palace	3589/3594	Medal	26.00
RMC136	17.7.14	Commonwealth Games, Glasgow	3619/3624	50p. coin	26.00
RMC137	28.7.14	Centenary of the First World War	3626/3631	£2 coin	26.00
RMC138	23.9.14	Ryder Cup, Gleneagles	S158	Medal	22.00
RMC139	18.9.14	500th Anniversary of Trinity House	3638	£2 coin	22.00
RMC140	24.1.15	50th Death Anniversary of Winston Churchill	3645	£5 Coin	26.00
RMC141	5.3.15	Alice in Wonderland	3658/3667	Medal	22.00
RMC142	6.5.15	175th Anniversary of the Penny Black	MS3710	Medal	22.00
RMC143	14.5.15	Centenary of the First World War (2nd issue)	3711/3716	£2 Coin	26.00
RMC144	2.6.15	800th Anniversary of the Magna Carta	3718/3723	£2 coin	22.00
RMC145	18.6.15	Centenary of the Battle of Waterloo (1st issue)	3724/3729	£5 Coin	26.00
RMC146	9.9.15	Long to Reign Over Us	MS3747	£5 Coin	32.00
RMC147	15.9.15	75th Anniversary of the Battle of Britain	MS3735	50p. Coin	32.00
RMC148	20.10.15	*Star Wars*. Battles	3758/3762, 3764/3767	Medal	23.00
RMC149	20.10.15	*Star Wars*. Vehicles	MS3770	Medal	23.00
RMC150	17.12.15	*Star Wars*. Characters	3758/3769	Medal	42.00
RMC151	5.4.16	400th Death Anniversary of William Shakespeare	3816/3825	3×£2 Coins	45.00
RMC152	21.4.16	90th Birthday of Queen Elizabeth II	MS3832	£5 Coin	30.00
RMC153	21.6.16	Centenary of the First World War (3rd issue)	3838/3843	£2 Coin	32.00
RMC154	28.7.16	*The Tale of Peter Rabbit*	MS3868	50p. Coin	32.00
RMC155	2.9.16	350th Anniversary of the Great Fire of London	3879/3884	£2 Coin	32.00
RMC156	14.10.16	950th Anniversary of the Battle of Hastings	EN51×4+label	50p. Coin	24.00
RMC157	6.2.17	65th Anniversary of Accession of Queen Elizabeth II	U3920	£5 Coin	30.00
RMC158	15.2.17	Windsor Castle	3920/3925	Medal	23.00
RMC159	6.4.17	Racehorse Legends	3940/3947	Medal	23.00
RMC160	5.6.17	50th Anniversary of the Machin definitive	MS3964	Medal	23.00
RMC161	31.7.17	Centenary of the First World War (4th issue)	3983/3988	Coin	23.00
RMC162	12.10.17	*Star Wars*. BB 8	4007/4014	Medal	23.00
RMC163	12.10.17	*Star Wars*. R2-D2	4007/4014	Medal	23.00
RMC164	20.11.17	Royal Platinum Wedding Anniversary	MS4031	Coin	23.00
RMC165	14.12.17	*Star Wars*. C3-PO	4007/4014	Medal	23.00
RMC166	23.1.18	*Game of Thrones*	4033/4042	Medal	30.00
RMC167	23.1.18	*Game of Thrones*	MS4043	Medal	30.00
RMC168	15.2.18	Votes for Women	4050/4057	50p. coin	26.00
RMC169	19.5.18	Royal Wedding	MS4092	£5 coin	30.00
RMC170	16.8.18	Captain Cook and the *Endeavour* Voyage	4118/4123	£2 coin	26.00
RMC171	13.9.18	Centenary of the First World War (5th issue)	4133/4138	£2 coin	26.00
RMC172	17.9.18	Centenary of the RAF	4058/4063	4×£2 coins	70.00
RMC173	17.9.18	Centenary of the RAF – Red Arrows	MS4064	£2 coin	26.00
RMC174	16.10.18	Harry Potter Dragon Alley	4041/4050	Medal	30.00
RMC175	16.10.18	Harry Potter Hogwarts	MS4153	Medal	30.00
RMC176	14.11.18	70th Birthday of the Prince of Wales	MS4163	£5 coin	30.00
RMC177	14.3.19	Marvel Spider-man	4182/4191	Medal	25.00
RMC178	14.3.19	Marvel Hulk	4182/4191	Medal	25.00
RMC179	26.4.19	Marvel Avengers	MS4192	Medal	25.00
RMC180	2.5.19	50th Anniversary of Introduction of the Harrier Jump Jet to RAF Service	MS4218	Medal	17.00
RMC181	24.5.19	Birth Bicentenary of Queen Victoria	4219/4224	£5 coin	20.00
RMC182	6.6.19	75th Anniversary of D-Day	4230/4235	£2 coin	17.50
RMC183	9.9.19	Centenary of Remembrance	3626, 3711, 3838, 3983, 4133	£5 coin	30.00
RMC184	10.10.19	*The Gruffalo*	MS4282	50p. coin	17.50
RMC185	26.11.19	*Star Wars*. The Skywalker Family	4292/4301	Medal	30.00
RMC186	26.11.19	*Star Wars*. A Galaxy of Vehicles	MS4303	Medal	30.00
RMC187	11.2.20	Professor Stephen Hawking	4323/4330	50p coin	26.00
RMC188	17.3.20	James Bond. Q Branch	MS4338	£5 coin	30.00
RMC189	27.4.20	The Design of James Bond	4332/4337	£5 coin	30.00
RMC190	7.4.20	William Wordsworth	4345/4354	£5 coin	30.00
RMC191	8.5.20	75th Anniversary of the End of the Second World War	4356/4363	£2 coin	26.00
RMC192	9.7.20	Queen Live	MS4396	£5 coin	30.00
RMC193	15.8.20	75th Anniversary of the End of the Second World War	MS4364	£5 coin	30.00
RMC194	18.8.20	Sherlock and Moriarty	4411/4416	Medal	30.00
RMC195	18.8.20	The Genius of Sherlock Holmes	MS4417	Medal	30.00
RMC196	13.11.20	*Star Trek* The Original Series	4443/4454	Medal	30.00
RMC197	13.11.20	*Star Trek* Movies	MS4455	Medal	30.00

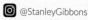

This index gives an easy reference to the inscriptions and designs of the Special Stamps 1953 to November 2020. Where a complete set shares an inscription or type of design, then only the catalogue number of the first stamp is given in addition to separate entries for stamps depicting popular thematic subjects. Paintings, inventions, etc., are indexed under the name of the artist or inventor, where this is shown on the stamp.

1. £.s.d. ISSUES 1953–70

Miniature Sheet Design Index

Stanley Gibbons receives, on a regular basis, enquiries concerning the allocation of SG Numbers to some of individual stamps included in Miniature Sheets. Stamps which are available from more than one source, usually from counter sheets in addition to the Miniature sheet, are allocated numbers.

From this flow of enquiries a decision was made, as part of the review of the design index, to include a new section identifying all the Miniature Sheets issued for GB. These are listed numerically by SG Number, alphabetically by title of sheet and finally (alphabetically) by the individual stamps printed within the MS.

QUIZ
What Kind of Collector are You?

START HERE

| COLLECTOR: | GENERAL ? | ADVANCED ? | SPECIALIST ? |

| BUDGET: | MODEST ? | MEDIUM ? | SIGNIFICANT ? |

YES

Unit Prices?
Per Stamp

Learn about **Top-UpTwenty**, On-line
Instant-Purchase Price-Drop Selling-System
e-mail updates

NO

Up to 20,000 l
NO Buyers Premi
£2M **World Auctions**

Consider **Approvals**
but Take Auction
1st £55 Free Offer

Try **Approvals**
Est 62 years—
1st £25 Free

Collect **Classic GB**
1840-1940 — send
wants list

Take
World Mixtures
1st 500 Free Trial

Join 2000+ Regular Bidders in 52 different
Countries – Unique, All Lots Guaranteed Reducing
Estimate **Auctions** + **£55 Free Trial Offer**
when you win £75+ – **It's easy to Request
your FREE Catalogue Now**

It's Easy to Select Yours Now at UPA

De-Mystifying Philately – QUIZ

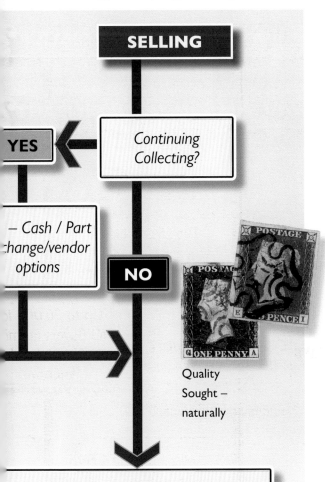

SELLING

Continuing Collecting?

YES

NO

– Cash / Part change/vendor options

Quality Sought – naturally

'money spent in the wrong way soon mounts up ...'

Successful and enjoyable collecting depends upon understanding the relationship of your budget to your interest.

Offers and services can be confusing can't they, and money spent in the wrong way soon mounts up.

In philately, sometimes it is hard to decide which way to go. Your passion may exceed your resource, so just what may be best for you?

Often, it is not what you collect but how you collect

This is the reason why my team and I have devised this quick and easy philatelic route-map QUIZ which does not ask you what you collect – but helps you to determine by your answers just which type of collecting service may best suit you ...

Presently you may find few philatelic companies other than UPA which can offer you integrated philatelic selling systems, but obviously once you determine which philatelic services best suit your collecting interest – you may have a clearer idea of which way is best to go – depending upon your levels of specialism and philatelic budget, of course

Check out our Philatelic QUIZ right now and see for yourself. To select your choice, visit our website or call my team

Dedicated to De-mystifying Philately

Andrew McGavin,

Veteran Philatelic Auctioneer
Philatelic Expert & Author
Managing Director
Universal Philatelic Auctions (UPA)

Contact Andrew Now or another member of his specialist Team to discuss the market/selling options:
andrew@upastampauctions.co.uk

☎ **01451 861111**

Visit: www.UPAstampauctions.co.uk

Fax: 01451 861297 ~ info@upastampauctions.co.uk ~ T: 01451 861111
Participate in this Philatelic Route-Map to Enjoyable Collecting.
Find UPA also on-line at www.top-uptwenty.co.uk
New Instant-Purchase Price-Drop Selling-System